Vehicle-dependent

Expedition

Guide

Tom Sheppard

Published
by

in association with

Published by

Desert Winds, 44 Salusbury Lane, Hertfordshire SG5 3EG, England in association with
Land Rover, Solihull, West Midlands, B92 8NW
Written, designed and produced by Tom Sheppard, MBE, ARPS, FRGS.
Copyright Tom Sheppard 1998

First published 1998. ISBN 0-9532324-0-9

Photography

pp 1.1-16, 2.3-47, 3.1-3, 4.1-16, 5.2-7, 5.4-3 left, 5.4-5 rt Simon Herd. p 2.2-14 Geoff Renner. p 2.2-16 LLBean USA. pp 1.2-6, 4.1-21 centre, 5.4-4, 5.4-12 top Land Rover. pp 2.4-9, 2.7-10, 2.7-17, 2.7-20, 2.7-23, 5.4-6 left Richard Mumford, South Midlands Communications, Hants. p 2.5-14 three lower shots, PreMac (Kent) UK. p 2.5-15 Katadyn Products Inc, Switzerland. p 2.5-18 Stella-Meta Filters, UK. p 2.7-13 left Ken Olney, Derby, Western Australia. p 2.8-5 BP Solar, UK. p 4.1-10 Francis Frost, UK. p 5.3-16 Automotive Technik Ltd, UK. p 4.1-16 top left The Colt Car Co Ltd, UK. pp 4.1-21 top, 5.3-4, 5.3-5, 5.3-20, 5.3-26 centre, 5.3-34 rt, 5.3-35 bottom left Chrysler Jeep Imports, UK. p 4.1-21 Honda UK. pp 4.1-22, 5.3-12 Leyland Truck Ltd. p 5.1-11 top Chris Caldecott/ RGS-IBG. p 5.1-11 bottom Simon Ferry/ RGS-IBG. p 5.1-13 left and rt Tom Craig/ RGS-IBG. p 5.2-13 NRSC, Farnborough, UK. p5.2-27 Trimble Navigation Europe Ltd. p 5.3-29, centre and left Toyota GB Ltd.   p 5.6-9 left to rt, Signature Industries, API Studio/B le Glatin, Jotron (UK). p 5.2-40 by agreement Rolex Watches.
All remaining photography Tom Sheppard.

Author's acknowledgements and thanks
As three years' phone bills and five boxes of research material attest, almost numberless people were involved in the distillation of the following material. I would like to express my grateful thanks to these many, even to those in outer offices who claimed to be 'not very technical' (have they no soul?), for their interest, help, patience and valuable contributions, however small, in the preparation of this book.
Individual thanks and credit is appended at the end of appropriate Sections. No less gratefully acknowledged, but driven from those pages by their wider help, the demands of layout or my own bad planning are :
Dave Clammer, Daniel Collins, Simon Herd, Dave Horner at NRSC, Michael James at the Royal School of Military Survey, Geoff Renner, the eagle-eyed Peter Wilson at Field and Trek, Val Ungless at NPA, Nigel and Shane Winser at the Royal Geographical Society and the amazing Lyn Corson who nobly waded through all 544 pages in the cause of proof reading and protecting the reader from my stylistic inattention and (most of) my enthusiastically long sentences – but not this one.

Contents

...contd

Section 2.3 Clothing, footwear

Human thermo-regulatory system, Clothing – general principles, Clothes, layers, The fibres jungle, Physics recap pt 2, Wicking, The truth about wicking, Breathables: Vapour pressure, Membrane breathables, Coated breathables, Tight weave breathables, External coatings, perspective, Breathables, perspective. The trade names avalanche. Design features – practicality: Practical points, Trousers, Shirts etc Workwear. Climate-specific clothing: Cold weather clothing, Hot weather clothing. Footwear: General criteria, Specification, features, Cold climate footwear, Hot climate footwear, Around the camp, Socks. Headgear and gloves: Headgear – types, uses, features, Gloves – types, uses, features. Vehicle upholstery as clothing. Catalogues to get. Sample specification comparison lists – Field and Trek, References.

Section 2.4 Cooking and food

COOKING. Stoves: Fuel availability, Fuel types: Liquid fuels, Fuel types: Gas. Stove types. Coolers. Need vs bulk, weight, cost, Types of cooler. Utensils. FOOD. Eating pattern, Diet, Dehydrated or tinned, Hygiene, Litter.
Sec 2.4.1 Typical kitchen list

Section 2.5 Water

Logistics. How much to take, Carrying and dispensing, Using it. Purification: Importance of clean water, Purification – filtration, chemicals, Bug sizes, action (table), Water purification hardware, Available filters, data (table), Selecting your hardware, Purification – heat, ultraviolet. Bulk water: Filtration and storage, Desalination. References

Section 2.6 Fuel, oil, fluids

FUEL. Logistics: How much fuel to take, Using it. Fuel types. Compression ratio. Petrol engines – fuel grades: Octane etc – why it matters, What can you do about it – gasoline, Petrol grades (tables), Unleaded petrol, What will run on what (table). Diesel engines – fuel grades: The variables, Cetane number, Sulphur content, High sulphur diesel fuels (table), Cloud point – waxing, CFPP. Water contamination. OIL, FLUIDS. Introduction, Oils – job and definition. Defining an oil – 1. Viscosity, What the label means (chart). Defining an oil – 2. Service categories. Defining an oil – 3. Synthetics. 'Best oil' - the Mk 2 syndrome, Oils for diesel engines. Engine oil – what to actually do, Engine oils snapshot (table). Running-in a new engine (box). Tractor fluids. Gear oils. Brake fluids, Engine coolant – antifreeze.

Section 2.7 Communications

The need – who talks to whom. The regulations and the medium: Regulations, The medium. Frequency vs distance. Vehicle to vehicle communications. Vehicle to field base comms. Vehicle to home country comms: Terrestrial radio, Satellite comms. Use/licensing overseas. Broadcast reception. Climatic conditions.

Section 2.8 Electrical power

Electrical power sources: Extra batteries, Portable generators, Solar panels, Inverters, DC/ DC converters.

SECTION 3. PEOPLE, TRAINING

Section 3.1 Team selection

Types of trip and team. Friends, Call for volunteers, Group development, Leadership, the leader: Leadership, The leader – characteristics. Selecting the team, training. Case study: Comments on report. Interview marking schedule.

SECTION 4. VEHICLES

Section 4.1 Expedition vehicles

What for? The task, Function vs fun and luxury, How many vehicles, load, type? Trailers. Vehicles – general criteria: Vehicle attributes (table), Ingredients, Size, power-weight, payload. Transmission systems: 4x2 or 4x4, Types of four-wheel drive, Viscous coupling (panel), 4x4 systems – general (diagram), Differentials (panel), Controlling left/right wheel-spin. Two-speed transfer box. Auto or manual. Suspension, weight distribution: Geometry, suspension, Weight distribution. Engine, configuration, service: Petrol or diesel, Configuration, Simplicity, service, spares. Inspection, preparation.

Section 4.2 Vehicle modifications

Why modify? Modifications – the spectrum. VEHICLE FUNCTION MODIFICATIONS. Engine and fuel system: Engine function improvements, Instrument sources, Oil system improvements, Fuel system improvements. Electrical system: Batteries, Typical battery specifications (table), Battery charging (box), Other electrical modifications. Vehicle security: Precautions, Alarm systems. Navigation system. EXPEDITION FUNCTION MODIFICATIONS. Tyres. Tyres overview (table). Speedometer calibration. Roof modifications. Underbody peripheral protection. Recovery add-ons. Maximise cargo space, Tie-downs to secure load. DIBS-mirror for virgin desert. CREW FUNCTION MODIFICATIONS. Floor, roof, sides insulation. 'Van' side window. Places to put things. Upholstery, ventilation. Audio.

Section 4.3 Loading and lashing

The overall picture. Liquid containers. Equipment boxes. Overall payload. Load distribution. Lashing.

SECTION 5. OPERATIONS

Section 5.1 Routine, operations

Pre-planning: Type of trip, Anchor points, Who does what. Routine – mobile expeditions. Routine and operation – fixed-base projects. Major fixed-base expeditions. Oman Wahiba Sands Project report.

Section 5.2. Navigation

THE PROBLEM, SOLUTION INGREDIENTS. Where am I? Where should I head? The attitude. Ingredients and applications. WHERE AM I? Maps and satellite imagery. Planning maps and working-area maps: Maps - what to look for, Maps – where to buy them, Satellite imagery. Position fixing 1: manual/terrestrial. Where am I? Position fixing, Guides and their limitations, Cross-bearings on landmarks, Astro fixing, Radio/electronic terrestrial navaids. Position fixing 2: satellites, GPS. Sat- fixes – Transit, GPS, Glonass, GPS, Other applications, DGPS et al, Which GPS? DEAD RECKONING. WHERE TO HEAD? Two components, The navigation log. DR - Heading measurement: Terminology: heading, bearing, course, Hand-held magnetic compasses, Magnetic errors – variation, deviation, Magnetic dip – needle 'weighting', Magnetic compasses in vehicles, Care of magnetic compasses, Electronic compasses in vehicles, Non-magnetic direction devices. DR - distance measurement: Vehicle odometers, calibration, 'Terrain factor' and the map. THE REST. Electronic equipment - care in the field. Navigation equipment (See p 2.1 – 19).

Sec 5.2.1 Map grids

Lat/long and grids. Basis of grid systems. Military grid based on UTM (diagram). National grids and others. Grids and datums. Grid north. Doing a cross check. Grid systems summary (diagram).

Sec 5.2.2 Satellite image selection

Case studies: Buy of middle market and low-budget satellite images to enhance poor mapping.

...contd

Section 5.3 Driving
Overall philosophy. Transmission, gearboxes: What 4x4's for, Main gearbox, Transfer gearbox – what it does, Transfer box 1: selecting 4x4, Transfer box 2: selecting low ratio gears, Table: Some 4x4 systems/vehicles, Transmission – the rest. Driving techniques: Mechanical sympathy, On-foot recce and marshalling, Use of transfer box, Suspension affects traction, Avoid wheel-spin, reverse out , Steep slopes – up, Steep slopes – down, Lateral slopes – traverses, Weak ground, Soft sand, poor traction, Mud. Panel: Low to high range on the move. Salt flat, Rocks, corrugations, Water, Driving in dust, Turbo-diesels – stopping.

Sec 5.3.1 Driver training

Section 5.4 Recovery
The big picture: Lift and pull, Don't make it worse, Take the right tools. Floating/lifting: 1. Floating. Bridging channels, PSP, Sand ladders, Digging under belly, Low tyre pressures, Off-load cargo. 2. Lift. Jacking the axle (or wheel), Jacking the body. Pulling/pushing: The gamut, Low transfer box, People pushing, Tow by other vehicle(s): Long tow rope, Co-ordination, Tandem tow. Winches: Winch types (table), Data on some winches.

Section 5.5 Vehicle maintenance
Philosophy – preventive maintenance. The expedition mechanic. Pre-expedition inspection. Lubricants. Nightly inspection. Tools. Spares. Fuel consumption and records. Cleanliness. Tips: Main battery disconnect, Dry fuel tank. Nightly inspection schedule.

Sec 5.5.1 Spares and tools list

Section 5.6 Emergencies
Contingency planning: Ingredients. The details: Convoy procedure, Simple rescue aids, Standard procedures, timing, Medevac. Vehicle insurance. Radio / satellite beacons: Cospas-Sarsat LUT coverage, Choice of beacon type, Cospas-Sarsat facilities (table), Next generation – GEOSAR, Buying your beacon, The rescue. Rescue plan.

SECTION 6. INDEX

Signposts

People open books in the middle. (If you opened this one here, well done; don't move yet!) People flick through books from the back, turn over chunks of pages, jolt at the flash of an interesting picture, half-scan the caption, resolve to read bits later when they have time, guess – not always correctly – the context of the piece that caught their eye.

Very few will read this book from cover to cover; or even from the front. So easy access and signposting has been one of the aims. Open any page and you will know where you are and what is under discussion.

The *Contents page* – repeated on the back flap of the dust jacket so you can use it as a page marker – summarises what's here.

Once you have that, use the first 20 mm down from the top of each spread to see *where you are* in the book. *Coverage of the section* – eg Section 2.3 – is summarised on the back of the title page of that section. Top right *summarises the spread*; the little italics side boxes *summarise each page*.

Additionally, every subject has a *column sideheading* or a *para-heading*. The *index*, we hope, will enable you to find *anything*.

First:
1. Section, title of section
2. Sub-section and title
3. In-a-phrase summary of what's on the **spread**

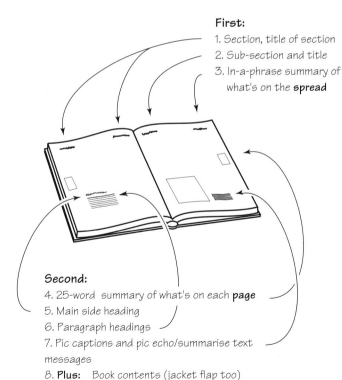

Second:
4. 25-word summary of what's on each **page**
5. Main side heading
6. Paragraph headings
7. Pic captions and pic echo/summarise text messages
8. **Plus:** Book contents (jacket flap too)
   Section contents
   Index

Introduction

I must go down to the sea again, to the lonely sea and the sky
And all I ask is a tall ship and a star to steer her by
Sea Fever... John Masefield

Much quoted; learned under duress, as sometimes happens at school, without its great perceptions really sinking in at the time, Masefield touches a nerve that tingles in all of us. You can see the distant horizon, the hugeness of the sky, sense the freedom from life's trivia and drudgery. It is the spirit of adventure. It is a lot more, and more worthy, than the mere urge to do something dangerous or risky. It is the need for freedom, to be in charge, briefly, of our own destiny; the urge to explore, to do things well, to see the new and the unseen, to have time for kindness, and, just as much part of the equation, to do so in a cocoon of our own making, designed to carry us through the hazards or discomforts ahead, a challenge to our ingenuity and planning. That cocoon – it can be a backpacker's backpack, a yachtsman's' yacht, NASA's *Columbia* space shuttle or an overlander's 4x4.

However down-to-earth our reasons for buying a 4x4, if we already have one, few of us do not nurture a yen really to use it to free the spirit, to take it to the mountains, the moors, to the bush or to the great deserts. In many cases it will be the other way round: we have our plan, our project or our dream and a 4x4 is the way to realise it, the only feasible core of our voyage of

exploration.

But however esoteric and lofty the concept of our plans, expeditions in practice can quickly fall back to earth with a bang if they lack the vital ingredients. Expeditions should be about total reliability, about planning the risks and problems out of the scenario. There will be enough to occupy and challenge us without having to deal with shortages of equipment, having the wrong documentation, being unprepared for the climate, having insufficient fuel or getting lost.

Help for your trip. Be it your first or your twenty-first expedition we hope this book will help to make your trip trouble-free. We have aimed to do this in a number of ways; first, by matching your vehicle and logistics to your project so that the one does not hazard the other; sectionond, by flagging-up selection criteria on the main categories of equipment, and thirdly, by giving guidance on keeping vehicle, equipment and crew in the best possible condition.

Context – maps and books. Navigation too is covered in some detail. Navigation is knowing where you are and where you are going in relation to everything else. When you are really on top of things and have good maps, it makes the trip twice as good. Preparatory reading is exactly the same in establishing context – the tourist blurb, the guidebooks, the entries in encyclopaedias, studying the maps. It sounds very obvious but too often the rush of organising things precludes your background and essential reading. Do the preliminary research and, as with the navigation, you'll get twice as much out of the trip.

Space technology. If the maps are poor, help is at hand. Like no generation of expeditioners before, we have breathtaking technology at our beck and call. The achievements of the space scientists and astronauts can provide us with satellite imagery to show us the earth in the most minute detail – or in just enough detail to bolster older maps. GPS and Glonass navigation systems will position us to better than tens of metres; satellite communications give us book-sized

telephones or messaging anywhere on the planet (with better to come); and if things do go wrong SARSAT and COSPAS satellites receive and re-transmit emergency calls. It is an exciting time to go expeditioning.

Tablets of stone? In the time it takes a finished manuscript and page design to be turned into plates and roll off a printing press, some information can be out of date. But we felt it would be more useful to have a snapshot of 1996/97 technology and product design, naming names and products, than to skirt round it as so many books do.

In putting this book together we have tried to highlight principles and the bases for the advice given so that it will remain valid irrespective of what equipment is on the market. In some cases this involves reference to actual products since the point can usually be made more clearly that way and often infers genuine endorsement of particular items. At all times the aim is to excite your interest, get you to weigh your own needs and make your own balanced judgement. As is so often the case, though, we have found that the more you research, the more there is to know and the more the new developments you see just around the corner. In swimming up this Niagara of information and progress we have done our best and would ask you to bear kindly any differences between what you read and the State of the Art at the date you pick up the book.

Planning, preparation and thoroughness. A successful expedition, however small in scope – even an afternoon in the hills – is about preparation and planning and thinking ahead. Beyond the reach of the invisible safety net of goods and services usually on call to meet the needs of your everyday life, on an expedition you have to adjust to a new net that often has huge holes in it. Expeditions are about planning, preparation and a thoroughness that means detail; naturally the big picture comes first but you will always have to follow it through to the detail. Even as leader of a great project, adopting the 'Don't bother me with detail' approach will not work. It is no use pretending that detail doesn't count; if you want to check the oil level of a Land Rover R380 gearbox in the bush and haven't brought along a Torx 55 adapter to remove the level plug then you will see the point. As a one-man expedition you just think of that; as the leader of a group you must make sure it has been thought of – and then check it.

Driving. There is repeated emphasis in the book on the care of vehicles and the acquisition of infallible driving skills since vehicles will, in almost every case, be the lifeline of your expedition. Whatever your project, it will be set at nought if your transport is wrecked on the first day off the tarmac by poor driving. Not much more than the basic principles can be touched on here but, acknowledging the limitations and context of this book, readers are advised to refer also to *The Land Rover Experience* or the subsequent book *Off-roader driving* (published in

a matching format) for a fuller treatment of the operation of four-wheel drive vehicles.

Ease of access. As with that book – see 'Signposts' before this Introduction – we have tried to make ease of access a feature of this one. Use the Contents pages, the Section Coverage pages, and the Index. Scanning across the top line of print will give you Section, Section title, sub-section and the subject dealt with on that spread. And the italics side boxes summarise the content of each page.

Keenness and enjoyment. Don't let all the talk of detail and perfection sound too forbidding. Taking the time to do things well matters a lot but remember that keenness – the spirit and ability to be absorbed in and enjoy what you are doing – is probably the most important prerequisite in preparing an expedition. This you have already. Enjoy your expedition.

Section 1
Preliminary planning

Section 1.1

Preliminary planning:

Initial scan

COVERAGE OF THIS SECTION

Repeat and refine. Parts of this section are covered in more detail in other parts of the book but a broad preliminary scan of the planning pigeonholes is appropriate at this point. Planning an expedition can be likened to taking a photograph using a zoom lens. First get the subject in frame to see the size and general shape of it; then focus roughly. When this clarifies the picture you may wish to zoom closer or further away – to alter what is in the frame.

Then you will want to focus more critically. It may be that when you focus this sharply you see something that may make you want to change the whole picture and select different lighting or another viewpoint. This is exactly the repeat-and-refine process that you will find yourself doing with your expedition project, be it a half day in the hills, a week in the Pyrenees or a trip in the game reserves of East Africa. Start with the big picture, zoom in on the details; repeat and refine.

Read about your destinations before setting out. Start getting 'Western civilization' into perspective ...

Know the aim

Practicality. An exhortation to 'know the aim' may seem superfluous but perhaps this could be better phrased as 'keep an eye on the aim'. The broad idea of 'let's go to Tombouctou' quickly gets overtaken by the all-consuming details of planning so that, for a while, the planning itself becomes the aim. Refining your ideas on what you will be doing when you get there must be a continuing process that will result from reading and research – very important, this, if you are to get the best out of your trip.

Reading. All too often, though sometimes understandably, reading on an area takes place after the visit. Understandable because the visit awakens a wider interest in the subject. Get the drop on the situation by making a conscious effort to research and read before the trip! Specialist shops are the kinds of places to go – Stanfords the map people in Long Acre London is one, and The Travel Bookshop in Blenheim Crescent, London has a formidable reputation. Sarah Anderson who started the latter establishment has put together an encyclopaedic work, *Andersons Travel Companion: A guide to the best non-fiction and fiction for travelling* (Scolar Press). It contains

Repeat and refine the planning process, narrowing your aim with more detail. Despite the urgency and momentum of planning, take time to read background.

a guide to guide-books as well as a catalogue of books of just about every specialist aspect on nearly every country in the world, including, for background, fiction – a Herculean and valuable piece of work.

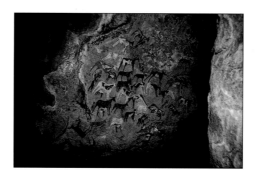

... indeed, 'civilization' itself. (Masjed-i-Shah, Isfahan, previous page; desert rock paintings above.)

Tourist information, guidebooks such as *Lonely Planet*, or *Rough Guide* will yield valuable background and day to day logistics information, albeit seldom related to vehicle-based expeditions. Probably the best place to start is your local library's *Encyclopaedia Britannica* which will give you a nicely rounded opening picture of the countries you are going to or through and without doubt open up areas of interest you did not know existed. These will be invaluable starting points and part of your close-focusing process as you research and refine your aim.

'Expansion joints' – planned gaps. Having an aim need not imply a non-stop frenzy of activity on your trip. Your aim in some sections of your journey could simply be to arrive, stay for three days and potter, doing as your fancy dictates – after the usual 'good shower, laundry and an oil change'. Indeed, building-in 'expansion joints' of this kind in your itinerary is wise since you will often find yourself wanting extra time to follow up items of interest along your route or simply to reassess the supplies position or savour the feeling of no urgency.

Nail the variables. Student expeditions, small scientific projects, sponsors, time and cost will often go hand in hand at the planning stage and in this arena an expedition will often change shape, size and direction as continuously as a primitive life-form under a microscope. Nail the variables one by one to establish the format and aim of the trip. Time away is usually a demanding cri-

Sounds obvious but do read as much as you can first. Plan your itinerary broadly first, including 'expansion joints' of spare time en route. Then go for the detail.

terion; consider time of year with great care (page 1.1 -8); your vehicle dictates the size of your team – or vice versa (see below and Section 4). If you get the size, shape, time and timing of your project right first time you have pulled off a minor miracle. Check now your original aim is still valid; should it be trimmed, can it be expanded? The Royal Geographical Society's *Expedition Planners' Handbook*, essential overview reading for all expeditions, is especially valuable in the context of scientific projects. Again, your aims should be as precise as possible and all too often the constraints of time and cost will demand a clear head to restrict your aims to what is feasible.

Plan ahead, basic philosophy

Important detail. No matter what the size and scope of your expedition, the importance of advance planning is fundamental. Even on a day-trip to the hills – wind and waterproof clothing, gloves, rubber boots as well as walking boots, jack, a baulk of wood to put it on, shovels, flask of hot drinks or a stove – the detail is important. Here, as on longer trips, when you will be away from other habitation and support there will be no opportunity to cushion planning shortfalls, to obtain the equipment you omitted to provision, to hone the knowledge or skills with which you should have come equipped or to make good the preparation of equipment you now find is not functioning in the field.

Pragmatic realism. Time and cost are especially unforgiving taskmasters and pragmatic realism must be brought to bear early in the planning stage – typically in the distances you plan to cover each day.

*Walking the ridge of a thousand foot dune
or the streets of a thousand year-old town –
no two 'expeditions' are the same in scope
or location. Yours is the one that is special.*

(Avoid the common trap of turning your trip into a mile-eating marathon, a blur of changing scenery you cannot absorb.) Allowing for these and other modifying factors at the planning stage will be good training for later. Accommodating the host of varying influences and events during the execution of your project will be the application of that training – typically, 'the place has just closed for the weekend', 'the fuel pumps don't work', 'it's a national holiday' 'the water is off' *et al.*

Keenness counts. Basic motivation in your team – keenness on the project and care in its execution – is paramount. From this will stem the commitment to plan ahead, to plan in detail and to allocate time and go to great pains to produce a situation in which the trip may be successful. Included as outcomes of this basic attitude will be training and preparation, thinking yourself into all the situations that can arise,

researching what others have done in the past and tirelessly seeking the best available advice and equipment.

Planning criteria – overseas trips

The general headings. Not all expeditions will be overseas but the planning sequence and considerations such visits demand are worth following for the thoroughness of approach they instil. The main influencing criteria at the planning stage will be scanned in the following paragraphs and in most cases also dealt with more fully later in the book:

- Cost – support by team and any outside agencies.
- Time – for adequate planning, preparation and training.
- Time – time of year, length of visit.
- Government permission – and preferably active co-operation – from the target country.

Plan to take time. Don't turn your trip into a mile-eating marathon. Allow time for pre-trip planning, training and getting things right – especially the vehicle.

- Personnel – ability to assemble a team of appropriate expertise and interests.
- Safety *vis-à-vis* political extremism, bandits and thieves – increasingly important, alas, to keep in mind.
- Logistics – access to and resupply in the target area.
- Equipment – availability/suitability of vehicles and equipment.
- Shipping – drive, ship or fly?

Cost, funding, media markets

Sponsorship is possible but think yourself into your sponsor's shoes. What is in it for them? The media are usually unreliable; treat sales as a bonus only.

Don't underestimate. The implications of cost are self evident. Your first-guess estimates will be done when your enthusiasm (and optimism) for your project is at its dizziest and your scan at its most global. Whilst this will also be the start of an appropriately anything is possible approach, beware of letting optimism take over too much in the area of costs. It is easy to underestimate by omitting such items as insurance costs, vehicle carnet indemnities (if required), the multiplicity of handling charges when sending vehicles by sea and other surprises such as the high cost of taking a sensible supply of photographic film. Reserve funds and contingencies (medical insurance) for possible medevac must be catered for after sober thought and consideration of what may be needed.

Don't bank on media sales. Especially beware of glib hopes of making a film or doing articles. Transmitted television standards for travel documentaries are dauntingly high in terms of visual (if not always intellectual) quality and are often associated with well known personalities. UK television companies are not a bottomless source of wealth and are reluctant to buy from non-union film makers, besides which production of a viable film is overall probably more work and cost than the whole expedition. Magazine journalism standards are generally low with coverage shallow and clichéd. The playing field is very seldom level and such assignments as are published have often come from an in-house 19 year-old 'travel editor'. In general, letters are rarely answered. Editorial attention span seems seldom to better that of a housefly (arguably a requisite qualification for the job) and you will be lucky to get an advance commitment firmer than 'submit material on return' – not unreasonable, in all fairness, unless you are an established author. Get by without the media if you possibly can or at least treat any sales as a post-expedition bonus.

Sponsorship. Regarding other sponsorship try, before going further into this jungle, to see your project through the eyes of the company you are about to approach. What, really, is in it for them? Your package of proposals must offer real prestige and a positive spin-off for your sponsor. Again, the Royal Geographical Society's *Expedition Planners' Handbook* gives a valuable

Hold your breath; cherish scenes like this. But be sure not to break down or forget to bring what you need. On far-ranging expeditions, detailed planning is all.

The planning (below) and the pay-off. That first cup of tea gives time to reflect on the night's strange animal noises. Mapping can be supplemented by satellite imagery (Section 5.2).

guide to sponsorship.

Transit costs. On costs overall, you will find in most cases that the expense of getting to and from the expedition operating area is by far the greatest constituent of total costs (see also Section 1.2 'Shipping'). Next will come fuel for your vehicle, especially if it is petrol rather than diesel powered. In the field you are very often self-contained and self-sustaining and living at a very low rate of expenditure so this will be the cheapest part of all.

Time

Plan ahead; well ahead. Having stressed the importance of time to plan, prepare and train, you are entitled to expect guidance on how long to allow; and this is very hard to give with any precision. 'Six to eighteen months' is the kind of advice, given a limit of four words, that would be offered but in truth every project will be different and the time requirement will vary according to the disciplines or tasks involved and whether anyone can be occupied full-time with the project – a very important proviso – or, if you have a vehicle ready to go from a previous trip. Suffice it here to say that this area is one of the first in which to apply the pragmatic realism mentioned above. List the things that have to be done, know which can

overlap or take place concurrently with other tasks, add margins, allow settling-in phases – typically, for example, a full-cargo check run in your vehicle after its mechanical overhaul or practice and familiarisation sessions with new scientific, navigation or photographic equipment acquired specially for the project. Your vehicle will be the lifeblood of your project; make no compromises with time or cost to ensure it is set up and prepared as perfectly as you know how for the trip ahead. Time to train and prepare may or may not then put you at the optimum time of year for the trip – see next paragraphs. To risk again stating the obvious, get the best value you can from the cost and effort of preparation and shipping. Maximise your time in the field. Consider, even, leaving your vehicle in safe storage and flying back for a second trip.

The no-reply syndrome. Most frustrating of all – and there is no easy solution – will be the time taken to get replies to letters; not just in the sphere of diplomatic clearances – everywhere. Read that again, photocopy it, pin it to your dart-board; you can vent your fury at the world's bad manners and score at the same time!

Getting to and from the expedition area is the expensive bit. It is cheap in the field. Ballpark figures: allow six to eighteen months planning and preparation time.

Space, respect, time to just look. Avoid the age-old trap of turning your expedition into a mile-eating marathon.

Time of year

Time for acclimatisation. Time of year can make enormous differences to climatic conditions and among the very first aspects of your research fact gathering should be examination of temperature and rainfall statistics. Michelin maps of Africa, as well as being exceptionally good planning maps, are the benchmark for presentation of this information which is to be found on every sheet. Tourist guides and atlases often show it too. University and school summer vacations are at the worst possible time of the year for northern hemisphere hot climate expeditions. That does not mean they cannot be utilised but you must allow time for acclimatisation which will take about a week during which the expedition routine can be developed. You may well be forced to go at particular times of the year but make a real and sensible allowance for acclimatisation; this is especially necessary if physical workloads are likely to be heavy and high temperatures are accompanied by high humidity. Where

Even if your choice is limited, take account of time of year. If going tropical in summer, consciously plan a low workload period of acclimatisation.

there is a rainy season or monsoon period study the effect this has on local roads, rivers, bridges and flood plains. Often the advice is to avoid this period altogether.

Check the weather data. Few better examples of the influence of the calendar on human operating conditions can be found than the Arabian Gulf coasts. The winter months are pleasant during the day, cold at night; July and August, on the other hand have probably the most enervating combination of high temperature and humidity to be found anywhere on the planet. Very little is impossible and plunging into these conditions has been done with appropriate buffer periods but do study meteorological data early on, whatever your destination, and get your planning criteria tuned-in accurately.

Government permission

Long-lead item? Government permission will be involved at the initial stages of most overseas expeditions – from the smallest to the largest. Establish at the outset how much of a bureaucratic marathon you are embarking on. Sometimes you can just jump in your vehicle and go without even the need for a visa; on other routes preliminary paperwork will be quite involved – visas, customs carnets for the vehicles, indemnities for the carnets, International Driving Permits, special medical/immunisation requirements, difficulties with insurance, import of currency and possibly special permission to visit or operate in remote areas. Get the picture early since this is the part that will take time to sort out and progress before you can get full permission to go.

UK government help. For some trips from the United Kingdom that permission – and certainly advice – may well involve the UK government too, the usual starting point being a call to the Foreign and Commonwealth Office (FCO) Travel Advice Unit on 0171.238.4503/4. This will give you a political overview of the current situation in a particular country but the sheer number of enquiries has eroded the quality of the service somewhat in recent years. Try to obtain the address and phone/fax of the UK Embassy in the country you plan to visit – see below.

Your label. Allow plenty of time for government permission. Letters are not always answered. To the overseas government you are dealing with, you are a foreigner and the nuances of your different culture can sometimes be hard to get the measure of. Worse, stereotypical preconceptions regarding 'Western tourists' may already be in place and you will likely wish to distance yourself from these; having done so you will be starting with a handicap that has to be overcome. After your homework, an actual reconnaissance visit to the country prior to the expedition itself can work wonders for tricky clearances. Personal relations can be established with those whose permission you seek and that can be worth a whole file of letters. You will need to give careful thought to whether you label yourself a tourist for the sake of trying to obtain a straightforward clearance, or take on a more serious mantle. This can

Getting government permission is a test of tenacity and patience; good training for later on. You will have a national label from day one and won't want to let it down.

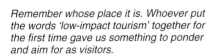

Remember whose place it is. Whoever put the words 'low-impact tourism' together for the first time gave us something to ponder and aim for as visitors.

help in cases where government organisations are suspicious. Even the space on an immigration entry form can be filled as 'tourist' (a wave-through) or 'business' leading to a 'What business?' type of grilling.

Diplomatic approach. There will be three possible avenues of initial approach when seeking permission to visit an overseas destination:

1. British embassies overseas. The UK embassy in the proposed country of your visit can steer you round obstacles, indicate where help will be available or put you in touch with appropriate government departments. It is usually worth checking with them anyway if there is anything unusual about your project. Remember that consular officials are invariably busy to the point of being harassed and your letter should be brief – one page if possible – and to the point. The FCO will be able to furnish the correct address and person to whom you should write.

2. European embassy of country concerned. If you are UK or Europe based you may find the European embassies of the countries you plan to visit provide very variable standards of assistance. Unfortunately they are sometimes staffed by 'city slickers' unfamiliar with the remote regions in their own country that you wish to see and are unsympathetic or suspicious of anyone planning to go there. Beware especially of those who will give you glib – and subsequently unattributable – assurances that there will be 'no problem'; you will recall these assurances when you are turned away from a border because you were unaware of a particular piece of paper that you should have brought with you. This will be a difficult snag to spot in advance. However, embassy staffs can be helpful and you have to establish an accommodation with them and gain their confidence before you can get any further. Remember that these are the people who will issue your visa. And remember too that embassy staffs probably have a high proportion of time-wasters on their client list making casual enquiries and not following

Be alert to experience levels and reliability of foreign embassy staffs in Europe. They may not have full knowledge of any remote areas you may want to visit.

through. Your ambassadorial role has started already – see below.

3. Corresponding organisation overseas. If you have any kind of scientific programme a brother university or research institution overseas in the country concerned can inevitably strengthen and authenticate requests for clearance. This will probably be the best way of assuring the visa-issuing authority in Europe of your serious intent.

Ambassadorial role. We have all seen the tendency for people to generalise from the particular, especially where foreigners are concerned. If preaching will be forgiven, it is not out place to flag up (appropriate idiom) a timely reminder on how this could apply to us; on overseas trips take on board at an early stage that you will be, throughout the project and in the wrap-up that ensues, an ambassador for your country and, if applicable, for your university or other sponsoring organisation. It will be manifested in your manner and manners, your sensitivity to people and situations, your attitude to the people whose country you are planning to visit, your dress and appearance, your administrative efficiency. The role applies, is necessary and will pay off, whether you are organising a major project, a two-vehicle initial recce or going somewhere on your own. Adopt and maintain, on the expedition, a sensitivity to the host country's sovereignty; tact and patience are essential. Though locked into it, the officials you will encounter will not like bureaucracy much more than you do. Recognise the rules they have to apply.

Personnel

Trusting gut feel. The question of personnel selection and training is covered in Section 3 by reference to a case history involving a demanding eight-person expedition. If you are mounting an expedition where the requirement for specialist skills demands that you 'go out to tender' and call for volunteers then you have a responsible task on your hands; one that must not be hurried and one that will demand first that

Give a little of yourself to those you meet, not necessarily a little of your possessions. The Touareg have a selective relationship with Western culture and are still very much their own people, preferring their traditional life style and the freedom of the desert. Climatic change has been cruel in recent decades.

you know yourself. A number of difficult criteria have simultaneously to be satisfied, some of which require mature subjective judgement and the courage to stick by it. The most demanding situations for the team leader in the wider context of the whole expedition will occur in relation to personnel selection or the resolution of difficulties in the field. Say to yourself early on, 'This is my judgement on what is best. Have I the courage to justify this decision, can I be influenced by rational argument without succumbing to appeasement or, if necessary can I trust, state and explain, gut feeling?'. Gut feeling need not be (indeed should preferably not be) a totally subjective decision. It will more likely be a mix of facts, objective judgements and subjective feelings that have to be acknowledged and balanced. From the pragmatic to the intuitive, these are some of the headings you will have to consider:

• *Skills and disciplines.* Getting the right skills within a given small group for the planned programmes plus linguists will be your first challenge. Pre-expedition training for (and proof-of-skills by) all team members is essential. If someone is a cook, see them cook – in the field under represen-

tative conditions. Ditto for mechanics, radio operators, climbers or drivers.

• *Availability.* Team members must realise that time away from other commitments has to be faced and accepted. This includes training and preparatory work prior to the expedition which cannot be shirked by any team member and will, indeed, be proof of all-important motivation towards the project. You will not be wanting team members to be less than totally committed.

• *Multi-role capability.* Few expeditions can afford prima donna single-discipline specialists. Everyone should be able, when called upon, to cook, change a wheel and, above all, drive delicately with mechanical sympathy.

• *Fitness.* Physical fitness is essential both from the point of view of the amount of physical exertion that may be required in, for example, unloading or digging-out vehicles and also from the point of view of resistance to disease. It is almost impossible to equate certain states of pre-expedition fitness with performance on an actual expedition, especially since that performance is so dependent on mind-set, but what can be said with certainty is that in given circumstances a fit person will be of more use to an expedition than one who is unfit.

• *Compatibility.* Compatibility between team members and with the conditions of the expedition is vital. Trust your gut feeling

Trust gut feel in the hugely important business of team selection. Allow training time, working together; have the team demonstrate their special skills.

at the selection stage.

Also look at yourself as objectively as you can in your role as leader or even as specialist; you may not be an expert in all the required skills but knowing what you have yet to learn and adopting the right attitude, not the least facet of which is knowing who to rely on, is half the battle at the planning stage. If you have got it right, who to rely on will include the whole team.

Safety

Risk assessment. Give it a grand name – 'safety audit' or 'risk assessment' – but do take a sober look at all the 'what-if ...' situations that could arise on your trip and what your fall-back plans are. The spread of crime and political extremism must be examined as objectively as possible. It is always hard to get a balanced picture and the views of those you ask are likely to be polarised at either the alarmist or complacent ends of the scale according to whether they themselves have or have not experienced problems. You would not take long to come up with a list a bit like this:

Undertake a thorough safety assessment of the planned trip. Include medical insurance, (and its shortfalls), anti-crime measures, and fly-out practicalities.

• *Medical risks.* Endemic diseases, precautions, inoculations, advice.

• *Medical facilities.* Nearest comprehensive medical facilities and likely costs (see also Section 5.6). How far does your medical insurance cover you? Can you make up the difference? How far to the nearest airport?

• *Spares.* Vehicle or other spares, are there any local dealerships, arrangements for fly-in, etc. (See also Sections 4 and 5.5.)

• *Calling home.* Can you be contacted? Can you contact home or office? (See below, see Section 2.7 'Communications' and Section 5.6 'Emergencies'.)

Anti-crime. Having established as best you can the overall ambience in the region you are going to, it behoves you then to take the fullest possible precautions in thief-proofing your vehicle. These measures, where possible, should be aimed at keeping the thieves away rather than merely sounding alarms after they have struck. Hijacking the whole vehicle is not unknown in some countries; ask the question if only to dismiss

it. Instead of having to break in and try to start the vehicle, the hijacker waits for the owner to do that and takes it from there, as it were. There are ways, even, of combating this – see also Section 4.2. Think too at this preliminary stage about the security of camp sites, use of school or police compounds; and the possibility, where the team is large enough, of using an all-night roster of guards.

Logistics dictates equipment

Position of supply points. Your distance from main supply points during your journey or whilst you are at a main base site governs the shape of an expedition and the provisioning task. How many kilometres between fuelling points, where good water is obtainable; 'how many people for how many days' will affect water, food and other logistic needs. Think about reserves and the specific criteria or scenario on which you base them. Many expeditions will be in regions where few, if any, of these problems will bother you; your route may take you through many little towns or villages where there are shops and filling stations which also have clean water on tap to fill your cans from. Or you may be using well maintained campsites. In other regions – classically in the great deserts – all these calculations will be far more critical. In this worst-case scenario, with a large group, the headings you should consider are:

• *Resupply.* Fuel, water, food resupply points (see also Sections 2.5 and 2.6).

• *Vehicles choice.* Availability of fuel, water and food affects choice of vehicles with appropriate payload and/or number of vehicles in convoy (see below and also Section 4.1).

• *Fly-out.* Availability of fly-out facilities for medevac or, eg sending out exposed film, live samples in natural history collections etc.

• *Communications.* Communications/rescue. Always plan to be self-sufficient if possible - multiple vehicles (three is the ideal minimum), experienced deputies to back-up essential specialist skills such as navigation, languages. Avoid relying on outside agencies for whom 'out-of-sight-out-of-mind' is a default philosophy; two-way communications such as radio or satellite, however, ensures you do get a response (see Section 2.7); the latter, particularly, can put a different light on this subject and can be invaluable for keeping in touch with families, transmission of data or reference to a sponsoring body (see also Section 5.6 'Emergencies').

Vehicles, equipment, people choice. Consideration of these combined factors will fundamentally shape your whole expedition – what vehicles you use (Section 4.1), what equipment you use (Section 2), who you take and their qualifications (Section 3.1). Typically, large vehicles (medium trucks such as ex-army 4-tonne Bedfords) will support the greatest distance without fuel or water resupply though they will be low on power/weight ratio and thus less agile off-road – see below. The size and payload of your vehicles is crucial to your logistics problems.

Equipment

A quick look at detail. Carrying on the reasoning started under Logistics above but now in more detail, a devil's advocate approach must be taken here too in order to establish a most-demanding and least-demanding scenario in which an expedition may have to operate. This will enable you to get an accurate perspective on the detailed equipment planning. Will there be a fully equipped workshop nearby or do you have to do all your own maintenance and repairs? If so tools and equipment will need to be looked at. Will you have mains-charging facilities for cine-camera or other scientific equipment batteries or will you have to bring it with you? Riffling quickly through questions such as these will give you, early on, the slant you will need on detailed equipment scales.

Vehicle. As indicated above, think about vehicle size, cross-country capability (irrelevant unless driver skills are also considered - see Section 5.3), fuel-limited range, and

Logistics and resupply will completely dictate the shape of your team, vehicles and equipment inventory and plans. The vehicle is the life-blood of the expedition.

It is hard to know which evokes the greater anger and frustration. In some countries the beautifully manicured 'No Entry' sign is almost a national emblem whilst in others its absence permits casual environmental vandalism and its validity is all too clear. Yahoo overland rallying without subsequent clear-up operations is desecrating huge areas of wilderness with non-degradable junk. Expeditioners who value the planet's spaces have a special responsibility.

payload (Section 2.6). Tools, spares and servicing aids must also be studied (Section 5.5). It is likely that in the majority of cases, ie those in which you already have the vehicle, you will be working this equation the other way round: knowing your vehicle and its payload you can work out how much it can carry and what its fuel-limited range is together with its off-road capability. This whole subject, then, amounts to matching the vehicle to the expedition or the expedition to the vehicle (see Section 4.1 'Expedition vehicles').

Vehicle power/weight ratio. Power/weight ratio falls off with vehicle size, in general terms – medium trucks vs 'light 4x4s'. High power/weight ratio is what you need for agile off-road performance where grip is poor – getting through soft sand or to the top of sand dunes, for example. This is all covered in more detail in Section 4.1.

Technical equipment. Apart from the obvious equipment associated with a scientific programme, where there is one, photographic, film, and especially navigation equipment and requirements must be considered. Again establish how near the 'edge of the graph' your plan is as early as possible; for example, if the piece of equipment is absolutely vital, should you take a spare?

Rescue/medical. Planning of medical supplies in a large expedition must be linked to assessment of the expedition's capability for diagnosis and administration of special medication – for example saline drips in cases of extreme dehydration. An inseparable part of medical planning is location of the nearest hospital and knowledge of medevac facilities. Think about, face and establish your approach on the question of rescue in the event of serious problems. Informing people of your route so that overdue action may be taken, the carriage of signal flares, whistles, heliographs, SARBE satellite-relayed radio emergency beacons, two-way satellite communications (voice or telex to lap-top) are among the wide spectrum of solutions. See Section 5.6 'Emergencies'.

Choose your vehicle(s) with enormous care and spare no effort to have them on the top line for the trip (see Section 4.1). Having the right papers is just as important, alas!

Paperwork

Bureaucracy takes time. Early in your initial planning be aware of the kind of paperwork you will need for your trip and double your first estimate of how long it will all take to get. When you find you have to treble it, put yourself in the position of those whose country you are planning to visit and ask yourself with what enthusiasm you would greet the idea of tourists trampling all over your backyard, whatever the benefits in hard currency, and whether you would not have a sneaking wish to install some kind of filtering and control process? That is what is going on when paperwork takes time.

Papers for them ... . Consider in careful detail exactly what paperwork you will take; it is a great tradition of all overseas expeditions that the bureaucratic obstacles are almost invariably more difficult to overcome than the natural ones; most of them are connected with having the right paperwork, the right number of copies, the right lists and all in the right language. Although by definition the world of bureaucracy is one of minutiae, grasp the big picture first and think in broad terms of what you are trying to do – the import and export of people, vehicle(s), goods and currency. The paperwork you need for national authorities and your own administrators will therefore be associated with these aspects:

- *People* – passports, visas, driving licences, health documents .
- *Vehicles* – log books, ownership, customs, insurance.
- *Goods* – lists, declarations, origin receipts, customs.
- *Finances* – declarations, exchange rates and records.

... and papers for you. There will then be your own paperwork requirements which will probably fall into the following compartments:

- *The trip, travel* – sea/air/ferry tickets, travel guides, books, maps, log.
- *The project* – textbooks, satellite photos, letters of authorisation.

- *The vehicle* – as above plus maintenance manuals, fuel log.
- *You and the crew* – diary/log, travellers cheques, cash, plastic, keeping your credit card people happy, post dated cheques, record of travellers cheques, address lists, emergency telephone numbers, medical insurance.

Paperwork – random tips

The book probably does not exist that contains all the tips that travellers in the past have to offer on the conduct of the war on paper. A few starting points are shown below:

- *Vehicle safe.* Have a cash-box or security box bolted into your vehicle somewhere out of sight to keep valuable documents and/or currency in.
- *Photocopies.* Have at least one high-grade photo-copy made of your passport front pages and the pages with visas on. Do the same for your driving licence, the registration document of your vehicle, and your equipment lists (so that these may be given to customs people).
- *Passport pictures.* Take spare passport photos in case special permits of any kind are needed that require a photograph.
- *Expedition file.* Make selections from the expedition file that you may wish to have with you on the trip – letters of authority and the like – and take photocopies or, in some cases, originals, leaving the photocopy on file.
- *Address list.* Take an address list on a single sheet of A4 (photo-copier-reduced to A5 if possible) of all the names, contact addresses, phone and fax numbers of people you may wish to contact in emergency while away. Include who to inform in case of loss of credit or bank guarantee cards.
- *Credit card cushion.* If you are likely to be away more than a month and intend using your credit card (or if your account was not cleared before departure) contact the credit card company and furnish them with one or more post-dated cheques to boost your account on the appropriate dates by which minimum payments have to be made when monthly accounts are submitted. Computers do not understand people being on expedition or extended absence and your account could be summarily shut down just when you need it most simply because a monthly minimum payment has not been received.

'Office' kit to take. A detailed list of 'Office' kit is at Section 2.1.1 'Typical kit lists', for a relatively simple overseas trip.

Not only the right papers but photocopies of passports, an on-board safe for storage are important. Your customs carnet (Section 1.2) is worth more than your vehicle!

Breath-taking Dali-esque landscape of almost surreal beauty has a unique magic. When you find one, freeze it in time and treat it carefully in case it shatters.

... but be prepared for this kind of thing every now and then!

Section 1.2

Preliminary planning:

Shipping

COVERAGE OF THIS SECTION

Major cost item. Shipping and all that goes with it will probably be the most expensive item in the majority of expedition budgets. Almost inevitably, when you are on site in the field you will be living under camp-out conditions and nearly always looking after your own food and accommodation at minimum cost. Unless you are lucky enough to be on the same continent as your project or chosen region and without any large intervening stretches of water, the cost of getting the expedition to that area will be the source of some pain to the expedition funds. It will be worth spending a lot of effort at the planning stage to minimise the effects of this financial storm zone.

Shipping options

Choices. The main methods of shipping, in ascending order of cost, include:

1. Conventional cargo. Here the vehicle is deck cargo or is craned into the below-decks hold of the ship. Usually passengers travel by other means. This is the cheapest method of shipping vehicles but they are at their most vulnerable to damage from falling cables and the like, theft and contamination from other cargoes. UK shipping professionals do not recommend this form of shipping for expedition vehicles but in certain areas overseas it may be the only means available and personal travel on the same ship is desirable to safeguard your equipment.

If a vehicle travels on deck for reasons, say, of inflammable liquids hazard, it will also be vulnerable to salt-water spray. This latter need not be as bad as it sounds if the vehicle is shipped on the aft well-deck of the ship (ie shielded from direct douching by waves or spray over the bow) and given a

'Conventional', uncontainered cargo is vulnerable to theft and damage unless you can travel with the vehicle.

Allowing time for planning is nowhere more important than when arranging shipping. 'Conventional' shipping as opposed to container is not normally recommended but here time allowed the vehicle crew to negotiate passage on the same ship.

Drive-on ferries are the ideal way of shipping and it is worth in-depth research on available services before firming-up expedition plans. Arrival formalities can be slow and chaotic; hone your easy-going patience and co-operation in advance.

also to exchange money and buy third party insurance – all before leaving the dock area. Arrival and customs clearance in some south Mediterranean ports can be chaotic and take up to six hours.

3. RO/RO (roll-on/roll-off). After delivery to an assembly area, usually at the port, the vehicle is driven by dock handlers onto and off a specialist ship designed to carry only vehicles – wall-to-wall in multiple decks. Passengers travel by other means. RO/RO services are not widespread and tend to be used by vehicle manufacturers despatching large consignments of vehicles. The vehicles being open to contract vehicle handlers at the ports, security is a major problem even with an empty vehicle. Unless the vehicle load is very well secured, a vehicle loaded with expedition gear could be taking a major risk from pilferage – mainly in the port assembly areas.

4. Container. The vehicle travels in a standard dimension, drive-in, steel container which is then locked and sealed and loaded onto a specialist container vessel. It is often possible to request 'inland delivery' after arrival at the destination port. Here the container, still sealed, is moved to an inland destination on the back of a large truck. Passengers travel by other means usually. The paramount benefit of container shipping is security against damage and theft which, in the case of a vehicle carefully loaded with a precise inventory of equipment, is vital. Pre-arranged, it is possible for you to drive the vehicle into the container yourself, be present when the container is sealed (you can note the container and seal number) and also be there when it is unsealed at destination. General-purpose containers come in lengths of 20 feet and 40 feet. As the diagram shows the former is well suited to carriage of single light 4x4 vehicles while the 40 foot unit could accommodate three Defender 90s or a pair of longer vehicles.

Note that the diagrams show vehicles without roof-racks. Clearance height of a standard general-purpose container entry portal is 2260 mm on the 40 ft container and

generous fresh-water hose-down on arrival. Given enough notice, expedition team travel on the same ship can usually be arranged. If that much travel time is available for the vehicle crew it can ease the security problem and usually forestall any bureaucratic difficulties on arrival at the destination port. In some parts of the world enjoying warmer climates, on-deck carriage of passengers is often the norm and it may be possible for you to live out of your vehicle when it too is on deck for a short journey. This kind of arrangement is very ad hoc and can be subject to last minute or en-route changes.

2. Ferry (drive-on/drive-off). Passengers drive their vehicle onto the ship, then travel in a lounge or cabin on the same ship. Standard procedure in Channel or Mediterranean ferries, this has enormous advantages in terms of (relatively) streamlined and timed departure and arrival rituals. A note of warning here. Not all drive-on, drive-off ferries are as quick to load and unload as those over the English Channel. Intra European travel requires little more than a valid passport but between, say, France and North Africa much more is involved – firstly a visa and, on arrival, the completion of immigration forms, declaration of currency and valuables, 'Carte Touristique' (a temporary import card for your vehicle, sparing you the aggravation of a carnet – see below). On arrival you have

If you have to ship your vehicle unaccompanied, a container is by far the best method. Be there for loading and unloading.

Container size options

20 ft container (top) will take any single Land Rover. 40 ft accepts three Defender 90s or two of most other light 4x4s; offers best economy for group.

Nominal 8 ft wide, 8 ft 6 in high general-purpose Container door aperture dimensions: width 2335 mm, heights 2290 mm on 20 ft, 2260 mm on 40 ft.

2290 mm on the 20 ft container. On the so-called '9 ft 6 in' 40 ft unit (ie a foot higher than the standard), the portal entry offers 2580 mm clearance.

Weights are unlikely to be a problem carrying expedition vehicles. Container tare (empty) weights vary between 1800 and 2500 kg for the 20 ft unit and between 3700 and 4400 kg for the 40 ft. Maximum gross weight (ie container plus its contents) are 22860 kg for the 20 ft unit and 30480 kg for the 40 ft, so even loaded vehicles are feather-weights in relative terms.

5. Air freight. Obviously expensive but not always as expensive as might be thought, air freight will have applications for special circumstances like getting a vehicle or a replacement vehicle to a particular destination in a hurry. Rates vary enormously according to destination and are not always based on air miles. Frequency of service (which reflects the volume of general air freight and thus how competitive the rates are) and the involvement of special all-freight aircraft will greatly influence cost. Use of 'wide-body' freighters (ie 747 type as opposed to 'narrow-body' 707 or DC8 aircraft) is relevant too. Most road cars (anything under 165 cm in height) will go in the under-floor hold of a passenger 747 but the 206 cm high Land Rover and virtually all other 4x4s have to go 'upstairs', ie on a specialist freight aircraft. Such vehicles can

Here shown in sea-freight container, vehicles need lashing when travelling as cargo. Be sure handlers have lashing rings to use and do not put chains or straps round axles to hazard brake pipes.

sometimes be squeezed onto 'narrow-body' freighters but only rarely with a roof-rack fitted.

Vehicles, except in one-off cases of travel on Hercules, Antonov or other military-type aircraft with a rear loading ramp, will be driven on to and attached to a pallet which in turn is loaded by fork-lift onto the aircraft and clamped to the freighter floor. Some operators will demand removal of internal kit such as expedition equipment, others can get round the problem. Advance notice is the nub of the question; security and dangerous goods hand searches may have to be carried out so arranging this in advance is crucial. Packing your kit in separate boxes within the vehicle, lashing those containers to the vehicle floor and covering the whole cargo area of the vehicle with a pilfer-proof net or similar will be fundamental to normal preparation for the trip anyway but it can

Know container door aperture dimensions. Most roof-racks will be ruled out.

Range Rovers paletted for loading onto the upper deck of a Boeing 747 freighter. Rate safety above possible loading crew irritation by developing concern about brake pipes; what is the routeing of the strop on the front wheel of the left-hand vehicle?

fundamentally help with air freighting. If you are not able to negotiate in-vehicle carriage of your expedition gear it will have to be packed into a separate crate and will be flown as a separate – expensive – item.

As with sea freight (unless a container is involved) air-freighted vehicles will spend time in a warehouse, hangar or on the tarmac and thus be vulnerable to pilferage unless you take the precautions above, and make sure they are thorough.

With air freight, a good agent can save you lots of money – as well as negotiating a loaded vehicle. Make contact well in advance.

Involvement of a resourceful specialist air freight agent is very much in your interest; they will invariably have negotiated per-kilo rates with the airlines way below the 'standard' rates. Like most things where maximum utilisation of horrifically expensive capital equipment like aircraft is concerned, air freight loading is modular, ie pre-loaded standard-sized pallets, are used. These pallets are 10 ft and 20 ft long so a Defender 110 would occupy 2 x 10 ft or a single 20 ft unit. Some carriers, Lufthansa for instance, have introduced a 16 ft pallet (4.9 m) onto which a 4.6 m Defender 110 will sit less wastefully.

The credo of virtually every expedition at all times is to be flexible and resourceful but this is no excuse for not making advance enquiries; always plan ahead. Preparation of

your expedition kit is one part of thinking ahead; knowing what vehicle preparation has to be done is another – see below under 'Vehicle preparation for shipping.' In general, airlines will require less than a quarter-full fuel tank; there is an even chance they will want batteries disconnected but some do not bother.

As with marine freight where *Lloyd's Loading List* is the 'bible', so Lloyd's own *Air Cargo Contacts* and the *ABC Air Cargo Guide* – the freight version of the passenger *ABC* guide – are the equivalent for air freight. Services, airlines, aircraft type, routes, will all be there. Getting hold of one and doing some DIY research can often bring potential solutions disinterested clerks do not come up with regarding choice of destination airport. As with ships, the port or airport is not always ideally situated so you'll probably find a long journey to final destination is involved; sometimes you will find you are weighing up alternatives. Again, as with ships, the quickest possible clearance of the vehicle, once it arrives, will save storage charges and pilferage risks.

Cost vs security. You will see in this spectrum of shipping options, especially in marine freight, the trade-off of cost against the security of the vehicle – and, in the expedition context, its carefully packed contents. Certainly security is a major concern where a vehicle is travelling already loaded with expedition equipment and is out of your immediate care. Even 'naked' vehicles, empty of cargo, can arrive at the destination dock gates bereft of wing mirrors, spare wheels and other sundries if not secured in containers for shipping or covered by special guards at the dock areas.

As already mentioned, crating removables and lashing the sealed boxes to the vehicle is one way of approaching this problem. Learn as much as you can about what is involved and try to ensure that it is only your vehicle that is taken for a ride.

Rubbing salt into this amoral wound is the fact that dock handling charges and sometimes-obscure peripherals – see typical-costs list – often comprise more than 50% of the total shipping cost. If the cost of departure and arrival add-ons hurt, remember a ship without a port to unload at would not be worth much and the infrastructure of ports – the cranes, the real-estate, the docks, the dredging, the warehouses and staff – all have to be paid for somehow and how more logically than by the cargo passing through.

Bottom line. Section 1.2.1 'Typical shipping costs' gives an indication of how costs are made up and also a comparison between shipping different combinations of Defenders to different destinations. Whilst the actual figures will date, the relationship between them is of interest.

The shipping process

Shipping agents. In general, ship operators are fed cargoes by one or more forwarding agents, sometimes confusingly referred to as 'shippers' though they don't operate the ships – you can find a sprinkling in *Yellow Pages* under 'Shipping'. This will be done, ideally, a ship-load at a time for a string of successive destinations on a given route. Knowing which ships go where and their timetable is your starting point. Your shipping agent will probably be referring, if you are in the UK, to *Lloyd's Loading List*, an encyclopaedic weekly publication which lists over 1100 worldwide destinations and the services available for the carriage of cargo from UK ports. Associated inland delivery road services are taken into consideration where applicable and the availability of wide-body air services also listed.

Shipping details. You will be informed of the receiving port (ie the port in the UK that receives your vehicle for shipping), the receiving period for cargo – usually a span of three or four days, the estimated time of departure of the ship, the en route time and estimated date of arrival at destination. Your 'receiving' or loading point may be inland – you can have a container delivered to your door provided you can load it whilst it is still on the truck.

Charges. In broad terms, charges will comprise the following (though they may not be listed under these exact headings):

- *Sea freight charges*
- *Outbound charges (on departure):*
  Container delivery (if you are using one and loading other than at the port) or transport within the port area.
  Strapping of vehicle in container.
  Customs inspection.
  Customs export clearance.
  Port charges.
  Marine insurance (covers en route and docks).
- *Inbound charges (at destination):*
  Port charges and/or 'wharfeage' based on value of cargo.
  Container transport within the port complex.
  Container unstrapping.
  FCL/LCL charges – see below.
  Customs inspection.
  Customs dues if any.

In general, the outbound charges and sea freight costs can be paid before departure but inbound charges will have to be paid on arrival at destination. Marine insurance is usually arranged by the agent and is based on the value of the cargo (and vehicle contents – a list will be required), 2.5% of the value of the vehicle and contents is a typical cost and there may an excess, ie you bear the first 1% of any claim. Some insurers

The peripheral charges associated with shipping will be an initial shock. But the infrastructure is huge and must be paid for.

Sometimes it is better not to look. With extra-ordinary skill or luck the Land Rover was inserted between the mast and the forestay without damage. Needless to say, this kind of ship-ping can rarely be booked ahead; turn up and start asking is the method.

will not insure vehicle contents on the grounds that they would have to spend unreasonable time checking pre-departure contents; with others there seems to be no problem.

FCL/LCL charges relate to 'full container load' or the extra handling involved when there is 'less (than) container load' – ie the container is shared with other cargo and some co-ordination is required during loading and unloading. This is unlikely to apply in the case of a vehicle where the whole point of using a container is to deny others access to it. Covered in more detail below is the question of customs dues and procedures.

Vehicles a special case. Cargo with wheels on always seems to attract its own vivid spectrum of special taxes and charges and even when temporarily importing a vehicle, special documents, procedure and sometimes large amounts of money in the form of indemnities etc are involved. Such vehicles on permanent import in many overseas countries would incur enormous customs duty – often well over 100% of its normal home value – so customs authorities take steps to motivate temporary importers to stick to their undertaking to re-export at the end of their trip! If you sell your vehicle overseas then duty is payable and the system in general operates on the basis of this

Bill of lading will be one of the most important documents you carry. It's the only way you will get your vehicle. You get the original.

duty being held available somewhere in case you do sell the vehicle. Inevitably in these sad times, shipping sometimes includes what can also take place at land border crossings – a random take-apart search for drugs. This will depend a lot on where you have shipped from.

Bill of lading. You will receive a bill of lading – in effect a receipt or consignment note – from the shippers or agent usually within a few days of the ship sailing. This is an essential and vital document and is what will enable you to claim your cargo at the destination. Be sure you get it and be sure it is not lost; there is only one original and that is what you or your agent will need to obtain your vehicle from the shipper at the arrival port.

Vehicle preparation for shipping

Regulations vary. Since regulations will affect the way you pack your vehicle and possibly the need for certain hardware modifications, be aware, well in advance, of any special requirements relating to vehicle preparation when it is to be shipped, containered, or flown to an overseas destination. These can include:

1. Lashing points. Most vehicles will have them but be sure your vehicle does have strong-points fore and aft to which deck/container lashings can be attached.

Paint them yellow or fluorescent to attract attention since throwing deck lashings around axle cases and crushing attached brake pipes is a tendency to which over-worked cargo-handlers are sometimes prone. There is something to be said for lashing a vehicle by its wheels so that the body is free to 'float' on its own suspension during a bumpy trip and the tightness of the lashings aren't compromised by the flex of the suspension; again beware brake pipes.

2. Fuel tanks. First ensure you have a fully serviceable fuel tank cap of the kind specifically manufactured for your vehicle – ie a good anti-slop seal and proper venting arrangements. Draining the fuel tank before loading is sometimes a requirement, some-times not; or a 'tank less than quarter full' requirement may exist. Sometimes, with equal disregard for logic and the laws of physics, draining down to around 4-5 litres is the requirement; whilst this will cover ter-minal area manoeuvring and thus make life a little easier, such a small quantity actually provides far more explosive vapour in the tank than a full tank. Petrol or diesel does not always make the difference you would expect though it should in most cases make the difference between a 'Class 9' hazardous cargo and a non-hazardous cargo.

Where draining is required this usually

will have to be done at the docks; know where the fuel tank drain plug is and what spanner is needed. The fuel will have to be drained into something and you may be the one to have to provide it.

Occasionally regulations even demand running the engine until the fuel in the fuel pipes is used up. *Warning!* Resist this if you can where fuel injection engines are con-cerned (diesel or petrol) since subsequent bleeding of the fuel system may be neces-sary on arrival at destination when you fill up and try to start the engine. Spill-return fuel systems often do not need bleeding; check the procedure on your vehicle before departure. **Important.** See page 5.5-7 regard-ing procedures for dry-tank fuel systems. If you have had to drain your tank for ship-ping you will, of course, need some cans of fuel on hand when you arrive too. Once again a dockside job possibly involving taxi rides to nearby filling stations.

3. Roof-racks. Note the height limita-tions mentioned on the preceding pages regarding containers. This is likely to be a very demanding limitation if air freight is concerned and checks on security of any roof load will be especially stringent – if such a load is permitted at all. The carriage of fuel cans or other heavy loads on roof racks (see Section 4.3) is not recommended

Find out 'prepa-ration for ship-ping' regula-tions well in advance. Finding out at the dockside can be a disaster in some cases.

One of the more challenging 'preparation for shipping' situa-tions. The three vehicles were too long for the Hercules so the Land Rover was driven onto the Bedford, de-wheeled, lowered and lashed. Plank 'ramps' were taken for the de-mount. Regulations demanded dry tanks, hence hand tow.

unless special and well-engineered modifications have been carried out to roof structure and suspension. Should these have been done, any roof mounted fuel cans will have to be empty before shipment by any means – with the possible exception of shipping as deck cargo and then only by special arrangement.

4. Batteries. Sometimes it is required that the vehicle battery is disconnected before shipment.

Warning! Beware of battery disconnect on vehicles with certain types of burglar alarms and follow the drivers handbook procedure; also vehicles may have one or more ECUs (electronic control units) that may have volatile memory and require re-programming. Important. See Section 4.6 for implications and effects of battery disconnection.

Do your home-work on the effects of battery disconnection – usually a shipping require-ment. Alarms and other electronic black boxes will be affected.

If you do have to disconnect the battery, keeping a ready-access spanner specially for this to be done in a hurry should be part of your expedition preparation anyway (a last-ditch procedure in the case of an electrical fire or harness-roasting short circuit on older vehicles). Well worth the trouble is ensuring that the spanner has an insulated handle so that when working in a dark container accidentally touching adjacent metal-work does not provoke a shower of sparks. Wrapping the handle copiously with insulation tape is effective.

For reasons of residual battery loads such as radio, alarms (even when not activated), disconnection of the vehicle battery before shipment can be beneficial when transit and possibly dockside storage periods are extended. Bureaucratic problems over claiming your vehicle will be enough without having to cope with a flat battery as well. (See also p 4.2 - 14 'Flat battery ...'.)

5. Battery vents and acid. Sometimes, especially with older batteries, air freighting will require the battery vents to be prevented from splash or spillage or vapour boil-off; stretching a toy balloon or a condom over each vent plug will allow expansion of the gas in each cell but prevent escape of the highly corrosive acid. If you are equipped

with the zero-maintenance or sealed type – and this, even with an old vehicle, will likely be part of your pre-expedition vehicle preparation – these precautions are not usually necessary.

6. Carriage of other special items. Inflammable fluids in the vehicle or explosives (such as rescue flares) are usually forbidden or may be subject to special regulations - eg having to be carried on deck or in special lockers on the ship.

7. Security against theft. It is in your own interests, however the vehicle is to be shipped, to ensure that unauthorised access to your valuable expedition equipment is impossible. Locked containers within the vehicle are the ideal since the appropriate keys can be retained by you. This is not always possible for everything so use a throw-over canvas or tarpaulin cover in the load area, strapped down and have bag-handles secured to strong points with bicycle cable locks or similar so that a quick lift of loose bags cannot happen – a favourite method of stealing.

8. Cleanliness. Pest and infection control regulations when shipping to some parts of the world such as Australia, New Zealand or the US require that the vehicle be steam cleaned to remove mud and dirt under the vehicle and within the engine compartment before departure. Do it in advance and avoid the implacable 'We won't ship it if it isn't clean and if you take it away to clean it you'll miss the deadline,' kind of situation so dear to officialdom.

9. Ventilated containers, deck cargo. Individual shippers' requirements regarding fuel tanks and the like are, clearly and understandably, concerned with the accumulation of potentially dangerous pockets of fuel vapour in a cargo area. Sometimes a container can be stowed above deck level and, additionally, be labelled with 'no smoking' warnings to indicate its inflammable status. Ventilated containers are available which permit air circulation around a secure vehicle without water ingress. There are also 'fan-tainers', open-top, even open-side – with bars – containers, but the standard general-purpose container does effect air change during a trip and these are the normal units used for shipping containered vehicles. Vehicles carried, uncontainered, on deck are obviously well ventilated and do not pose a problem.

10. Carriage of expedition fuel. Occasionally an expedition, for reasons of local logistics or costs at destination, may wish to ship drums of fuel and this, again with the appropriate advance discussion, can sometimes be arranged by stowing the drums separately at a certain part of the ship, usually on deck. As mentioned above, advance knowledge and discussion with the shipper is the key. Do not be tempted to regard this as a detail that can be attended to at the time – and be sure that your agent doesn't either; you could find yourself compelled to offload fuel and equipment on the dockside if the right amount of planning has not been applied.

Vehicle and driver documentation

Registration documents. Documentation for the shipping of a vehicle is fairly common-sense – ownership and registration papers being the most important. Registration documents – the UK 'Log Book' (V5), French 'Carte Gris' or your local equivalent – will tie the vehicle's registration number to:

• the registered owner
• the type of vehicle
• the engine number
• the chassis number or VIN (Vehicle Identification Number).

The engine number and VIN will be stamped or plated somewhere on the vehicle; be sure you can find these as customs (and any subsequent border) inspection will certainly involve your showing the customs officer the actual numbers. Sometimes these will be in dirt encrusted or inaccessible areas of the vehicle and may even need the use of a mirror to see them properly – engine numbers beneath exhaust manifolds used to be a favourite challenge though visibility is easier on modern vehicles.

ICMV. In the UK the AA or RAC can

provide a kind of vehicle passport, the International Certificate for Motor Vehicles (ICMV), valid for one year, which provides the registration document information in a slightly grander format for those countries unfamiliar with local UK paperwork or other specifically national forms; importantly, the information is shown in a range of different languages and scripts including Arabic. The list of contracting states is small (though it includes Iran, Iraq, Kenya, Cameroon, Nigeria, Pakistan and Tanzania) but, though the ICMV is mandatory in these countries, the document is worth having elsewhere for its translation of information. It also provides a way of stamping a vehicle in and out of a country.

Permanent export. In the UK the Driver and Vehicle Licencing Centre (DVLC) needs notifying of permanent export. This is done by issue of a Certificate of Permanent Export (Form V561) in exchange for the V5 'Log book'. The V561 will facilitate registration overseas. See also DVLC booklet V526 : 'Taking a Vehicle out of the Country'.

International Driving Permit. Also provided by the AA or RAC is the International Driving Permit, again valid for a year, which is in effect a translation of your driving licence data into an internationally recognised and multi-lingual format. Usefully, it includes a photograph. As above with the ICMV, the IDP is inexpensive to obtain and well worth having even when

Impassive officials can kill an expedition on the dockside if you don't have all the right papers. 'Internationalise' where you can – eg with the use of the ICMV.

specific regulations do not require it.

Letter of authority. Where you are driving a vehicle of which you are not the owner, for example vehicles loaned by a sponsor or commercial organisation, you will have to have a clear letter of authority in your possession from the owner shown in the registration document permitting you to drive the vehicle to the countries you are visiting.

Customs documentation. Customs documentation is dealt with more fully in the following section but a reminder here is appropriate. Take with you a list of the equipment carried in the vehicle; have it duplicated so you can leave copies with customs officials. Have it translated into the local language, and copied again. Special rules will apply to and papers be required for the vehicle – see below.

Customs procedures

Woo customs officials with lists, detailed knowledge of where everything is and a smiling willingness to unpack everything for them.

Principles. The principle behind all customs activity is that dutiable permanent imports have appropriate duty levied and paid. If temporarily imported they are normally not liable to duty though a small *ad valorum* levy, sometimes called 'wharfeage' may be charged; in South Africa, for example, this was 2.89% inbound and 0.89% outbound in 1995. Payment of duty is a well-enough known procedure but expeditions are usually in the temporary import business so, before letting the complexities of any one system overwhelm you, keep the broad aim in view – that of convincing the customs people that you will re-export the equipment you have brought into the country and possibly providing for them a bond or indemnity to cover the possibility of its not being re-exported. Establishing a bona fide temporary import is done in a variety of ways at destination or subsequent border crossings according to the regulations prevailing in the country you are visiting. Some of these procedures are:

• *Before departing your home country*
Obtaining a 'Carnet de passage en Douane' ('Carnet') – see below.
or

• *On arrival at subsequent countries*
Stamping the vehicle into your passport.
Use of the ICMV (see above).
Use of a visitor's 'Carte Touristique' (eg as in Algeria) which achieves the same procedure.
Depositing and later recovering a duty on the vehicle.

Lists of equipment. As mentioned above, step one, before getting to the vehicle itself, is to define your equipment by box and contents – 'Grey box 1, ..., Grey box 2...' etc. In general, lists should be sufficiently detailed to indicate you have nothing to hide and can locate any item the customs inspector may randomly point to but should not be unduly detailed so as to raise difficulties of minute translation or make it look as though you are importing a very large amount of equipment. Whilst most bags of 'personal effects' or 'clothing' etc will pass without comment, it is useful to have a list you can put your hands on if required showing camera equipment (with lens numbers etc) or other valuable items which customs officials may feel you could dispose of.

Electronic equipment. Like vehicles – as opposed to any other goods – when crossing borders, electronic equipment seems to occupy a special place in the perceptions of customs people. On many borders it has clandestine overtones and this comes down to the suspicion that the traveller is a spy. At the same time there do exist special international regulations regarding the use of radio transmitters – frequencies have to be cleared, approved and licences granted. (See Section 2.7 'Communications'.) Thus CB or other intercom radios will excite bureaucracy, curiosity and – if not properly licensed – confiscation (or worse) at borders. In general, to import a radio transmitter of any kind is a major undertaking that will require a great deal of preliminary leg work. That said, with proper advance clearance, two-way HF radios can sometimes be regarded by officials as part of an expedition's equipment and be waved through without comment.

Though in fact belonging to a completely

different category, electronic navigation aids can arouse similar suspicions in the uninitiated border official, albeit those in port areas will probably be more au fait with them. Whilst many that you meet will recognise that such equipment is a sensible and necessary part of your equipment and an aid to safety, you would be advised to accord it a low profile. Keep it out of sight if possible. Remove it and lock it away when approaching officialdom if you can (or, if it is a dashboard installation, throw a sweat-rag over it) and list it in your equipment as something innocuous such as 'electric compass' (an accurate description of one of its functions). Similarly, satellite-relayed UHF distress beacons (SARBE et al – see Section 5.6) are best kept out of sight.

Use of the passport. At its simplest, some border posts will stamp valuable items into your passport, writing a short list so that the existence of the items can be confirmed when you leave the country. This is a very elegant approach since it gets back to the overall aim of not disposing of dutiable goods within the country you are visiting. You can sometimes persuade officials to list any contentious items in the passport if they have doubts. Some countries will even list vehicles this way – infinitely simpler and more straightforward than the Carnet system – see below. You will, after all, always have to show your passport on leaving the country and the list alongside the entry stamp is a perfectly straightforward way of alerting the exit port of what you brought in.

Currency and valuables declaration. In some countries, declarations of foreign exchange on arrival will also include space for declaration of high-value items such as watches or cameras. These declarations, usually done in duplicate with the holder keeping a copy, can be checked by customs outbound to see that you still have the declared hardware and also that you have appropriate records of currency or travellers' cheques exchanged. Do keep these records or you may be liable to accusations of changing money on the black market.

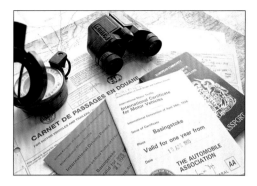

Carnet (photocopy shown) is an extremely valuable document; losing it could cost you a great deal of money. IDP (International Driving Permit), ICMV (International Certificate for Motor Vehicles) are most useful for their multi-lingual descriptions of driver and vehicle even though they are not a requirement in all countries.

Customs carnet

Purpose of a carnet. The concept of the customs carnet revolves around the ignoble assumption on the part of the customs authorities that, despite your stated intentions as an expeditioner, you are likely to sell your vehicle at a substantial profit within the country you are visiting and thus be liable for payment of a great deal of customs duty. To ensure that there is no trouble over this, if and when it should occur, these dues are held 'up front' by the means outlined below and, should your vehicle check-in to the country and not subsequently check-out, they will be claimed by the customs authorities. The amount of money involved is considerable and is routinely 150% of the home value of the vehicle or even up to 400%. Thus in the 150% case, the owner of a £16000 Defender might have to arrange for £24000 indemnity to be held on call against the possible selling, theft or write-off of the vehicle in a country he or she may be visiting.

Carnet procedures. The carnet, sometimes more descriptively called a triptyque, has a page for each country, each page consisting of three parts. One part is retained by the owner, and the other two are used at

Don't flaunt electronic equipment. As well as arousing suspicion, your vehicle can be noted by thieves' networks in foreign ports.

entry and exit points of the country concerned. On entry to the country the owner's section is stamped, and the entry section is also stamped and removed. On exit, the owner's section is stamped again to show the vehicle is leaving and the exit section of the page is stamped and removed. The owner thus has an authorised record of entry and exit for the vehicle and the country's customs authorities, by comparing paperwork from each border crossing or port, can also ascertain that a certain vehicle has entered and then left the country. The responsibility for getting the document stamped in and out of the country rests with the owner and, with at least 150% of the value of the vehicle riding on the correct discharge of the carnet, its importance can hardly be over-emphasised.

Carnets can involve indemnities up to four times vehicle value. It really is important to have it discharged properly entering and leaving a country.

Obtaining a carnet. A customs carnet can usually be obtained through the national motoring organisations – in the UK the Automobile Association (AA) or the Royal Automobile Club (RAC); local Chambers of Commerce issue carnets for consignments of goods (including vehicles on transporters) but not for driven vehicles. Depending on how many pages it contains (remember each country transited will require one page) a vehicle carnet will currently cost around £55-65. The AA or RAC usually will have the latest information so first find out whether the countries you wish to visit require a customs carnet when you enter at the border or port. Not all countries do and you are fortunate if this is the case. Then double check this information with the Embassy or High Commission concerned; don't be too surprised if you find the motoring organisations have the more accurate and up-to-date information. Your own and your vehicle's full details are required plus the all-important indemnity – the £24000 in the example above. Rates will not always be this high – or may be higher – but the issuing authority will be able to ascertain the correct figure to cover the worst case for the countries you propose to transit. The carnet will usually take about three weeks to prepare but you must arrange the indemnity

before that so allow five to six weeks for the whole transaction. A carnet is valid for a year but there are means of extending it. The carnet is a very important and valuable document and should be kept under secure conditions.

Disposal of carnet. On completion of the trip the carnet is returned to the issuing authority with each page showing the vehicle stamped-in and stamped-out from the countries visited. With this evidence the issuing authority can then declare the carnet discharged and release the indemnity. If for any extreme circumstances you were unable to get the carnet stamped-out, there is provision for a Certificate of Location to be signed at appropriate police or customs offices in your home country; this in effect is telling the issuing authority that all is well, the vehicle really is back home.

Carnet indemnity. Be clear about carnet indemnities from the start. Divest yourself of the idea that often prevails when large sums of liability are discussed, namely that 'the insurance' (or whoever) will look after that. With a carnet indemnity, whoever you raise the money through, it is you yourself that is, in the end, liable to find the money if customs dues are payable. Although in the case of failure to re-export, the country concerned will make their claim for customs dues on the motoring organisation issuing the carnet, that organisation will then invoke the indemnity you have provided for them and the cost of that will finally gravitate to you. That is why in practice, the authority raising the carnet – let us say the AA – will require proof that the required indemnity is in position before they can issue it.

DIY indemnity. The best and cheapest way to provide the indemnity, if you can, is to raise it yourself by transferring from another account the appropriate figure to be held by your bank for this specific purpose. The bank will raise a letter of 'set-off' – the form is impenetrably obscure so be sure it spells out what the money is for in plain English, even if you have to add it yourself in handwriting. They will hold the money, usually on an investment account, issue a letter indicating its purpose and then sign the indemnity form for the AA enabling them to issue you with the carnet. As indicated above, the AA will release the indemnity on receipt of the properly discharged carnet after the expedition. This way, although it is you that are providing the large sum involved, the money will earn interest whilst it is held and there is no residual non-returnable cost as in the case of a broker – see below

Indemnity brokers. If you are unable to raise the indemnity money yourself then there are brokers who can do it for you – two such in the UK being Campbell Irvine or R L Davison in London. In principle they will raise the money, sign the AA or RAC's indemnity form and charge you for the service at an appropriate rate. A recent quote for a figure around £24000 indemnity was £1500. This latter figure was roughly equivalent to the current base rate of interest on a loan of £24000 for a year and is a non-recoverable charge. Note however, that, as indicated above, if you sell the vehicle or it is stolen or destroyed and the customs people claim on the carnet then the buck still stops with you; ultimately you will still be required to make good the amount of the claim. Situations such as these emphasise what a hard world it is – you could have lost your vehicle and then be required to pay, on top of the £1500 for the carnet indemnity, the actual charge itself which could be a further 150% of the home value of the vehicle.

Double indemnity. If this prospect is too spine-tingling a risk, your broker can offer what is called a double-indemnity, which in effect amounts to you taking out an insurance policy against the loss of the vehicle and your having to repay the customs duty. In this case you would be paying, as before and as a non-recoverable payment, the fee (in effect the interest) on raising the indemnity money plus the 'insurance' premium against possible loss of the vehicle. As a very rough indication of costs here, the £24000 indemnity required for the Defender above would have cost £1500 to raise plus a

further £1200 for double indemnity – a total non recoverable charge of £2700. Rates, of course, will vary according to the current base rate of interest and the percentage of vehicle home value applicable to the countries to which you are going but the benefits of the 'DIY indemnity' above start to become clear – in this case £2700 saved. If the whole world of carnets and the safely ensconced 'ten percenters' on its periphery seems to you like taking a tightrope ride across the maw of a volcano then you are not too far off the mark. More soberly, however, it just requires that you do not sell your vehicle, take the greatest care it doesn't get damaged or stolen and drive it out of the country you brought it into. After all, that was probably your intention anyway.

Border deposit. Occasionally you may encounter a country that is not a signatory to the general AIT carnet system agreement that, caught on the hop, will require you to pay a deposit on entering the country which you can reclaim on leaving. In a perfect world with perfect communications between the 'in' and 'out' borders this can work. More often it can take months to get your deposit back and then possibly in a 'soft' or non-convertible currency. Try to avoid this at all costs; try to persuade the border officials to enter the vehicle in your passport alongside their entry stamp so that those checking you out can see that you should be taking a vehicle with you.

Be under no illusion: if customs claim on a carnet, unless you have taken out the already expensive double indemnity cover, the bottom line is down to you.

Even high-priced sheet metal like this can survive loading onto a dhow – albeit the railway sleeper slung under the chassis for the lifting ropes came close to demolishing the exhaust system. Don't be afraid to be a mother hen; it pays!

Waiting to be craned on board as accompanied deck cargo (above) and being there (right) when unaccompanied container is opened. These roof-racks (below) would preclude use of a standard container though may fit a 9 ft 6 in high version.

Section 1.2.1

Preliminary planning:

Typical shipping costs

COVERAGE OF THIS SECTION

Some typical shipping costs – 1997

Variations on a theme. Freight charges to different destinations will change almost monthly for a wide variety of reasons often having little to do with inflation. Competition, changes of service frequency, changes in major traffic patterns and fuel prices are among reasons for rates to go up and down. A snapshot of the early-1997 situation is provided here with quotes for shipping various combinations of Defender vehicles to Mombasa, Freemantle (Perth) in Western Australia and Buenos Aires. It gives an indication of how the total charge is made up; port activities and insurance add significantly to the basic freight charge. It is also an indication of how different operators levy not only different rates but charge for different services that may not even be defined by a competitor. And finally it shows that the final cost is surprisingly unrelated to distance shipped and depends more on who will have otherwise empty containers returning from port A, B or C and is trying to optimise the revenue.

Shopping around. What is also clear is the value of shopping around, especially if time forces you in the direction of air freight. Specialist vehicles-by-air concerns will have negotiated the best rates from the airlines on the basis of a large 'buy' of space and can invariably offer a single customer a sharper rate than you will get by approaching the airline direct. This is actually of some benefit to the airline who that way do not have to become involved in the minutiae of individual one-off customers. Moreover, a specialist will also be able better to handle the expeditioner's problem of expedition equipment going with the vehicle; he can either persuade the airline to let the kit travel in the vehicle or, if not, will certainly negotiate a better rate for it than if it were travelling as separate freight on the same aircraft.

The same will apply with sea freight shippers used to dealing with individual vehicle owners rather than large contracts for manufacturers – especially so in the case of RO/RO services. Container specialists often have set and routine vehicle collection and drop-off procedures should you wish to take advantage of them (albeit the optimum to go for, always, is to be there when the container is sealed and be there when it is opened at the far end).

Large containers pay. The cost per vehicle benefits of using a 40 ft shipping container for a small group of vehicles is well brought out as is the advantage of going LCL (less than full container load) though you will have to be especially sure, with a shared container, that you are present when the container is opened. What may be casual opportunist thieving to some dockworker could be a piece of vital expedition equipment from your vehicle. The diagram in Section 1.2 'Shipping' shows how 20 ft and 40 ft containers can carry various combinations of Defender.

Which method? Inevitably from the viewpoint of price and security against theft, the sea-borne container is the best bet for an expedition vehicle. Time, as ever, is worth money, and if you are really pushing the budget, a RO/RO passage could be made less risky by appropriate preparation of the vehicle, given the time to do it properly – classically by using a padlocked wire mesh cover over the cargo area of the vehicle or securely crating and lashing-down the other equipment you want to send with it to ensure it can survive the hazards of dock handling and time on the dockside.

Bottom line. The figures shown here do not all include destination costs and are unlikely to be indicative of costs when you decide to ship. It was deemed better, however, to show something – even a snapshot tied to a particular year like this – than nothing at all. The tables do indicate relative costs to the three destinations plus the relationship between light and heavy traffic routes. Sort out your UK and destination agents early. Few things will get you a better deal than the agent knowing you are in no hurry and are shopping around.

Costings for the ensuing tables are mid-1997 but will give an idea of make-up and relative costs for different destinations.

UK to Mombasa or Nairobi – sea and air

SHIPPING: UK TO MOMBASA – TYPICAL COSTS (£) EARLY 1997 – QUOTE 1
(Gibbons – Origin: Tilbury)

Shipping method/ item	RO/RO			Container 20 ft	40 ft	40 ft	Notes
Type and number of vehicles, eg 1 x Defender 110 = 1 x 110 (See container diagram)	1 x 110	3 x 90	2 x 130	1 x 110	3 x 90	2 x 130	
Container delivery – 100 miles	N/A	N/A	N/A				
Lashing in container @ £150	N/A	N/A	N/A	150	450	300	
Port charges	34	102	68	75	75	75	
Insurance – based on value	1.80%	1.80%	1.80%	1.50%	1.50%	1.50%	
Export documents	20	20	20				
Shunt				75	95	95	
Bills of lading				15	15	15	
Sea freight costs	974	2704	2127	1475	2945	2945	
TOTAL COST £ stg (Insurance not included)	1028	2826	2215	1790	3585	3430	Add insurance at *ad valorem* rate shown.

Sea freight time: Ro/Ro 8-10 day frequency. 23-26 day transit. Container: Weekly, 28 day transit

Destination costs: Not known

SHIPPING: UK TO MOMBASA – TYPICAL COSTS (£) EARLY 1997 – QUOTE 2
(P&O Containers – Origin: Tilbury)

Shipping method/ item	RO/RO			Container 20 ft	40 ft	40 ft	Notes
Type and number of vehicles, eg 1 x Defender 110 = 1 x 110 (See container diagram)	1 x 110	3 x 90	2 x 130	1 x 110	3 x 90	2 x 130	
Container delivery – 100 miles				245	265	265	
Lashing in container @ £60				60	180	120	
Port charges				75	75	75	
Customs				15	15	15	
Insurance – based on value							Est: £750, £1200 and £1200
Bills of lading (£15 & NSSN)				30	30	30	
Sea freight costs				1250	2500	2500	
TOTAL COST £ stg (Insurance not included)				1675	3065	3065	Includes container delivery but not insurance

Sea freight time: Weekly, 21 day transit

Destination costs: Agent's and customs charge not known							
Container delivery – 100 miles				531	1163	1163	
Port charges				44	50	50	
Wharfeage				63	125	125	

SHIPPING: UK TO MOMBASA – TYPICAL COSTS (£) EARLY 1997 – QUOTE 3
(Medite – Origin: Tilbury)

Shipping method/ item	LCL container – ie shared with other cargo			FCL container 20 ft	40 ft	40 ft	Notes
Type and number of vehicles, eg 1 x Defender 110 = 1 x 110 (See container diagram)	*1 x 90*	*1 x 110*	*1 x 130*	*1 x 110*	*3 x 90*	*2 x 130*	
Container delivery – 100 miles							Not quoted
Lashing in container				115	115	115	
Port charges @ £15 per cu m	215	254	284	-	-	-	
Customs	15	15	15	15	15	15	
Insurance							Not quoted
FCL port handling				75	75	75	
Sea freight costs	1105	1309	1467	1397	2759	2759	
TOTAL COST £ stg (Insurance not included)	1350	1593	1781	1599	2979	2979	Add insurance at *ad valorem* rate shown.
Destination costs:							Not known

AIR FREIGHT: UK TO MOMBASA – TYPICAL COSTS (£) EARLY 1997 – QUOTE 1
(Medite – Origin: Heathrow)

Shipping method/item	Air	Notes
Type and number of vehicles, eg 1 x Defender 110 = 1 x 110	*1 x 110*	
Air freight costs	4378	Air freight costs only. All other peripherals and insurance extra.

AIR FREIGHT: UK TO NAIROBI – TYPICAL COSTS (£) EARLY 1997 – QUOTE 2
(Lufthansa direct – no agent. Origin: Heathrow)

Shipping method/item	Air	Notes
Type and number of vehicles, eg 1 x Defender 110 = 1 x 110	*1 x 110*	
Airline handling @ £0.50 per kg	200	Based on 16 ft pallet, ie notional 2 x 10 ft @ notional 2000 kg ea, ie 4000 kg chargeable
Dangerous goods check	22	
Dangerous goods certificate	25	
Customs	22	
Insurance		Not specified
Documentation	5	
Air freight costs @ £1.1 per kg	4760	
TOTAL COST	5034	NB Insurance not included. Destination costs not known.

UK – Mombasa/Nairobi contd ...

AIR FREIGHT: UK TO NAIROBI – TYPICAL COSTS (£) EARLY 1997 – QUOTE 3
(Benco – Origin: Heathrow)

Shipping method/ item	Air	Notes
Type and number of vehicles, eg 1 x Defender 110 = 1 x 110	*1 x 110*	
Airline handling @ £0.50 per kg	200	Based on 16 ft pallet, ie notional 2 x 10 ft @ notional 2000 kg ea, ie 4000 kg chargeable
Security search @ £0.08 per kg	80	
Dangerous goods certificate	22	
Insurance		Not specified
Documentation	5	
Air freight costs @ £1.15 per kg	4550	
TOTAL COST	4927	NB Insurance not included. Destination costs not known.

UK to Freemantle/Perth or Melbourne – sea and air

SHIPPING: UK TO FREEMANTLE – TYPICAL COSTS (£) EARLY 1997 – QUOTE 1
(Gibbons – Origin: Tilbury)

Shipping method/ item	RO/RO			Container 20 ft	40 ft	40 ft	Notes
Type and number of vehicles, eg 1 x Defender 110 = 1 x 110 (See container diagram)	*1 x 110*	*3 x 90*	*2 x 130*	*1 x 110*	*3 x 90*	*2 x 130*	
Container delivery – 100 miles	N/A	N/A	N/A	-	-	-	Not quoted
Lashing in container @ £60	N/A	N/A	N/A	60	180	120	
Port charges	30	90	60	78	176	176	
Insurance – based on value	1.80%	1.80%	1.80%	1.50%	1.50%	1.50%	
Bills of lading	15	15	15				
Sea freight costs	1000	3000	2575	1054	2600	2600	
TOTAL COST £ stg (Insurance not included)	1045	3105	2650	1192	2950	2896	Add insurance at *ad valorem* rate shown.

Sea freight time: Fortnightly, 28 day transit.

Destination costs: Not known

SHIPPING: UK TO FREEMANTLE – TYPICAL COSTS (£) EARLY 1997 – QUOTE 2
(P&O Containers – Origin: Tilbury)

Shipping method/ item	RO/RO			Container 20 ft	40 ft	40 ft	Notes
Type and number of vehicles, eg 1 x Defender 110 = 1 x 110 (See container diagram)	*1 x 110*	*3 x 90*	*2 x 130*	*1 x 110*	*3 x 90*	*2 x 130*	
Container delivery – 100 miles				243	329	329	
Lashing in container @ £60				60	180	120	
Port charges				88	176	176	
Customs				15	15	15	
Insurance – based on value							Est: £750, £1200 and £1200
Bills of lading (£15 & NSSN)				30	30	30	
Sea freight costs				1219	2438	2438	
TOTAL COST £ stg (Insurance not included)				1655	3168	3168	Includes container delivery but not insurance

Sea freight time:	Fortnightly, 28 day transit	

Destination costs:	Agent's and customs charge not known						
Unlashing				$550	$1650	$1100	Australian $ – est
Port charges				$250	$750	$500	"
Wharfeage				$120	$120	$120	"

SHIPPING: UK TO FREEMANTLE – TYPICAL COSTS (£) EARLY 1997 – QUOTE 3
(Medite – Origin: Tilbury – FCL only)

Shipping method/ item	RO/RO			FCL container – ie your vehicles only cargo 20 ft	40 ft	40 ft	Notes
Type and number of vehicles, eg 1 x Defender 110 = 1 x 110 (See container diagram)	*1 x 110*	*3 x 90*	*2 x 130*	*1 x 110*	*3 x 90*	*2 x 130*	
Container delivery – 100 miles							Not quoted
Lashing in container				88	176	176	
Bill of lading				15	15	15	
Customs				15	15	15	
Insurance							Not quoted
Sea freight costs				1493	2987	2987	
TOTAL COST £ stg (Insurance not included)				1611	3193	3193	Add insurance at *ad valorem* rate shown.

Destination costs: Not known

AIR FREIGHT: UK TO MELBOURNE – TYPICAL COSTS (£) EARLY 1997 – QUOTE 1
(Medite – Origin: Heathrow)

Shipping method/ item	Air	Notes
Type and number of vehicles, eg 1 x Defender 110 = 1 x 110	*1 x 110*	
Air freight costs	15478	Air freight costs only. All other peripherals and insurance extra.

AIR FREIGHT: UK TO MELBOURNE – TYPICAL COSTS (£) EARLY 1997 – QUOTE 2
(Lufthansa direct – no agent. Origin: Heathrow)

Shipping method/ item	Air	Notes
Type and number of vehicles, eg 1 x Defender 110 = 1 x 110	*1 x 110*	
Airline handling @ £0.50 per kg	200	Based on 16 ft pallet, ie notional 2 x 10 ft @ notional 2000 kg ea, ie 4000 kg chargeable
Dangerous goods check	22	
Dangerous goods certificate	25	
Customs	22	
Insurance		Not specified
Documentation	5	
Air freight costs @ £2.75 per kg	11000	
TOTAL COST	11274	NB Insurance not included. Destination costs not known.

AIR FREIGHT: UK TO MELBOURNE – TYPICAL COSTS (£) EARLY 1997 – QUOTE 3
(Benco. Origin: Heathrow)

Shipping method/ item	Air	Notes
Type and number of vehicles, eg 1 x Defender 110 = 1 x 110	*1 x 110*	
Airline handling @ £0.50 per kg	200	Based on 16 ft pallet, ie notional 2 x 10 ft @ notional 2000 kg ea, ie 4000 kg chargeable
Security search @ £0.08 per kg	80	
Dangerous goods certificate	22	
Insurance		Not specified
Documentation	5	
Air freight costs @ £2.40 per kg	9550	
TOTAL COST	9927	NB Insurance not included. Destination costs not known.

A funny thing happened on the way to...... Algiers

Visa rules having changed between planning and arriving in Algeria we were sent back to Marseilles for the missing stamps; the Discovery was left in the port police compound for safe custody. Returning triumphantly visa-ed we found it had been broken into and three camera outfits taken; back to UK for a new window and cameras. A bad start; it pays to know the latest regulations...!

UK to Buenos Aires – sea and air

SHIPPING: UK TO BUENOS AIRES – TYPICAL COSTS (£) EARLY 1997 – QUOTE 1
(Gibbons – Origin: Tilbury)

Shipping method/ item	RO/RO			Container			Notes
				20 ft	40 ft	40 ft	
Type and number of vehicles, eg 1 x Defender 110 = 1 x 110 (See container diagram)	*1 x 110*	*3 x 90*	*2 x 130*	*1 x 110*	*3 x 90*	*2 x 130*	
Container delivery – 100 miles	N/A	N/A	N/A	-	-	-	Not quoted
Lashing in container	N/A	N/A	N/A	85	255	170	
Port charges	16	48	32				
Insurance – based on value							2.30% *ad val orem* – not included below
Bills of lading	20	20	20	15	15	15	
Sea freight costs	655	1718	1472	735	1425	1425	
TOTAL COST £ stg (Insurance not included)	694	1789	1526	835	1695	1610	Add insurance at *ad valorem* rate shown.

Sea freight time: Ro/Ro fortnightly. 25 day transit. Container: Weekly, 24-26 day transit.

Destination costs: Not known

SHIPPING: QUOTE 2 and 3. P&O Containers and Medite – no service to Buenos Aires

AIR FREIGHT: UK TO BUENOS AIRES – TYPICAL COSTS (£) EARLY 1997 – QUOTE 1
(Medite – Origin: Heathrow)

Shipping method/item	Air	Notes
Type and number of vehicles, eg 1 x Defender 110 = 1 x 110	*1 x 110*	
Air freight costs	9084	Air freight costs only. All other peripherals and insurance extra.

AIR FREIGHT: UK TO BUENOS AIRES – TYPICAL COSTS (£) EARLY 1997 – QUOTE 2
(Lufthansa direct – no agent. Origin: Heathrow)

Shipping method/item	Air	Notes
Type and number of vehicles, eg 1 x Defender 110 = 1 x 110	*1 x 110*	
Airline handling @ £0.50 per kg	200	Based on 16 ft pallet, ie notional 2 x 10 ft @ notional 2000 kg ea, ie 4000 kg chargeable
Dangerous goods check	22	
Dangerous goods certificate	25	
Customs	22	
Insurance		Not specified
Documentation	5	
Air freight costs @ £3.21 per kg	15000	
TOTAL COST	15274	NB Insurance not included. Destination costs not known.

AIR FREIGHT: UK TO BUENOS AIRES – TYPICAL COSTS (£) EARLY 1997 – QUOTE 3
(Benco – Origin: Heathrow)

Shipping method/item	Air	Notes
Type and number of vehicles, eg 1 x Defender 110 = 1 x 110	*1 x 110*	
Airline handling @ £0.50 per kg	200	Based on 16 ft pallet, ie notional 2 x 10 ft @ notional 2000 kg ea, ie 4000 kg chargeable
Security search @ £0.08 per kg	80	
Dangerous goods certificate	22	
Insurance		Not specified
Documentation	5	
Air freight costs @ £2.40 per kg	9550	
TOTAL COST	9927	NB Insurance not included. Destination costs not known.

Agents

Where to start? Shipping agents often specialise in different parts of the world, specific shipping lines, or specialise in RO/RO, general cargo, or containers. Whilst agents have all the inside knowlege they are not always prepared to pull out the stops for you. Private customers with tall 4x4 vehicles, usually loaded with expedition equipment and wishing to meet vehicles on arrival represent a discrete portion of the market: not always what a car-manufacturer-oriented agent is looking for. Others do specialise in individual customers.

Lloyd's Loading List – **the starter.** Some early research will pay off. Talking to the motoring organisations like the RAC or AA, to the shipping lines or airlines themselves will often get their recommendations of who can help or who their regular feeders are.

But *Lloyd's Loading List* is an invaluable expedition planning document in its own right. In many cases you will find yourself shaping an expedition around the existence of certain cargo services. *Lloyd's* is published weekly and is liberally interspersed with agents' advertising – there is usually a five or six page *index* to advertisers – so, as well as being able to contact those agents specialising in the particular route you are interested in (Assab and Djibuti leaving on a Thursday, San Juan via Baltimore?) you will come straight to the sharp end by contacting those buying space. They will usually have a special office or agent who handles private cars.

Lloyd's Loading List is not easy to obtain off the shelf but the odd copy (which is all you will need at first) can usually be ordered through WHSmith or you can ring Lloyd's of London Press on 0171.250.1500; they also, six monthly, publish *Air Cargo Contacts.* The *ABC Air Cargo Guide* is published by ABC International of Dunstable, tel 01582.600111.

Some shipping agents seem unusually afflicted by the 'NERB syndrome' (No-one Ever Rings Back) and you will be well advised to drop further enquiries at once if you encounter this. If you are outside their attention span at this stage it bodes not well for the future.

Some of the following have been very helpful in the preparation of this preceding material.

- *Container freight*

  Gibbons Freight Ltd
  Powell Duffryn House
  21 Berth, Tilbury Docks
  Essex RM18 7JT Tel 01375.843461

  Medite Shipping Company UK Ltd
  Medite House, The Havens
  Ipswich
  Suffolk IP3 9SJ Tel 01473.277777

  P&O Containers Limited
  College Road, Perry Bar
  Birmingham B44 8DR Tel 0121.252.4242

  Tilton Sons and Co Ltd
  58 Southwark Bridge Road
  London SE1 0AZ   Tel 0171.928.0175

  Kuhne and Nagel Ltd
  Cargopoint Heathrow
  Old Bath Road, Colnbrook
  Berks SL3 0NW   Tel 01753.686848

- *RO/RO (and other methods)*

  Cutler Freight
  2a South Gipsy Road, Welling
  Kent DA16 1JB Tel 0181.301.6626

- *Air freight*

  Benco Freight Service
  Unit 14, Trident Industrial Estate
  Blackthorn Road, Colnbrook
  Berks SL3 0AX   Tel 01753.686699

  Lufthansa Freight   Tel 0181.750.3100

  Dynamic
  Unit 1, Trident Industrial Estate
  Blackthorn Road, Colnbrook
  Berks SL3 0AX Tel 01753.682222

Lloyd's Loading List should be in your first-batch planning documents. AA/RAC, and ABC Air Cargo Guide are also valuable.

Section 2
Equipment planning

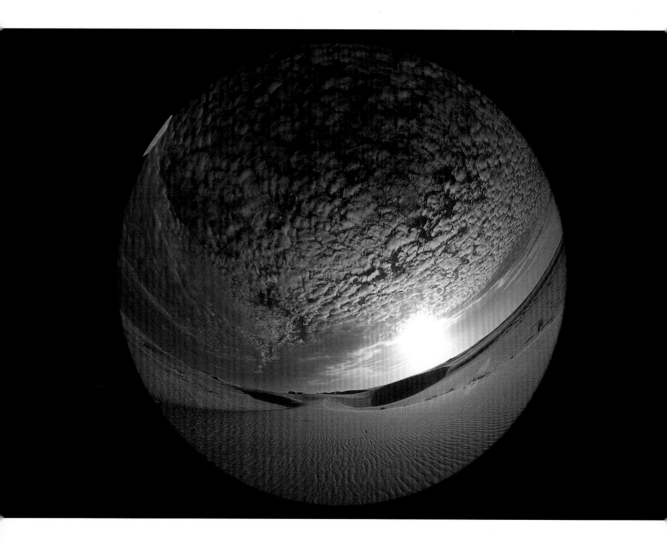

Section 2.1

Equipment planning:

Equipment basics

COVERAGE OF THIS SECTION

Succulents do it pretty well; humans have lost the art of 'living on nothing'. For an expedition, plan ahead – in detail. It's fascinating.

Signpost. Section 1.1 provided some broad philosophy signposts and a preliminary scan of planning parameters with references to later more detailed treatment in the book. Section 2.1 will treat equipment in the same way, though vehicles, as a special class of equipment, will be treated in more detail in their own section. Here in Section 2, after this 'basics' scan, individual sub-sections are devoted to:
- Camping – tents and sleeping equipment – Section 2.2
- Clothing and footwear – Section 2.3
- Cooking and food – Section 2.4
- Water – Section 2.5
- Fuel, oil, fluids – Section 2.6
- Communications – Section 2.7
- Electrical power – Section 2.8

Other equipment-related sections are:
- Vehicles – Section 4
- Routine – mobile, fixed base – Section 5.1

Detail – the essence

Plan with care. There is little doubt that part of the fascination of any expedition is in the planning – an appeal that extends, at the execution stage, to the situation you have built for yourself. Unlike day-to-day life where the burden of other people's bureaucracies, probably low standards and disparate aims bear down on you, here you are rebuilding a smaller, more ordered world centred on your expedition vehicle. You are in charge and can face, address and solve each problem according to your judgement. You will find the formulation and implementation of this judgement extremely satisfying, in some cases exhilarating, and it will be based on detail.

In a hundred instances you will be

It's your expedition. Few other projects will yield the satisfaction of planning it in well-judged detail to the highest standards you know.

assessing a need and matching the solution to it, facing up to influencing criteria, to pros and cons and realities. In selecting the equipment that will comprise a great part of your expedition world you will be balancing needs, solutions, function, cost, weight, durability and you will be seasoning the resultant brew in many cases with gut feel. How well you do this is crucial to the success of your trip and is a fascination in itself.

That said, all the detail on everything, all at once, will overwhelm you and, as with the rest of the book, precise access to what you want at a particular time is the aim here.

Need for thoroughness. There are few areas in which detailed planning and generally thinking things through count as much as in the field of selection of equipment for expeditions. When you are out in the desert or the bush, the forest or the tundra you are stuck with what you have brought with you and there is no opportunity to change or modify it – so choose well. One of the reasons why preliminary training (see Sections 3 and 4) is so important is that, apart from its obvious benefit in honing the skills required for the trip, it will help bring potential problems to light relating to the environment in which you will be operating – heat, humidity, cold, wet, sand, dust, wind, the need for lightness.

Plan, prepare and above all train with an eye for detail. Only that way will you be able to select the right equipment for your trip.

As in all aspects of expedition work, there is no substitute for detailed planning. You will make endless lists of equipment, and lists of where it is all stored, but it is the only way to ensure you have the right equipment when you need it – for living, surviving, keeping your vehicle fit, doing your project work – or just enjoying the trip.

In this section the emphasis is on equipment that will be part of a mobile, vehicles-based group. Where equipment is chosen for a base-camp operation the need for lightness and robustness will be less severe but bear in mind that even when gear is brought in and carefully unpacked for use at base, it will have had to be brought in by vehicle in the first place so that lightness is still important (see also Section 5.1 – Report on fixed-base operations).

Outdoor equipment – up-to-date advice. An ebullient market place for outdoor equipment – especially in the field of tents and clothing – together with the sheer inventiveness of the industry lead to continual product evolution and development. Adding in the less laudable swings of fashion makes it hard to give definitive advice in a section like this. An attempt has been made to distil the bedrock criteria affecting selection of equipment in the appropriate sub-sections, however. In some cases it has been necessary to go back to first principles and generics to help you see what is going on.

Some suppliers of outdoor equipment offer regularly up-dated catalogues that are extraordinarily comprehensive in terms of what is on the market. A few also give advice on the underlying design concepts and technical principles involved; these will be the best suppliers to deal with as this information is indicative of a product knowledge and standards that are prevalent throughout the chain and which they are not afraid to commit to paper. And it shows an ability to cut through competing promotional material to get, on behalf of you the customer, to the real selection criteria. Such a bedrock of written advice is a safety net for any variability in the standard of shop service though it should be said that most outdoor shops are staffed by enthusiastic users of outdoor equipment, often with the glow still in their cheeks.

A catalogue in which every product is uniformly hyped is of little use; listing a range of products against a set of relevant functional criteria and design features in a table so that you can see exactly what you are getting is more helpful. Such an approach is followed by the Field and Trek group (see Section 2.3) in a technical guide at the end of their brochure; the tabular comparison clarifies an otherwise complex task and enables you to select with precision according to your needs – there are a dozen criteria more important than price; for example, you do not always want the warmest sleeping bag or the stiffest boot.

Hours spent planning your storage (and that is what it will take) will pay off every mile of your journey. High density loads (fuel, main water, spares) go close to the mid-wheelbase point. Rations and the can-in-use go nearer the rear door for easy access. The boxed, modular approach is best; all containers lashed down. Elasticised net for featherweight items.

Weight – the main enemy

To those coming from hiking and hill-walking expeditions, it may be a surprise to learn that weight and bulk, in that order, are still overriding considerations in choosing equipment for a vehicle-dependent trip; the explanation lies in logistics. Vehicle-borne expeditions go further and for longer; vehicles need fuel, people need supplies. There is always a conflict between what you would like to take and the spare payload available on the vehicle. Never overload your vehicle; respect absolutely the manufacturer's figures for maximum gross weight. In the heat, grit, rough ground, corrugated tracks and dust that prevail in desert regions or the steamy wet grind of a rain-forest track, vehicles will already be operating in conditions close to their limits of strength and durability; to exacerbate the mechanical stress by overloading is foolishness that could provoke breakdown or mechanical failure in dire conditions of isolation.

Lightness is of fundamental importance – every list should have a column for weight. The spare payload of the vehicles used on your expedition will be dictated totally by the demands of the longest leg without refuelling or water availability; on these legs most of your payload is going to be fuel and water. Calculations of fuel consumption and time-in-the area (for example, litres per head per day of water) will govern what load is left over for other equipment or personnel. (Yes, personnel. You will have to limit the number of people in each vehicle according to your ability to carry their supplies and equipment.) These will be the governing figures for the whole expedition and, as already indicated in Section 1.1, will determine choice of vehicles, size, shape and duration of the trip.

Storage

Liquid containers. One of the pervasive logistical problems you will encounter from an early stage in your planning will be the transport of liquids in bulk. It is dealt with in detail at Section 2.5 and 4.3, 'Water' and 'Loading and lashing', but suffice it here to mention the following:

• *Fuel.* Consider the pros and cons of built-in long-range fuel tanks. In general modern vehicles do not easily accommodate this approach, certainly not on a 'do-it-your-

Any equipment overview must be based on a sober realisation of the importance of lightness. Never exceed your vehicle's maximum gross weight.

The desert is the ultimate test of your equipment planning – anything missing off your lists at this stage generally stays missing. Thoroughness of packing is also given a good test by the roughness of the tracks – usually in the form of corrugations (see p 5.3 - 33). This Discovery has had a bolted-in wooden 'skip' made to contain the plastic packing boxes and serve as a base for lashing-down.

Jerry cans areusually the best way of stowing fuel and water – but not on the roof. Modular plastic box storage is best for hardware. Strap them down.

self' basis because fuel systems often incorporate fuel return lines. Properly engineered modifications are sometimes available that will offer a useful contribution to – but not a total solution for – the problem. The main advantage of a built-in chassis-mounted auxiliary tank, of course, is that of stowing fuel low down and other than in the cargo compartment, thus holding on to cargo space and keeping the centre of gravity low. Remember, though, that the maximum GVW (gross vehicle weight) of the vehicle must still be respected. More usually and for ease of stacking and offloading, lightness and safety from the effects of a single leak, fuel containers such as 20 litre jerry cans are the best solution – but *not* (see Section 2.5 and 4.2) stowed on the roof.

• *Water.* Similar arguments apply to water with probably even more validity since you will almost invariably need to transport the containers to a tap in a corner of some courtyard or up some stairs in order to fill them. Only plastic jerry cans made of 'hard' polythene should be used.

Storage boxes. Regularise your equipment storage system. Make it modular using lidded, stackable, robust, plastic boxes of the kind found in DIY stores; they will protect the equipment from damage and dust. Eliminate rattles, strap things down. Label the boxes on the tops and the sides so you know where to find things – this will also ease your provision of lists for the customs people. Dealt with in more detail at Section 4.3, such boxes are the optimum answer to the storage of rations, spare parts and scientific equipment, even oils and hydraulic fluid. Take great care in selecting your boxes and try a few in the vehicle before going firm; some will be the right dimensions to get two-abreast snugly in the cargo-well of a Defender, others may be awkwardly over-sized or too narrow so that you have spare, wasted space. The right lidded plastic containers in which a top box will locate into a slight recess in the lid of a lower box will enable you to go to two layers or even three without danger of the load sliding about.

Cooking equipment – quick look

(See also Section 2.4). Early planning thought must be given to the way the expedition will cook and camp and what it will eat. For cooking, gas is the instinctive choice – for controllability, cleanliness and safety – if you have no gas supply problem, but this is unlikely in many expedition regions and you soon have to turn to liquid fuel stoves. Ideally, a stove that runs off vehicle fuel is to be recommended since that way no special container for cooking fuel has to be taken. This is becoming harder to accommodate as the specifications of vehicle fuels change. Most, to a greater or lesser extent, will 'coke-up' a stove so you must aim for a stove that can be cleaned to remove deposits in the field. Many can't be and in this case you must accept a gradual deterioration of performance and take a (fairly expensive) spare 'generator' – the coil of pipe that sits in the flame to generate gas from the liquid fuel.

Again the length of your trip will influence your choice; for example, a short trip would possibly enable a petrol stove to run on motor fuel for long enough before coking-up terminally. In most trips longer than around two to three weeks, you are probably going to have to plan a five or ten litre stove-fuel can into your load (see Section 2.5). If it is a short trip you will probably be able to fit in a can anyway.

Think about the number of people in the group. Do you need a multi-burner stove? Will it be on the ground, on a box, on a table? What about a windshield? An early mental note about pots and pans is worthwhile. As in the home kitchen, even more so

in the field, cheap thin aluminium pans will be very hard to keep clean, especially if used on a fierce-burning petrol stove. Thick-bottomed stainless steel utensils, carefully and frugally chosen, can be worth the extra weight.

'Washing up' is sometimes done in sand so take a stainless steel plate. Mugs made of double-skinned stainless steel can be obtained and these keep your tea hot for long periods as well as resisting the scratches. Aladdin make double-skinned insulated mugs in plastic (with non-spill lids) which are even more effective but not so robust.

Camping gear – quick look

(See also Section 2.2). The main pre-planning variables to decide on at the equipment initial scan stage concern the country, climate and time of year in which you will be camping and whether you will be using one big tent, two small tents, one small tent or no tent at all. If you are camping at all, the mix of hotels, rest houses and overnight camping in your itinerary will have only a small effect on the sort of equipment you take and its all-important weight and bulk.

Covered in detail at Section 2.2, slotting your camping conditions into the categories of cold/wet, hot/wet (tropical) or hot/dry (desert or bush) will dictate the type of tent you take. Hot climate tents ideally are tall, roomy and well ventilated compared to the low-profile cold/wet/windy European

Making the right choice of cooking fuel and method early on is important. Can you get gas canisters en route, use vehicle fuel or will you need a special fuel?

A funny thing happened on the way to.... Amadel-n-Anir

On the most micro-featherweight trip of all time I reckoned breathable motorcycle kit that kept out the morning chill at speed would, with just a bivvy bag, be warm enough to sleep in. Shivering, I couldn't believe the night ambient of 16°C – but noticed how crystal clear the sky was. Radiation would be strong. I pulled the wafer-thin 'space blanket' over me and bingo! Instant warmth!

*The heart-stopping grandeur of
the world's wildest places should
never blind you to your vulnera-
blity. The need for safety is paramount. Who knows you're there?*

*One tent, two
tents, or no
tent? Sleeping
mat, air bed,
camp bed? Do
you need com-
munications?
Safety is para-
mount.*

type. Depending on your group size, two
small tents will generally be easier to erect
and use than a single larger one but may
weigh more and take up more room. A vehicle-based tent – roof tent or add-on tent – is
another solution yielding safety, room and
convenience against bulk and weight.

What you sleep on – bed, inflatable mattress, self-inflating mat, foam mat – will be
influenced by whether or not tents are used
and which kind. This will also equally influence the kind of sleeping bag, inner and/or
bivvy bag used. Consideration of insect, reptile or animal hazards will also enter the
equation. A matrix of choices will present
themselves.

Whilst the great deserts are in many
ways a special case they exemplify the no-
tent case for sleeping out under the stars on
a low camp bed, garden lounger or safari

bed using a sleeping bag inside a bivvy bag
– with or without a mosquito net as the conditions may demand. In the bush, fenced-off
campsites and/or tents for protection would
be essential, of course.

All these variables are also influenced by
storage space. Whilst this book (see Section
4.2) does not in general favour roof-racks for
expedition work (certainly not heavy-laden
ones), the storage of *lightweight* camping
gear is one of the few recommended roles
for them. Camping gear is classic, low-den-
sity equipment (ie bulky but light weight)
that is only needed at the end of the day and
thereafter is best kept out of the way while
other access to the cargo area is made.

Communications – quick look

(See also Section 2.7.) A decision on the
need for and extent of on-board communications needs to be taken at an early stage
since there will be considerable cost, space,
weight, bureaucratic and probably training
implications. This will be especially so – and
particularly relevant to – fixed-base or field

base expedition projects where teams will operate at some distance. Consult specialists early to get a broad idea of equipment, official permission and cost implications.

Electrical power – quick look

(See also Section 2.8.) Depending on the size and role of your expedition and whether you will be using communications, you may find you have a need for electrical power. Mobile electrical power, charging sets, AC mains supplies, and solar panels for battery charging are some of the applications. All are quite feasible but cost and the ever-present and unforgiving enemy – weight – will be the problems.

Personal kit – quick look

The variables. (See also Section 2.3 for principles and design features in detail.) As with tents and sleeping gear, climatic and task-related variables will influence choice of personal kit. The obvious demands of cold/wet vs hot/wet or hot/dry will each present their own spectrum of clothing possibilities but to this should also be added considerations of operating conditions – routine outdoor, extra rugged, rocky, sandy, muddy, strong sun, heavy rain, need for leg protection against animal life. The need for various types of protective clothing against weather or for work (overalls, gloves etc) and the availability and frequency of laundry/washing facilities will influence the amount of kit taken and its bulk and weight.

Weight and baggage. What you wear plus between 15 and 20 kg, excluding sleeping bag, is a fairly generous maximum allowance for a long expedition. Plan your kit, put it together, pack it and weigh it a long time in advance to be sure you have the right gear; no one set of equipment will have so much effect on how you enjoy or function over the next few weeks as that in your personal luggage. Especially if a team is involved, be firm about weight limitations. Have people actually weigh their complete kit; it will foster the discipline and attention to detail that the trip will demand. Use nylon stuff-bags for peeled-off clothing,

a 'small kit' zip bag for regularly used items and having a 'best' bag for clean clothing ensures that what you take is safe and clean. Immensely strong, very lightweight nylon holdalls are currently available and have the advantage of stowing easily in odd corners of vehicles without rattling.

Framed rucsacs are space-hungry, puncture other containers or bags, are maddeningly difficult to stow and catch on everything in vehicles; avoid them. Day-sac rucsacs for trips away from camped areas are acceptable and practical but as regular luggage are rarely dust-proof enough, are forever falling over and the item you want is always at the bottom. You may find yourself putting up with this for their general convenience.

What to wear. Clothing is dealt with in technical and functional detail at Section 2.3 but the well-tried multi-layer principles of all outdoor clothing applications are always valid – an outer breathable wind/waterproof shell garment in Gore-Tex or similar with, beneath, a number of layers of thin garments that can be peeled off as required. If you are in the tropics or other hot climates, the constituency of that first layer next to the skin is very important; it will probably be all you wear for most of the time and getting the right 'feel' is vital.

It is worth reiterating the uses of nylon stuff-bags for peeled-off clothing which otherwise gets strewn round inside the vehicle and usually ends up under a jerry can or getting something unsavoury spilled on it. Despite a growing general awareness of the dangers of skin cancer through excessive exposure to UV radiation, it is still timely to repeat the warning about sunburn and keeping covered. In clear desert or mountain air – or *anywhere where the sky seems to be unusually blue* – sunburn can be ferocious in its severity and speed. Parts of the body unused to exposure can burn in as little as 15 minutes and cause the victim pain and inconvenience for a number of days as a result. In so far as wearing shorts or allowing undue exposure of the skin can also give offence in some Arab countries, long

Plan your personal kit a long time in advance. Try it, weigh it, know it in detail, reduce it as much as possible. Stick rigidly within the weight allowance.

Payload and range are acutely interdependent. Distance and time between replenishment points determines fuel and supplies load and the size/payload of vehicle required. <u>Never</u> exceed manufacturer's maximum gross weight.

trousers have a dual benefit.

In general, loose clothing that can breathe well is the principle to adopt – whatever the climate, but see Section 2.3 'Clothing'. Thin leather gloves and an oversize boiler suit (roomy and cool to wear over just underwear when it is hot) will keep you clean and unlacerated in mucky mechanical jobs or jobs around the camp – washing water will be scarce so it pays to keep yourself clean. Overalls will also give protection from sunburn in open vehicles. Beware of using ex-military camouflaged clothing in foreign countries as this can cause trouble until it is explained. In sunny climates, hot or cold, take a cloth sunhat with a wide brim to keep sun off your nose and ears.

Appearance. Being on an expedition is not a mandate for being unwashed, unshaven and scruffy. Even when water is scarce, washing is not impossible – see Section 2.5. Keep fresh clothes to change

Scruffy appearance is not part of being on an expedition. Washing and shaving is perfectly practicable and looking presentable will enhance border crossings.

into before entering towns after long periods out in the field if there will be contact with officials or you seek police/immigration permission for the next leg; the courtesy will often pay off. Officials are not normally impressed by unwashed or inappropriately dressed foreigners.

Be especially careful not to offend local sensibilities in relation to dress – or the lack of it. If in doubt, cover up. In most African countries it is considered offensive for men to be seen without shirts in public. In Muslim countries men should wear long trousers; in some countries it is an offence for women to wear shorts or slacks – dresses below the knee are more appropriate.

Footwear and gloves. Again, see Section 2.3 for detail. In cold or wet/muddy conditions there is a strong case for taking the usual outdoor walking boots and also a pair of rubber gumboots (big enough to take a lining of extra-thick stockings as well as robust socks). Getting walking boots wet on the inside by inadvertently sinking up to your knees is an error that will stay with you for some days. Invariably take a wet-proof bag in which to store the pair of boots not in use; stowage for these bulky and supremely awkward items is enough of a nuisance without them depositing wet mud over everything they come in contact with.

In hot climates there are two schools of thought in regard to footwear. One favours sandals for their ventilation and sand-between-the-toes; the other finds this produces dirty feet when water is scarce and affords easy access for insects. Desert boots of breathable soft thick suede leather are a good halfway house; they are light, very comfortable and not too hot but they do let in the sand (as there is no bellows tongue) and are not terribly robust. Lightweight walking boots – the type with flexible soles and Gore-Tex fabric panels in the sides – keep the feet clean and the sand out, are comfortable and provide ankle support and protection when walking or climbing on rocks. Contrary to expectations, they are not too hot. Canvas jungle boots, if you can get them, are worth seeking out.

A pair of featherweight moccasins or slip-ons are invaluable for end-of the day relaxing when in the camp; it is close to bliss when your feet break free of your heavy-duty boots and get into something light, airy and flexible. With care at the choosing stage these can be made to double as 'respectable' shoes when in hotels or on social occasions.

Choose gloves with great care too. The balance of warmth, grip and digital agility will need monitoring – Section 2.3 again.

Keeping comfortable. You can have a refreshing and effective daily wash with a wet Kleenex or paper kitchen towel. A Braun 'Sprint' battery shaver will give over two months shaving on one set of alkaline cells. Take a spare pair of sunglasses, lots of lip salve and Nivea, sun cream, a wide brimmed hat and a really reliable torch; a Petzl head-mounted torch is invaluable, leaving both hands free for what you are doing. List and weigh all your kit well in advance.

Typical personal kit list. See Section 2.1.1 for a typical personal kit list – an example of one man's personal kit taken on an eight week desert/bush expedition with minimal en-route replenishment.

'Office' equipment, paperwork

As your planning progresses the extent of the paperwork requirement both before and to take on the expedition will become clear. A very general overview was given at the end of Section 1.1 of the categories of paperwork with which you will be involved. In an overseas trip you are basically going to be involved with the export and import of people, goods and motor vehicles – motor vehicles, as you will see, always seem to occupy a discrete category and are treated differently from other goods.

Typical office kit list. See Section 2.1.1 for a typical office kit list.

Take care choosing footwear (and gloves). Suitable hot climate footwear is seldom available in European equipment shops. You will have to do some searching.

Briefcase on top of grey boxes (centre right) comprises 'office' equipment, documentation, maps. Orange-topped box lower right was film cooler; not really necessary – see Section 2.4.

Section 2.1.1

Equipment planning:

Typical kit lists

COVERAGE OF THIS SECTION

Personal kit

The following lists comprise one man's kit taken on a two-man, single vehicle, eight-week trip in desert and bush in early summer – night temperatures 5-25°C, day 20-40°C; 'smart' clothes were taken for formal meetings at embassies etc.

(Additions for winter departure/operation based on previous trips would be: Berghaus Alpine Extrem Gore-Tex jacket, Gore-Tex over-trousers, towel neck-scarf, Helly-Hansen fibre-pile jacket, fibre-pile sleeping-bag inner)

Wearing. T-shirt/vest, pants, Thorlo socks, lightweight Clarks 'Brecon' leather boots, lightweight polycotton trousers with zip pockets, LL Bean 100% cotton twill shirt, autumn-weight blouson.

Thin wallet worn round neck beneath clothes for max security
Passport
Travellers cheques (TC numbers in bag)
Cash – Francs, US$, UK£
UK drivers licence
Eurocheque card
Credit cards
NOK card

Samsonite zipped belt-pouch (13 x 19 x 4 cm) attached to belt
Travel insurance papers
Photocopy of passport
Photocopy of driving licence
Ferry tickets – Channel/Med
Eurocheques
International drivers licence
Vaccination certificates
Small calculator
Tiny torch (1 AAA cell)
Avomine
Immodium
Address stickers
Spare passport pics
Pencil/ball-point
Keys to luggage mini-locks
Spare vehicle keys

Lowe-Alpine small rucsac overnight 'ready-bag' – 50 x 25 x 38 cm
In Tupperware 125 mm sq sandwich box (used also as tiny washbowl): soapdish/soap, face flannel. Toilet bag with: Braun battery razor, pre-shave, toothbrush/paste (50 ml = 7 wks), shampoo (150 ml = 7 wks), Nivea, Lotil, spare lip salve, nail clippers, tweezers, scissors, clear plasters, hairbrush.
Also:
Light track suit (sleeping gear)
Small towel
1 T-shirt/pants underwear
LL Bean Trailblazer canvas shorts
Short sleeve shirt
1 pr spare Thorlo socks
2 handkerchiefs
Gem French dictionary
Heliograph and whistle
Mycota foot powder
Sunglasses
Sun screen – Ambre Solaire No 10
Sony SW1 short-wave radio
BBC World Service frequencies
Receipts for cameras showing origin
Insect repellent spray

Maloprim anti-malaria
12 Nurofen
Spare boot laces
Fly whisk
Alarm clock
Digital thermometer
Record of travellers' cheque numbers
Petzl head torch

Main bag, nylon zip-grip – 50 x 25 x 33 cm
'Embassy' kit:
        'Smart' polycotton trousers
        'Smart' polycotton shirt
        Tie
        Lightweight leisure shoes
Light sweater
Long sleeve 'Camel' thin cotton shirt
1 T-shirt/vest
1 pants
2 prs socks
2 handkerchiefs
Floppy sunhat
Spare reading glasses /sunglasses
Moccasins
Medium towel
Sewing kit
Plastic coat hanger
Bottle of liquid detergent for clothes wash
10 m nylon clothes line, 10 pegs
Wide range of strong polythene bags
Spare Jcloths (face flannels)
Spare batteries. Equipment, number and type of battery shown. Some stored in personal kit, most stored in Spares box 3 (electrical spares):
Shaver 3 AA, Sony radio 2 AA, Petzl head-torch 2 spare 3LR12 (MN1203), Canon flash gun 4 AA, GPS in portable mode 4 AA (2 sets taken), Philips tape note-book 2 AAA (2 sets taken), tiny torch 1 AAA. Canon EOS camera 2CR-5M lithium (4 spares taken), Pentax Spotmeter 1 4LR44 6v.

Top clothing for work/chores. (stuff bag). Feather-weight waterproof jacket and trousers, roomy boiler suit, light leather gloves, gardening gloves, floppy hat, woolly hat, water bottle and carrier.

Stored elsewhere
Compact camera (may be worn on belt-loops)
Philips 596 pocket memo – nav kit
Small binoculars – in door pocket

Sleeping/camping kit
(See also Sec 2.2) LL Bean 'Woodlands' #2 polyester tent or garden lounger/chair/bed, Thermarest sleeping mat, Gore-Tex bivvy-bag (Field and Trek), Mountain Equipment Lightline 550 sleeping bag, Mountain Equipment 'Sleepy' cotton sleeping bag liner, 'space-blanket' ground-sheet.

'Office' and navigation kit

For maximum mind-jogging value to the reader, the following lists are an amalgam of kit taken on three separate trips: a two-man, single vehicle, five-week trip in the Algerian Sahara and two trips round southern Africa totalling 11 weeks. It was convenient to keep the expedition paperwork and navigation equipment (including maps) together in the same brief-case to keep them clean and flat – hence their inclusion in the same section here.

Since much log-writing and other 'office-work' will be done in the vehicle, a flat working surface (a piece of hardboard) just over A4 size is very useful. Log-writing, navigation planning and similar pen-pushing activities were done in the evenings using a fluorescent light running – as was all ancillary equipment – off a second vehicle battery, not the main battery that would be used to start the engine in the morning (see Section 4.2 'Vehicle modifications).

Office' equipment and papers

'Official' papers:
*Passport with visa plus photocopy
*UK and International drivers licences
*Channel and Med ferry tickets
*Travellers cheques
*Eurocheques
*Cheque and credit cards
*Foreign currency cash
Vehicle registration document
Photo copy of vehicle registration document
(Further copy left at home)
International Certificate for Motor Vehicles (ICMV – see Sec 1.2)
Vehicle insurance papers, green card
EuropAssistance medical insurance papers
Purchase receipts for cameras etc
Customs carnet (see Sec 1.2)
Bill of lading (shipping – see Sec 1.2)
* = kept in belt pouch/wallet – See previous spread

Lists, files:
Expedition file with selected papers
List of UK addresses
Photocopies of proposed route
Photocopies of equipment lists
Photocopies of equipment lists in French (if needed)
Equipment location/box contents lists
Records, notes:
Diary/notebook, A4 spiral bound
Photo records notebook
Expedition purchases notebook
Vehicle fuel input/mpg notebook

Books, publications:
Accommodation guides (Logi, Auberges, B&B)
Ferry timetables
Sahara Handbook with town sketch maps
Hachettes *Guide Bleue, Algerie*
Appropriate *Lonely Planet* guides
BBC *London Calling*, current edition
Latest *Financial Times* World value of the £
French dictionary (in personal kit)
AA multilingual car parts guide
Desert Animals
Appropriate scientific monographs etc

(Office kit – contd)

Stationery etc:
Hardboard A4+ work surface
Air mail envelopes
Blank postcards
Carbon paper
Business cards
Address stickers
Elastic bands
Sellotape, masking tape
Spotstick glue
Scissors
String
Marker pens
Ball-points, Pentel pencil
Pencil leads
Stick of chalk (for marking cans)
Magnifier
Pocket calculator
Spare polythene bags
 (also in personal kit)

Other:
Key to vehicle cash-box
Spare vehicle keys (hidden)
Keys to any external equipment stowages

Navigation equipment – may be in second briefcase
(See also Section 5.2 Navigation)

Maps, etc:
Transit maps: France, Marseilles, Algiers
Map envelope – contents sketch maps
Map envelopes:
Michelin 953, 955, 972, previous exped map
 1:1m topographical
 1:500,000 topographical
 1:200,000 topographical
Satellite photos of special areas
Photocopy working copies of sat pics
Predictions of magnetic variation for spot lat/longs
Plastic protective map cases for maps and satellite images

Main navigation gear:
Sun compass
Silva 'Nexus' marine GPS, enlarged-scale cockpit readout, roof aerial
Philips 596 tape recorder note-book for nav log (with personal kit)
Spare batteries – see personal kit
Sony ICF 7600 short-wave radio – ditto
Sat-pic magnifier lupe with graticule
Hand-held magnifier
Silva type 80 fluid damped sighting compass (±0.5°)
Spare lightweight compass
Spare heliograph
Spirit level for sun compass
Spare gnomons for sun compass
30 cm plastic ruler
360° protractor
Dividers
Scalpel

Books, publications:
GPS instruction books
Nav logs from previous trips
Nav stationery:
       Pencils (various, to 4H)
       Eraser
       A4 graph paper for DR plot-outs
       Reporter's notebook (spiral) pre-ruled for nav and DR log

Nomad Mona Lisa

Section 2.2

Equipment planning:

Camping

COVERAGE OF THIS SECTION

CAMPING – TENTS

Tents – principles

Three functions. Few will be unfamiliar with what a tent is trying to do in general terms but, particularly in the context of the different climatic environments covered below, a quick recap on the three main functions will not come amiss:

- Protection
- Insulation
- Ventilation

The principle of the outer tent (flysheet – to keep out the wet) being teamed with the inner is well known. On its own an impervious outer will keep the rain off but cause unacceptable condensation of breath moisture inside as well as being the very worst sort of thermal barrier – a heat-losing radiator at night and a greenhouse to soak up heat during the day. However, a waterproof outer allied to – and spaced from – a suitable inner will at least provide the thermal barrier you need. If the inner is also made breathable and, important this, a degree of air circulation in the space between inner and outer is encouraged, then the problem of internal condensation will be addressed as well.

The amount of this circulation between inner and outer must be judged according to conditions. Too much will kill off the thermal insulation in cold conditions, albeit preventing excessive heat build-up in hot conditions. Too little inter-layer circulation and the condensation will run down the inside of the flysheet (or freeze on it) when it is cold and, when it is hot, will permit heat build up. When it is very cold you will probably be happy to accept some condensation on the flysheet in order to maximise heat insulation.

This initial recap is worthwhile since your decision on types of material and tent for the conditions you are targeting will depend on how you weigh the pluses and minuses involved.

The optimum mix of function – protection, insulation and ventilation – will vary according to where in the world you plan to use your tent.

Tents – materials

Selection parameters. As ever, selection of your favoured tent materials will involve balancing pros and cons in the light of prevailing conditions for your particular trip:

- Hot or cold, wet or dry
- Weight sensitivity
- Cost sensitivity
- Static camp or a daily move

Outer tent fabric. Most outer tents are made of coated nylon which is light, strong, waterproof, compact, can be shaken almost dry and will not rot if packed away wet (albeit it should be dried before packing away for any length of time). Polyurethane coating is the commonest and here the seams can be tape sealed. Elastomer coating actually strengthens the base fabric but seams cannot be tape-sealed; some designs go for this but with polyurethane coating on one side so that sealing can be carried out. Coated nylons are adversely affected by prolonged ultraviolet exposure – sunshine – causing it to fade, tear or leak.

Where a tent is left set up for an extended period, for example, as a base tent, deterioration of nylon in strong African sunlight has been reported in as little as six weeks. This has to be seen in perspective; six weeks continuous overhead sunlight is more than

UV light can cause deterioration of nylon tents when they are used in strong sunlight for long periods. Proofed polyester or cotton is better for these conditions.

many tents will see in a lifetime but the information is worth digesting. Many higher specification nylon tents are treated with a UV-resistant silicone elastomer coating to reduce deterioration.

LL Bean, the well known US manufacturer, produces a range of tents featuring polyester flysheets which resist the damaging effect of UV light and outlast nylon by more than 2 to 1 under constant sunlight.

Cotton outer tents are hard wearing, less affected by sunlight and robust enough to survive inexperienced or repeated handling such as that to which youth groups might subject them. Cotton, tightly woven, becomes waterproof when the wet causes the fibres to expand. Cotton is inherently heavier than nylon and when wet cannot be shaken dry – the water soaks in making the fabric even heavier. It does, however, breath while a coated nylon does not. It can be given a water-repellent treatment to reduce the amount of water absorbed and this also acts as a rot inhibitor. Cotton is a better heat insulator than nylon – cooler in summer, less cold in winter.

Inner tent fabric. Inner tents are usually made of lightweight breathable (uncoated) nylon, polyester/cotton or pure cotton fabric. This will be a of a sufficiently dense

Materials-wise, polyester flysheet is more UV resistant than nylon and, unlike cotton, is non-absorbent so dries quicker. It is also lighter but seems less 'boot proof'. Very light at under 5 kg, this LL Bean 'Woodlands 2' has the added height and airiness required for use in hot climates without sacrificing rain or wind resistance.

weave to preclude condensation drips from the outer tent reaching the occupants but breathable enough to permit the moisture caused by their breath to escape. As with outers, nylon wins on weight but cotton wins on insulation and its ability to absorb moisture and re-evaporate it across a temperature or humidity gradient.

Groundsheets. A point on construction first: the desirability of a groundsheet to be sewn-in passes almost without argument but do check as some tents are made without this feature. In this 'sewn-in' construction the groundsheet becomes part of the inner tent and doors and closures zip to it so that crawling insects and animals are kept out. It is usually also of the 'bathtub' type, ie it has shallow walls 5-10 cm high to keep out water as well. Only large heavyweight military-type canvas tents will be found without built-in groundsheets; separate tarpaulins, proof against soldierly boots usually do the job in that context. As for groundsheet materials in camping-type tents, coated nylon is again the most usual choice. PVC coated nylon is the most durable and the heaviest, again suited to group-use tents. Next in line, gaining in lightness but a little less durable, is neoprene-coated nylon. Polyurethane-coated nylon comes next and

is the most-used fabric. The lightest mountain tents sometimes have multi-coatings of polymer, and other combinations. If your tent has one of the lighter but less robust groundsheet materials take extra care in selection of your site; and if you are in a vehicle and can spare the small extra weight, use a protective 'pre-groundsheet' to lay first.

Poles. Ridge-tent poles and A-poles will usually be of simple alloy tubing, often in sections with each section linked to the next by rubber shock-cord or a spring to preclude inadvertent loss or confusion during assembly and putting away. Flexible rib-poles as used in geodesic tents (see below) are made in alloy or fibreglass – the latter being cheaper but liable to be brittle in cold conditions and not as robust as a well chosen alloy; the latter are usually the better bet, especially for an expedition in remote areas. For this job they are not just 'aluminium' which in pure form can be soft and 'soggy'; a carefully selected alloy that can take the bending and spring loads will have been used in the best tents. Group tents – those likely to be used by a succession of unskilled clients (see also below) – often have extra-robust spring steel rods as frame members and pay an appropriate price in weight.

Use a 'pre-groundsheet' to protect your tent from stones. Opt for poles of high grade alloy rather than fibreglass which can snap – at the worst times.

Inner of the LL Bean tent opposite offers mesh or rainproof door apertures as well as breathable mesh roof panels for bug-proof ventilation. Inner clips to springy alloy frame without need for fiddly 'threading' of poles. Detail design of tent is exemplary; T-section nylon pegs (left) seemingly indestructible.

Tents – weight.

Seeing the light. Never let it be said that this book departed from its near obsession with weight saving (!) but perspective is all and it is important to remember that the lengths tent manufacturers go to in order to keep weight down is usually based upon the precept that the tent – and a lot of other kit – will have to be man-hauled to the campsite. This inevitably also reflects on cost where the most exotic materials are used. On a vehicle-based expedition man-hauling is not always the case and there is little point in paying a higher price for a tent weighing half a kilo less than another version if you are going to use the tent by the side of your vehicle. That said, alas, many 'best spec' tents do assume that weight must be minimal and to get a really well designed tent you will sometimes get the 'added lightness' thrown in.

Tents – environmental conditions

Weather, terrain

Weather dictates. Once the decision is made (Section 2.1) that tents are to be used – the alternatives of huts or sleeping out having been ruled out – choice of tent is straightaway influenced by the weather conditions you will encounter and the nature of the terrain on which you will be pitching. Flysheets, tent material, porches, covered cooking areas, stowage areas, ventilators, netted windows and entrances, valances for snow or rocks, groundsheet type, build and material, the tent's basic structure and reliance on guys and pegging – all these items are influenced by weather (more accurately, climate) and terrain.

Terrain – pegging. Many tents are self-supporting – the geodesic ones, once assembled, will stand on their own without pegs or guys and can thus be moved around in the erected condition before any pegging or guying is done. The traditional ridge tent in effect uses the earth as a structural member and, once pitched cannot be moved unless it is disassembled. Rock will not take pegs, and sand or snow will hold them insecurely unless they are a special length and build. Even self supporting tents will blow away so valances (flaps at the bottom of the flysheet which can be weighted down with rocks, earth or snow) or a guying system may be essential for where you are going.

Conjecture a quiet valley meadow where every peg can be inserted in the right place and the inner and outer kept taut and apart on the simplest ridge tent and then, in contrast, think of a windy, rocky, open site where pegging is a challenge and wind flap and touching inner and flysheet will cause insecurity and wetness to intrude. Your position between these two extreme scenarios is what you must consider for your particular usage of a tent.

Pegs. Whilst on this subject, pay close attention to the tent pegs you use. Some manufacturers supply bent wire or thin metal rod of circular cross-section as tent pegs. A tent peg's function is invariably to supply resistance to a strong lateral force and the larger the side area it can present to the ground the better it will be able to do this job. Bent wire or thin rod pegs have a very small side area so pull out laterally fairly easily; they also have a tendency to bend when being hammered in. Use a T-section peg if you can (see photo previous page); it has greater side area. Surprisingly, they don't take up a lot of extra room in the tent bag. The special nylon ones appear to be indestructible and are light too.

Seasons usage. A 'seasons usage' rating (three seasons, four seasons, etc) is sometimes allocated to tents to distinguish – usually in the context of cold climates – a tent that is more or less robust; those that will flap frighteningly in strong winds or merely

Euro-catalogues major on tents for overnighting on K2 – low, small, aerodynamic. If you are going tropical you'll want different design features. T-section pegs are best.

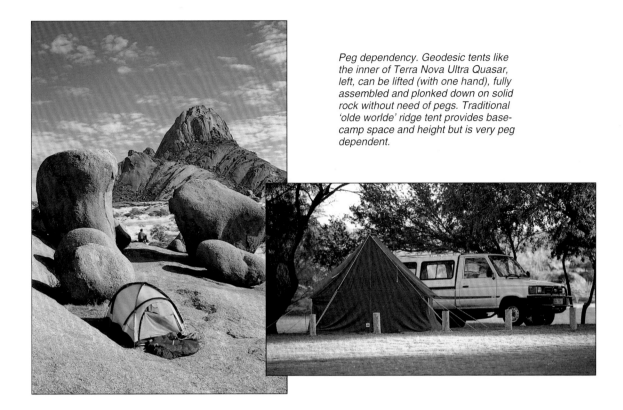

Peg dependency. Geodesic tents like the inner of Terra Nova Ultra Quasar, left, can be lifted (with one hand), fully assembled and plonked down on solid rock without need of pegs. Traditional 'olde worlde' ridge tent provides base-camp space and height but is very peg dependent.

give a little and shudder, those that will succumb to condensation, those that will bear snow or those that will not. The seasons rating is a good indicator to the resistance of a tent to rough weather but beware since it invariably gets used in the context of cold/wet/windy climates and does not always indicate suitability in other climatic regimes.

Cold/wet tents

Match specification to conditions. Illogically, a common ideal of a 'good' tent seems to be one that has been on an expedition to Mount Everest or other extreme cold/wet/windy environments. Such tents, to have done well, will clearly be 'good' but it pays to remember that these are tents for one set of conditions only – dramatic and demanding conditions, certainly, but by no

means conditions that encompass all expeditions. An ideal tent for hot/wet and hot/dry conditions will be very different but must be no less well designed – see below.

In cold wet conditions thought will have to be given to the basic design in relation to the practical implications of being both cold and wet; ease and speed of erecting the tent, stowage of wet kit, cooking under a canopy or in the teeth of a gale. A front and rear 'porch' – the space outside the inner tent but still covered or shielded by the flysheet – will be essential to accommodate both these requirements and the need to remove boots on entering all but the most robust of group tents (see below) will have to be remembered too.

Ease of pitching. Give a lot of thought to the ease with which a tent can be pitched and the conditions under which this will

Cold/wet usually means windy too. Low-profile tents with covered porches for kit and cooking are usually the best for such conditions with flysheets down to the ground.

Terra Nova Ultra Quasar from previous page with flysheet in position. An excellent design, very light (3.6 kg) and optimised for cold/wet/mountain conditions, many will find tents of this size and design claustrophobic and lacking ventilation when used in hot climates.

have to be done. Will it be so cold that you will be pitching your tent with gloved hands, and if so how 'fiddly' is the tent? How easily do the geodesic poles thread through the channels? Some geodesic tents are erected framework-first so that the tent inner is then 'hung' from the frame and the flysheet put on afterwards. This has an initial appeal but such tents are sometimes less taut than ones in which the geodesic poles are threaded through tunnels first. This is not always so; the L.L.Bean 'Woodlands' tent has a 'hung' inner which is as taut as you could want.

Design criteria for 'cold/wet' tents almost invariably assume man-haulage so lightness is a pre-requisite. Though valuable, this can add considerable cost.

Some tents are pitched flysheet first so that the inner can be inserted beneath a sheltering flysheet if it is raining when you pitch or strike camp. This is a useful way of preserving a dry inner but does mean you must crawl around inside to reach the back of the smaller tents and you will probably need a small sheet of plastic in order to keep your knees dry whilst doing this. There may be problems getting the inner taut enough when you do things this way in windy conditions.

Lightness is expensive. Especially in the cold/wet scenario the material from which the tent and flysheet are made will be important (see above) – even more so if your vehicle will be at 'base camp' and there will be tenting that has to be man-carried to a site farther up a mountain. Here the subtleties of the materials manufacturer's skill – performance without excessive weight – will be very important. It is this 'technical' aspect that is most reflected in European vendors' catalogues – very clever materials, strong, very light. For example UK manufacturer Terra Nova Equipment use a material they call 'Watershed' for their top of the range fly sheets. This is a polyurethane-coated rip-stop nylon with a strong ultra-violet protecting silicone elastomer on the outside that permits full hot-sealing of seams as well as minimising UV damage to the nylon at clear-air high altitudes encountered on mountains.

Hot/wet tents

Rare breed. Nearly all the sophisticated design and materials technology evident in European equipment has been directed at tents for ultra cold/wet/windy or high altitude conditions. Profiles are low to combat wind and shed precipitation. Tropical, subtropical or even temperate zone summer conditions demand a totally different approach and here the compact Euro-tent, however brilliant technically, will almost certainly feel unacceptably claustrophobic and stuffy.

Height, space, air. Height, spaciousness, ventilation, roll-down windows, robust fine mesh panels in sides and roof to let in air and keep out moths and mosquitoes – plus the ability to withstand sudden storms – become the design criteria for tents to be used in tropical or sub-tropical regions. Difficult to obtain in Europe, such tents will be more widely available in the areas to which you are going. Expeditions to those areas could make advance enquiries and buy on arrival or choose during recce visits. These tents produced, for example, in South Africa tend to be of a less 'technical' type; well made, very robust canvas, with solid steel rib poles (and a much higher basic weight) is a typical specification – but they are extraordinarily strong and ideal (see below) for the rough and tumble of group use as well. Their use of light strong canvas instead of nylon confers a certain amount of breathability, good heat insulation and immunity from the destructive effect of prolonged UV exposure – especially important where tents are used as base units and left standing all day in the sun.

Whilst there is no substitute for seeing, examining and feeling the goods, tents of this airy, roomy kind (actually suitable for hot dry as well as hot wet – see earlier spread) are however available by mail order to anywhere in the world from the American LL Bean leisure equipment organisation. Very well designed and light for their size, the Woodlands series of tents offer the high quality construction of a European tent in an airy tropical format; non-nylon, coated polyester flysheets are used for resistance to UV. As with many 'fine' tents, an additional under-ground-sheet is advisable to protect the tent floor fabric from stones or rough ground. LL Bean have a manned, 24 hours-a-day UK mail order service operating a freephone line to the US (0800.962.954) and incoming duty and VAT are included in the prices.

Netting, extended flysheets. Where a fairly wind-sheltered site can be assured, the use of a net-enclosed awning area (see photo LL Bean Space III Tent with Net Enclosure on page 16) could be invaluable where sit-down evening paper-work – or just relaxing – in a mosquito-free area is required. This kind of tent could make a practical and sensible base tent – see below.

In tropical monsoon conditions you will be seeking tents of this roominess and vol-

Height, space, air, roll-down mesh windows and UV resistant flysheet become important design criteria when tent is to be used in tropical conditions.

This tent (Cristy Sport, Cape Town) is excellent for hot humid or hot dry conditions. Outer is more a shade awning and will have a hard time in a tropical downpour. Where regular heavy rain is expected, ridge tents with ample stand-up headroom and steep sloping extended flysheets will be needed; surrounding dug drains also an advantage.

Compact two-metre Cristy Sport design, left, and four-window type above have high-sill built-in groundsheets and epitomise bush-optimised tents used in Southern Africa.

'Dull' colours – greens, beige – best for tropical tents. Built-in groundsheets most important to keep out ground-life. Shielded camp-sites preclude wind buffet.

ume with extended flysheets so that really heavy rain can be shed well away from the base and groundsheet. You will likely be digging small drain channels around the base of the flysheet so that water can in turn be led away from the tent area and reduce the magnitude of the quagmire that will otherwise ensue.

Colour. Colour will be important in so far as the flysheet should cast a deep enough shadow to be cool and in this case a light coloured inner could be beneficial for the spread of light within the tent. The traditional khaki or olive exterior, as well as being sufficiently unobtrusive not to offend human or wildlife, will fulfil this requirement without absorbing (and re-radiating) the higher heat load that a very dark fabric incurs. Yellow or light coloured tents often attract insects – another reason to opt for a khaki/olive exterior.

Groundsheets. Groundsheet requirements will be similar to those of tents opti-

mised for cold wet conditions, ie a 'tray' or 'bathtub' groundsheet with small vertical sidewalls to keep wet out. These will need to zip closely to door closures to prevent entry of inquisitive insect, animal or reptile life; such life may in any case seek the space between the ground and the groundsheet for protection and it is only a matter of time before they become upwardly mobile. Clearing the tent site of sharp objects before pitching and not wearing boots in a tent that could snag or tear the groundsheet and thus allow water or insects into the tent is doubly important in tropical conditions.

Wind buffet. The spacious, well ventilated tents you seek for hot conditions, sometimes with awnings as well, will inevitably be tall and more susceptible to wind buffeting. This is an inevitable trade-off for the characteristics you want but jungle and bush conditions by definition usually imply surrounding trees which will keep wind speeds moderate. You will probably also be seeking to pitch tents under (carefully vetted!) trees in order to keep internal temperature as low as possible anyway.

Hot/dry tents

Space – again. See hot/wet above – virtually all the choice criteria applicable to the selection of a tent for hot/wet conditions also apply to one for hot/dry bush or desert environments. One of the differences regarding optimum tent specification would be in relation to terrain/pegging (see above also). A moment's thought will at once conjure the difficulties regarding pitching tents on stony or rocky surfaces, the problem of clearing a site so that stones do not damage the groundsheet or of setting tent pegs on rocky ground or on sand; importantly too, the exposed nature of desert terrain and the frequency of strong winds at certain times of the year must be considered.

Self-supporting, strong. Especially in desert regions, tents can often be dispensed with for sleeping (see below) but if a tent is to be used a self-supporting geodesic tent would again be recommended. In most cases full flysheeting can be dispensed with

for lightness and simplicity though it does enhance heat insulation; worth it if weight permits. As well as accommodating the shape, size, ventilation and roominess criteria referred to above under 'hot/wet' tents, the South African tents of the kind illustrated are first class for hot dry or bush conditions. The Cristy Sport tents (Diep River, Cape Town, tel 021.72.4616), for example, either have no flysheet or a small 'top cap' and awning solely for shade. Very strong and durable even with prolonged exposure to strong sunlight, such tents – in either the 2.0 or 2.5 metre square size are very practical where tents are needed in hot dry conditions to keep out insects and animals at night and provide shade during the day. Their relatively high weight – less critical for a vehicle-borne tent than one to be man-carried – is offset by their extraordinary robustness, ability to withstand being tripped over or trodden on during inexpert erecting and striking by novices in a group.

Tent sizes and types

Base/group tents

Group 'HQ' requirements. Some expeditions, involving groups of people, will find themselves with the need for a headquarters or assembly shelter, often static for a period of time. Such a role is ideally met by use of a local hut if one is available but if this is not possible an 'HQ' tent for eating, briefing or evening work is one solution to the needs of a static expedition. When truck-based, the role can often be met by the truck itself or by an awning extending from the truck side though this solution ties the shelter to the presence of the truck which may well be required for use during the day. This particular requirement should be seen as separate from the need simply to sleep a group of 10 or more people, this latter being far better solved by the modular approach – a number of roomy two/three person tents

that occupants pitch themselves.

Weight, durability, heavy-use groundsheets. Large base tents or the smaller sleepers to be used by a single or successive groups are worth separate consideration from those referred to on the past few pages since the concept highlights the problems and requirements of heavy use, people trudging in and out of an HQ tent, and possibly inexpert users pitching and striking accommodation tents. The instinctive and natural solution to these heavy traffic problems is the right one – a robust, heavy, canvas tent of the kind used by the military with boot-proof tarpaulin groundsheets laid as a separate item before the tent is erected. Sleeping tents should of course still have a sewn-in ground sheet to keep out animals and insects; the criteria affecting selection of these smaller tents are covered above.

A roomy, heavy-duty HQ tent is often a necessity for an expedition with a semi-fixed base camp or a group-use requirement. Consider a bug-proof 'lobby'.

'Boot-proof', strong canvas tents with plenty of space is the ideal for group use – especially where people may be inexperienced in the niceties of putting tents up. Large ebullient groups are often perceived as overwhelming campsite facilities and much else. The low-impact approach is best – even in choice of tent colours, as here!

Big, HQ tents are best selected by reference direct to specialist manufacturers , suppliers of ex-army equipment or youth group suppliers such as Cotswold Camping (Cirencester, tel 01285.860.123) who have a range of 'patrol' tents and mess tents. Be aware, however, that tents of this kind are extremely heavy and bulky, usually including wooden tent poles of two metres in length and requiring medium trucks for transport and a team of people to erect them. They are not likely to be practical for an expedition comprising only light 4x4s such as Defenders or Discoverys or even an expedition that is constantly on the move; they should be considered in the context of fixed-base operations – see Section 5.1.

For groups, a number of small tents is better than one large one. Be generous with space if you can – two people in a three-man tent, for example.

Two/three/four person sleepers

Selection of two/three/four person sleeper tents is critically dependent upon the weather/climate criteria in which they will be used – cold/wet, hot/wet/, hot/dry – and this will dictate small low profile, close-cowled tents or tall roomy ones, each of which would be totally unsuitable in the other's operating environment. It is essential to give detailed consideration to these criteria and the subject is dealt with fully under the relevant climatic regime headings on previous pages.

On a vehicle-dependent expedition be as generous as you can with tent space, especially in hot climates – two people in a three-man tent, for example. Man-carried equipment has to be more tightly specified on weight and bulk but a well selected tent on a vehicle-based trip should be able to afford you the relative luxury of a little more room in the tent.

Vehicle roof tents

Elegant but heavy. (See also Section 4.2). So elegant does the idea of a roof tent seem at first that it is hard to remember sometimes that there are cons as well as pros to the idea. First of all your vehicle must be equipped with an appropriate roof-rack, indeed a special rack often designed especially for, and coming with, the roof tent you select. This in turn must be properly mounted and in many cases specially reinforced. The Defender (see Section 4.2) is particularly in need of engineering attention if a substantial roof-rack is to be fitted; some models have aluminium gutters completely unsuited to the absorption of heavy roof-rack stresses and they will fatigue.

In the context of an expedition and the higher stresses and rough roads likely to be encountered, an internal roll-cage taking loads through to the chassis frame is the

Classic roof tents offer comfort and security from animals and insects. Choose carefully; awning side apertures, above, a thoughtful design.Steel-topped pick-ups take roof-rack loads better than alloy Defender structure on rough roads. Ladder to ground can get kicked away; better as shown here

best basis for any kind of heavy duty roof rack, especially on a vehicle with a light superstructure like the Defender. Bear in mind in any case that a heavy-laden roof rack, whatever other logistical problem you may have on your hands, should be avoided on an expedition vehicle for reasons of handling and centre of gravity position; also remember that the vehicle's maximum gross weight must still not be exceeded.

Limit roof load. All this said, once the roof rack, its credentials and structural integrity have been established, an appropriately designed roof tent, with stowage limited to low density items of bedding and sleeping bags, should not put more than 100 kg load on the roof – indeed *that would be a sensible upper limit figure for any roof-rack on any vehicle*. Provided this is the target figure, structural and handling problems will prob-

ably be avoided.

As the illustrations show too, nearly every installation will involve the roof tent unfolding so as to be cantilevered over the vehicle bonnet and supported there by an access ladder or other struts. This enables a kind of 'patio' area, aft of the tent to be available on the roof. There will also be noticeable aerodynamic drag and some noise penalties to be paid with the tent folded and the vehicle in motion; somehow the unit never folds down to the size and thickness that theory would lead you to expect. Be very careful about the height of the folded structure in the pre-expedition days when you are still negotiating car park booms and even your own garage.

Safety from animals – of all sorts. The advantages of a roof tent, however, are considerable and particularly so in bush coun-

Conceptually appealing, roof tents do incur a high roof-rack weight penalty. Rack itself must be properly mounted structurally – specially important on Defenders.

try where there may be danger from animals. The hazards and difficulties of pitching a tent in the dark, on soft wet ground, when you are late or when there is no official campsite – even the hazards of theft – are elegantly and reassuringly overcome at a stroke. The benefits will not be universal, of course, being, as already indicated, more applicable in warm climates.

Susceptible to wind. Cold, particularly windy climates, highlight the very high side profile of the roof tent and will result in considerable canvas flap and rocking of the vehicle to the extent that some sites will be too exposed to be acceptable. Remember that frequently when there is a wind you tend to use the vehicle as a windbreak for a ground-borne tent; in the case of a roof tent the unit is probably three times as exposed. Consider this when planning your itinerary; the shelter of barns, trees, scrub – or the absence of wind – are important. Few, if any, roof tents are equipped with flysheets as such so performance in heavy rain will bring its own problems.

As with conventional tents there are designs more and less suited to the various climatic regimes. Once again the criteria mainly concern side or end ventilation panels with appropriate anti-insect netting.

Vehicle-attached tents

Ground level accommodation. A variation of the side- or back- awning is the vehi-

When weighing comfort and convenience against weight , remember the roof tent has enormous side area and will be susceptible to wind rock in exposed sites.

cle-attached tent. Where height of the vehicle must be kept within specific dimensions, where a roof-rack is not available or you wish to avoid one, where the overall height and susceptibility to winds on exposed sites is likely to be a problem or where you want stand-up height or don't like climbing ladders, a vehicle 'annexe' could be the solution. One such annexe, the well-established UK-made Caranex model, has a very significant weight advantage compared to roof racks and roof mounted tents, weighing in all, under 8 kg including the extra poles for the 'free-standing' feature.

And remember, if you are trying to devote the maximum proportion of your permitted gross weight to actual goods rather than the means to carry them, the weight saving of not having to have a roof rack is enormous. Though bulkier than a small tent to stow – the bagged unit measures just over 1m by 30 cm – it compares well with a frame tent of similar size.

Basically comprising a rearward awning/tent extension to the back of the vehicle with a 2.1 m by 1.53 m (7 ft by 5 ft) floor area, the Caranex – or similar units – has the advantage of joining up with available space in the back of the vehicle to make a single large area rather than separate small ones so that cooking or other operations involving access to storage within the vehicle can be undertaken without leaving shelter. The sewn-in groundsheet would offer normal tent protection against crawling insects and the like. Unlike a lot of tents

Terra firma, less weight, no roof rack. Vehicle-attached tents such as the Caranex sacrifice some off-the-ground security for stand-up space, continuous access to back of vehicle and huge weight savings. Free-standing arrangements enable vehicle to be driven off.

Field and Trek catalogue tech guide product analysis table – tents

Catalogue Code	Manufacturer and Model	Page Number	£ Price	Number of Sleepers	Seasons Usage	Weight (grams)	Packed Pole Length (cm)	Porches	Inner Tent Shape	Inner Tent Fabric	Outer Tent Fabric	Ground Sheet Fabric	Poles	Pitching
TENT FEATURES														
32046	D of E Hoop	141	219.95	3	3	4150	55	1	T	Breathable Nylon	PU Nylon	Neoprene Coated Nylon	A3	O
32039	D of E Ridge	141	219.95	3	3/4	4150	47	2	R	Breathable Nylon	PU Nylon	Neoprene Coated Nylon	A3	O
32072	Khyam Explorer	136	269.00	3	2	7500	80	1	D	Breathable Nylon	2oz PU Ripstop Polyester	2oz PU Nylon	F	S
32055	Khyam Igloo	136	199.00	3	2	5000	73	1	D	Breathable Nylon	2oz PU Ripstop Polyester	2oz PU Nylon	F	S
32054	Khyam Highlander	136	159.00	2+	2	4400	77	1	D	Breathable Nylon	2oz PU Ripstop Polyester	2oz PU Nylon	F	S
32080	Khyam Vis a Vis	136	319.00	4	2	8500	96	1	2xR	Breathable Nylon	2oz PU Ripstop Polyester	4oz PU Nylon	F	S
30047	Macpac Nautilus	133	249.00	2	2/3	2600	40	2	T	Breathable Nylon	Nylon	Nylon	E	S/I
32057	Macpac Microlight	133	199.00	1+	1/2	1800	40	1	H	Breathable Nylon	UV40 Nylon	Nylon	E	S/I
32040	TNF Mountain 24	128	350.00	2	4	3820	62	2	D	Ripstop Nylon	Silicone Elastomer Ripstop Nylon	Scotchguard Coated PU Taffeta Nylon	E	I
32012	TNF Expedition 25	128	450.00	3	4	4420	49	1	D	Ripstop Nylon	Silicone Elastomer Ripstop Nylon	165 PSI Nylon Taffeta	E	I

ivi Bags Technical Guide

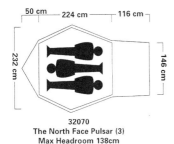

50 cm — 224 cm — 116 cm

232 cm   146 cm

32070
The North Face Pulsar (3)
Max Headroom 138cm

Tent buying in UK is hugely clarified by acquisition of a good catalogue such as Field and Trek (tel 01277.233122; see p 2.3 - 53).Table shows analysis by size, weight, usage, scale diagrams, left.

however, with room to stand up or use camp chairs in, this kind of unit provides a useful 'doing things' area that can be utilised the whole time and then be used as a sleeping area at night. With the appropriate extension poles to lend it extra stability when the vehicle is removed, it can be left as a free-standing headquarters if you are in one location for more than one night or, having arrived at a campsite, wish to use the vehicle.

Spacious, can be customised. Like the roof tents referred to above, the Caranex does not have a flysheet but since the

enclosed volume is a lot greater than a tent and the seals where it meets the vehicle sides will not be perfect, condensation and run-down in cold climates will be less serious.

In standard form the Caranex is temperate climate optimised but there is available a customising service where any modifications can be carried out on purchased units. Thus to 'tropicalise' a Caranex with the fitment of one or more mesh windows for extra ventilation would be a simple matter. In hot climates the lack of a flysheet may increase heat load internally when the sun is high but the larger size of the unit together with the vent aperture and large door will make it, even before 'tropicalisation', less hot than a small, low tent.

Caranex is at Oban, Argyll, Scotland, PA34 4RB, tel 01852,300258.

Vehicle-attached tent extensions offer stand-up space, access to the back of the vehicle for food preparation etc in bad weather and do not need weight of roof-rack.

Security – animals, insects

Mosquito nets – in-tent and outside, head-nets, repellents. Market place offerings are always changing but face squarely your needs in relation to excluding mosquitoes and other insects and creatures from

your sleeping accommodation. Literally, the problem will not go away. In big tents, mosquito nets can sometimes be hung inside; in smaller ones, netted windows and doors and the use of a spray before going to sleep is the alternative. If you are sleeping outside LL Bean have a 'Bug Bivvy' that provides a netting awning over the top end of a sleeping bag or the 'Bug shelter' that can be used on a hammock or on the ground. Netted hats are also available but these are more suited to waking wear than for use in a sleeping bag. A repellent sprayed around the head also helps.

Mosquito nets themselves can be treated with a mosquito-killing or repellent treatment so that the insects cannot bite any part of your body that rests against the net inadvertently. Permethrin is one such compound. It ensures that a mosquito that finds its way into your net will not stay around very long to bite you; a treated net – treatment lasts 3-6 months – can be of a less fine mesh than an untreated one and will enhance ventilation and movement of air in tropical conditions.

Animals and crawling things. In some areas of the bush it is essential to sleep in a tent rather than outside because of the danger of animals. Some authorised campsites are unfenced and the implications are clear. Even when leaving the tent at base for a day's outing, be sure it is zipped up and secure. Baboons and monkeys are very quick to learn the 'benefits' of human habitation – chief of which is rummaging in dustbins or inside tents for scraps of food. It is widely said that elephants have an almost

In some areas – game parks typically – sleeping outside a tent can be recklessly dangerous. Taking measures against insects, groundlife and thieves is important too.

uncontrollable liking for oranges, can smell them from extraordinary distances and will do anything to get to those that they scent. Whilst this cannot be personally confirmed the shortage of volunteers willing to undertake a controlled trial probably indicates discretion – and storage in polythene bags and sealed containers – being the better part of valour!

Human hazards – security of vehicle, equipment. Sad but almost inevitable is the need to secure your camp against thieves. Before turning-in for the night, pack all equipment into the vehicle and lock all doors and windows. Even in your tent do not leave equipment around on the floor; there are numerous tales of sharp knives slicing into tents whilst the occupants sleep. Disillusioning though these stories are, the remedies are fairly straightforward. Sleep with your vehicle keys, wallet or whatever actually in your sleeping bag. Vehicle burglar alarms are obviously beneficial though most work only after the window or door has been forced or broken. Alarms do exist – the Clifford 'Sense and Tell' synthesised voice warning, see Section 4.2 – that sound off before any breakage has occurred. A demonstration to local inhabitants never fails to produce top entertainment value and laughter but also subtly gets the message across to pre-empt the possibility of criminal behaviour.

Maddening if you are trying to catch up on paperwork or just eat, moths and other insects attracted to lights at night, mosquitoes at any time and flies by day can be kept out of your expedition by a net enclosure such as LL Bean's here shown on their vehicle tent. Useful for a group 'base camp' in wind-sheltered spot.

CAMPING – SLEEPING EQUIPMENT

Sleeping out

Sleeping with no tent

Lightness, simplicity, bivvy-bags. No tent equals lightness, speed and simplicity. Sleeping under the stars is an experience not to be missed and there will be certain expeditions where this is both safe and practical, allowing elimination of a tent's weight and bulk which can usually be allocated to more important items. If cold will be a problem use a fibre-pile 'inner' to your sleeping bag (see under 'Sleeping bags' below), plus a Gore-Tex bivvy-bag.

A bivvy-bag is in effect a loose, hooded 'outer cover' into which you insert your sleeping bag; it can be zipped up at the top end, is proof against wind, rain or sand-storms and, in Gore-Tex, is breathable. Over a sleeping bag on cold nights or used on its own in summer, it keeps out warmth-seeking spiders or other crawling creatures. A mosquito net is necessary (one-point suspension type can be hitched to the side of your vehicle) in some parts of the world; it will often stop enough breeze to double as a ventile form of tent.

Killing radiation. Because of the contrast with day temperatures and the very high radiation rate it feels very cold indeed under clear skies at night. This is especially noticeable in the desert despite temperatures being no lower than 0 to 10°C. A 'space blanket' – the type with one side aluminised – spread loosely over the sleeper and weighted on the ground with stones, bright side towards the wearer, is spectacularly effective in reducing warm-body radiation under clear-night conditions.

Sleeping off the ground – safari beds. If weight – and space – allows, a lightweight aluminium alloy garden lounger that converts from a chair into a bed is a good multipurpose investment with a pay-off of a very

Lying down under the stars can be so beautiful it's a shame to go to sleep! A bivvy bag forms a breathable wind barrier if needed. Cooling by radiation can be strong.

A garden lounger (left) is awkward to pack but can be used as a chair or bed to keep you off the ground and very comfortable. Despite some reports to the contrary, aluminised 'space blanket' (below) reduces radiation cooling. Doubles as groundsheet.

good night's rest and, in chair mode, respite for aching backs around camp in the evenings. Such a bed will keep sleepers 20 cm off the ground and away from crawling wildlife. Put a storage box under the head-end when you get into it or else you will find the bed will tip as you get into your sleeping bag. Particularly if you are bony and lack 'natural upholstery' you will get a remarkably comfortable night's sleep, especially if you use a sleeping mat between your sleeping bag and the bed for insulation against heat loss.

The disadvantage is that this sunbed type of device folds no smaller than around 60 cm square by 12 cm deep and is awkward to stow in a vehicle; it is a natural candidate for roof-rack stowage (bulky, low weight) if you have one. It will also be too high to use in many tents. Unlike the traditional (1930s!) wooden camp bed it has feet that comprise horizontal bars that will not sink into the ground or penetrate a tent groundsheet.

Ex-services Safari beds of spring steel and canvas are a little closer to the ground, are far easier to stow but are slightly heavier than the garden lounger and do not offer the convertible chair arrangement. They have

Clumsiness of folded sunbed for packing contests its sleeping comfort. Using this or a Safari bed, you'll still need a foam sleeping mat to prevent downward heat loss.

similar bar-type feet but these, being small diameter steel bar, will sink into sand unless simple spreaders are used (ordinary cardboard will do),

Sleeping on the ground. If weight or numbers of personnel preclude tents or the chair/bed approach there will be times when it is possible to sleep on the ground though many will prefer the security of being raised above it. If you do sleep on the ground, a bivvy-bag is a good way of discouraging warmth-seeking wildlife since it is just that – a bag – and can also be zipped right up if required. This arrangement has been used without unheralded visitations from insects on lightweight motorcycle trips in the Sahara. Sleeping mats (see next section) are warm and comfortable on most surfaces provided a shallow 'grave' is scooped out initially with a shovel; try this during pre-expedition training. A mosquito net tucked in round the sleeping mat is further protection against larger insects if the operation is conducted thoroughly. (When getting up in the morning, pull out the tucked-in mosquito net with some verve and this will dislodge with the requisite speed any nocturnal visitors who might have dropped by for the warmth.)

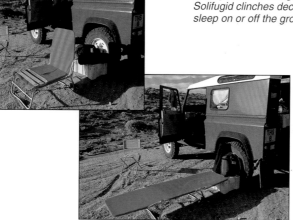

'Super lounger', left, DIY-performance-enhanced with rubber chair webbing. Needs box under head to prevent overbalancing when entering sleeping bag. Solifugid clinches decision on whether to sleep on or off the ground!

Things to sleep *on*

Dual role. The temptation was to label this section 'sleeping mats' since this is what many people use. Again, at the risk of stating the obvious, the role of 'things to sleep on' comprises:

- Insulation from heat and cold.
- Cushioning hard ground.

It is worth remembering to separate these functions; they are carried out by a number of different equipments available under the general heading of 'things to sleep on'. In anything that comes between you and the ground or your bed the first function, insulation, is as vital to a warm night as a good sleeping bag. A sleeping bag relies on loft (trapped air) for most of its insulation and the part underneath you of necessity is flattened, precluding most of this function. That insulation must be put back by some other means – invariably using air as the medium in one way or another. This may or may not also contribute a cushioning function:

- *Sleeping mat.* Closed-cell polyethylene foam encapsulates thousands of tiny air bubbles in a stiff plastic to act as insulation; these mats, usually of 8 mm thickness (standard) or 12 mm depth, give 'four season' or 'extreme' (ie severe cold) standards of heat insulation beneath the sleeper. Around, or less than, half a kilo in weight, they are feather light, cannot be punctured, and are extremely efficient. The stiffness of the foam does give some comfort cushioning (and for this reason the 12 mm mat is the better to use on a vehicle expedition) but it usually behoves the user to make sure the basic contour of the 'bed' is suitable. Go for the thickest, widest mat you can get. The Karrimor Karrimat is one of the best on the market.

These mats are usually rolled up and for that reason are a little bulky to carry. If you want to save space and also be able to use them as a kneeling pad, unroll the mat and make transverse scalpel incisions alternately front and back at around 30 cm spacing and then fold the mat like a concertina. It will take up less space as well as being easier to pack. The incisions must be precise; use a depth stop and leave 1-1.5 mm uncut at each fold.

Don't think you can dispense with a sleeping mat when you use a camp bed. Downward heat loss through your compressed sleeping bag will be high if you do not use one.

Cushioning hard ground and providing insulation against cold (sometimes hot) ground are aims. Mats: a million backpackers can't be wrong – or are there alternatives?

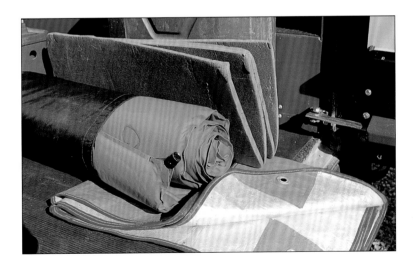

Sleeping mat carefully cut and folded, concertina-style, takes up less room, can be used as kneeling mat too. Thermarest self-inflating mat (left) is vulnerable to punctures from burrs and thorns – note patch. Space blanket is useful as groundsheet and to keep radiation heat losses down.

• *Self-inflating air beds.*
One of the best known makes
of self-inflating air bed is the
Thermarest. In some ways
these could be regarded as the
'opposite' of the sleeping mat.
Where the sleeping mat outlined above consists of a
closed-cell foam, ie each tiny
bubble of air is self-contained
and sealed, in the self-inflating
air bed the foam used is open-
cell so the opposite is the case
– every cavity is connected to
every other cavity in effect
rather like a bath sponge. This
means that, when enclosed in
an airtight sac and provided
with a valve, as self-inflating
air mattresses are, the thing can be blown up
and deflated like a tyre. Its self-inflating
aspect results from the foam having a natural tendency to retain its original shape; thus
when the valve is opened the 'springiness'
of the foam sucks air into the mattress. With
a top-up puff, the valve is then closed and it
is ready for use. To deflate it, the valve is
opened and the bed is rolled up slowly
towards the valve squeezing the air out.

The Thermarest comes in various thicknesses from 25 to 50 mm so has slightly
more of a cushioning capability than the
closed-cell mat mentioned on page 2.2 - 19.
They are a great deal more expensive than
the Karrimat type of item and some types
have the disadvantage (except in the most
expensive model) of being slippery to sleep
on, narrow and, in the context of African
expeditions, very susceptible to punctures
by small burrs and thorns – exacerbated by
the need to press down hard while rolling it
up. Spray-on anti-slip is available. The
widest, longest, most expensive Thermarest
is already coated with an anti-slip
('Staytek').

• *Waffle-foam.* Waffle-foam – flat on
one side and covered in protrusions on the
other side in the form of a waffle or egg-
crate – is another approach. When purpose-
designed, this foam is around 65 mm thick

*Inflatables of
some kind are
very effective –
and appropriate
– for cold condi-
tions but burrs
and thorns in
Africa do them
no good at all.*

*Cool of the
evening. Sleeping
on the ground here
in summer requires
a sleeping mat to
prevent heat gain
from the ground!*

and of a closed-
cell type thus
offering a mois-
ture-barrier as
well as a maxi-
mum of heat insu-
lation and cush-
ioning against
lumpy ground.
However, open-cell foam is sometimes
offered for this job – conceptually like a
Thermarest without its airtight cover. This is
simply a piece of open-cell upholstery foam
around 50 mm thick; it compresses too easily when lain on and is not wet proof. Be sure
you are aware of the difference between the
closed-cell and open-cell foams; the latter
would not normally be recommended.

Regrettably many will find that neither
type compresses enough for packing conveniently in a light 4x4 and takes up a lot of
space in the vehicle; a single-bed item
would be around 70 x 30 cm when rolled
up. Though robust, puncture-proof and
comfortable its bulk would probably rule it
out unless a base-camp operation is being
set up and trucks are available to transport
equipment.

• *Airbed.* An inflatable, blow-up airbed
is an old-fashioned concept but combines
insulation almost up to sleeping mat standards with a considerable capability to cushion hard or stony ground. A box-edged one
has a flat rectangular cross section and, like
those with longitudinal bolsters down each
side, is thus less liable to precipitate your
rolling off it in the night. An airbed of suitable robustness is quite heavy, requires an
airbed foot pump and, though most are
thicker skinned than a Thermarest, is still
liable to damage by thorns.

Things to sleep *in*– sleeping bags

Rating, types, fill

High-profile item. Although a sleeping bag is only a single item of equipment you are going to spend a long time in it on an expedition. If it isn't right then, like a steering wheel with a patch of half-dried sticky marmalade on the rim, it will cause you a lot of irritation for a long time; a high-profile item. Put more positively, a well-chosen sleeping bag will be almost worth its weight in gold for the comfort, rest and opportunity to recharge your batteries that it will afford. Choose with great care in relation to the climate and weather you expect on your particular trip and in relation to you as an individual.

As with so many other items of equipment it is not just a question of price or the 'maximum' specification. You will need to look at all the design and construction parameters. As we have seen in the case of tents, the annual Field and Trek catalogue has an excellent detailed rundown on this and then relates it to a wide, pre-vetted range of equipment; and it is right up to date.

Seasons rating, your rating. All sleeping bags have a 'seasons' rating – one to four covering suitability for summer-only or an all-year-round usage. (Two seasons is late spring to early autumn, three seasons is early spring to late autumn). There is also a 'five seasons' rating which covers year-round use at high altitudes plus an 'expedition' rating which covers the most severe conditions in polar or high-mountain regions.

Think hard about what you need but do amend this according to whether you are a 'cold' person or one who seems to be happy in shirtsleeves when your colleagues are in pullovers. Some people get warm when 'metabolising' a meal, some may be 'cold' people who get warm very quickly when they exert themselves and then cool down again equally quickly when resting – or are sleeping. This variation in personal heat generation has been seen on expeditions where, using the same issue sleeping bags, team members climb into bed wearing just underpants or swathed in track suits and pullovers.

Clothing, inners and liners. And here, of course, is a way of fine-tuning your warmth requirement – clothing, inners, liners and the use of a bivvy-bag. A track suit is in any case a very practical form of expedition 'pyjamas'; when you stop to camp you can have a wash before it gets too dark or cold, change into the track suit, don a pair of overalls on top, be comfortable for evening camp chores and then be ready to get into bed after taking off the overalls. A sleeping bag liner of cotton is a very good way – essential on virtually any expedition – of keeping the inside of the sleeping bag clean; it also contributes about 'half a season' of warmth. (Whilst sleeping bags can be cleaned this takes its toll and it is far better to not let them get grubby in the first place.) The Mountain Equipment sleeping bag people do their own liner called the 'Sleepy', an all-cotton item for best comfort and easy washing; a simple enough item but this one also has a hood to pull over your head that keeps greasy hair from making the pillow area grubby.

Other liners come in the form of a thick fibre-pile liner which will add a 'full season' to any sleeping bag you have; there are also fleece liners which are less bulky but still add significant warmth.

Seasons rating – the solution. A moderate seasons rating plus liners, bivvy-bag and available clothing is probably the best approach to accommodate the span of temperatures you will get. If you are sleeping outside without a tent, the amount of cloud cover will affect your radiation rate so even temperature on its own is not a reliable indication of how cold you will feel. As mentioned above, an invaluable weapon in this context is an aluminium-coated 'space blan-

Choose your sleeping bag specification to the climate you will encounter and accessories you'll use. The warmest is not necessarily the 'best'.

Combination that served for a trip with night temperatures spanning 5-27°C, used in and out of tents. Field and Trek Gore-Tex 'Freedom' bivvy-bag (right), Mountain Equipment 'Lightline' 2-3 seasons rating bag (550 gm duck down) and Mountain Equipment 'Sleepy' cotton hooded liner – all used in various combinations with track suit 'pyjamas'. As here, home-store sleeping bag uncompressed.

ket'; laid over your bivvy-bag, shiny-side innermost, it is very effective in cutting down radiation heat loss on clear nights.

When you hit warmer conditions or hot humid nights you can peel away the layers, sometimes using just a bivvy bag and track suit, lying on your sleeping bag until that inevitable time at two in the morning when the warmth leaves you.

Filling – down

Down is extremely effective as a sleeping bag fill – both for its insulation properties and springiness. It needs specialist cleaning, is poor when wet and slow to dry.

Nature's design triumph. The sight of serenely content ducks, geese or swans on a river in winter may be routine but is jaw-dropping testimony to Nature's ability to meet the challenge of thermal insulation. The down from these birds is soft, springy (important, that) and has 'loft' to encapsulate the maximum amount of insulating air. Not surprisingly it makes the most effective filling for sleeping bags from the point of view of insulation alone.

A feather is probably one of Nature's most beautiful and truly elegant pieces of functional design – note how the neck of a pigeon maintains perfect aerodynamic smoothness as the head moves. This immaculate sealing system excludes water from the down that keeps ducks and geese warm and this highlights one of the special needs of a down-filled sleeping bag – the need to keep it dry. Being so fine and fibrous, down 'absorbs' a lot of water, takes a long time to

dry and in that time becomes a very poor insulator.

Down is also expensive, part of the expense being in the quest for homogeneity. Even this, however, can be quantified: 'fill power' is an indication of loft and is the volume in cubic inches occupied by one ounce of fully lofted filling. The best quality bags will always quote this figure. The higher the value the better the insulation – duck down is typically 600, goose down 700. If no fill power figure is quoted it may indicate poorer quality down mixed with tiny feathers.

The springiness mentioned earlier is an indication not only of how small a sleeping bag can be compressed when it is bagged in the morning but also how much it will expand and loft, naturally, when it is unpacked to do its job of keeping you warm.

Care and cleaning. Finally the question of care and cleaning. Down sleeping bags can be cleaned but it is far better that they never get dirty – invariably use a liner inside and take care of the outside. Natural fillings need more care and should be washed in a special down cleaner such as Loft – not a detergent or fabric softener. The washing and drying processes must be gentle; if it has to be done it is probably better to use one of the specialist down cleaning services on offer in the outdoor magazines small-ads. Don't store a down sleeping bag, long term, in a compression sac; use a large loose weave pillow case (Mountain Equipment bags come with a large netting bag of roughly this dimension for storage) or, if you can, hang the unrolled bag by one end.

Filling – synthetic

Catching up with ducks. Despite the acknowledged excellence of a down bag in terms of warmth and lightness, man-made fillings – various types of polyester fibres combed together to form a thin 'batt' which looks like a thin layer of cotton wool – have a special place in the small spectrum of alternatives. Down adapts very well to sleeping bags but Nature's original design brief – keeping ducks and geese warm – did not include 75 kg bodies rolling round on it whilst giving off copious water vapour. Polyester fibres are now getting pretty clever. The original mono-fibre can now be replaced by hollow fibres (DuPont Hollofil), fibres with four microscopic hollow tubes at its core (Quallofil) or fibres with seven internal tubes for lightness and enhanced insulation (Quallofil 7). Other treatments enhance slip and loft of adjacent fibres.

A synthetic fibre, of course, can be made totally homogenous so quality control is easier and the product can be cheaper than down, albeit within the spectrum of man-made fillings there is still a significant price and quality gradient.

Successive 'batt' layers are combined to effect the right thickness and the mat is then quilted to a fabric from which the sleeping bag is made – see construction details below.

Easy to clean, quick to dry. Because they are made of polyester, synthetic bags, as well as being cheaper, are easier to clean and dry more quickly than down. They are heavier for a given seasons rating – or conversely, offer less insulation for a given weight. A bag weighing 1.1 kg rather than 2 kg is significant where backpacking is involved but is likely to be immaterial on a vehicle-based expedition.

Synthetic-filled bags may thus actually be more suitable than down for certain environments and an investigation of the top technical quality bags is well worthwhile at the equipment planning stage of your expedition.

Filling – fibre-pile

'Instant fur'. Fibre-pile, also polyester, sometimes polypropylene, and used widely in mid-layer jackets for outdoor activity, can also be used in sleeping bags. Buffalo manufacture a modular sleeping bag system called Buffalo Double P based around a series of inners, outers and liners made of fibre-pile and Pertex. This system is interestingly outside the more conventional sleeping bag type of manufacture and is extremely logical in concept. It utilises the layering principle widely accepted as the basis for clothing (see Section 2.3) so that various outers and inners may be combined or separated to give the degree of insulation required.

More bulk, handles wet well. Fibre-pile compresses less than most insulators, bags lose least performance when wet and are easiest to wash when compared to other types as well as drying with surprising rapidity. It thus commends itself, like the synthetic fillings above, to particular conditions where you may be reluctant to take an expensive and relatively vulnerable down bag. Again, fibre-pile bags are bulkier and heavier than an equivalent down unit but this could well be relatively unimportant when using a vehicle; it may also be, in warm climates, that you do not need the performance that a combination of layers offers so you might need only one bag.

Sleeping bags – construction

Different types, different construction. Down sleeping bags are essentially a series of contiguous or overlapping compartments which are filled with down. This is done to eliminate the possibility of the down bunching up in one part of the bag and thus leaving a 'bald' spot without insulation. A lot of small compartments rather than fewer large ones will be better since the smaller the compartments the less the possibility of this

Synthetic fillings – fibres or fibre-pile – have much to offer where super compact packing is not vital. Advantages: washing, quick drying, wet performance.

Open country, gin-clear skies equals cold nights. Ensuring you sleep well is one of the most important aspects of planning.

Sleeping bags – features

Tops and tails. As well as the baffling, look at zip lengths, whether the zip is double-ended, on the left or the right and the general shape of the bag. A snugger fit equals more insulation so the tapered 'mummy' shape will be warmer than the rectangular type of bag; some bags even have a very slightly elasticised inner lining which gravitates more to the sleeper than the outside of the bag. Rectangular type bags are so inefficient at head and shoulders heat retention that they can be ruled out for expedition use in most cases.

That said in relation to a snug fit, go for a fully 'boxed' foot end to the bag. Like the proverbial hospital bed, tightly tucked in at the end, there are few features so uncomfortable as a sleeping bag that precludes your feet sticking up as feet are meant to do. Top-ends have several important design features too; a shoulder/neck collar with separate draw cord will keep out draughts, and, very important, a shaped cowl hood, again with its own draw cord. A great deal of heat can be lost at the head and as ever this will probably not be apparent until some hours into the night. A cowl-shaped hood that you can draw-cord around your face will be very useful; often you will find yourself using this feature in combination with a bivvy-bag that zips to a tiny aperture at your nose.

Once the seasons rating and fill has been decided, check into the other design features, construction, drawcords, hoods, zips, 'boxed' foot end.

happening. Contiguous circular tubes of down would only touch at their peripheries so a box-wall construction is usually employed, ie adjacent rectangular tubes so there is never a zero down-thickness point.

Further refinements of this approach is the slanted box construction (in which each compartment has a rhomboidal cross section) and also what may be termed the 'interlocking Toblerone' build in which a double stack of triangular cross section tubes are layered first layer point up, second layer point down; this is the V-baffle Mountain Equipment system and is even more effective in eliminating cold spots.

Synthetic-filled bags being, as indicated above, made of layered batts quilted (sewn) to fabric are constructed differently. Once again, in this single-layer construction, the danger is of zero insulation-thickness areas and these would naturally be where the machined stitching runs. The way round this is to overlap two quilted sections in such a way that the stitching in one piece of material comes opposite the maximum batt thickness in the other; this is the double offset layer method. The third method is the 'shingle' method where batts of fibre in transverse strips are sewn to outer and inner layers alternately and staggered so that the final effect is like overlapping roof-tiles lying over one another.

Equipment catalogues – what to buy

Latest ranges. The above is a generic overview of principles. What is on the shelves in the shops will continually be changing as products are refined. Use only the most 'technical' equipment suppliers and study their catalogues in detail and unhurriedly before deciding what to buy. Get the catalogues from the right suppliers – see conclusion of Section 2.3 – 'Clothing'.

Field and Trek catalogue tech guide product analysis table extract – sleeping bags

Catalogue Code	Manufacturer and Model	Page Number	Price	Seasons Rating	Total Weight (Grams)	Filling Details	Construction	Shoulder/Neck Collar	Total Length (cm)	Length to Neck (cm)	Shoulder Width (cm)	Foot Width (cm)	Outer Fabric	Lining Fabric	Packed Length (cm)	Packed Diameter (cm)
Natural (Down Filled) Sleeping Bags																
35066	F&T Rolling Cloud 750	143	109.00	2+	1700	750g Duck Down 550+	Box Wall	S	220	186	75	48	Nylon Taffeta	Nylon Taffeta	34	24
35067	F&T Rolling Cloud 1000	143	129.00	3+	2000	1000g Duck Down 550+	Box Wall	S	220	186	75	48	Nylon Taffeta	Nylon Taffeta	38	25
35068	F&T Rolling Cloud 1200	143	149.00	4+	2200	1200g Duck Down 550+	Box Wall	S	220	186	75	48	Nylon Taffeta	Nylon Taffeta	41	25
35061	M.E. Marathon 300	146	99.95	1	810	300g Duck Down 550+	Box Wall	-	203	173	70	40	Ultrasoft Nylon	Toray 40/40 Nylon	25	14
35011	M.E. Classic 500	146	139.00	2	1100	500g Duck Down 550+	Box Wall	S	205	173	70	40	Ultrasoft Nylon	Toray 40/40 Nylon	27	18
35012	M.E. Classic 750	146	159.00	3	1340	750g Duck Down 550+	Box Wall	S	205	180	70	40	Ultrasoft Nylon	Toray 40/40 Nylon	30	23
35024	M.E. Classic 1000	146	183.00	4	1625	1000g Duck Down 550+	Box Wall	S	205	180	70	40	Ultrasoft Nylon	Toray 40/40 Nylon	33	26
35001	M.E. Glacier 500	145	164.00	2	1080	500g Duck Down 550+	Box Wall	S	205	180	70	40	Drilite Ripstop Nylon	Toray 40/40 Nylon	32	18
35004	M.E. Glacier 750	145	209.00	3	1380	750g Duck Down 550+	Box Wall	S	205	180	70	40	Drilite Ripstop Nylon	Toray 40/40 Nylon	34	22
35005	M.E. Glacier 1000	145	182.00	4	1625	1000g Duck Down 550+	Box Wall	S	205	180	70	40	Drilite Ripstop Nylon	Toray 40/40 Nylon	33	26
35015	M.E. Lightline	145	189.00	2/3	1150	550g Duck Down 650+	Slant Wall +EXL	S	205	180	70	45	Drilite Ripstop Nylon	Toray 40/40 Nylon	33	21
35022	M.E. Snowline	145	239.00	3/4	1500	750g Duck Down 650+	Slant Wall +EXL	S	210	180	70	45	Drilite Ripstop Nylon	Toray 40/40 Nylon	31	25
35000	M. Mountaineering Spr Antelope	144	205.00	4/5	1420	740g Goose Down 700+	Slant Wall	S	205	176	70	40	1.7oz Taffeta Micro	30 Max Taffeta	43	25
SYNTHETIC (FIBRE FILLED) SLEEPING BAGS																
31169	Ajungilak Kompact Lite	149	69.95	2	1160	Microloft Hollofibre	Stitched Through	-	217	190	72	48	Pertex	Pertex	37	20
31045	Ajungilak Nordic Lite	149	49.95	1/2	1260	Polyester Hollofibre	Stitched Through	-	205	170	65	48	Nylon	Nylon Viscose	32	18C
31168	Ajungilak Kompact	149	94.95	3	2020	Microloft Hollofibre	Double Offset	-	200	180	69	44	Pertex	Pertex	46	23
31049	Ajungilak Nordic	149	69.95	2/3	1700	Thermofill	Double Offset	-	205	170	65	48	Nylon	Nylon Viscose	33	22C
31170	Ajungilak Kompact Super	149	125.00	4	2100	Microloft Hollofibre	Double Offset	S	220	190	72	48	Pertex	Pertex	49	24C
31055	Ajungilak Nordic Super	149	89.95	3/4	1900	Quallofil 7 2x130g	Double Offset	S	220	176	65	40	Nylon	Nylon Viscose	36	20C
31090	Vango Q7 400	151	72.95	4	2000	2x200 Quallofil 7	Double Offset	S	200	190	66	45	40in 240 Ripstop Nylon	270 Micro Polyester	48	21C
BUFFALO DOUBLE P (FIBREPILE) SLEEPING BAGS																
31060	Buffalo L/W Outer Large	152	49.95	1*	1060	Fibrepile	-	-	215	185	74	40	Pertex	Fibrepile	34	22
31059	Buffalo L/W Outer Medium	152	48.95	1*	820	Fibrepile	-	-	200	170	74	36	Pertex	Fibrepile	30	17
31064	Buffalo 4S Inner Large	152	42.95	+2*	1340	Fibrepile	-	-	205	180	74	36	Pertex	Fibrepile	37	26
31063	Buffalo 4S Inner Medium	152	39.95	+2*	1100	Fibrepile	-	-	190	165	74	34	Pertex	Fibrepile	27	20

Have a clear idea of what you want before going to the shops. Only you can decide and to do so without this kind of detail would be foolish. Get it right first time.

As with tent buying and the table featured a few pages back, an analytical table of the kind in the Field and Trek catalogue is virtually essential in sorting out your requirements before you go to any shop. See page 2.3 - 53 et seq, phone numbers, addresses etc.

Section 2.3

Equipment planning:

Clothing

COVERAGE OF THIS SECTION

Quite a long section, this one. It comprises:

Theory – what is going on
'Wicking' and 'breathability' are two buzz-words of the fabrics business specially applicable in expedition clothing. To set up your discernment you need to look at a bit of theory and scan over generics first. All is not as sometimes portrayed.

Practicalities – what to buy or consider
With a little bit of theory covered, you can marshal your ideas better and the equipment brochures will make a lot more sense.

Non-apologia. Clothing is with you all the time. No part of expedition equipment is so close to you, so all pervasive, so involved in the way you feel and look; few so contributive to how you work, relax, rest and, in many cases, survive. Clothing is very important. The subject is therefore treated in some detail so that you know what is going on. Once you have the basics you can take as many or as few 'doesn't bother me' short cuts as you wish.

Today's commercial techno-baffle and miracle-claim thicket in outdoor clothing is so dense that an attempt will be made here to treat the subject of clothing generically first – the human temperature regulating system, then the different sorts of fibres and then the various generic types of fabric and clothing systems. Dusting off your knowledge of Nature's own system and the physics of heat, moisture and what clothing does will be the best way of re-priming your discriminatory faculties when selecting gear for your expedition. Reading the brochures and catalogues, the genuine claims will then

Clothing is a very high-profile aspect of expedition equipment. Choosing it well can mean comfort and functionality. Getting it wrong will make life a misery.

Hot and humid or biting cold – these are the conditions in which clothing must do its job of helping the human thermo-regulatory system function at its best.

become more convincing, the areas of doubt more obvious. Equipped with these criteria, the whole picture becomes clearer. To tie it all together a 1996 snapshot of fabric trade names and how they relate to generic fibre types and processes is provided also.

Human thermo-regulatory system

Nature got there first. It is always humbling, just when we think we are at our cleverest, to ponder what Nature has been doing for countless thousands of years. The human thermo-regulatory system is an astonishingly ingenious basic mechanism that seems to be available in different states of tune according to race, tribe, colour and – in the last few dozen millennia – the modifying effect of the widespread use of clothing. Eskimos can take the cold better than south American Indians but we all have a pretty clever basic system aimed at keeping the vital organs – brain and the core of the trunk – at a steady 37°C. That has to be achieved at varying states of energy workload, at varying states and rates of metabolising food energy intake and different rates of heat output or input due to conduction, convection and radiation. The basic mechanisms used are:

Animal thermo-regulatory systems are among Nature's design triumphs but they still have limits. Know how it all works and make your clothing work in harmony.

• Use of blood flow to move heat or shut down the movement of heat and

• Use of evaporation to achieve surface cooling.

Handling cold. The head, arms, hands, and feet are equipped with a relatively large number of blood vessels near the surface and these are the areas most used for heat exchange – to get rid of heat or to reduce heat loss. In cold conditions and especially if our energy output is low these areas of high blood vessel density are the first to undergo a constriction of blood vessels to reduce the blood flow and thus reduce heat loss. Being 'blue with cold' is one of the visual symptoms of what is going on though this is more often merely a paling of the skin indicative of the blood flow shutting down and thus moving less heat out of the core regions.

Nature's next move is to initiate shivering which is a way of producing heat energy – at the expense of energy reserves. Even this elegant system has its limitations and eventually, when taken beyond the limits of these autonomic devices, the core temperatures will start to drop and hypothermia sets in. This can lead to death.

When extreme cold is local on exposed parts of the body – a finger, toe, foot or part of the face – the reduction of blood flow actually exacerbates the situation and frost nip or frost bite results with severe pain and tissue damage.

Handling heat. The converse happens when you are working hard on a temperate kind of day. We get red in the face, feel the urge to roll up our sleeves, loosen our collars so that the areas of high blood vessel density can shift heat more efficiently by contact with the cooler outside air. More blood is diverted to the surface of the body in these conditions – the opposite of the constricting blood vessels that occur when we are cold. Heat is being moved by conduction/convection – conducted away by a cool fluid (air) passing over a warm surface (our skin); the warm air also rises and that is the convection. We may begin to sweat as well. And this is where the scientifically elegant part of the system kicks in.

When we want to warm a baby's bottle we often put it in warm water; the cold bottle gradually acquires the temperature of the warm water by heat transfer (conduction, in this case). So why, when a human body at 37°C is placed in a desert where the ambient temperature is 40°C does it not heat up to the local temperature? Perspiration is, of course, the answer. The thermo-regulatory system causes us to sweat and the evaporation of the sweat has a cooling effect.

Evaporative cooling. When anything wet or damp dries it cools. 'Drying' infers the evaporation of liquids from a surface and it is the evaporation that causes the cooling.

When you paint-spray a panel with an aerosol evaporation of the solvent is part of the cause for the panel being cold to the touch; a damp cloth on your forehead cools you due to the evaporation. Very relevant to wicking and breathable fabrics that we look at later on, the real textbook concept of tem-

Evaporation – kinetic theory

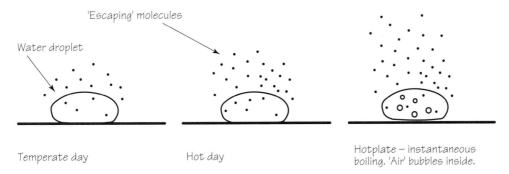

'Escaping' molecules

Water droplet

Temperate day   Hot day

Hotplate – instantaneous boiling. 'Air' bubbles inside.

perature, liquids and evaporation is so elegant it is worth recalling – memories from school will probably be rekindled.

A water drop is full of water molecules in motion. Liquid water is topped by a thin cloud of water vapour represented by the molecules that broke through the surface (see 'Surface tension' later). The speed of this molecular motion is dependent on temperature – higher temperature, faster molecules – so the higher the temperature the greater the cloud of molecules 'breaking free' into the space near the surface. With molecules breaking free from the liquid the average speed of molecules at the surface is reduced. Lower speed equals lower temperature; QED evaporative cooling. This brief and elegant kinetic theory explains all the phenomena required to get a grip on how the human thermo-regulatory system and any clothing system works. We shall see it is fundamental to 'breathable' and so-called 'wicking' fabrics.

Evaporation occurs at all temperatures and, inevitably from the above, occurs more rapidly (and provides more cooling) when:
- Temperature is high.
- There is a large surface area
- There is a wind over the surface (to shift the molecule cloud and make room for others).
- The humidity is low. Dry air allows more molecules to 'escape' than steam where the space is already 'full' of water

molecules – the tropical jungle case.

Applying this theory to the human temperature system, clearly the sweat evaporating causes considerable surface cooling. The evaporation will be more rapid – and the cooling stronger – if the local air is very dry and/or there is a wind blowing. In fact, in the desert you will probably not be aware of sweating at all because the perspiration goes from liquid to vapour virtually the moment it appears. Conversely we will all remember the sweltering feeling of still air on a humid day in the tropics – or worse still, a large city.

Thinking on a little, you'll recall the same sweltering feeling when you are working hard and have too many warm clothes on. What is happening here is that your thermo-regulatory system is feeling the

Body heat regulation is largely by blood flow enhancement or constriction aided by evaporative cooling. This moisture needs to be moved and also replaced.

A funny thing happened on the way to .... Uweinat

Rising straight out of the desert, Jebel Uweinat in south east Libya is high enough to trigger its own rainfall when conditions are right. Near the top a cavern had its own pool of rainwater. Walking into the cave was like entering an air conditioned room; outside it was 40°C. In a region of exceptionally low humidity the water was demonstrating evaporative cooling. We took its temperature: 16°C below ambient!

excess heat, increasing the perspiration rate to try to cool you down and, because the cooling is not working properly – ie the sweat can't 'get away' by evaporating and cooling your skin – the system then causes you to sweat even more.

You will be well aware of most of all this but it is worth recalling since it influences greatly our choice of clothing to work in harmony with our own thermo-regulatory system.

Fluid loss – Bedouin and Indians. Of course, a 75 kg body wandering about in the desert at an ambient temperature of, say, 45°C is getting through a fair amount of fluid to keep the evaporative cooling system going when you are just standing still, never mind the addition of a heat-generating work load. (Unless you keep your fluid intake up you will soon be into a dehydrated condition – see Section 5.4). The contrast in how desert-dwelling Bedou and jungle-dwelling south American Indians handle heat is worth a few seconds thought for it polarises the methods we take advantage of today.

A desert nomad wears a surprising amount of clothing and it does two things. Firstly it keeps radiant heat off by providing shade (also preventing sunburn) but second-

ly it prevents *excessive* fluid loss by evaporation by creating a slightly moister micro climate next to his skin. As we have seen, evaporation is much more vigorous when there is a hot dry wind and finely judged loose clothing in really hot dry conditions will permit enough evaporation to afford skin cooling but not permit runaway fluid loss by excessive contact with a desiccating wind.

In contrast, jungle-dwellers usually go around naked or certainly with bare chests. Firstly from the point of view of radiation they do not have the need to cover their skin because there is tree cover; from the point of view of effective sweating, the much higher ambient humidity demands that the skin get all the help it can in effecting evaporative cooling from an unhindered airflow.

Both environments demand insulation. The Mauritanian traveller's expertise is almost second nature – insulation from solar radiation and from ultra dry air; the loose clothing permits only slow evaporation of body moisture but is ventile enough to feel cool.

Clothing – general principles

Clothes, layers

What for? If the past few hundred millennia have narrowed the spectrum of conditions in which human beings can comfortably survive *au naturel*, they have also honed our ingenuity in making up the shortfall. The first hominid to realise that the protection offered by sheltering under a tree could be made portable by *wearing* an animal hide will have regarded clothing as being about keeping warm. Milestone though his discovery was, he was only partly right – at least in the context of what modern clothing can and therefore must do.

Mankind's other propensity – finding uses for ingenious discoveries – gives today's clothing the task of:

• Insulation – not quite the same as just keeping us warm.

• Keeping us dry – protection from rain without and sweating within.

• Protection from the sun.

• Protection from physical damage and abrasion.

Why the analysis. To keep up with the last thirty years' heady pace of development in fibres, textiles, clothing and design – overlaid with the ephemera of fashion – would require a steady eye, a lot of ink and almost a weekly update if expedition clothing was comprehensively to be covered. The aim of this section, therefore, is to scan the aims and principles at work and note some of the generic ingredients and methods used to achieve solutions; to equip you with a few criteria with which to make your own judgements.

Taking the exploratory scalpel to what clothing is for already reveals the feasibility of tasks hitherto regarded as inherently impossible. Where, once, wearing a waterproof could be relied on to provoke excessive sweating in certain conditions, the clothing manufacturers are now finding ways round the problem. Similarly the chill-inducing sweat-soaked T-shirt, the heavy warm coat, the clumsy waterproof, the clammy socks are all falling to the skills of the fabric manufacturers and designers.

So a little analysis is helpful to give context – and a bedrock usefulness – to modern clothing-speak about wicking, micro-fibres, breathables, permeable coatings and hydrophobic sprays,

And since, unlike the majority of outdoor equipment catalogues or magazines, the requirements of hot-climate expedition clothing will be addressed in this Section too, the brief 'rusty recap' of school-book physics and what water molecules get up to will be continued. Resist any latent urge to regard this as scientific nit-picking; with any luck it will establish judgmental criteria that will stand the test of time – for the moment, at least!

The plethora of new fabrics, registered trademarks and enthusiastic manufacturers' brochures will hopefully then mean a little more and be greeted with an 'Ah!' and a knowing nod rather than wide-eyed bewilderment.

The layer system. Well enough known to most these days, it is worth a formal introduction to the 'layer system'. The implication of the term 'layer system' is to emphasise that a number of thin layers of clothing are better than one thick one, firstly because there are more layers of insulating air and secondly because with many layers it is easier to fine tune the degree of insulation required, peeling off layers as you get hotter with exercise, taking off windproofs to let some ventilation in – or vice versa in deteriorating weather. Classically – or by usage – the layer system is seen to comprise three layers:

• *Base layer*, next to the skin; much concerned, as we shall see, with the movement of moisture away from the skin to keep it drier, less chilled, less clammy or less prone to blistering according to what area of skin is involved.

• *Mid layer* for insulation. In practical terms this can actually comprise a number

Insulation from heat and cold, protection from sun and physical abrasion; clothes now can also assist keeping us dry from internal moisture as well as external. Layers are key.

of separate garments such as shirt, pullover or fleece.

• *Outer or shell layer* whose function is to keep out wind and rain from the insulating layer. Additionally, as again we shall see, the capability to 'breathe' water vapour from the body is an important role in order to prevent internal condensation.

• *'Warm jackets'*. An extra class of 'layer' is the 'warm jacket' kind of garment that effectively combines an insulating mid layer with a waterproof shell – or may have the capability for an insulating mid layer to be zipped into a shell garment if needed.

The fibres jungle

Generics. 'There's wool, cotton and clammy nylon shirts...' – a Blimpishly apocryphal summary of the traditionalist view reflects the caution many people still feel about synthetic fibres in what has become known as activewear. Faced with the never-ending procession of magic new fabrics whose names end in '-tex' and ®, an almost inevitable mental block results. As with medicines, however, sorting trade names from generics is a very good start. The first breakdown would be among the generics themselves – a division into natural fibres and synthetic fibres.

A few of the more usual sub-headings here might be:

• *Natural fibres*
Wool
Cotton
Linen
Silk
• *Synthetic fibres*
Polyamide (nylon)
Polyester
Acrylic
Polypropylene

Viscose used to be called rayon and sits between the two categories being a 'man-made' or regenerated fibre coming from a natural cellulosic source. A bit fragile, but very absorbent and extremely 'comfortable', its early origin does not disqualify it from modern textiles where it is usually used in a blend with another fibre.

Natural fibres soft, absorptive – too much so for some applications. Synthetics very strong, non-absorptive, rapidly catching up on skin contact suppleness and comfort.

Fabrics and people in harmony. Fibres become yarns and yarns become fabrics. Natural fibres have an irregular and complex construction and thus a large surface area; conceptually they also have 'a lot of air mixed in' and these characteristics contribute to their pleasant 'feel', good insulation and absorption properties as we shall see.

A synthetic fibre is, in effect, an extrusion (like squeezed toothpaste) – the result of the fibre material being extruded through a very small hole in something called a spinneret. Normally this means the fibres will have a straight rod-like shape with a round cross section – which does not do much for the feel of the material. This was the main cause of the early 'clammy shirt syndrome' with nylon. Fibres can, however, be 'texturised' to improve bulk and feel and be made with different cross sections to greatly increase their surface area and improve their handling of moisture; superfine filaments will also affect feel. So don't expect polyamide (nylon), say, always to have the same characteristics; a great deal will depend on the fibre cross section, the fineness and the weave of the textile.

The straightness and uniformity of the fibre is important too. Cotton has a nice feel because, amongst other characteristics, it is an uneven fibre with a natural twist and crimp in it so touches the skin at uneven intervals. Incredibly, that most versatile, tough, flexible, self-healing and sensitive of substances – the human skin – can sense the micro-difference between this and 'old style' nylon. Modern synthetics in fine or micro-fibre format can be made to feel every bit as welcoming as cotton – see 'Feel – ..'p26.

Of fundamental importance in assessment of the performance of a fabric in relation to its task is what part of his or her operational envelope the wearer is in. Are you sitting still in cold conditions, cruising in balanced conditions of heat output and heat dispersal or working hard enough for the human thermo-regulatory systems we examined above to be starting to kick in and begin some surface cooling? And are you in cold, temperate, hot/dry or hot/humid environmental conditions?

The fibre and the fabric must work in *harmony* with our thermo-regulatory system and that is the clever bit as we shall see a bit further on.

Properties of fibres. Just before getting on to this working together it is useful to know the variables in fibres; how they differ and in what respects. To help you get an idea of what you will be getting with a textile it is useful to select just a few of the couple of dozen properties the textile technologists use to define the characteristics:

• *Tenacity.* Textile-speak for strength. An indication of durability and, along with elastic-plastic nature, of resistance to abrasion. Tenacity varies wet or dry.

• *Elastic-plastic.* How much it stretches and recovers. The elastomers like Lycra/Spandex are extremely elastic, cotton is inelastic.

• *Handle.* What it sounds like; how the fibre handles in an otherwise untreated form – soft-limp, soft-waxy, hard-very crisp (linen), medium/hard-waxy (nylon, polyester). Sometimes also referred to as the 'hand' of a material.

• *Hygroscopic nature.* Absorbency. Anything hygroscopic absorbs water vapour (humidity) or liquid from the air – salt is a classic example. Cotton is very absorbent (hygroscopic). Polypropylene is exceptionally non-absorbent (non-hygroscopic) – about 1/400th the absorbency of nylon which is already less than 1/10th that of cotton.

• *Hydrophobic/hydrophilic.* The terms *hydrophobic* (tending to make water droplets ball on the surface as on the bonnet of a just-waxed car) or *hydrophilic* (tending to be wetted by water) are also used in connection with a textile's behaviour. Hydrophobic and hydrophilic relate to the behaviour of water (or other liquid) on the *surface* of a fibre or fabric – not to whether it is absorbent or not; that is hygroscopic (absorbent) or non-hygroscopic (non-absorbent). It really is important to remember the distinction; some equipment catalogues get it wrong.

This is fundamental to an understand-

Cross sections of some modern synthetic fibres. DuPont's diagrams of Tactel polyester compared to 'standard nylon' (left). Second from left is normal Tactel, then trilobal Tactel as used in Aquator. The tri-lobe cross section gives a greater surface area for dispersion of moisture. (Aquator – see trade names tables – is a two-sided fabric; polyester inside, cotton outside). Far right is Tactel micro-fibre – an indication of how fine modern microfibres are.

ing, firstly, of wicking of moisture or sweat from within a garment (hydrophilic good) and, secondly, of water repellency – rain on the outside of a garment (hydrophobic good). Polyester and polypropylene are both termed hydrophobic but there are subtle and important differences between the two – see 'The truth about wicking' later.

• *Thermal properties.* How readily does it soften, melt, burn.

• *UV resistance.* Of interest (see Section 2.2) in tent materials, degradation under prolonged UV seldom affects clothing to any noticeable degree.

Armed with some of the above information you will be getting an indication of what to expect if 'Spondulex'® the latest wonder-fabric, is announced as a Spondulized 65/35 blend of polyamide/viscose microfibre with a hydrophilic pro-wicking treatment and an external water-repellent Teflon coating. Though we have some way to go yet, islands of comprehension begin to poke through the receding flood waters of unfamiliar gobbledygook; 65% nylon means strength and abrasion resistance plus quick drying, the viscose would give a soft warm feel and make it absorbent, the hydrophilic treatment would help the nylon to wick better than it would otherwise, and the Teflon external treatment will make the outer layer hydrophobic making it showerproof (but not waterproof).

Synthetics have to be (can be) fine-tuned to what Nature did all along. Hydrophobic/ hydrophilic characteristics, fineness of fibre are most important.

SOME COMPARATIVE CHARACTERISTICS OF FIBRES

Fibre	Strength	Elastic/plastic	Hygroscopic nature	'Handle'	Heat of wetting
Wool	Weak	Elastic	Very absorbent	Med/soft, warm	113
Cotton	Strong	Inelastic	Absorbent	Med/hard, crisp	46
Viscose	Fair	Plastic	Extremely absorbent	Med/soft, limp	106
Acrylic	Fair/strong	More plastic than elastic	Hydrophobic	Soft, waxy	7
Polyamide (nylon)	Strong to very strong	Elastic	Nominally hydrophobic and 'non absorbent' (compared to natural fibres)	Med/hard, waxy	31
Polyester	Strong to very strong	More elastic than plastic	Nominally hydrophobic and 1/10th absorbency of nylon	Med/hard, waxy	5
Polypropylene	Strong and light		Very hydrophobic and 1/40th absorbency of polyester	Hard, waxy	
Elastomeric (PVC – Lycra etc)	Very weak	Extremely elastic	Hydrophobic	Medium waxy	

1. The combination of strength and elastic/plastic characteristics yields abrasion-resistance.
2. In blends such as polycotton one fibre can overcome shortcomings of another.
3. Elastic/plastic. A plastic material stretches and stays stretched, an elastic material recovers.
4. 'Heat of wetting' is not fully understood phenomenon whereby a fibre gives off a steady amount of heat whilst absorbing moisture – until saturated (another reason why sheep shake themselves ? – see text). Figures are joules per gram from dry to saturation.

Physics recap – part two

Air is the cheapest and most effective insulating medium. Its encapsulation and minimising convection is central to good insulation in fabrics.

School books out. What you can expect from given fibres will be starting to become clear but another recap of possibly long-forgotten school physics will give you an indication of how the building blocks of yarns and fabrics can best fulfil the aims of clothing that we saw at the beginning of this Section. We need to look at:
- Insulation
- Vapour pressure.
- Surface tension and capillary action of liquids

We will soon cover in a little more detail the fairly well known notion of three-layer clothing – base layer (next to the skin), mid layer (providing insulation) and shell (providing wind and waterproofing); also thermal insulation as well as the newly coined concept of 'wicking' – sucking-up, if you like, the perspiration the body gives off under hard work conditions and transferring it from the 'wet' end of the wick to the 'dry' end as does the wick in a paraffin lamp.

Insulation. 'The non-transfer of heat' is a clear, down-to-earth definition of insulation. The laws of Nature dictate that equilibrium rules – just as high pressure tends to discharge and move towards low pressure, so heat tends to migrate towards cold and 'insulation' has the job of stopping it, be it a cold-box keeping cool drinks from taking on the heat of a summer's day outside the container or the body-heat of a duck not being lost to the freezing water in which it is swimming.

It will be no surprise to know that air is

the principal constituent in both cases of insulation (low mass so low thermal capacity and poor conductivity) but the secret of its success here and elsewhere is that it is provided in very small parcels so that there can be negligible convection (and thus movement of heat) within each parcel. Closed cell polyethylene foam sleeping mats have already been mentioned (see Section 2.2) but in clothing we want breathability as well so an *optimum* constriction of the air is needed – not too much and not too little and the constriction should be via a medium (fibres or whatever) that themselves are poor conductors of heat.

Design constraints are legion. Greater thickness usually means better insulation but can mean little if the insulating medium is poorly conceived – a suit of armour fashioned from half-inch copper plate would be a very bad idea (even if you had the strength to stand up in it) because it would have an enormous thermal capacity – ability to soak up heat – in comparison to heat stored in the human body it was supposedly 'insulating'. This absurd example is quoted because, due to its weight and the thermal capacity of water, wet clothing has been quoted, in conditions of extreme cold, as leading to 25 times the heat loss of dry clothing; the thermal resistance of dry clothing is dramatically better than that of wet clothing – a point of some relevance when we come to look at moisture transportation in wicking.

Adding thickness (of proper insulation material) is not always possible in items such as boots or gloves so a reformulation may be necessary; Thinsulate, a well-known and very effective insulating medium used in outdoor clothing, has a different formulation for gloves and boots as compared with the type used for jackets. Springiness in the insulating medium is essential so that it will recover loft after compression – one of the claims of down and some of the better synthetic materials.

Without headlining them, we have here considered the reduction of convection and conduction as the means of losing heat –

bearing in mind that for what may be termed habitability we are also stuck with a breathability requirement without too much convection.

Radiation, however, must be considered too. Remember how matt black bodies take up and radiate heat more than light colours; anything chrome plated radiates and takes up least radiant heat of all: the idea behind shiny foil survival bags and, aluminised foil linings to some jackets. Here the shiny lining is reflecting back the warm-body radiation – albeit tests have shown them less effective than once regarded, principally because reflection is of the surface temperature of the clothing, not the internal body. However, as mentioned in Section 2.2, the use of a 'space blanket' when sleeping without a tent in the desert (clear sky, ideal radiation conditions) makes a dramatic difference to how cold you feel.

Vapour pressure. Although belonging here in the physics recap section, vapour pressure is of particular interest in the context of breathable shell garments so has been moved on a page or two.

Surface tension and capillary action. Water droplets beading on a waxed car bonnet, an old old cotton dishcloth or a piece of blotting paper drying up a spill are familiar enough phenomena yet have a direct read-across to how fabrics behave in wet conditions – whether the moisture is external or internal. Keeping rain or drizzle out of a treated garment (by causing it to bead and run off) and wicking perspiration away from the skin with a base-layer garment rely on related manifestations of the principle of surface tension. In selecting expedition clothing it is important to know when these completely opposite concepts – repelling or soaking-up – are likely to apply.

Intermolecular forces in a drop of water – the forces of attraction between adjacent molecules – cause it to behave as though the surface of the water had a tensioned elastic skin; that is why water droplets try to be round. (We already saw that evaporation is fast-moving molecules breaking through this 'skin'.) Water from an eye–dropper

How water droplets interact with a surface determines how it wicks and breathes moisture from within or without the garment.

Principle of wicking – capillary rise in thin tubes

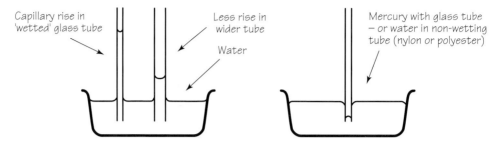

Capillary rise in
'wetted' glass tube

Less rise in
wider tube

Water

Mercury with glass tube
– or water in non-wetting
tube (nylon or polyester)

'Wetting' permits capillary rise – wicking   No capillary rise because no wetting

*'Spread' or
'beading' of
water droplets is
crucial to how a
garment works.
You want it to
'spread' from the
inside but 'bead'
on the outside to
keep you dry
and comfortable.*

onto your bonnet bead tightly on a waxed vehicle, less so when the vehicle has not been waxed and, when there is detergent in the water it spreads out with virtually no beading at all. What is different about these three cases is the angle at which the edge of the droplet meets the surface – the contact angle.

The *surface with which water interfaces modifies the (apparent) surface tension* and the behaviour of the droplet. Thus the waxed surface may be classed as hydrophobic – tending to repel water (as on the outside of a treated garment) – and the detergent acts as a 'wetting agent' or hydrophilic treatment encouraging it to spread out in a thin film. This latter, importantly, would be the same

if the wetting agent was on the surface itself – such as a bar of soap – rather than pre-mixed with the water. The connection with the earlier mentioned hydrophobic and hydrophilic fibres is starting to emerge.

The ability for water to 'wet' a surface (clean glass) or not (block of beeswax, to quote the other extreme) gives rise to the phenomenon of capillary action – the ten-

Just as the textbooks say (below). Water on clean glass (right) is hydrophilic, a small contact angle tending to promote surface wetting. The wax candle to its left is highly hydrophobic, tending to make the water bead. The same effect is seen in the photograph (left) where a fabric has been treated to make it more hydrophobic.

dency for a liquid to spread along or even climb another surface. Water will climb very thin glass tubes immersed, say, in a tumbler of water, to a particular height above the water's surface in the tumbler depending on the diameter of the tube. If the tube was (conceptually) wax-lined, the water would not climb the tube – quite the opposite, the level would be below that of the surface the tube was dipped into. Water on wax or mercury on glass are both examples of this repellency because the surface does not 'wet'; the contact angles are different. This is capillary action at work – note the relevant parameters; the fluid rise in the tube (wicking) occurs more in a small diameter tube (or when fibres are really close together) than in a large tube, and only when the surface is hydrophilic, ie has a small contact angle and 'wets' well. (Even without skipping a page or two, you will see the relevance of all this to 'wicking' in outdoor clothing.)

The diagram opposite will ring distant bells of recollection of school physics experiments but the captions relate to what happens, or can happen, in base- or mid-layer expedition clothing that claims to wick moisture from your body by capillary action. If the fibres wet properly then the capillary action on the left keeps you dry; if

it is hydrophobic and doesn't wet then the drawing on the right could be the sorry result. With so many synthetic fibres listed as hydrophobic how can they wick? Firstly 'hydrophobic' is not always a strictly accurate term; it is, literally, a matter of degree – the size of the contact angle.

Looking at the diagram a bit more closely you can see, in the situations depicted above, what the contact angles are.

Although the classical school lab experiment depicted in the previous diagram shows water/glass and mercury/glass interfaces, as has already been mentioned, when a liquid of known properties contacts a solid, the surface characteristics of the solid determines the nature of the solid-liquid interface. So the diagram below could conceptually be, on the left, water and a cotton fibre and, on the right, water and a fibre of polypropylene; wetting in the one case, non-wetting in the other.

Nylon and polyester are somewhere in between – but on the low side of the all-important 90° contact angle. Although something of a simplification, 90° might, literally, be termed the watershed when it comes to all the clever things we are asked to believe about modern fabrics – wicking moisture or shedding it off the outside. See 'The truth about wicking' on the next page.

'Contact angles' quantify the 'spread' or 'bead' characteristic of a fibre and its ability to move internal moisture out from a garment.

Contact angles – liquid/solid interface

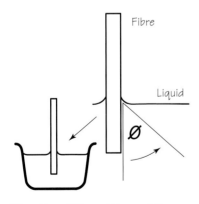

Fibre

Liquid

Ø

Ø less than 90° = wetting = wicking

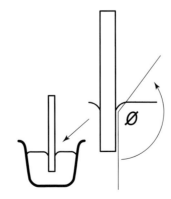

Ø

Ø greater than 90° = no wetting = no wicking

Wicking

The truth about wicking

Absorption and adsorption. There is 'insensible' sweating and 'sensible' sweating; the former is the skin giving off moisture vapour to keep cool and the latter – sweat you can 'sense' – is liquid sweat which the body gives off when the thermoregulatory apparatus goes into high gear to get rid of more heat. Keeping a garment-wearer dry thus involves dealing with both these types of sweat:

• Vapour sweat
• Liquid sweat

Usually a ventile, loose-weave, breathable fabric helps move the water vapour that is the insensible sweat. To deal with the sensible sweating (the liquid) we need a fabric characteristic that might be both absorptive (to soak up the sweat) and hydrophilic to cause it to spread over the surface of the fibres to enhance evaporation and also promote capillary movement of the liquid between the 'tubes' formed by adjacent fibres. These functions are generally taken to be wicking which thus can thus be broken into two types:

• Wicking by absorption
• Wicking by capillary action.

Put wicking by absorption on hold for a minute – remember that which is absorbed has to be re-evaporated. Cotton's benchmark ability as an absorber (albeit viscose

ABsorption sucks moisture into a fibre; aDsorption is a measure of moving moisture along its surface and wetting – essential for wicking effectively.

actually out-performs it) is a two-edged weapon – long drying times, chilling in cold conditions when a sweat-soaked shirt or vest can feel cold to the skin for a long time, and clamminess in hot conditions are quoted disadvantages of varying validity and are discussed later under 'Climate-specific clothing'. Synthetics, in comparison to cotton, are virtually non-absorbent although there is some moisture take up with nylon, a good bit less with polyester and far, far less with polypropylene.

What we need to look at a little more closely is capillary wicking and the closely allied aDsorption (with a 'D') – the movement of a liquid over the surface of a fibre (as opposed to aBsorption, which is liquid taken into the internal structure of the fibre). Of course the two can get very intermingled when modern synthetics (poor aBsorbers) are produced as micro-fibres with such fine fibres that good aDsorption almost amounts to the same thing. It is still useful to know the difference; you will certainly feel it when you wear a sweat-soaked, chilling-out vest after a hot climb.

No wicking without wetting. Leaving moisture transportation by aBsorption aside for the moment, capillary wicking depends primarily on a low value of liquid contact angle since it is this that determines 'wetting' and only with wetting will capillary

Absorption and adsorption in fibres

Absorption – fibre soaks up moisture

Adsorption – moisture moves over surface; enhanced if hydrophilic

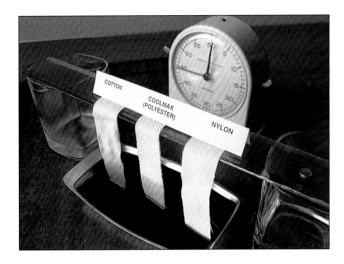

Simple wicking tests – in the kitchen table lab. Strip from 100% cotton T-shirt (left) is standard wicker/absorber here compared with 'clever cross section' polyester (Coolmax pique, centre) and lab-coat strip in 'old nylon' (right). Height of dyed-water stain (here at 45 secs after dipping) shows wicking. Note untreated coarse nylon does not wick at all. Cotton a little ahead at 10 secs but Coolmax soon caught up. Earlier test with cotton weave vs knit showed little difference. Samples here pre-washed, no softener – but see next photos.

rise and surface spreading take place at all. Not something you measure by slapping a protractor over it, contact angles are usually calculated from other phenomena so, with sample-to-sample variations thrown in too, there is not always consensus. However, the following is a broad guide to which fibres (untreated) are going to wick best – and which not at all (remember the significance of keeping under 90°):

Viscose (rayon) – 45°
Cotton – 40-50°
Acetate – 50-55°
Nylon – 60-73°
Polyester – 68-81°
Polypropylene – 95-110°

Wicking enhancement. Where synthetics may be having problems with high contact angles, wicking performance can be improved by special treatments:

• *Hydrophilic treatment.* Some fibres, with varying degrees of success and durability in the washtub, can be given a hydrophilic treatment of some kind that reduces the contact angle with water, promotes capillary wicking and helps to make the liquid flow along the fibre. This is usually a surfactant – in crude terms a surface detergent – that enhances wetting. The improved wetting also spreads out the moisture and enhances drying time.

The US outdoor clothing manufacturer The North Face offers VaporWick in their Tekware range of nylon and polyester clothing. This addresses precisely the problem outlined above – '.. a fabric treatment that alters the surface of the fiber so it is more hydrophilic .. to allow the moisture to move along the fiber. The finish is permanent; however fabric softeners will inhibit the fabric's performance'.

• *Surface texturing.* Other treatments that can enhance wicking by reduction of the contact angle include what may be regarded as a surface roughening (also used by North Face in 'sanded' finishes).

• *Fibre cross section.* Altering the cross section of the fibre can increase its surface area; going from round to tri-lobal (three lobes like a clover leaf) has been done and the latest manifestation of this is DuPont's 'Coolmax' which has a peanut cross section giving a claimed 20% increase in surface area as well as, in effect, four vestigial 'channels' along the length of the fibre to give polyester's moderate wetting angle a better chance of wicking well.

• *Non-use of fabric softeners.* Noted later under 'Washing', fabric softeners though giving fabrics a soft feel actually impart hydrophobic charactertistics and inhibit hydrophilic ones.

Inherently, synthetics don't wick as well as natural fibres; micro-fibre and fancy cross sections help – as do hydrophilic treatments. Don't use fabric softeners.

Fibre contact points, fine fibres.
Capillary tubes used in classroom experiments have straight parallel sides whereas a forest of fibres in a garment will be mostly curved. However where fibres diverge this will have the effect of decreasing edge contact angles across a meniscus thus initially enhancing capillary rise. Also the thousands of fine-angle fibre contact points each form points for capillary condensation. Whilst this is not the place to treat this hypothesis rigorously, commonsense indicates what will be going on. It will further encourage capillary activity if there are many fine fibres rather than fewer thicker ones; the advent of micro-fibres helps the process. Whilst the contra side to this is that coarse pores hold more liquid, they don't necessarily *move* it (the wider tube in the diagram on page 12); better to have thousands of tiny pores moving tiny amounts of liquid than fewer large ones not actually moving anything.

Wicking of vapour. Whatever its hydrophobic/hydrophilic characteristics, a synthetic fabric will not impede the movement of water vapour, intrinsic to the initial stages of moisture movement, especially if it has an exceptionally low absorbency (moisture 're-gain') like polypropylene. Some researchers believe that vapour movement is actually enhanced in hydrophilic fabrics compared with hydrophobic ones through *surface* moisture movement. (See 'Breathables' on page 19.)

Sweat vs water? A further consideration to lob into the theoretical arena concerns the fact that sweat and water will have different contact angles on a given solid. Sweat, having a salt content will have the lower contact angle and will enhance aDsorption (movement along the surface of the fibre) – good news in the context of moisture transportation in skin contact garments.

The actual liquid being moved at any point within the clothing is worth a thought too. Body *vapour* will condense as water on the clothing. Liquid sweat that 'boils off' as vapour will do the same but liquid sweat that migrates as a *liquid* will do so in that

Body moisture as vapour gets out through any ventile fabric – but will likely condense into water so capillary wicking and adsorption still very important.

form – a salt-rich solution. Though the concentration of salt is low (well under 1%) the tell-tale white deposits on a sweat-soaked shirt drying out in desert conditions is unmistakable. In many cases, then, liquid sweat will probably start off as sweat, evaporate into water vapour, re-condense within the clothing as water and move on in that form.

Skin contact. Skin contact garments such as underwear, T-shirts, polos, should be able to cope with the movement of moisture in vapour *and* liquid forms so if synthetics are involved these should be of a 'clever' cross section fibre or ideally should have had a durable hydrophilic treatment to reduce their contact angle and enhance capillary wicking; micro-fibre configuration also helps. Sometimes, where this has not been done or the treatment is not durable enough, a cotton/synthetic mix is used – enough cotton to soak up liquid without getting too clammy – but again, the synthetic ideally should have been treated if it is to do its bit. Tactel Aquator in the trade names table in the following pages, as a two-layer fabric (hydrophilically treated polyester on the inside to wick, cotton on the outside to spread and evaporate away from the skin) has elegantly addressed all these points and comes up with a construction and treatments formula that makes sense to the selective and intelligent buyer. So too does The North Face use of Supplex (nylon) microfibre treated with VaporWick.

The promoters of Coolmax claim that its unique 'grooved' cross section and very fine denier fibres obviate the need for surfactant treatment and have comprehensive test results that appear to support impressive wear comfort criteria and liquid moisture transport even in hot humid jungle conditions. (See also wicking photographs.) Certainly if a fibre will perform without a hydrophilic treatment then the possible demise of that treatment in the washtub cannot be a problem.

Helly Hansen 'Lifa' underwear in the same table bravely stamps the product as untreated (and totally hydrophobic) polypropylene on the basis that for the Arctic conditions for which it is designed moisture movement by vapour will be sufficient. (The totally non-absorbent nature of polypropylene also makes it very quick drying.) They do, however, also make 'Prowool' – a paradoxical mix of polypropylene and wool.

Mid-layers. Where there is no skin contact, as in mid layers, moisture transportation is more likely to be by vapour under the 'power' of the temperature and humidity gradients (see diagram at 'Breathables' on page 19) so the need for hydrophilic treatment is less important. Wicking in the context of mid-layer garments is an incorrect use of the term if it is dealing with vapour rather than liquid but is often taken to indicate a non-hygroscopic material that will not absorb moisture but 'pass it on' to the breathable shell garment. Remember that wicking mid layers are only as effective as the final 'gate' – shell garment or boot – that the moisture has to pass through.

Summary. The following table sums up some moisture transportation criteria:

Natural fibres move moisture by absorption and adsorption but must then 'de-sorb' by lengthy evaporation. Synthetics move by capillary action and adsorption alone.

UNTANGLING 'MOISTURE TRANSPORTATION' IN FABRICS

Characteristic	Fibre type	
	Natural – cotton, viscose, wool, linen	Synthetic fibres – nylon, polyester, polypropylene
Absorbs moisture, ie hygroscopic, (liquid and vapour)?	Very absorbent so dries the skin – but itself slow drying because it takes in and holds so much moisture. This can, in some climates be an advantage as it provides a greater surface for evaporation and thus more cooling. But – see two boxes down.	Compared to natural fibres, these are non-absorbent so quick drying. [There is some moisture re-gain in nylon (compare your current toothbrush to a new or hardened-off old one). Polyester's vapour/moisture uptake about 1/10th that of nylon. Polypropylene virtually impregnable – 1/40th re-gain of polyester.]
Naturally hydrophobic or hydrophilic, ie repels or 'wets' surface moisture?	Hydrophilic, wets well.	Nylon and polyester relatively hydrophobic compared with cotton but contact angles (see above) less than 90° so will wet to some extent.; process further enhanced by fine fibres, texturising or other hydrophilic treatment. Polypropylene hydrophobic.
Wicks moisture – liquid?	Yes. Wicking by absorption mainly which then has to be 'de-sorbed' by evaporation; thus dependent on airflow and temperature. This slow wicking by absorption can lead to chilling in cold weather.	Nylon and polyester yes by capillary wicking only. Polypropylene does not 'wet' naturally so there will be little or no capillary wicking.
Wicks* moisture – vapour?	Yes, through a relatively open weave textile though hygroscopic nature of fabric causes it to 'hold' moisture (vapour condensed to a liquid) unless favourable humidity/temperature gradient exists **.	Yes, through a relatively open weave textile but only with a favourable humidity and temperature gradient. Synthetics are virtually non-hygroscopic so such gradients are the only way vapour can move through a fabric of synthetic fibres. Beware the case of tropical conditions where such gradients can be absent – same temperature/humidity inside garment as outside! No gradient, no vapour movement**.

* Misuse of the term – 'water vapour permeability' is more accurate. Strictly speaking 'wicking' refers to capillary action and can thus only take place in a liquid (which wets a surface). Here is meant moisture migration in vapour form, ie evaporation in one place (skin) and condensation somewhere else (hopefully ambient air outside!)

** Humidity or temperature gradient – see 'Vapour Pressure' – implies progressive decrease in humidity or temperature over a given distance, specifically, distance from the skin.

Practical implications – summary. The practical implications of all this is that the main synthetics (polyester and polyamide – nylon) will wick moisture (liquid) but in basic constructions less effectively than cotton. As the photographs of basic wicking comparisons show, their performance can be considerably enhanced with hydrophilic treatments (these must be durable), and by fine fibres of ingenious cross sections that increase surface area. Polypropylene is inherently a non-wicker of liquids and has the potential for being insufferable in hot humid climates.

Absorptive wicking is most efficient in cotton (and almost negligible in synthetics) but the problem of re-evaporation in cotton can sometimes present itself as slow-drying chill in cold climates and heavy wetness in hot. As we shall see, some hot-climate 'chill' – not 'heavy wetness' but the light extended coolness of a synthetic/cotton mix – can be just what the wearer wants in some kinds of tropical or desert environments; it amounts to 'getting the most mileage' – evaporative cooling – from a given amount of sweat! See below 'Hot weather clothing'.

Wicking and washing – beware softeners. Take care to follow washing and drying instructions with the garments and fabrics you use. Especially beware of fabric softeners which function by depositing what amounts to a very fine waxy coating on the fibres to render them soft. This, however, will incapacitate hydrophilic coatings and actually make a naturally hydrophilic textile more hydrophobic while it lasts. Good wicking becomes poor wicking when you have used a fabric softener as the photographs show; you can check this any time with domestic towels or kitchen wiping-up cloths. Use fabric softeners only when you really do want the softening effect and the wicking is immaterial – usually wicking is far more important in the context of virtually all expedition clothing.

Some garments carry instructions 'Cold wash'; this is usually done to safeguard any Lycra or Spandex against the effects of excess heat and to guard against the possibility of loss of dye intensity especially in deep colours. If your washing machine cannot undertake a cold wash, a 30°C or even 40°C wash will be the next best thing and is unlikely to damage your clothing. If in doubt check – with the manufacturers if need be. Don't accept a fudged 'It should be alright..' from someone who has never even noticed the label!

Check drying instructions too which are usually concerned with creasing, the lofting of an insulating medium and/or the maintenance of an external hydrophobic coating. Some garments are listed 'Do not tumble dry', others 'Tumble dry only' – just to keep you guessing!

Abide by washing instructions with your clothing. Especially, do not use softeners, wash cool rather than hot – both easy to accommodate on an expedition!

Beware of fabric softeners in any performance fabrics used for expeditions or outdoor activities. Even with cotton where wicking is aBsorptive as well as aDsorptive, the reduction in wicking performance after washing with fabric softener is very noticeable. With synthetics the effect is even more marked.

Breathables

Vapour pressure

The driving force. 'Breathables' as shell garments aim to keep wind and rain out yet allow water vapour from the body to escape so that it does not condense inside the garment. Breathables function through temperature and humidity gradients, of which vapour pressure is an integral part. The little clouds of water molecules we saw in the evaporation diagram is a simple way of visualising vapour pressure.

Tiny though they are, the cloud of molecules exerts a minuscule pressure called *vapour pressure* that gives the vapour the energy to diffuse, ie move to areas of lower vapour pressure – fewer water molecules equals drier air.

If you have been tempted to query why the water vapour from your body should want to move through your breathable jacket, vapour pressure and diffusion is the motive force behind it. Like evaporation, common sense dictates that vapour pressure is proportional to temperature (for a given humidity) so there is in fact both a temperature and a pressure gradient across the surface of your jacket. Badly worded in some promotional literature, this 'pressure' is more an energy state seeking to diffuse than, as one wearer of a breathable jacket, tightly draw-corded at neck and hem envisaged, lots of pounds per square inch forcing

the vapour out! *Vapour pressure* is the term, not just *pressure*, which gives the wrong image to many people.

Wide spectrum. A traditional interpretation of 'breathable fabric' is one that allows air or moisture vapour to pass through it fairly easily – an in-the-shop test is to bring the fabric to your mouth and then exhale quite vigorously; the amount of air movement on the far side that you feel is an indication of how ventile the fabric is. In present day parlance the meaning of the word concerns the ability of a waterproof (or water resistant) shell garment to permit body-generated water vapour to pass through it whilst keeping wind and rain out. This is in contrast, for example, to a sheet of polythene which is unquestionably waterproof but just as unquestionably, does not 'breathe'. (The sheet of polythene does have an application, though, as we shall see later.)

Although the point has seldom to be made in the European context since it is almost always colder outside the garment than in, remember from the start that breathable shell garments were conceived as an outer layer in an insulating, weather protecting system. Firstly this means that, acting with other clothing, you have first to get the moisture vapour through the inner layers before any breathing through the shell can take place and secondly that the driving

'Vapour pressure' makes breathables breathe. It is more of an energy state than lots of pounds per square inch. Needs temperature and humidity differential.

Vapour pressure – concept

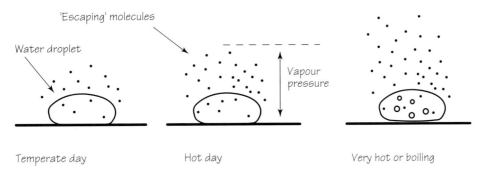

'Escaping' molecules

Water droplet

Vapour pressure

Temperate day   Hot day   Very hot or boiling

Notional temperature/humidity gradients at skin/clothing interface

Temperature gradient

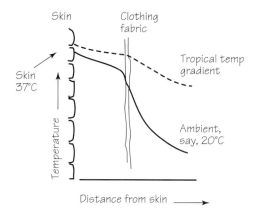

Humidity gradient

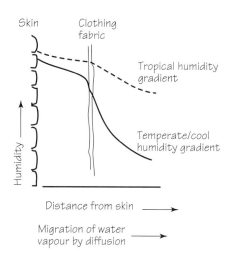

force of the 'breathables', as has already been hinted, is the difference in humidity and temperature between the inside and the outside of the garment. That's what makes it work at all.

Three types of breathable: 'membrane', 'coated', and 'tight-weave'. All need temperature and humidity gradients between inside and outside garment.

'Ah, Gore-Tex', is what many would say when breathables are mentioned but in truth there is quite a wide spectrum of shell layer fabrics that breathe to a greater or lesser extent. Breathing is a matter of degree and even Gore have a comprehensive and cunningly targeted range of fabrics to

address. So long as there is a micro space for molecules to get through – be it a special membrane like Gore-Tex or a very tight weave – movement of vapour will occur under the right conditions of temperature and/or humidity gradient. 'Breathables' for shell garments can, in fact, be categorised as follows:

• Membrane breathables.
• Coated breathables.
• Tight-weave breathables.

We'll deal with membranes first.

Steamy River Niger; the dotted lines on the picture/graphs above sum up this kind of environment; not a great drop in temperature or humidity as distance from skin increases – a weak gradient in both so not ideal conditions for breathables to function in. See 'Climate-specific clothing' on page 38.

Membrane breathables

Very, very small holes. Membrane breathables, such as Gore-Tex, comprise a very thin membrane, in this case expanded microporous PTFE (microporous polyurethane film in the case of Aquatex, hydrophilic polyester with Sympatex) , which is usually bonded to a face fabric to give it strength and stability.

• *The membrane(s).* In the case of Gore-Tex, for which detailed data is available, 'microporous' here means there are in the PTFE membrane billions of holes per square inch, each one hundreds of times larger than a water molecule but many thousands of times smaller than a water droplet so that water vapour can easily escape without letting in water droplets. 'Gore-Tex 2' membranes (ie all recent and current Gore-Tex) has an additional component – a very thin hydrophilic, oleophobic (oil repellent) layer on the inside to stop pore blockage by skin oils.

A little note here. Hitherto we have regarded 'hydrophilic' to be a surface wetting characteristic in the context of wicking. In the context of breathable coatings it is still a strictly accurate description but here refers to the propensity of water molecules to migrate *through* the coating. You will find descriptions of waterproof garments utilis-ing a 'hydrophilic coating' and may other-wise be temporarily confused by the appar-ent use of wicking terminology.

The hydrophilic characteristic acts like blotting paper on a molecular scale, ie dri-ven by the temperature and humidity gradi-ent, water molecules will migrate outwards through the film; the oleophobic characteris-tic, in basic terms, stops performance degra-dation through dirt.

Aquatex use a film or membrane too but this one is made of microporous polyurethane. They also use a thinner hydrophilic polyurethane membrane on some of their fabrics. Hydrophilic film, this time of polyester, ultra-thin and 'stretchy', is also used by Sympatex. All three manufac-turers use 2-ply and 3-ply versions – see below. (The difference between micropor-ous and hydrophilic films is shown dia-gramatically under 'Coated breathables' on the next spread.)

• *3-ply and 2-ply.* The face fabric is the outside of the garment so is usually a tough nylon which is itself externally given a hydrophobic treatment to help it repel water – or more specifically, encourage the water to bead and roll off so that it will not 'wet-out' and impede the passage of water vapour through the fabric – see photo at 'External hydrophobic coatings', page 24.

Membrane breathables usu-ally breathe best but more expen-sive and bulkier. 2-ply better than 3-ply but less robust. Activent type breathes best but is only water resistant.

Membrane breathables – 2-ply and 3-ply Gore-Tex

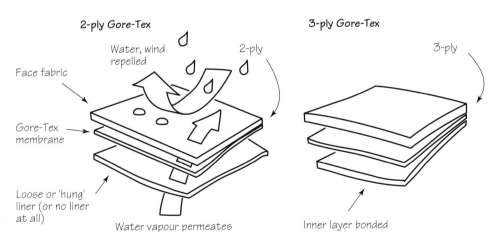

2-ply Gore-Tex

3-ply Gore-Tex

Water, wind repelled

2-ply

3-ply

Face fabric

Gore-Tex membrane

Loose or 'hung' liner (or no liner at all)

Water vapour permeates

Inner layer bonded

This two-ply sandwich – face fabric and membrane – requires internal protection for the delicate membrane against chafing or other damage resulting, for example, from the carriage of rucsacs. This can be achieved by a further internal face fabric laminated-on – the whole thus becoming a 3-ply fabric – or it can take the form of a separate 'hung' liner and in this form the material is referred to as 2-ply. The 3-ply fabric is the more rugged and durable since the membrane has more protection but the 2-ply is 50-100% more breathable and, being a lighter, less rigid laminate, has a softer feel and drape. This 2-ply breathability bonus is only around 20% in the case of Sympatex.

• *Activent.* Mentioned in the list of trade names at the end of this section, Activent is worth a special note here for it is, at least at its introduction, something of a milestone in the design philosophy of breathable membrane fabrics. Coming on the market in the winter of 1995/96, this fabric by W L Gore represents recognition that even a 2-ply Gore-Tex is, for some vigorous activities, not breathable enough. Activent is more than twice as breathable as normal Gore-Tex and to achieve this Gore have accepted reduction in status from 'waterproof' to 'water resistant', implying it is suitable for use in only light rain. As well as providing a fabric for a well defined sector of the market this also seems to represent, face to face with the customer, a mature and laudable acceptance of the laws of physics rather than denying the existence of swings and roundabouts.

• *Washing.* Washing and in-use care should be considered before selecting a garment. Gore-Tex membrane, for instance, is not harmed by detergents, bleach, dry cleaning fluid or UV light and a straightforward machine wash and tumble dry is appropriate. Sympatex and Aquatex go for drip-drying. Naturally the particular garment manufacturer's washing instructions should be consulted also since this will take into account any dyeing or hydrophobic surface treatments that may have been carried out. Almost invariably, this latter treatment benefits from thorough rinsing and application

Gore-Tex seems to test as benchmark membrane breathable – so far! Activent a response to need for more breathability yet at slight cost to waterproofing.

of a 'cool' iron or warm tumble drying. Warnings to use powder detergents and no fabric softeners often feature. (See page 24 'External hydrophobic coatings'.)

• *Which brand of membrane is breathable?* The Ultimate All-brands Objective test has yet to be carried out on membrane breathables but the well respected US outdoor equipment manufacturer The North Face (TNF) had the courage, in their 1996 brochure, to quote tests done by two independent organisations – the Hohenstein Institute of Bonningheim in Germany and the US Testing company of Hoboken, New Jersey. Here they not only quote Gore-Tex as 'the most durably waterproof breathable fabric' (ie testing wet flexing and abrasion) but quote the names of those that did not reach the same standard. Similarly in terms of quantified breathability among fabrics that claim to be waterproof and breathable Gore-Tex came top. Equally, among water resistant fabrics, Gore-Tex Activent was found to be the most breathable; again, the losers were quoted by name.

There would appear little doubt of the wide acceptance of Gore-Tex in its many forms as the benchmark breathable waterproof fabric system but that is not to dismiss all other systems. Relatively static or low physical work-load situations, for example, do not require the high breathability (and higher cost) of Gore-Tex. Other systems sometimes offer a softer feel to the fabric and less weight. Cost and packability also enter the equation when tight budgets, occasional use or groups are concerned. And this leads neatly to coated breathables.

Coated breathables

New capability. Lightweight, tightly woven nylon with an inner coating of impermeable polyurethane will be familiar to many as a 'Pacamac' or easily stowed waterproofs to use in emergencies. Not so widely known is that these coatings can be made breathable – microporous (tiny holes), hydrophilic ('molecular blotting paper') or a combination of both – and can even be fine-tuned to favour waterproof or breathable

'Waterproof' vs breathable in coated fabrics

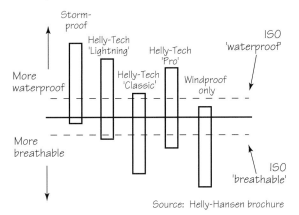

Source: Helly-Hansen brochure

• A microporous layer 'breathing' through the permanent, air-permeable pore structure – this favours breathability at the expense of waterproofing.

• A hydrophilic layer transmitting water by a molecular mechanism of absorption, diffusion and desorption – this favours waterproofing over breathability.

As can be seen from the diagram left, Helly Hansen mix these to get exactly what they want but many manufacturers go for one or the other.

Remember that the effectiveness of coated breathables, as Helly Hansen are conscientious enough to point out, is dependent – as with membrane breathables – on the temperature and humidity gradient between the wearer and the outside conditions. It is hard not to add 'even more so' since the coated breathables are inherently less good breathers than the membranes such as Gore-Tex. Remember too that in cold conditions you are relying more on humidity gradient than temperature gradient for the breathing to happen.

'Coated breathables' use two types of coating – microporous and hydrophilic – in various combinations to favour breathability or waterproofness.

characteristics. It is, however, usually an either/or, roundabouts and swings, situation; these characteristics can range from stormproof (and not very breathable) through to very breathable (and far enough short of the ISO definition of waterproof for it to be classified water-resistant or just windproof).

Using the Helly Hansen system as an example, their coating consists of two constituents:

Coated breathables – microporous and hydrophilic layers

Microporous – more breathable, not so waterproof

Vapour

Microporous coating

Vapour – easy passage

Hydrophilic – waterproof, not so breathable

Waterproof barrier

Vapour

Hydrophilic coating

Water molecule chains move through hydrophilic groups

Vapour – slower passage

The reason for this, of course, is that your mid layer of clothing whose job is to *insulate*, will, if it is doing its job properly, have reduced the temperature difference between the outside ambient air and the surface of the mid layer to the minimum. Conversely, if this is not the case and the outside of the mid layer is quite warm then the breathing will be going very well but you will be losing heat and feeling cold! More roundabouts and swings.

The validity of the exhortation to use good-wicking mid layers if you want your breathable shell garments to work does become clear, though.

All breathables need hydrophobic external coating to 'shed' water droplets rather than allow them to wet the surface and impede egress of vapour.

Tight-weave breathables

Flexible breathability. Tight-weave breathables are what they sound like; a really tight weave with a fine hydrophobic yarn is a good formula for shedding water and also letting vapour through. Such a formula does work – Pertex or Trevira Finesse synthetics on their own are often used this way – but frequently the garment will be classed only as water-resistant rather than waterproof. Invariably such fabrics are used with a hefty hydrophobic coating (the durability of which you should check) and they may also be used with one or other of the internal coatings mentioned above under 'Coated Breathables'. Lightness, flexibility and lower cost are among the advantages.

Within this category, elder statesman of tight-weave breathables and, with many devoted followers who revel in its feel and quietness, is the all-cotton 'Ventile' fabric. The manufacturers sternly eschew coatings of any kind and achieve waterproofness by the well-established principle of outer layer cotton fibres absorbing moisture and swelling to keep the remainder dry. Cotton's extended drying time is the disadvantage.

External coatings, perspective

External hydrophobic coatings. This is a good place to slip in a note about hydrophobic coatings for shell garments. As will have been clear this far, such coatings encourage the falling rain to bead on the surface and roll off rather than spreading, wetting and thus forming a barrier to the sinuous drift-out of water vapour through the fabric. Teflon, Scotchgard, Helly-guard (in Helly Hansen's case), Nikwax TX Direct, Granger's Superpruf spray and many others (generically often a fluorocarbon coating when used at the production stage) are typical examples. Be aware that these are variously durable and will get tired or wash out or may suffer from grubbiness. Be aware also that for the reasons just stated it is important that the performance of the hydrophobic coating be maintained. It can often be rejuvenated by washing the garment as instructed (with thorough rinsing to get the detergent/surfactant out) and tumble drying warm; it is the heat from the tumble drying that causes the restoration (a cool iron will also work).

Some of the above processes (the Nikwax and Granger's) can be used as do-it-yourself, hand spray in the garden or garage and allow to dry, re-proofing agents when required – and again rejuvenated as necessary by warm tumble drying.

Breathables – perspective

Water vapour resistance – the big picture. The breathability of modern outdoor fabrics is usefully compared with everyday

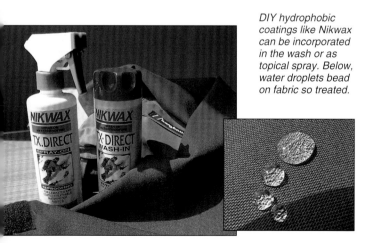

DIY hydrophobic coatings like Nikwax can be incorporated in the wash or as topical spray. Below, water droplets bead on fabric so treated.

TYPICAL WATER VAPOUR RESISTANCES
(R LOMAX)
(Low values equals best breathability)

Fabrics	WVR*
Outer shell materials	
Neoprene, rubber or PVC coated	1000-1200
Conventional polyurethane coated	300-400
Waxed cotton	1000+
Wool overcoating	6-13
Leather	7-8
Woven micro-fibre (nylon or polyester)	3-5
Closely woven cotton	2-4
Ventile ™ L28	3.5
2-ply PTFE laminates	2-3
3-ply laminates (PTFE, PE)	3-6
Microporous polyurethane (various types)	3-14
Open pores	3-5
Sealed pores	6-14
Hydrophilic coated (various types)	4-16
W'proof breathable liners (coated/laminated)	2-4
Inner clothing	
Vests (cotton, wool)	1.5-3
Shirting (cotton, wool)	0.8-3
Pullover (lightweight wool)	3-5

*WVR = water vapour resistance, ie thickness in mm of
layer of still air having same resistance to water vapour
diffusion.

items of clothing in the paper by G Robert Lomax presented to the British Textile Technology Group in 1990 (*J Coated Fabrics, Vol 20*). The table above shows water vapour resistance (WVR) – defined as the thickness in mm of a layer of still air which has the same resistance to diffusion of water as the item considered; thus low values mean good breathability, high values mean poor breathability.

Note the span of WVR – 3-14 is nearly 500% – on the coated fabrics (microporous polyurethane and the hydrophilic coatings). This reflects different manufacturers' techniques, coating thickness, material and base fabric. Note, significantly, that the best of breathable waterproof fabrics have WVRs comparable to that of inner clothing; and provide a reminder that a breathable shell garment can only transmit the moisture that gets to its inner surface – through the base and mid layers.

Breathables compared. A similarly down-to-earth summary is provided by Dr Richard Scott in *Chemistry of the Textile Industry* (Blackie, 1995) comparing water vapour permeability, waterproofness and cost of the three main types of outdoor clothing breathables on a simple star rating basis – table below.

Remember the gradients. Remember, finally, that no shell garment will 'breathe' unless driven by a sizeable temperature and/or humidity gradient. Take these away – as in the tropics where, worst case, both temperature and humidity could be as high outside the garment as inside it and thus provide no gradient – and no breathing will take place. The sheet of polythene we mentioned at the start or a cheap old-style impermeable Pacamac looks to be a good bet! (See 'Hot weather clothing'.)

Avoid theory-saturation. Check table for a breathability comparison with other known fabrics. Gradient-dependent breathables can not work well in the tropics.

BREATHABLE BARRIER FABRICS – PERFORMANCE OVERVIEW – (R SCOTT)
(One star = poor, five stars = excellent)

Type of breathable	Water vapour permeability	Waterproofness	Cost	Comments
PTFE laminates	★★★★★	★★★★★	High	Market leader; versatile usage, expensive.
Microporous polyurethanes	★★ to ★★★★★	★★ to ★★★★★	Medium/high	Widely used, reasonable durability, coated or laminated forms.
Hydrophilic polyurethanes and polyesters	★★ to ★★★	★★★ to ★★★★★	Low/medium	Polyurethanes very cheap, some de-lamination can occur in use.
Conventional **impermeable** coatings	Nil	★★ to ★★★★★	Low/medium	Waterproof but uncomfortable

Note the variability of performance within generic types. This is due to different manufacturers' methods and standards of construction and correlates well with Lomax's findings in the table above left.

The trade names® avalanche

Tactile appeal

Feel. Before looking at what some trade name fabrics consist of, be aware of your own subjective appreciation of the 'feel' of fabrics. Develop it and accommodate it. As already remarked, the human skin is an astonishing combination of toughness and sensitivity and can often determine on a virtually microscopic scale how a fabric is made. The industry has woken up to and accepted this over the past 25 years and, especially since the advent of micro-fibres, shown itself able to produce soft comfortable-feeling fabrics out of most fibres. Despite the leaps made in just the last two or three years there are still differences, though. Enough to keep you on your guard – specifically and invariably in the case of skin-contact fabrics; trousers included.

The feel of the fibres and the question of moisture transportation are what will affect you most and as we have seen, this latter is very dependent, in synthetics, on temperature/humidity gradient. Are you moving moisture out into cool dry moving air or trying to push it out into a static tropical steam bath? What will the fabric feel like then? Not surprisingly from what has gone before and as we shall see under hot and cold weather clothing sections below, the interface between your body microclimate (the 'weather' between your chest and your vest) and the outside world determines this and will influence your choice of the real wickers, the claimed wickers or a bit of good old-fashioned cotton absorbency.

As befits its seniority in the fibres hierarchy wool is a bit special. Whilst there is rarely any reason to feel doomed to accept apparel that you 'hope to get used to' – itchy wool against the skin being the classic we can all remember – skin and wool can work well together. The itchiness derives from the springiness of the wool fibre and

The feel, 'hand' or tactile appeal of fabrics made from synthetics has improved enormously. Still beware, though; heat,and damp make a difference. Test first if you can.

the inevitable result of there being fibre ends 'pointing down' as it were, into the skin. That said, this very itchiness and the minor irritation it causes, can stimulate local blood supply and promote a feeling of warmth. Even if you can't take a woolly vest, a wool scarf around your neck is remarkably effective in keeping you warm; the moisture evaporation and re-absorption also utilises the 'heat of warming' to good effect – damping generates heat.

Hard fibres. The more obvious comfort contrasts like abrasion-resistant nylons in fabric boots can manifest themselves in microcosm and blends of this Cordura in trousers may be hard for some. Roll the fabric between your fingers; does it 'grate' or is it cosy-soft or airy-soft? What will it feel like, sweat-soaked, against the seat or between you and a rucsac? Even some polycottons can feel hard and prickly and clammy. That said, soft and clever knits, fine fibres and texturising can make a lot of difference; rolling a soft knit Coolmax between your fingers has you not believing it is pure polyester and a fine Supplex is a thousand miles from 'old nylon'.

The fabrics – what they are. The rationale for considering generic fibres characteristics as a basis for establishing selection criteria will become especially clear when confronted with the babel of trade names on the market at any given time. As already indicated, this is constantly changing but in the context of this Section it was judged that a snapshot, if only valid for a given period, was better than the frustrating habit books of this kind too often resort to – that of stepping round the challenge to name names. The following, therefore is a snapshot of (some of) the trade names on the UK and other markets in summer of 1996 and a brief indication of what each represents and claims to be.

SOME CURRENT FABRICS LISTED BY TRADE NAME (SUMMER '96)

(Application: Base layer = B, Mid (insulation)= M, Outer = O, Insulated outer layer = OM, Ins = insulating medium)

Fabric name or term	Basic fibre, detail, and manufacturer (or main user)	Layer	Uses and special features claimed, based on manufacturers' information plus opinion. (Note difference between waterproof and water-resistant which implies showerproof only.)
Coolmax	Polyester (Dacron) DuPont	B	T-shirts, athletic vests, socks, skin contact garments. Multi-lobe 'peanut' cross section greatly increases surface area of fibre compared with round extrusion. Wicks well without hydrophilic treatment due to longitudinal channels in fibres. Fast drying. Very soft and comfortable. Sometimes combined with a cotton outer surface or Lycra.
Tactel	Polyamide (nylon) DuPont	B, M, O	DuPont brand name for range of nylon 6.6 fibres that can be used for all types of clothing from coated, abrasion-resistant out wear, mid layer fleeces to soft base layer or shirting.
Supplex	Polyamide (nylon) DuPont	B, M, O	Another name for Tactel used in certain market areas such as the US. Made in different weights and softness texturing according to application.
Tactel Micro	Polyamide (nylon) DuPont	B, O	Light thermal wear. Ultra-fine filaments. soft touch, quick drying. In tight weaves can be used in showerproof, breathable outers.
Tactel Aquator	Polyamide (nylon) DuPont	B	T-shirts etc. Two-sided fabric. Inner surface of Tactel tri-lobe microfilaments for increased surface area and improved 'touch' combined with outer surface of cotton for cool evaporation of moisture. Tactel has been treated with Sandatur HV surfactant to promote wicking – see paras above on wicking.
Thermastat	Polyester DuPont	B	Base layer thermals. Hollow-core fibre provides extra insulation. Wicking coating.
Polartec 100	Polyester Malden Mills	B	Base layer thermals. Knitted in two weights: light and medium pique. Anti-bacterial treated, odour resistant
Polartec 100M	Polyester Malden Mills	B,M	Tight construction in micro-fibre fleece gives very soft chamois-like feel and enhances windproofing. Also known as Micro.
Polartec 200	Polyester fleece Malden Mills	M	Well established double-sided fleece mid-layer insulation. Sometimes usable as outerwear. Series 200S stretch fabric incorporates Lycra. 200R contains 50% post-consumer recycled polyester.
Polartec 200 DWR	Polyester fleece Malden Mills	M,O	As 200 but DWR (durable water repellent) treatment to outer pile resists water, aids faster drying. Outer-only treatment makes sense.
Polartec 300 (DWR)	Polyester fleece Malden Mills	M/O	As 200 but heavier; about 30% more insulation power suits it to colder conditions. Available with DWR and also as 300R with 89% recycled polyester.
Polartec Windbloc DWR	Polyester Malden Mills	M/O	Double-sided fabric with breathable, windproof, water-resistant intermediate barrier. High pile velour inner, high pile velour outer with DWR (durable water repellent) finish. See also Gore-Tex Windstopper.
Tundra Haze 300	Polyester Malden Mills (Berghaus)	M,O	Double-sided fleece. Similar to Polartec but outer face close cropped and treated with water-repellent, inner face deeper for greater insulation.
Tundra 200	Polyester Malden Mills (Berghaus)	M	Double-sided fleece similar to Tundra 300 but lighter weight and less bulky.

Polyester, nylon micro-fibres with 'smart' cross sections dominate skin-contact fabrics. Large Polartec family of polyester fleeces has band of feel-alike competitors.

Ultrafleece	Polyester (Mountain Equipment)	O	Tight-knit water and wind resistant lightweight fleece, Teflon treated for further water repellency. Often used with seat, knee, arm and shoulder reinforcement panels
Aquafleece	Polyester (Mountain Equipment)	O	Similar concept to Polartec Windbloc – waterproof membrane between two layers of Microfleece. Breathable, water and windproof.
Drilite	Polyamide (Mountain Equipment)	O	Tight construction, breathable, down-proof, windproof, water resistant, with water-repellent treatment. Used for sleeping bag outers and jackets. (See also Gore Dryloft below.)
Waterlite	Polyamide (Mountain Equipment)	O	A 'coated breathable'. Nylon with waterproof inner coating. Breathable but less so than Gore-Tex which is a 'membrane breathable'.
Karisma	Polyester fleece DuPont (Field and Trek)	M,O	Dense, lightweight fleece; thermal properties roughly equivalent to Polartec 100 or Ultrafleece. Used for jackets and trousers.
Alchemy	Polyester and nylon (Field and Trek)	M/O	Pertex (tight weave nylon, water resistant) backed Polartec 200
Buffalo	Polyester and nylon (Buffalo)	M/O	Pertex (tight weave nylon, water resistant) backed Polartec 200 (Buffalo also make a unique sleeping bag system using quick-dry synthetic piles.)
Pashm	Polyester fleece (Berghaus)	M	Own-brand double-sided fleece similar to Polartec.
Pertex	Polyamide (nylon)	O	Tight-weave breathable' available as Pertex 4.5, 5, and 6 indicating increase in fabric weight, thread count, and degrees of weatherproofing and toughness. Breathable and treated with flourocarbon hydrophobic water repellent. Sometimes (Pertex 5, for instance) seen with polyurethane 'coated breathable' coating.
Gore-Tex (3-layer)	Expanded PTFE membrane W L Gore	O	A laminate comprising a shell or face fabric, the Gore-Tex PTFE membrane and a lining tricot knit fabric. The fabrics protect the PTFE membrane which is porous to water vapour but not water or wind and is thus 'breathable'; there are degrees of breathability and water resistance – see also Dryloft, Activent and Gore-Tex Windstopper.
Gore-Tex (2-layer)	Expanded PTFE membrane W L Gore	O	As Gore-Tex 3-layer but lacking the inner fabric and thus lighter and more supple. 50% higher MVTR (moisture vapour transmission rate) more breathable than 3-layer Gore-Tex but not so robust in areas of wear or chafing – eg where backpacks are used.
Gore Immersion Technology	Expanded PTFE membrane W L Gore	O	Very robust version of Gore-Tex used for fishing waders and the like. Given appropriate temperature gradient it will 'breathe' away body moisture vapour under water.
Gore Ocean Technology	Expanded PTFE membrane W L Gore	O	Very rugged version of Gore-Tex fabric optimised for offshore sailing etc with accent on waterproof durability.
Gore Windstopper	Expanded PTFE membrane W L Gore	O	Highly breathable membrane laminated to a polyester knit, durably windproof after repeated washes but not water proof or resistant. Often combined with fleeces or other fabrics in sandwich construction. See also Polartec Windbloc.
Gore Dryloft	Exp'd PTFE membrane W L Gore	O	Extremely breathable, water resistant; designed for use with down-filled garments or, more usually, sleeping bags, windproof so 'warm air pumping' eliminated, insulation enhanced. (See also Drilite above.)

W L Gore started membrane breathables with expanded PTFE. Product range now large, tipping over into extra-breathable showerproofs rather than waterproofs.

Gore Activent	Polyamide (nylon) DuPont and W L Gore	O	Gore's response to need for greater breathability in highly aerobic activities. Over twice the breathability of Gore-Tex, wind proof. Water resistant not waterproof. The most breathable of 'water resistant' fabrics. May be 2-layer or 3-layer in construction. Launched Autumn 1995
Cordura Gore-Tex	Polyamide (nylon) DuPont and W L Gore	O	Extremely tough, abrasion-resistant coarse nylon fabric combined with Gore-Tex membrane. Used on boots.
Ardura Gore-Tex	Polyamide (nylon) DuPont and W L Gore	O	Tough, highly abrasion-resistant nylon fabric combined with Gore-Tex membrane used on high-wear areas of outdoor garments such as arms, elbows, shoulders.
Ultra TZ Gore-Tex	Polyamide (nylon) DuPont and W L Gore	O	Texturised, durable nylon face fabric combined with Gore-Tex membrane used on high-wear areas of outdoor garments such as arms, elbows, shoulders.
Impact Gore-Tex	Polyamide (nylon) DuPont and W L Gore	O	A 3-layer reinforcing fabric combined with Gore-Tex membrane for arms, elbows, shoulders. Used by Sprayway.
Taslan Gore-Tex	Polyamide (nylon) DuPont and W L Gore	O	Medium duty face fabric combined with Gore-Tex membrane used 2-layer or 3-layer.
Supplex Gore-Tex	Polyamide (nylon) DuPont and W L Gore	O	Lighter, more supple face fabric combined with Gore-Tex membrane. Sometimes used 2-layer with Thinsulate in warm jackets. NB Supplex = Tactel in different markets.
3x3 Ripstop Gore-Tex	Polyamide (nylon) DuPont and W L Gore	O	Lightweight ripstop (see below) nylon combined with Gore-Tex membrane with high tear resistance but less resistant to puncture or abrasion
Tenslite	Polyamide (nylon) (Mont Bell, Japan) W L Gore	O	Supple, light weight 30 denier nylon face fabric for a 3-ply Gore-Tex. Face fabric treated with SR water repellent to prevent 'wetting-out'.
Aquatex	Polyurethane film laminate. Porvair (Many manufacturers inc Field and Trek)	O	'Membrane breathable' uniquely using polyurethane film in either 30 μm (micron) microporous or 12 μm hydrophilic form laminated to appropriate face fabric. Used in 2-layer and 3-layer configuration by many manufacturers from marine industrial to light leisurewear. Breathability claimed on a par with Gore-Tex. Aquatex also do lightweight microporous polyurethane coating on some fabrics. Soft handle, 2-yr guarantee. External Teflon hydrophobic coating.
Sympatex	Polyester membrane, various face fabrics. Akzo Nobel. (Austin Reed, Vau de)	O	'Membrane breathable', polyester membrane hydrophilic (not microporous) waterproof laminate with adhesive applied in dots to external face or to liner fabric. Very thin at 10μm, very plastic (stretchable with permanent elongation). 2-ply or 3-ply applications but little difference in breathability. Breathability claimed similar to 35μm microporous PTFE. Thin, flexible, light enough for fashion applications also.
Aquafoil	Polyurethane coated polyester (Berghaus)	O	A 'coated breathable' using a polyurethane inner coating on a DWR (durable water repellent) treated polyester microfibre face fabric. Light weight, 2 yr waterproof guarantee. Not as breathable as Gore-Tex. Also available as Aquafoil Lite based on ripstop nylon.
Aquabloc (on Pertex)		O	For 'coated breathables', a coating to make the Pertex (nylon) waterproof and breathable. Not as breathable as membranes such as Gore-Tex.
Trevira Finesse	Polyester Hoechst	O	Tightly woven, texturised (crimped) microfibre, without coating, membrane or film. Breathable, 'impermeable to wind and weather'

Gore membranes often applied to robust face fabrics for boots, jacket high wear areas. Aquatex, Sympatex offer softer, flexible breathables using PE and PU membranes.

Ventile	Cotton Ventile	O	Old established tight-weave 100% cotton working on old tent principles of cotton fibres swelling when wet to exclude further water ingress. Not coated, laminated or as 'efficient' as synthetics and has usual problem of drying time. Windproof, soft, quiet and with a lovely feel.
Ripstop	Polyamide (nylon)	O	A type of weave, usually in nylon, in which a thin light fabric is strengthened by incorporation of a grid of thicker yarns to give extra strength without excessive weight. So-called because a rip in the thin fabric will be stopped by the stronger filaments.
Lifa	Polypropylene (Helly Hansen)	B	Thermal', non-absorbent, lightweight skin-contact base layer designed to permit maximum body moisture movement to mid layer in vapour form. Totally hydrophobic and untreated, it will absorb virtually no vapour but equally cannot wick liquid moisture; thus unsuitable for high sweat-rates or hot climates. Made in three product ranges to favour moisture transportation or max insulation. Also branded as Ultra Net (thin open net), Prolite 5000, Arctic and Pro-wool which paradoxically contains wool.
Meraklon	Polypropylene (Helly Hansen)	B	Brand name of the polypropylene fibre used in Lifa (above).
Propile	Polyester (Helly Hansen)	M	Own brand light, medium and heavy weight fibre-pile (3, 4, 8mm). Double-sided (shorn on outside, lightly brushed inside), breathable, hydrophobic; claims, because of 'W-system fibre lock' to have more loft and loft durability than fleeces, plus resistance to pilling.
HellyTech	Polyurethane coated synthetic (Helly Hansen)	O	Coated breathable'. Combination of microporous and hydrophilic layers graded to favour waterproofing (Lightning), breathability (Classic) or a balance of both (Pro). External DWR (durable water repellent – Helly Guard) to help prevent total surface wetting which would inhibit breathability. Not as breathable as a membrane such as Gore-Tex.
Helly-tech Extreme	(Helly Hansen)	O	Details not yet available.
Helly Tech F1 3-ply	(Helly Hansen)	O	Breathable and breathable-when-wet ocean racing equipment aimed as competitor to Gore Ocean Technology. Light weight, good external hydrophobic beading.
Thinsulate	65% polypropylene 35% polyester 3M	Ins, O,M	Well established and very effective thermal insulation medium used where excessive garment thickness is not required. Different grades (C, U, B, THL etc) for jacket, glove or boot applications. Also 200, 100, 40 gm weights for body, sleeves, etc. Breathable, good recovery after compression, withstands repeated washing. Also marketed as LiteLoft sleeping bag filling.
LiteLoft	65% polypropylene 35% polyester 3M	Ins	See under Thinsulate above
Primaloft	Polyester Albany International (Helly Hansen)	Ins, O,M	Thermal insulation for sleeping bags, jackets, etc. Bonded, ultra-fine polyester fibres claiming to be fractionally warmer than goose down and notably better than other synthetic insulation. Maintains loft and insulation properties when damp, dries quicker than natural downs.
Microloft	Synthetic DuPont	Ins, M	Thermal insulation for sleeping bags and jackets etc. Synthetic microfibre-based. Claims include better insulation properties than down (weight for weight), exceptional softness, machine washable and dryable.
Rhovyl	70% chlorofibre (PVC) Rhône Poulenc, plus 30% viscose (North Cape)	B	Minimal technical information available from Rhône-Poulenc but practically described by North Cape as a spring and autumn base layer, a combination of wicking and warmth. The viscose contributes the warmth and makes it more absorbent than an all-synthetic and not so quick drying. Not so suited to hot weather as Coolmax.

Synthetic insulation mediums claim performance very close to down. Advantage is machine washability, quicker drying, better wet/damp performance.

Cyclone	Polyurethane coated synthetics. Carrington (North Cape)	O	'Coated breathable' using microporous or hydrophilic polyurethane on nylon or (as a microfibre) polyester face fabrics usually flourocarbon hydrophobic proofed to enhance 'beading' water repellency. May be seen with more durable Teflon hydrophobic external coating. Microporous generally more breathable than hydrophilic coating. As with all coated breathables, cheaper than but not as breathable as a good 'membrane breathable'.
Sofitex 2000	Polyurethane coated polyester. Sofinal (North Cape, Adidas)	O	'Coated breathable'. Microporous polyurethane coating with a top layer of hydrophilic coating on a polyester microfibre. Water and wind proof, breathable but not as breathable as a membrane such as Gore-Tex. Machine washable but biological powders, fabric softeners and tumble dryers should not be used.
Exeat	Polyester or polyamide (nylon) with polyurethane coating. Coating Applications Group (UK)	O	'Coated breathable' process, essentially a polyurethane hydrophilic (only) coating system applied to a dedicated range of fabrics optimised for particular applications. Exeat 'Professional' (specified by police and other public utilities), 'Performance' for sailing, climbing etc, 'Endurance' for industrial applications (which sacrifices some breathability for ruggedness) , and 'Leisurewear' for lighter applications. Variations in breathability/waterproof characteristics. Like all coated breathables, less expensive than membranes, suited for group use.
Nike Dri-F.I.T. (F.I.T = 'Functional Innovative Technology')	Polyester microfibre. Some versions add cotton, some have also Lycra. (Nike)	B	Skin-contact micro-fibre, aiming to wick moisture from skin to surface. 11 different versions, all comprising polyester micro-fibre; 3 with a combed cotton face, 4 have Lycra (Spandex) for stretch/fit. Various knits, jerseys etc. Brands: Dri-F.I.T. plus Base Layer, Swiss Pique, Terry-loop/Spandex, 4-Way, Raschel Stretch Liner, Jersey, Pique, Jersey-Spandex Lite, Microfibre-Spandex Jersey, Crepe, Mini-Mesh.
Nike Therma-F.I.T. (FIT: see above)	Polyester micro-fleece (Nike)	M/O	Mid-layer insulating double-sided dense micro-fibre fleece, 'lighter and less bulky than other fleeces', plus a degree of wind-proofing. May be used as an outer garment. Microfleece and Microfleece Lightweight.
Nike Clima-F.I.T. (FIT: see above)	Polyester micro-fibre (Nike)	O	Tight weave breathable' in micro-fibre with hydrophobic external treatment OK 'for 20 washes'. Windproof, water resistant, not waterproof. Available as Microfibre and Microfibre Lite – 'crushable, packable'.
Nike Storm-F.I.T. (FIT: see above)	Polyester micro-fibre (Nike)	O	'Membrane breathable (PTFE)', 2-ply, shell garment with microfibre base. Waterproof, 'as breathable as Clima-FIT'. 'For the highly aerobic athlete'. 'Soft, supple, not noisy or crunchy'. 'Exclusive Nike technology'.
Waxed cotton	Cotton with liquid wax coating	O	Many as are its traditionalist devotees, it is hard not to dismiss waxed cotton as, at best, an endearing anachronism. At worst it contaminates vehicle upholstery; mud, dust and dirt stick to it irremovably. If re-proofing (and stickiness enhancement) is recent enough for it to be waterproof it will promote internal condensation.
Teflon HT	Hydrophobic water repellent silicone proofing. DuPont	M,O	External, hydrophobic silicone coating or proofing of any face fabric. Promotes water beading and run-off rather than 'wetting-out' a fabric which would inhibit any breathing characteristics. More durable than flourocarbon proofing – reputedly 80% still present after 10 washes.
Scotchgard rain and stain repeller	Hydrophobic water repellent proofing. 3M	O	Fluorochemical treatment (not a film) applied at textile mill under 3M licence though certain dry cleaners can re-treat. Main effect is to cause water to bead and roll off though reduction in hygroscopic absorption also apparent. Fabrics' breathability unaffected. Normal detergent washing possible but thoroughly rinse; tumble dry or light iron rejuvenate repellency
VaporWick	Hydrophilic treatment for synthetics (The North Face, DuPont)	B,M	One of the few named, stand-up-and-be-counted hydrophilic treatments for synthetic fibres. Permanent chemical treatment for synthetic fibres to enhance wetting/wicking characteristics and thus promote moisture movement along the fibre. Fabrics thus treated should not be washed with fabric softeners which would inhibit fabric's performance.

Even membrane breathables won't handle the highest sweat rates, so lighter,cheaper 'coateds' make sense. Hydrophobic external coating very important.

Design features – practicality

Practical points

Detail counts. In terms of design features and the practicality of expedition clothing, know in advance what you are looking for. Experience is important. Once you have lost your first three lens caps you will look at shirt pockets with special interest. Bunches of tiny keys that unlock the zips on your grip or rucsac probably need a pocket of their own to prevent them springing free of your pocket when you take out your handkerchief. The inside pocket of your jacket with its nice slippery lining will likely disgorge your passport and travel documents loose into the airline overhead baggage bin unless it has a zip closure. Draw cords on the bottoms of anoraks or shell garments stop the wind blowing in. Anything white seems to be impossible to launder properly on an expedition.

Time will provide you with an ever more precise list of requirements in terms of pockets, closures, reach, fit, pleats, colour, showing the dirt, washability, multi-role use, and 'smartness' values. As with all expedition equipment you will be consciously seeking to get the most from the least.

Expedition clothing should be firmly function-oriented albeit presentable as well. Look for detail design features indicative of painstaking designer.

Shell garments

Wind, rain; moisture within. Features to look out for or decide on in shell garments, especially in cold climates, include:

• *Material.* Fabric alternatives: membrane breathable, coated breathable, tight-weave breathable, 'don't bother with it for the tropics' non-breathable. Waterproof – or just water-resistant with higher breathability (the Activent approach).

• *Coating.* External hydrophobic coating or treatment (such as Teflon or Scotchgard) to ensure that water will bead and roll off rather than wetting out the surface of the garment – see above under 'Breathables'.

• *Seams.* Taped seams that cover the path of stitching and preclude water leakage.

• *Frontal zip.* High-zipped, neck to chin-level with room for scarf.

• *Hood.* May either roll into the collar or be free-standing, with or without a soft-iron wire frame, or draw cord. Wire-framed hoods (difficult to stow) are really only necessary in extreme weather conditions. Some garments (The North Face) claim specially enhanced neck swivel hood arrangements.

• *Drawcords* – elasticised preferably – at waist (to prevent 'ballooning') and at the lower hem. These will keep the wind out and preclude the 'bellows effect' where pre-warmed insulating air is in effect pumped out of the shell garment by body movement. Elasticised cord will enable it to be drawn tight and still give enough should you bend or sit down.

• *Cuffs.* Should have variable Velcro closures so they too can be drawn tight keeping out the elements and giving a slim enough wrist to work unencumbered or slip the hand into a gauntletted glove.

• *Pockets.* Number and type of pockets and their uses – maps, spectacles or sunglasses, lens caps, hand-warmers, inside pockets for passports and the like; all with zip or Velcro closures to keep the contents safe. Inside pockets with closures are especially sensible. External pockets with waterproof fold-over closures. Water drain holes in external pockets let out rain that may have got in.

• *Ventilation.* Zip vents for underarm ventilation are available on some garments to obviate need to take the garment off when the workload is high in difficult situations such as mountaineering.

• *Hot climates.* In hot climates shell garments still have a role – notably windproofing in the desert (a case for super-breathable water-resistants like Activent) and waterproofing in the tropics. A few of the features mentioned above will, on a common-sense basis, be less important in warm climates. Making a shell garment body-moisture breathable in extreme jungle conditions

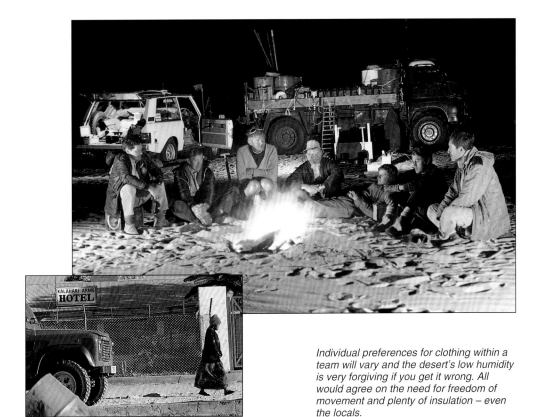

Individual preferences for clothing within a team will vary and the desert's low humidity is very forgiving if you get it wrong. All would agree on the need for freedom of movement and plenty of insulation – even the locals.

would defy the laws of physics in most instances so a case exists for using simple polyurethane-coated ripstop nylon garments, light, cheap and easily stored, on such expeditions. You will still want pockets that hang on to their contents and hoods that keep the rain from going down your neck

Trousers

Function first. Fabric type, the cut for full freedom of movement, pockets (as ever) and closures – the mix of practicality and presentability for 'civilised' parts of the trip will dominate the selection process.

• *Fabric selection, cut.* Much affected by whether shorts or long trousers are considered. Since no stretching across bent knees and thighs is involved, shorts can be accented in the direction of toughness without sac-

rificing comfort – light canvas or Cordura blends, for example – to make them virtually indestructible. There is not much skin contact with shorts so feel is not so important as in longs. With longs, cut and fabric type should be considered together since loose cut makes fabric-feel less important; both should take account of the amount of crouching that seems part of every expedition – lighting fires, setting up stoves, cooking at ground level.

Despite an all-synthetic content, Cordura and Supplex blends, for example (providing bomb-proof durability) can feel acceptably soft and habitable with a full cut – albeit the case in mind (photo, diagram next spread) did also benefit from VaporWick treatment.

For other reasons (see below) you may find yourself selecting polyester/cotton for trousers – a good blend of breathability,

Trousers: fabric choice and cut are interdependent. Go for at least part-synthetic for quick-drying with reinforcements at knees and seat.

Trousers – cut for comfort

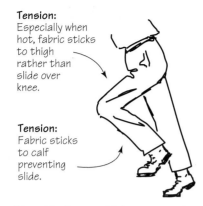

Tension: Especially when hot, fabric sticks to thigh rather than slide over knee.

Tension: Fabric sticks to calf preventing slide.

'Hate it' tolerance. With constricted cut we subliminally 'live with' these irritations without analysing them – contributing to general fatigue.

Fashion: Straight-leg cut can work, but go for a generous fit, double front pleats.

Function: 'Articulated knee' – bent-leg cut. Kneeling, climbing, uphill walking easier.

Expeditions involve lots of kneeling, bending, squatting, walking up hills or over obstacles. Only full cut trousers or articulated knees will accommodate this

comfort, quick-drying, crease-shedding and acceptability in the hotels or banks you visit. Often these are made with sensible reinforcements at the knees and seat and zipped pockets.

• *Reinforcements.* Whatever the fabric, these reinforced knees and seat areas are a good practical feature to look for. Kneeling on the ground (involved in most camp activities) and sitting on rocks take their toll.

• *Space to move.* Knees bent as far as they'll go or even knees involved in walking uphill need fully cut trousers, 'articulated knees' or elasticised stretch materials – not tight jeans which are far too constricting for free movement. Similarly, and especially where trouser pockets are likely to contain bulky items (such as Swiss Army knives), pleated fronts will give room to bend and stretch and twist without feeling they are doubling as a truss. Jeans denim is widely criticised for use 'on the hills' – all-cotton, very absorbent, quick to chill, very slow to dry – but they have a comfortable tough cosiness in the right conditions provided the cut is generous (but see below re pockets).

• *Belt loops* – number and positioning is one of those features that can subliminally

irritate over a period of time. Not enough of them is a common problem, positioning so that there is a great lump of sewn material positioned precisely over your spine when you lean back in your seat is another. Rant a little when you shop; the message may eventually filter back to the manufacturers one day. A built-in belt tunnel at the back is the best solution.

• *Pockets and closures.* Never consider pockets without considering pocket closures. Pockets on jeans are hopeless in this respect; breathe or bend the wrong way and your wallet will pop out of your back pocket like an orange pip; anything in the front pockets will dig into your groin when you bend, probably (if your Swiss Army knife has unfurled) performing an impromptu appendectomy in the process.

Zipped pockets and lots of them are virtually essential for expedition longs or shorts. Sometimes the latter (eg the excellent LL Bean 'Trailblazer Cargo Shorts'), where robust canvas enables them to take the strain, have pockets with Velcro quick-fasten, seal or tear-open-one-handed closures. Zips are sometimes hard to operate one-handed and a lens cap or keys safely Velcro-

Robust 7 oz cotton canvas on LL Bean Trailblazer shorts (left) would be too heavy for longs which here (centre) are in 65/35 % polycotton, and (right) very strong all-nylon Cordura/Supplex mix with VaporWick (North Face). Both longs quick drying (the nylon especially so), cool. Polycotton crease-holding enough to look presentable, the nylon loose-cut with belt tunnel, articulated knee (diagram left). Note bellows pocket and good closures – zips and Velcro.

ed into a pocket while you scramble over rocks or sand dunes to catch the scene will always be better than in an open-topped pocket.

And check the actual design of the pockets. If you think such details should be left to the manufacturer you would be right but, alas, look at the back pockets Rohan sometimes install; anything you put in them gravitates right down to settle beneath the 'bones of your backside' and when you sit down a painful and destructive crushing takes place.

At the other end of the scale The North Face offer mesh pockets on some garments to let water drain out should you be caught in heavy rain or wading streams. These pockets also give a lighter cooler feel to the garment. A very thoughtful detail though there may be a problem if very small keys are kept in the pocket.

Get into the habit of zipping-up pockets; especially when involved in energetic activity and, classically, when removing your trousers to enter your sleeping bag – one time when pocket contents can get nocturnally distributed around the tent, the snow, the sand or the bush never to be seen again.

• **Dust bellows.** Another unusual and thoughtful feature offered by North Face on their Tibetan Hiking Pant long trousers is dust gaiters – a lightly elasticised bellows within the lower end of each trouser leg that keeps dust out. An ingenious and effective feature to be weighed against slight loss of coolness. (Top right in photo above.)

• **Colour etc.** See below.

Shirts etc

Personal choice but... The basic choice criteria for shirts are pretty much as for trousers – fabric, cut and features – again majoring on freedom of body and limb movement. Personal preference and choice greatly influences 'torso-wear' and some will favour stretchy-knit pocketless polo shirts no matter what; to these it must be said, at least skim the following list of features, if only to finish with, 'OK I hear you, but ..' Vehicle-dependent expeditions, like it or not, will have frequent contact with officialdom at borders, banks and embassies and the scruffy traveller apparition is invariably counter-productive in such interfaces. Arguably, then, there are protocol/self-interest reasons for the 'proper shirt'

Make sure most of your pockets have closures – buttons, zips or Velcro. Loss of keys, wallets, cards, lens caps can have inconvenient – or near disastrous – implications.

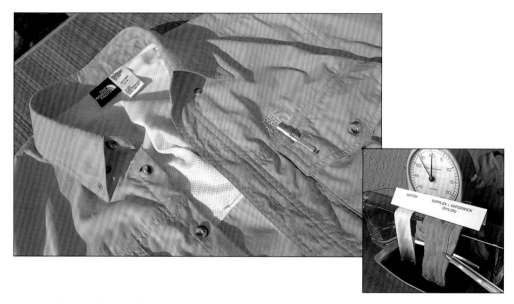

Designer of this North Face 'Ventilation Shirt' should be awarded Oscar or equivalent. Pockets have side-bellows, drain holes, mesh backs, space for a high-top pen, button closure. Yoke area is lined with wicking Coolmax front and back. Cut is loose. Main fabric is cotton-feel ultra-fine Supplex nylon; quick-drying and VaporWick treated to aid wicking. Wicking test with dyed water matches 100% cotton but drying will be far quicker.

approach as well as, see below, practical ones:

• *Sleeves.* Long sleeves give sunburn protection and will be essential to have a shirt like this available even for the most seasoned traveller in desert or high plateau clear-sun conditions; they keep mosquitoes off too. Short sleeve shirts are comfortable, airy; for use with caution and regard to mosquitoes and sunburn. Again, twin pockets with proper closures should be sought.

• *Collar.* A collar can be turned up to protect against sunburn.

• *Cut.* Look for a full cut in shoulders and sleeves, especially at the armpit; this ensures complete freedom of movement but also facilitates ventilation and ensures you can roll the sleeves up without the roll becoming a tourniquet on the upper arm.

• *Pleats.* A pleated back gives more freedom of arm and shoulders.

• *Closures.* Poppers rather than buttons are a convenience if the shirt is robust enough to take them – Levis 'Western' shirts can and do and are worth looking at where climatically appropriate, albeit they are 100% cotton – see below.

• *Pockets.* Pockets are inevitably important (twin breast pockets) and must have closures so that if you bend down the con-

Roomy fit is important in a shirt. Be able to move shoulders and arms fully forwards without feeling tug across back. Torsos generate sweat so choose material well.

tents do not shoot under the wheel you are digging-out or bounce out when you run. It is an advantage if the pocket, buttoned shut, will take a passport. Shuffling through a border-post immigration queue, you never seem to have enough separate pockets. Someday a shirt designer will make a shirt whose pocket can be closed over a ball-point pen the top end of which is invariably a centimetre or two higher than the clip. It is worth looking out for so that appropriate celebrations can be organised. (Late correction: somebody did – see photo!)

• *Tails.* Long shirt tails are always beneficial (assuming you wear them inside your trousers). If you don't, especially in hot climates, there is much to be said for the polo shirt approach as it keeps the torso well ventilated and cool.

• *Material.* In practical terms, mid-range, some form of polycotton – comfortable, crease-shedding, quick drying, easy to wash – is what you will probably gravitate towards with appropriate variations at each end of the climatic extremes and activity (sweat generation) spectrum. It is important to take cognisance of these variables and any conditions that put you in the liquid sweat range for any length of time should be accommodated; consider too if it will be sweating in cold or hot conditions and whether it will be sweating within a shell garment or with your shirt in free air. These factors will influence your need for, or indifference to, best moisture wicking properties.

Material selection (cold to hot) will range from all-synthetic micro-fleece through cotton-flannel workshirts, to polycotton, wicking-synthetic/cotton blends of different types through to thin loose soft cotton on its own. Synthetics, especially the micro-fibres these days, can be soft and welcoming but their degree of wicking ability will be dependent on what wicking enhancement has been done – clever cross sections, hydrophilic treatments and the like (see above – 'The truth about wicking').

For climate-oriented detail see 'Climate-specific clothing' below.

Skin-contact garments. See 'Climate-specific clothing' below.

Colour etc. The difficulties and infrequency of expedition laundry facilities demand that some matching of the clothing colour to the colour of the expected dirt would be wise. Commonsense will yield the right answers; clothing that will not show the dirt too much does not, of course, include black which manages to look dusty quicker than almost anything else. Bright colours and white reputedly scare wildlife in game parks, yellow is known to attract some insects and flies. Fawn, beige, sage green, jungle green are widely used in warm-climate expeditions for practicality and the maintenance of self-esteem when the calendar demands that you find a place to do some laundry pretty soon.

Workwear

Keeping clean. What you do have, keep as clean as you can; it sounds obvious but many expeditioners appear to cross an invisible threshold at the start of a trip, spiralling happily down into a walking museum of spilled baked beans, patches of engine oil, mud, black rubber from the last puncture, soot from the stove and sun oil enriched with dust. Some, but not all of this is inevitable. Donning a boiler suit or overalls for the vehicle inspection and camp chores not only keeps your day clothes clean but enables them, hung around the vehicle or in the breeze, to air while you are working. Cotton gloves and an old beret will keep gearbox oil from migrating from your hair to your pillow and other kit after the chassis inspection in the evening. The little extra trouble is enormously worthwhile; as already mentioned in the opening sections turning up at border posts looking like a tramp does little to speed your progress. With just underpants beneath, loose-fitting overalls are also refreshingly cool.

In hot climates (see below) simple rainwear – a 'coated breathable', or, cheaper still, a straight PVC coated nylon – can double as workwear for short periods and as a means of keeping your main clothing clean.

Overalls of some kind keep your 'proper' clothes clean when you're doing mucky jobs or chores. They're cool too – literally, that is.

Sensible workwear lets you concentrate on more important things than keeping your clothes clean.

Climate-specific clothing

Putting it together. With what has gone before in this Section – a fairly detailed and segmented coverage of principles and generics – little more is required here than a recap followed by reference to current equipment catalogues in the light of that knowledge. A particularly recommended catalogue is, amongst others, that of Field and Trek; equipment is listed by groups (base layer, mid layer, etc) and it contains a well-written technical section at the back with a listing of all current (ie the latest) items – jackets, sleeping bags, boots, tents – in a direct-comparison specification list. This is invaluable for sorting out the features that are important to you so that you can concentrate on these items and not be confused by the sheer extent of the choices available.

Cold/cool weather clothing

Clothing 'peel-off' capability is important to incorporate into high workload situations. And moisture wicked from skin level will re-condense unless helped on its way.

Layer system. The layer system was 'invented' – or at least coined – for cold weather conditions. Your base layer will likely be fairly constant. The shell layer – fundamentally there to keep out rain and wind but nowadays, in deference to the extra comfort it can afford, will certainly be a 'breathable' of some kind. It will be affected by the extreme end of the climatic spectrum and you will use more, or less, of the 'extreme' design features outlined above to cater for your needs. The main climatic tuning will be in the type and number of garments in the mid layer.

Workload. All the above will be influenced by the type and duration of workload, the ratio of 'standing around' to hard graft. The former must be comprehensively catered for plus margins to accommodate the extra subjective cold brought on by fatigue and time since the last meal. High-end workload will govern the need for 'peel-ability' of your clothing, the need or otherwise for ventilation without disrobing – underarm vents and the like. Most important, too, for high workload conditions, are the factors governing moisture transporta-

tion as covered above. Where there is mainly standing around, traditional fabrics will in many cases suffice but even a short burst of energy climbing a hill can highlight the need for efficient wicking base and mid layers in order to move the moisture to beyond the outer layer and not have it hanging around causing body chill. Cold climates have by definition the right temperature and (usually) humidity gradients to make wicking clothing work properly.

Fabric-help – moisture moving. What to make of the clamour of commercial claims about base layers and moisture transportation? The disadvantages of sweating profusely into all-cotton vests and chilling when you reach the top of the hill or end of your task are obvious and valid. Equally, sweating enough to produce liquid perspiration (as opposed to only vapour) and wearing a totally hydrophobic non-wetting polypropylene base garment would also be pretty unpleasant.

Inevitably there are solutions halfway between these extremes and you will have to judge their suitability in relation to your particular activity and operating conditions. Polyesters and polyamides (nylons), especially if hydrophilically enhanced by treatment or other factors (see 'The truth about wicking' above) , will wick liquid by capillary action and in the presence of a sensible temperature/humidity gradient.

This liquid has to be passed on – either as liquid or more likely as a vapour – and an appropriate mid layer will be required; in all probability a wicker such as polyester fleece will do quite well, again performing better with hydrophilic treatment. You may, however find that in coats-off, coolish temperate conditions a bit of 'king cotton's' cooling would be welcome in a synthetic/cotton mix. Something like the two-sided Aquator (there may be others but this is known to have been hydrophilically treated) is a good example; the polyester content will lift the liquid off the skin into an absorbent outer side to the fabric where the increased surface area allows some local evaporative cooling without the excessive chilling of all-cotton. Gauge how important moisture movement and non-absorbency is and that will push you in the direction of the 'clever' synthetics.

You have all the facts and it is worth taking some trouble with your choice; any fool can get it wrong!

'Civilisation interface'. The degree to which you can choose clothing entirely for functional reasons – and these must never be compromised when the well being of the team and even survival itself may be concerned – will be influenced to a degree by the amount of 'office bashing' you may have to do with local communities. 'Proper trousers' vs stretchy, light fleece knit 'activity pants' or baggy-kneed trekking pants will be the kind of area affected albeit in Western communities there is probably less susceptibility to the conflicts between functional and 'official' dress patterns than there is in developing parts of the world.

Footwear, gloves, headgear. See below. (See also 'Vehicle upholstery as clothing'.)

Hot/warm weather clothing

Hot weather types. It is surprising how much thought hot weather clothing requires if you are keen to get things right. Part of this is due to the fact that coverage in equipment catalogues is usually sparse. Nowhere is the working of the human thermo-regulatory system so clearly laid bare as in the different types of hot climate –

- hot dry
- warm wet
- hot damp.

Humidity matters a lot and affects the efficiency of your body's evaporative cooling apparatus. Deserts at 45°C are usually more comfortable than jungles at 35°C – the latter will leave you dripping and exhausted; in the former you'll probably not even know you are sweating till you note how often you top up your water bottle.

Fabric-help – moisture moving. Harmony between the wearer and the cloth-

A funny thing happened on the way to .... Kerzaz

In the Sahara in June it seemed to me the sun flicked from the eastern horizon to its zenith by about 9 o'clock where it stayed stock still till tea time. I opened my helmet visor to keep cool until it occurred to me that, at an ambient of 44°C, I was actually going to be cooler riding with it shut – a frigid 37° inside! It was like being 'cooled' by a thousand hair driers.

ing is especially important in hot climates. The fabric must be ventile (ie must facilitate ventilation) by the type of fabric it is and by its being not too close to the skin. Regarding the usual temperate-climate moisture transportation mechanism that operates mostly by temperature and humidity gradient, remember three things:

- *Firstly temperature gradient* – in many cases there just is no gradient; the temperature outside the garment may be the same or even higher than inside. Ambients of 37°C are fairly common.

- *Secondly humidity gradient* – in hot-wet conditions there will probably be little or no humidity gradient either; hot sweaty body in hot sweaty ambients. You remember from the start of this Section the south American Indians in the rain forest going around stripped to the waist. In hot-dry conditions (desert) the humidity gradient will be very strong so given a reasonably loose-fitting and ventile shirt, evaporative cooling on the skin will be effective. However, moisture transportation by temperature and humidity gradient will probably not be enough to keep you comfortable in humid conditions and you will find yourself reliant on...

- *Thirdly, wicking, absorbency and air* – an important factor in warm/hot climates. With no gradients to do the job, you will need help from capillary wicking to move excess moisture from your skin to your gar-

Hot is hot and magic fabrics won't alter that but aim to maximise the effects of evaporative cooling and minimise clammy wetness. Some cotton helps.

ments, then absorbency and lots of air to aid desorbency, ie re-evaporation of the absorbed moisture over as large an area as possible. If all-cotton is too chilling or too clammy (lots of sweat) or too scruffy, then blends can be used – polycotton being a typical one or, more elegantly (in at least a scientific sense) the Aquator and Coolmax solution, ie a clever wicking operation to keep your skin fairly dry but back-to-back with a cotton outer surface to maximise evaporative area and cooling effect.

These 'clever' fabrics – unlike the old days of 'clammy nylon' – can feel soft, welcoming and promote moisture movement. They will not, however, reverse the laws of physics and a hot day or high level of physical activity will still feel hot. Arguably any shirt that mops you chalk-dry with wicking could leave you less comfortable than one that leaves a little liquid around to do some minor chilling – again a case for the Coolmax/cotton blend kind of approach. (The laws of physics also decree, of course, that any shirt under a rucsac or leaning against the wrong sort of seat back will get soaked with sweat whatever it's made of.)

Cotton good in hot climates but if too slow drying for comfort: mix in Coolmax, Supplex, Aquator for less absorbency. Don't bother with breathable rainwear!

Incisively revealing if inelegantly titled, the 'leaning forward in your seat on a hot day' test will show whether you have got it right or not in regard to base/shirt fabrics. Doing that on a 42°C desert noon wearing a 100% cotton shirt delivers an icy and wholly welcome onslaught to the skin on your back as cotton's absorption and huge surface area get instantly to work on your behalf. In rain forest the effect will not be the same but it is probably as good as you will get. It may be that you prefer a more cushioned effect and the Aquator/Coolmax type of garment would in this case be preferable; the cooling would take place a couple of millimetres 'out' so that you get cooling without the icy chill.

If your interest in the science of clothing occasionally exceeds your interest in tennis, observe Wimbledon centre court players plucking their clammy shirts off their backs as they wait, shifting from foot to foot, for the next service. With their minds on other things, they probably don't realise their sweat rate exceeds the capability of their shirts to move the liquid. Everything has a limit; this could happen to you.

Layer system. After such imagery, the thought of layers may come as a surprise but, certainly in desert regions, the layer system is just as appropriate as anywhere else. Temperature drop due to the sun going down and virtually unrestricted radiation into clear skies is quick and considerable. Mid layers in the form of track suits or fleece with a wind-blocking outer shell are very much part of the desert traveller's equipment. A lightweight microporous shell (top and trousers) with the accent on breathability rather than waterproofing will probably be best – a classic if unusual Activent application though cheaper shells would do almost as well.

In hot-wet conditions something to keep the rain out is obviously desirable (a top with a hood is usually enough) and in tropical conditions such precipitations can just as easily fall during the high temperature part of the day. A second's thought flags up at once that there will be little or no air temperature or humidity gradient across a shell garment in a tropical downpour so there is no point in going for anything breathable or expensive. The actual temperature of such rain (unsurprisingly considering where it has just come from) can be very low so it is still worth trying to keep it off your skin despite the building internal condensation that will be going on within the garment while it is raining.

Shorts vs longs. Local sensitivities and customs (see below), personal taste and sunburn are the principal deciding factors in selection of long or short trousers in hot climates. Subjectively, shorts can confer enormous freedom of movement compared with long trousers that, especially on damp and sweaty legs, seem to pull and tug with every bend and stretch – but see under 'Design features – practicality' above. Do beware of sunburn, however, especially on European skin unused to strong sun; the thinner skin behind the knees is especially vulnerable

Shorts top the hot climate poll for comfort, freedom and movement but have to be weighed against sunburn, abrasion, mosquitoes but, no less importantly, local susceptibilities and customs.

and bad sunburn here, as well as creeping up on you, can be agonising. Another sunburn trap for shorts-clad legs is the upper part of the leg catching sun through the open window of your vehicle. Unless you are operating in isolation in remote areas, however, local sensitivities and customs must come first – see below.

Correct dress. Be aware that many African and Arab countries have strict codes of dress relating to shorts, the dress of women and the wearing of shirts. If in doubt always wear long trousers; in some countries women give offence if they wear short or long trousers. Women should always take a 'long', below the knee, dress where such codes apply. Men going bare chested in public can cause considerable offence and this can sometimes lead to arrest. (See also Section 2.1, 'Appearance'.)

Footwear, gloves, headgear. These are treated separately below. (See also 'Vehicle upholstery as clothing' – very important in hot climates.)

Be scrupulously careful about local dress codes. Shorts, wearing of shirts, long dresses for women are typical areas demanding attention.

Footwear

General criteria

An initial thought that crystallises the usual criteria for all expedition equipment – namely that it should be light, multi-purpose and there should be as little of it as possible – is that footwear generically is probably the most awkward, bulky, space-hungry and often mucky of items to try and pack in a vehicle. Resist, therefore, any nascent tendency to take any more sets of footwear than you have to. Some of the headings you will consider in making your choice will be:

• Multi-purpose? Smart/practical? How many pairs and of what?

• Physical flexibility – support vs freedom

• Keeping moisture out vs letting moisture out

• Cold climates – 'moorland', stony, rocks, climbing, ice/snow

• Hot climates – letting air in vs keeping dirt out

• Sandals, 'desert boots', bellows tongue boots

• Around the camp

• Socks – absorption vs wicking

Footwear for vehicle-based expeditions is in something of a class by itself, somewhere between the stout shoe for the garden fete, the suede chukka boot for the Arabian deserts and steel-rigid technical crampon-laden toe-hold grippers used for rock climbing. This latter class of footwear could well dominate your thinking as being the only serious contenders because this features so prominently in the outdoor equipment catalogues. This may be – but seldom is – the case. To make matters more difficult, possible contenders for your selection like Timberland and Camel are not informatively advertised or knowledgeably sold in many cases. Some sound contenders will be from ordinary high street shops like Clarks.

A lot of vehicle-based expeditions may be involved in little more than infrequent scrambling over rocks and footwear requirements in the field can then be more directed towards comfort, keeping feet dry in wet conditions and the avoidance of twisted ankles. Since drivers require easy foot movements, always go for comfort, flexibility, lightness and best ventilation; depart from these optima only at the behest of the expected specific conditions.

It is again a case of establishing your own criteria and not being overly influenced by sectors of the market where there is a plethora of information or being put off those sectors where there is little or none.

Specification, features

Multi-purpose footwear. The multifunctional aspect is important to start with, albeit you will in the majority of cases find yourself taking two sets of footwear. You will often need something strong enough to give you grip, ankle support, protection against rocks and sharp stones, mud or water a couple of inches deep or even sand that will find its way into your shoe/boot if it doesn't have a bellows tongue. Equally what you wear must be comfortable and flexible enough for driving and you will probably not wish to be clumping around hotels and embassies in boots seemingly made for lunar perambulation.

Support vs freedom. The inevitable amalgam of commonsense, roundabouts and swings applies in the selection of footwear for expeditions. Tougher, stiffer boots are good for rough ground and heavy loads but their extra weight and stiffness may be more fatiguing; such boots, custom-

Catalogue boots tend to be too stiff, rock oriented for most vehicle based expeditions. Drivers' ankles must flex. Go for lightness, flex, comfort with just enough ankle support.

arily associated with demanding snow/mountain conditions are usually made from the thickest most waterproof leathers.

On the other hand, lighter and more flexible designs – often with suede, suede/fabric or plain fabric uppers – are more applicable for paths and lowland walking but sharp rocks may be felt through the soles and protection from turned ankles may be less than from a stiffer boot.

Boots graded for purpose. Assess with care the functional requirements for your boots beforehand. Outdoor equipment catalogues are inevitably angled towards the extremes of activity and just as with other equipment (eg you don't always want the warmest sleeping bag – see Section 2.2), the most expensively specified is not necessarily what you need for your particular trip.

As mentioned above, UK outdoor equipment suppliers Field and Trek's approach of classifying equipment is excellent – and unique. In the case of boots a figure for flexibility is allocated plus a functional application guide. Berghaus' boots catalogue likewise categorises boots for 'adventure', 'trail', 'trekking', and 'mountain' indicating an increase in weight, strength and stiffness, suitability for crampons etc; here the categories indicate ascending orders of rigidity.

Stiffness – fore and aft, lateral support. Don't confuse longitudinal stiffness – how much a boot will bend fore and aft – with lateral support, the amount of resistance to a twisted ankle. Longitudinal stiffness depends almost entirely on the type of midsole or shank that is fitted (between the external sole and the insole). Longitudinal stiffness can vary not only in amount but in distribution – for instance it can be very stiff all along the boot, very stiff under the arch and allow most flex under the ball of the foot, or it can be flexible throughout the length of the boot rather like a tennis shoe.

Lateral support against twisted ankles on rolling rocks derives somewhat from the overall stiffness of the boot but is also critically dependent on the height of the boot – how far up the ankle and lower leg the boot

Best foot forward – but which boot? Hot, humid and wet; ideally you need to have done it before to know your preferences. Options: try to keep it out with a waterproof boot (but if you let it in it'll never get out), have a boot that lets water in but equally well lets it out again, use 'adventure sandals' that take this approach to extremes and leave you unprotected against groundlife into the bargain. And if you are going onto the rocks you will need ankle support. See main text ...!

and lacing goes. Dedicated followers of function rather than fashion, military boots have to keep soldiers operational (possibly after a parachute landing) rather than hopping about clutching turned ankles and most military boots go quite a long way up the lower leg.

Military boots. Military boots are worth scrutiny for other reasons too, for they come close to being ideal for many expeditions. The leather is often quite thin and flexible – soldiers have to run, leap and be nimble – and lining is minimal so that the high-ankle support and lacing does not impede flexing of the ankle in the fore and aft plane. Air Force aircrew boots also are very expedition friendly – designed for easy ankle flexing (toe-brakes and rudder pedals) yet as good for cross-country walking as for any bale-out situation.

Keeping/letting moisture out. Problems exist for boot designers very similar to those faced by shell-garment makers. The rain and the mud must be kept out but the feet must be able to breathe as much as possible so they do not get too sweaty, ie uncomfortable and susceptible to blistering (see also 'Socks' below). As with shell garments the more waterproof a boot is the harder it will be for it to breathe. So a tough waxed-leather,

shiny side out, will be more waterproof and less breathable than a suede where the 'shiny bit' has been skimmed off; both will be less breathable than a fabric boot. Note, though, that fabric boots are often available with a waterproof, breathable Gore-Tex inner membrane (see 'Breathables' above) and if flexibility is what you are after you can get this plus breathability and a waterproof boot at the same time.

Jungle boots. These are a separate item again. In European terms a jungle boot is a bit like a basketball boot with a stronger, cleated sole – mainly canvas, lacing to or above the ankle, it will give support and protection against hostile insect life and leeches. Its mainly canvas construction will make it supremely breathable – essential for tropical conditions – but as such cannot hope to keep the wet out. Instead it works sometimes on the principle that what it lets in it also lets out, a practical approach in conditions where you may constantly be wading through streams or shallow mud holes to check their suitability or otherwise for vehicles. Such boots will also dry more quickly in conditions where it is hard to get anything to dry properly; though again a synthetic content (typically Cordura) will help quick drying. (See item references at

Military boots, jungle boots have flex with support and a better potential for breathability than a lot of mountaineering or trekking footwear.

'Hot climate footwear' below.)

Other boot design features. The stiffness and waterproof or breathing qualities of expedition footwear are of prime importance (to optimise not maximise) but a number of other design features should always be considered:

• *Sole grip.* The grippiness of the soles will be decided in much the same way as you would select tyres for your vehicle – the Vibram, Timberland (and a hundred other types) of cleated pattern is best for a combination of grip in and durability. Again as with tyres, some patterns are too deep and close and serve only to trap pebbles; an open pattern is better than a close fussy one as it will enable mud to drop off and the tread to 'de-clog' itself more readily. Some rubber mixes are hard, others softer and more grippy on rock though may not last so long; unless you will be doing a great deal of walking over rugged rock go for a slightly softer more grippy mix. Many slips occur going downhill and the design of the heel should be examined – look for a pronounced 'step' at the front of the heel block and appropriate 'claws' at the back for the slippery downhill case.

• *Sole and heel cushioning.* Consider sole cushioning, a shock absorber of some kind in the area of the heel. Some sole designs in softer compounds are such that it is less important but in general it is better to have shock absorbing than not. Beware of too-soft 'cosmetic' cushioning; as with car seats it is the firmer, 'slow' (high hysteresis) padding that is most effective. Some boots have dual-density rubber soles or incorporate an EVA (ethyl vinyl acetate) inserts.

• *Bellows tongue.* The bellows tongue, in which the tongue is stitched to the shoe at the side as well as at the lower end and is wide enough to enable the foot to slip in, is invaluable for keeping water, grit or sand out of the shoe that might otherwise get in through the lace holes or at the side of a standard shoe tongue. Even if trainers or basketball boots will fit your purpose for general expedition use, make sure they have a bellows tongue; too often there is access

Do look at all the footwear design features – if only to decide some don't affect you.Giving your feet plenty of fresh air usually gives them plenty of dirt too!

for random bits of gravel to get in within only three inches of the tip of the toe but sometimes a 'half bellows' is fitted.

• *Pull-on loop.* Amazingly, some manufacturers still do not fit a pull-on loop at the rear of a boot. Its absence is not the end of the world but it is remarkably useful when pulling on a snug boot over thick socks and remarkably irritating not to have one. (Some provide the ultimate in frustration – a loop that is too small to get your finger into!)

Bellows tongue keeps out sand, grit, wet and live visitors. Fabric (Cordura) and Gore-Tex is more breathable than leather; sole is on the grippy side of hard and boot flexibilitiy rates a 1 (most flexible) on the invaluable Field and Trek scale of features. A very good light boot for temperate summer or winter; some may find it too much for warm climates, others not. Maitres d' would not welcome it in the dining room!

• *Lacing eyes, hooks.* These are virtually standard on all walking boots these days – lace-eye holes at the bottom and the last few towards the top of the boot are hooks. Three sets of hooks are better than two for quicker putting on and taking off.

• *Fit.* An oft-quoted method of ensuring proper fit (for length, at least) when buying boots is to put on the socks you propose wearing, undo the laces till they are fully loose, slip your foot into the boot, tap the toe of the boot on the floor until your foot is as far forward in the boot as it will go; at this point you should be able to get one finger between your heel and the heel of the boot.

Gumboots. Those brought up to North European off-road exploration will be forgiven for thinking that gumboots are part of a Land Rover's tool kit for these knee-length rubber boots are unbeatable for English mud, wading and all that goes with it. Fording shallow streams on foot to recce for rocks and potholes can be done in nothing so well as 'Wellies'. Even here, though, there is scope for fine-tuning what you buy. Being rubber, a gumboot (Wellington boot) does not breathe so get them sized big enough for you to wear two pairs of thick socks. Both these socks will get thoroughly damp or wet with perspiration; the laws of physics again – it would be that much worse if you only had one pair of socks on.

Be sure, when buying gumboots, that they have a heavily cleated tread and a really robust sole – foot-pushing a shovel will otherwise crack them quickly. In the quest for cheapness some manufacturers skimp this aspect. In muddy conditions the tread will soon at least partly fill with mud but, as with tyres in mud, a deep tread is better than a shallow one.

Needless to say, gumboots are not suitable for walking any distance in but as footwear for getting in and out of your vehicle to get it through demanding cold/wet muddy conditions they are hard to beat. Taking the booby prize for breathability they deserve similar awards for stowability in a vehicle – awkward, bulky, unlashable and seldom fitting in with anything else no matter where you put them. Have a boot bag – either purpose designed or use a really robust garden fertiliser-type of plastic sack. Often in North European conditions you will find, on top of this, that gumboots are probably your third set of footwear – but they are useful!

Gaiters. Conditions on moors or hills will often demand a walking boot but undergrowth may be high enough to soak trouser bottoms. If it is too warm to use waterproof trousers, gaiters can keep debris from entering the top of your boot and will keep you dry below the knees. At the other end of the temperature scale, gaiters can be useful in snow – an extra layer of insulation and a buffer to keep snow from compacting on the front of your boots. Remember that some gaiter systems apply to certain boots only and vice versa. There are full over-the-boot gaiters (which work best on stiff boots and generally need to be designed for the particular type of boot sole and toe) and others less enveloping with a simpler under-the boot strap retention system.

Cold climate footwear

Study the catalogues. The choice and variety of fine-tuning of specification is legion in the field of temperate/cold climate footwear. Once again the Field and Trek specification and categorisation list cannot be too strongly recommended for here role, construction, materials, flexibility, weight are listed against common criteria and a skim down this list – preferably before looking at the illustrations – will narrow your choice according to proposed usage. This way you will probably find a short list of four or five boots that meet your specification requirements rather than having to trawl the pages of illustrations in the main catalogue. Inevitably, choice of footwear is inseparably tied up with choice of socks, leggings, waterproof trousers, gaiters or other add-ons such as crampons.

Crampons. Crampons for ice and snow can be attached to leather walking boots but be sure yours have a stiff midsole and well padded, protective uppers.

Gumboots are infuriatingly space-hungry – but useful. Gaiters often a good alternative. Cold climate footwear well covered in catalogues.

• *Strap-on crampons* will need a boot with strong uppers to protect your foot from the effects of the straps – needless to say any movement between boot and crampon can be dangerous. Unless the use is occasional and for short distances, be sure the boot is compatible in stiffness with the crampon. Using too flexible a boot can strain the crampon to the point where it can break.

• *Clip-on crampons* will need a very stiff boot specifically designed for these items so that they may locate properly – and safely – without danger of damaging the boot and welt seams.

Scarpa, the well-known boot manufacturers, have established an invaluable boot/crampon compatibility code and system to ensure correct matching.

Gaiters. See above.

The final perspective. The previous page or so will have alerted you to matching the boot to the terrain and, for the sake of comfort and minimising fatigue, not over-specifying your footwear. Lowland, moorland, stony, rocks, climbing, ice/snow are ascending classes of terrain; go for the lightest, most flexible, most breathable formula that your proposed usage will permit. In temperate climates there are some followers of the 'adventure sandal' – see below.

Hot climate specially highlight problem of letting air in, keeping dirt out but fabric booted feet in fact cope well even with membrane fabrics. Anything airier is bonus.

Benchmark breathability for hot climates. Merrell's M2 Ventilator a bit stiff for driving and general use.

Hot climate footwear

Air in, dirt out. As with tents and clothing, the difference between cold wet, hot wet and hot dry conditions will be major influences on your choice of footwear. The consequences of getting it wrong in hot climates are high profile, to put it mildly and terminated only with that gasp of relief when you take your boots off at the end of the day. The aims are the same as for cold weather footwear above but probably matter more in hot climates – the least weight, the most breathability, and the optimum sufficiency of flexibility and ankle support. These factors plus those mentioned in design features above will zero in on the perfect footwear for your purpose.

Think hard about the need or otherwise for waterproofing. If you can get by without complete waterproofing the Water Vapour Resistances table a few pages back shows there are considerable benefits in breathability to be had by resorting to canvas – though a really open canvas will sieve dirt onto your foot if its 'breathing' gets too enthusiastic. Despite these advantages, Gore-Tex and fabric boots – which have been used without discomfort motorcycling in the Sahara (good strong humidity gradient!) – is still up to twice as breathable as leather.

The philosophy of the 'jungle boot' has already be raised above – a canvas boot that is supportive, light and, with no attempt at serious waterproofing, works on the principle that it lets water in but equally lets it out as well. Such boots are not routinely available in European markets though if you can tolerate their 'styling' excesses, some footwear in the generic 'trainer' category can go some way to fulfilling the same role. Camel Adventure Wear do the 'Zaire' boot with canvas sides, Item 10944 and Merrell have a new (mid '97) benchmark breathability standard in their new 'M2 Ventilator' boot (see photo), albeit some will find it stiff.

'Desert boots', bellows tongue boots. 'Desert boots' – ankle-high suede chukka boots with flexible, fibre-backed crepe soles – are part of hot climate heritage with intrepid explorer overtones for good measure.

They are unquestionably very comfortable for everyday wear but are objectively pretty disastrous from a number of points of view on an expedition. Being a two-hole lace up there is virtually no ankle support, the soles are so flexible that when walking over sharp stones you can almost feel each stone and furthermore, after a while the fibre backing to the sole cracks across the ball of the foot. To make the point indelibly, this crack often forms an open-pinch-close sequence on your sock every time the boot flexes thereafter.

Nor does a desert boot have a bellows tongue so that sand, pebbles and infuriated ants have free access from the front end of the boot. The breathability and comfort of the desert boot concept, however, can sometimes be found in high street shop variants – more lace holes, stronger soles, higher ankle support; but do look for the bellows tongue. The bellows tongue proviso applies to canvas boots too.

Sandals. Any product with the 'fashion', 'style' and high price designer-label overtones of 'adventure sandals' should have you immediately on your guard. Retaining objectivity, however, get back to conceptual fundamentals first. These concern the opposite-poles philosophies of well-protected but sweaty and less comfortable feet (boots), versus well-ventilated, airy but dirt encrusted feet (sandals) which for good measure are afforded no ankle support, toe protection or barrier against stones that come in from the side. The pro-boot camp will also, rightly, cite the extreme vulnerability of a newly-bared Euro-foot to sunburn from sun at a day-long, high, max-burn angle. (The skin on that part of the foot is usually very thin, very white and very vulnerable albeit,

of course, socks may be worn.)

Unlike most 'normal' sandals, however, the sports sort usually has comprehensive strap adjustments that enable a well-integrated fit to be obtained at the front of the foot where the slip-and-twist would otherwise occur. Some also manage a well-designed heel cup for good location at the rear. The better brands have shaped insoles that locate the foot centrally and without wobble; often these sandals additionally provide a slightly upswept toe to give vestigial protection against stubbing. Some have very grippy 'sticky' rubber soles but overall this is only as effective as the firmness and stability with which the sandal can be attached to your foot.

Sports sandals have an increasing following and are well reported for trail walking. In hot-wet conditions a sandal will give your foot sole protection when, for example, foot-recceing/wading a Zaire track bog-hole and will allow the incoming water straight out again; in such jungles, however, you will also be looking for foot protection against inadvertently disturbed insects, snakes, spiders, leeches and the like. For less demanding, after-hours campsite use, of course, a sandal can be ideal albeit still not keeping dirt and dust out of your newly-

Be sure before committing to sandals only. Deck shoes offer similarly featherweight airy option but more discouragement to irate groundlife.

No bare feet, whatever other solution you opt for! It is desirable to 'walk the course' before committing a vehicle to conditions like this but splintered bamboo can be among the hazards. Sandals or deck shoes might do but ankle support is desirable so a canvas jungle boot is probably best. Avoid bilharzia infected water and take gumboots – yes, gumboots – if necessary.

showered extremities!

The final perspective. Dissecting the specifications is one thing but the subjective knowledge of 'how your feet feel' must probably be the strongest influencing factor in choice of footwear. Probably more important than any other expedition equipment, be absolutely sure you have the right footwear way in advance of departure date.

Around the camp

After-hours comfort. As mentioned at the start of this Section on footwear, there is almost always a need for a second pair of shoes of some kind for 'around the camp' or 'office' use where boots are too cumbersome. The usual problems of weight and awkward packing prevail but other footwear is a virtual necessity. Desert boots, moccasins, light deck shoes or – mentioned above – sandals will fill the bill according to taste but something squashable, easy to pack, light and which does not require special polish would be sensible.

Socks

Another jungle. Once again, as with fabrics, an item you once took for granted has almost become a sub-culture. With the market seemingly providing a specially formulated technical sock for table tennis, pilota, crochet contests and philately, the techno-hype often masks the fact that things really are a bit more clever. Many will recall when socks for outdoor activities were always wool for warmth and absorbing the sweat to 'keep your feet dry'. Now, with some justification, absorbency is perceived as the *bête noire* and wicking is the aim – getting the moisture away from your feet (so long as there is the temperature/humidity gradient already mentioned) to leave them drier and more blister-resistant.

But be careful; one current manufacturer whilst claiming two years' research has gone into a sock composed of materials 'which quickly wick moisture from the skin without holding any itself' goes on to say in the same paragraph that it contains 30% wool 'for warmth'....! We have seen, a dozen

'Boots and one other pair' is common expedition footwear plan. After-hours comfort around the camp or hotel demands a treat for your feet too.

pages ago, that wool is the most absorbent fibre of all.

So be cautious and selective without being dismissive.

Blister-resister? Know thyself. Whilst clinical scientific analysis resulting in a light flashing above one particular sock would be nice there does seem to be an irritatingly subjective and variable factor which bears strongly on the question of socks – differing sensitivities among wearers to heat, dampness, even the sensed prickliness of certain types of wool. Experience with different types of boot and sock in different conditions is what will tell you what sort of feet you have or how strongly they 'mind' certain ambient conditions. With this in mind, try to build up a picture and, as with boots, be as sure as you can before your expedition that you are on the right track. You may be one of the lucky ones whose feet don't much care one way or the other; equally some readers may already have experience of expeditions where one member 'had trouble' with his feet and will know what it means both to the sufferer and to his companions.

The market and technology. A quick overview of what is now on offer and why:

• Two-layer sock system. Many prominent manufacturers go for a liner (thinner, skin-contact sock), often incorporating Coolmax, to do the major wicking and a main sock to give blister protection and carry on the moisture transportation to the boot and outside world.

• Some liners are wicking-optimised (Coolmax), some insulation-optimised (Thermax, Hollofil) for cold weather and made in extended calf lengths.

• The task of keeping the foot dry relates not only to perceived comfort but makes the skin less soft and thus less prone to blistering.

• The two-layer system will enhance insulation in cold conditions and moisture movement away from the skin in hot conditions.

• The main sock is the 'layer' at which warm or cool characteristics are conferred –

ie some wool for warmth or more Coolmax for extra moisture movement.

• The main sock is often equipped with heel and ball-of-the-foot cushion pads (or Padds as Thorlo would have it) of a thicker construction for shock absorption and the prevention of blisters.

• Some of these padds (Thorlo) are like terry-towelling in appearance and absorb the blister-generating shear that would otherwise occur within the skin at the upper heel and ball of the foot.

• Most makes are available in different thicknesses to suit different activities – Thorlo particularly and Bridgedale.

• As well as the feeling and the wicking and the absorption and the drying and the warmth or the coolness there is durability too to consider and this is likely to mean the incorporation of at least some robust synthetic fibres such as nylon, probably with some Lycra or Spandex to make the sock elastic at the top.

• Some socks have extra ribbing over the instep to give cushioning against lace pressure and tongue folds of the boot.

• There is sometimes the marginal incompatibility of synthetic fibres with true capillary wicking (see 'The truth about wicking' above) – albeit, if wet, a synthetic will dry quickly because it is non-hygroscopic.

Does it work? The overall system of

Thorlo socks – liner below – showing padds and variable thickness structure to the Coolmax-rich mix. Shown here inside out.

inner wickers keeping feet drier than otherwise seems to work when compared to a single sock of cotton or wool but remember that the socks can only wick what they can get 'out through the gate' – what will go through the boot. Use the most breathable boots. Some have found, using a fabric/Gore-Tex boot and a different double-sock system on each foot to effect comparison, that there is little dampness difference between a traditional system and the more 'technical' Coolmax-rich items. This may be due to high sweat rates, insufficient boot breathability or it might just be true in general. The padds do seem a good idea.

Bewildering availability of 'tech' socks usually have wicking/robust synthetic fibres and 'padds' in common. Usually two socks better than one, choice is personal.

Headgear and gloves

Sensitive extremities. When we took a look at the human thermo-regulatory system the importance of the head and hands was noted in relation to cooling and movement of heat – lots of blood vessels opening up, closing down to move or restrict movement of heat. Hats and gloves are a means of assisting the body's own system to regulate temperature. Even gardening on a cold day or on a walk to the shops, you will have noticed the surprising difference a woolly

hat will make; or, if you've put on too thin a jacket, wearing or not wearing gloves with it can sometimes make the difference between feeling cold and not feeling cold.

Headgear: types, uses and features

Hats for cold. Balaclavas and woolly hats – preferably without a 'bobble' for it will then nestle easily beneath the hood of an anorak without becoming dislodged – are probably the most practical, packable and versatile headgear for cold conditions. The rolled-up portion of a woolly hat can be rolled down over the ears if necessary. Both can be worn on their own in moderate or still air conditions, or beneath an anorak hood (which affords neck protection) when it is windy or snowing or wet. Either can be worn in a sleeping bag to assist a draw-string system to prevent heat loss. Where conditions are particularly severe balaclavas made of Gore Windstopper laminated fleece (by Outdoor Research at Field and Trek) will keep the wind out. (For rain hats and mountain caps, see 'Hats for hot/wet' below.)

Hats for hot. Here insulation is again the main aim – but for keeping heat out rather than in. In these conditions there will be the additional benefit of keeping sun off the head, neck and edges of the ears which, without protection, will otherwise burn and peel a dozen times in the course of a long trip. Note, a peaked 'baseball' hat (even worn with the peak at the front) will not provide shade for the ears. If you don't want the end of your nose to follow the same pattern as your scarred and peeling ears (and contrive to look semi-leprous in the process) make sure your hat has as wide a brim as you judge the prevailing winds will permit. Some form of draw cord system and cord lock to prevent the hat blowing away in wind gusts or in an open vehicle is useful though rarely provided in bought hats. Soft, cloth hats – army, 'Gulf War' types with a brim all round – are unquestionably the best for hot dry climates; easy to pack and immune to damage.

Hats for hot/wet. A 'Gulf War' hat sodden with tropical rain will be better than no hat at all because tropical rain is surprisingly cold but there are better solutions available for warm climate rainy conditions if this will be constantly on your weather menu. It may be that you will not wish to wear an anorak hood in hot wet conditions so a broad brimmed hat that is waterproof and with a wide enough brim to shed water away from your collar can be the answer; it will be cooler and give you greater freedom

Head is a prime output/input centre for heat/cold. Keep it warm, cool, shaded or dry and you'll do your body a considerable favour. A hat also keeps off sunburn.

Mauritanians had the message long before we started writing books about it – insulation. The dark fabric gives a darker shadow, the many layers better insulation. The puppy's forebears made their own arrangements even further back.

of movement than a hood. Less easy to buy, such hats do exist – LL Bean's wide brim breathable ripstop Gore-Tex Mountain Guide Hat with removable draw cord and cord lock is one that is close to the ideal specification. Field and Trek market similar items by Outdoor Research and the versatile Lowe Mountain Cap aimed more at the cold end of the spectrum is also rainproof.

Hats for work. See also 'Workwear' above, an old beret – not a hat with any kind of peak or brim – will keep your hair from taking on sand or engine oil when grovelling under the vehicle for the evening inspection.

Gloves: types, uses, features

Design conflicts. Gloves will usually be considered in the context of insulation against cold and wet but there are other roles too – anti sunburn, anti dirt, anti cuts and nicks and abrasion. Although it is the most usual application for gloves, cold weather glove design nearly always mitigates against some of the ergonomic functions required. You may find a conflict between:

- Insulation.
- Grip – lack of slipperyness, eg on smooth objects, poles, cameras, ropes.
- Digital dexterity (agile fingers) – the ability to write, operate switches, cameras, technical equipment.

For expedition use look for gloves in outdoor equipment shops but also in industrial hardware outlets where effective gear at very competitive prices is available. Motorcycle gloves and gauntlets are designed to cope with exceptionally high wind chill factors and low ambients and most good designs take a high-tech approach to the problem – Gore-Tex, Thinsulate, curved fingers, wear patches, gauntlet closures etc; summer weight gloves from this sector are also worth looking at. With the selection criteria and design feature summaries here you should be equipped to make your own decisions on gloves for your particular expedition.

Be on your guard against constriction of movement due to poor thumb articulation – a surprisingly common fault with gloves, especially the cheaper ones whose designers (or accountants) seem happy to torpedo the functionality of the glove for the sake of saving less than 10 mm of material. Proper articulation should enable you to grasp large diameter objects or put your whole hand flat on the ground with your thumb close to its maximum angle to the hand.

Gloves for cold. Leaving aside household rubber gloves which have good digital dexterity and grip but virtually no hot/cold insulation capability, a moment's thought will highlight the trade-off between waterproof insulation and the ability to grip or do even slightly complex things with your gloved fingers. There is thus usually the need to keep bulk and insulation to the functional minimum relative to the particular task in order to retain as much as possible of the other two faculties. Modern gloves and some mitts (and some industrial gloves) are sometimes made with 'sticky' palms and fingers to enhance grip on otherwise slippery items though this material will obviously not be as durable as palm material like leather. A tight glove is a cold glove. In general, if using a glove (rather than a mitt) in cold conditions go for a generous sizing to preserve circulation and air insulation. This does not cost dexterity as much as may be thought since a tight glove will usually also limit finger movement.

Glove or mitt, one layer or two, lightweight rain proof over-mitt, long cuff or short cuff, even half-finger lengths are among the available options to decide on according to role. In general the features may be arranged, in descending order of insulation properties as here:

- **Double-gloved mitt** – sacrifices digital dexterity, also grip unless 'sticky'.
- **Double gloves** – improved dexterity but still poor, limited grip unless 'sticky'.
- **Single glove with Gore-Tex and Thinsulate.** Very effective insulation, dexterity better, grip better but still improved with 'sticky'.
- **Windproof fleece gloves.** Not waterproof. Warm but very poor grip and poor dexterity.
- **'Sticky thicky' gloves.** Warm thermal with special grip treatment, moderate dexterity.
- **'Thinny' gloves.** Inner layer gloves with some Lycra content to enhance snug fit without excessive loss of dexterity.
- **Unlined leather gloves.** Clearly these will be low in insulation power but, if you have selected well – probably, for this kind of item, from industrial or motorcycle sources – they can be effective in keeping temperate winter cold out without much sacrifice in dexterity or grip. It is relevant to note that air force pilot gloves are of this kind made of a soft cape leather so that switches and push-buttons can be operated unambiguously.
- **Wool mitts**. Rather like wearing World War 2 army socks on your hands.

Insulation, grip, finger dexterity the three conflicting design aims in gloves. Select with care. Hands come close to heads in ability to disperse heat. Keep them warm.

Thick enough, usually, to stop wind fairly well but disastrous grip and dexterity.

• *Wool gloves.* Not wind/rain-proof so less warm. Very poor grip, poor dexterity.

• *Rain mitts.* Intended purely to keep rain out for running or biking, often made in ripstop Gore-Tex. Inevitably very poor dexterity, poor grip.

Cuff or gauntlet length tends to be short and elasticated in normal outdoor equipment gloves, longer in mitts and motorcycle equipment where there is a definite need to seal the glove/sleeve join as well as possible. A zip-close gauntlet or Velcro closure is sometimes provided on gloves and can be very useful for preventing water running down your arms and into the glove. the other approach is a glove with a small gauntlet that can fit inside your shell garment sleeve with the Velcro cuff on the latter effecting the seal. Consider the garment the glove will mate with; if in doubt err on the side of the longer cuff. Surprisingly (see below) this is also important in hot weather gloves.

Think hard about what you want. There are conflicts but the frequently encountered one of equipment operation (cameras, instruments etc) in cold conditions can be approached with the inner/outer glove solution – thin inner gloves that give best dexterity whilst still keeping cold out long enough to turn the knobs and switches – then put the outers back on. Make sure, for handling expensive cameras, that you do not sacrifice grip; human fingers make up a prize-winning design that we all take for granted. It is not until you try to hold a heavy camera one-handed with a glove on

Don't forget gloves for hot conditions and workwear. Swinging jerry cans, boxes, shovels and inspecting vehicles can result in unwelcome scratches, nicks.

that you realise how little grip there is.

Gloves for hot. That there should even be a glove requirement for hot conditions may come as a surprise to some but the benefits are worth some thought. The classic application is for sunburn prevention. Driving open vehicles or other plant can leave the backs of the hands and especially the wrists open to attack from the sun's rays from high angles for very long periods of time during which severe sunburn can take place. Cotton gardening gloves or especially the thin leather aircrew gloves mentioned above (with their longer cuff) can be ideal for keeping hands cool but protected. A thin leather glove will give better grip than cotton. 'Driving gloves' or what motor cycling shops display as 'racing gloves' – similar to aircrew gloves in thin leather – are also effective but you may have to shop around to find an acceptably thin and even grade of leather and obviously a driving glove with large back-of-the hand cut outs will not be what you are looking for!

Gloves for working. This has already been touched on under workwear above but work gloves – again gardening gloves are hard to beat – will protect the hands from cuts and nicks as well as dirt when doing vehicle inspections, refuelling from jerry cans, box loading and the like. During vehicle inspections there is always part of a hose clip or bolt or bracket waiting to draw blood and mix it with the ambient overlay of dust and dirt and sweat; on expeditions you never have enough water for washing and cleaning. Wear working gloves and you will keep clean as well as avoiding damage to yourself.

Vehicle upholstery as clothing

Part of the system. Vehicle upholstery is very much part of the clothing system and it is essential to choose carefully for an expedition vehicle. You are in contact with it for long periods every day and it is a very high-profile item in your immediate comfort environment. There are very few occasions when cloth upholstery is not the best and most practical for expedition use – hard wearing, breathing, warm when it is cold, cool when hot, it is virtually unbeatable. Vinyl seat covering is usually made avail-

The Defender has probably the best expedition vehicle seat ever for shape, support, ruggedness and immunity to dirt. Cloth immeasurably better than vinyl though for hot climates 'behind the surface' breathing could, ideally, be improved.

able in a product range for reasons of price for fleet operators or where soiling – dirty overalls, mud, wet – is going to be a constant problem.

Unless there are specific reasons where this will be intrinsic to your operating spectrum do not opt for vinyl upholstery. Clammy, sticky, used for any length of time in hot climates it will promote a sweat rash with the possibility of serious consequences. If there is no alternative or your expedition vehicle already has vinyl, fit thick cloth seat covers of the highest quality you can obtain – or have them made. Better still, try to obtain replacement seats. This is especially important in hot climate operations where, even with cloth upholstery you will already have problems of sweaty shirt backs.

If sections of your route will involve wading, or deep mud and you are tempted to go for vinyl, stick with cloth seats anyway and use slip-on waterproof covers which can be washed and removed as soon as conditions improve.

Leather unquestionably confers a smell and air of quality to a vehicle interior unmatched, almost, by any other single item but it is not the upholstery for an expedition vehicle. Slippery on corners, cold when it is cold, clammy when it is hot and prone to soaking up (and holding) sweat, it will not breathe like cloth and will probably lose its condition as well. Keep leather for luxuriating in at home (in temperate climates only) – it makes no sense in any other role.

Regard vehicle upholstery as clothing. Cloth facing only sensible solution – vinyl and leather almost equally disastrous in expedition context.

Catalogues to get

From generics to specifics. Detailed as the last few dozen pages have been – essential to establish your own selection criteria and necessary to make sense of the modern equipment market place and the sometimes ill-defined manufacturers' claims – you will need to consult current catalogues when you come to actually buy your equipment. Do use catalogues rather than just wandering into a shop to see what they have. Though others may emerge in the years sub-

sequent to this edition, the only current UK catalogue recommendations would be:
• Field and Trek plc, 3 Wates Way, Brentwood, Essex CM15 9TB, Order line 01277.233122. Six stores, mainly SE England. Annual catalogue, c. 220 pp, colour. Comprehensive, incisive product description backed by a unique, analytical and even handed Technical Guide that categorises, quantifies and compares products – invaluable.

• YHA Adventure Shops, 19 High Street, Staines TW18 4QX, 01784.458625. Total of 17 shops in England, of which 10 operate an equipment hire service and six mail order. Expedition and party discounts available. Their 'Technical Guide and Trevellers' Companion', c 70 pp, black and white, covers all budgets with rather fewer products; comprehensive product descriptions and invaluable general advice sections. Thorough, practical and recommended.

• LL Bean Inc, Freeport, Maine 04033 USA. UK order line 0800.962.954 (mail order service – air – to the UK with free-phone order line. Prices include customs, VAT etc; flat $9.75 carriage). Four-times a year catalogue plus annual 'Sporting' equipment catalogue. Very thorough product and materials description. Most goods own brand, design, manufacture to high standards of quality and practicality. Mainly straightforward leisure gear rather than cut-throat hi-tech mountaineering stuff.

• Cotswold Camping Ltd, Broadway Lane, South Cerney, Cirencester, Glos GL7 5UQ Order line 01285.643434. Seven stores. Annual catalogue, c. 200 pp, colour. Full product description but not as materials-informative or analytical as Field and Trek.

• The North Face, PO Box 16, The Industrial Estate, Port Glasgow, Scotland PA14 5XL. Tel 01475.741344 or through UK agents: First Ascent, Units 3-5, Limetree Business Park, Matlock, Derbyshire DE4 3EJ. Tel 01629.580484. Catalogue is thorough and technically makes sense but deals only with North Face products. Equipment is angled at 'serious' hi-tech pursuits – cutting edge mountaineering, Himalayan trekking etc.

Buying – team-up with the shop. The fact that stores such as Field and Trek or Cotswold are very often staffed by young, enthusiastic actual users of the hardware they sell means that the service you get in-shop will be refreshing and far better informed than virtually any other consumer retail outlets in the UK. Naturally, exceptional breadth of experience is hard to acquire at such an age, despite sometimes astonishing detail product knowledge, so you will be advised, as with all aspects of expedition planning, to do your homework with the catalogues as thoroughly as you can before setting out.

Don't attempt to buy equipment 'cold' in the shops without doing homework with the catalogues. Field and Trek recognise importance of analysis in their equipment tables.

Example of Field and Trek tech guide product analysis table – waterproof jackets

Catalogue Code	Manufacturer and Model Title	Page Number	Price	Size Range	Fabric and Lining	Weight (Grams)	Neck to Waist cm	Neck to Hem cm	Base Pockets	Chest Pockets	Internal Pockets	Hood Type	Hood Visor	Stormflap Arrangement	Waist Drawcord	Hem Drawcord	Cuff Arrangement	Suitability
Waterproof Jackets																		
4088	Berghaus Meridian	49	139.00	10-16	Aquafoil + Dry Mesh Liner	700	46	77	2ZS	_	M1	R	S	2S	D	D	V	1,2,4
4132	Berghaus Palisade IA*	49	139.00	S-XL	Aquafoil + Dry Mesh Liner	670	48	76	2ZS	1ZS	M1	R	W	1S	D	D	V	1,2
4173	Berghaus Quattro IA	49	149.00	S-XL	Aquafoil + Dry Mesh Liner	670	52	78	2ZS	2ZS	M1	R	-	1S	D	D	V	1,2
4014	Berghaus Cornice IA	50	187.00	S-XL	2 Layer Sultra GTX + Dry Mesh Liner	680	51	79	2ZS	_	M1	R	_	2S	DE	D	V	1,2,4
4089	Berghaus Glissade *	50	187.00	10-16	2 Layer Sultra GTX + Dry Mesh Liner	660	47	75	2ZS	1ZS	M1	R	_	1S	D	D	V	1,2,4
4005	Berghaus Meru	50	179.00	S-XL	2 Layer Taslan GTX	600	50	79	2ZS	_	M1	R	W	2V	D	D	V	1,2
4011	Berghaus AlpineLite	51	219.00	S-XL	3 Layer Ripstop GTX/Ultra TZ	800	50	77	2ZS	2ZS	M1	F	W	2S	SE	S	V	6,7
4003	Berghaus Kalanka	51	219.00	10-16	3 Layer Ripstop GTX/Ultra TZ	780	46	72	2ZS	2ZS	M1	F	W	2S	S	S	V	6,7
4002	Berghaus Lightning	51	145.00	S-XL	3 Layer Ripstop GTX/Ultra TZ	780	52	87	2ZS	_	M1	F	W	1V	DE	D	V	2,4,5
4033	Berghaus Meru Peak	52	279.00	S-XL	2 Lyr Taslan/Ardura GTX + Dry Mesh Liner	880	48	76	2ZS	2ZS	M1	R	_	2S	DE	D	V	1,4,6,7
4017	Berghaus Trango Extrem	52	249.00	S-XL	2 Lyr Taslan/Ardura GTX + Dry Mesh Liner	920	52	78	2ZS	2ZS	M1	F	W	2S	S1	S	V	4,5,6,7
4091	Berghaus Ultar Extrem	52	234.00	S-XL	3 Layer Ultra TZ GTX	840	50	79	2ZS	2ZS	M1	F	W	2S	S	S	V	5,6,7,8
4062	D of E Breathable Jkt	27	59.95	XS-XL	Exeat Coated Oxford Nylon	550	_	81	2ZS	_	M1	F	W	1V	_	_	V	2,4
4000	D of E Neoprene Jkt	27	52.95	XS-XL	8oz Neoprene Coated Nylon	000	_	84	2S	_	M1	F	W	1V			V	

Other tables in catalogue giving similar product treatment cover rucsacs, boots, sleeping bags, stoves, tents (+ scale layouts).

Detail dimensions, design features, pockets, hood, adjustable cuffs etc

Numbers key indicate suitability: leisure wear, hillwalking, winter climbing, group use etc

References:

Brownless, NJ et al. *The Dynamics of Moisture Transportation Pt 1: The Effect of Wicking on the Thermal Resistance of Single and Multi Layer Fabric Systems*. J. Textile Institute 1996

Brownless, NJ et al. *The Quest for Thermophysiological Comfort*. J. Clothing Technology and Management, 1995

Carr, CM. et al, *Chemistry of the Textile Industry*, Blackie Acadmeic and Professional, 1995

Chatterjee, PK, *Absorbency*. Elsevier Science BV 1985

Cheng, KPS, and Cheung, YK. *Comfort in Clothing*. Textile Asia, 1994

Duncan, T. *Advanced Physics*, John Murray, 1985

Farnworth, B, Lotens, WA and Wittgen, PPMM. *Variatioln of Water Vapour Resistance of Microporous and Hyrdophilic Films with Relative Humidity*. Textile Research J., 1990

Gohl, EPG and Vilensky, LD. *Textile Science*, Longman Cheshire, 1990

Holmes, DA, Grundy, C, Rowe, HD. *The Characteristics of Waterproof Breathable Fabrics*. J. Clothing Technology and Management, 1995

Hsieh, Y-L, and Yu, B. *Liquid Wetting, Transport and Retention Properties of Fibrous Assemblies. Pt 1: Water Wetting Properties of Woven Fabrics and Their Constituent Single Fibres*. Textile Research J., 1992

Hsieh, Y-L, *Liquid Transport in Fabric Structures*, Textile Research J., 1995

Lomax, GR, *Hydrophilic Polyurethane Coatings*. J Coated Fabrics 1990

Li, Y, Holcombe, BV and Apcar, F. *Moisture Buffering Behaviour of Hygroscopic Fabric During Wear*. Textile Research J., 1992

Mecheels, J. *Comcomitant Heat and Moisture Transmission Properties of Clothing*. Clothing Physiology Institute of Hohenstein, Bönningheim.

Osczevski, RJ and Dolhan, PA, *Anomalous Diffusion in a Water Vapour Permeable Waterproof Coating*. J Coated Fabrics 1989

Rees, WH. *Physical Factors Determining the Comfort Performance of Textiles*. Shirley Institute. (Now British Textile Technology Group)

Spencer-Smith, JL. *Some Aspects of Tropical Clothing*. Lamberg Industrial Research Association

Thomson, H. *Fibres and Fabrics of Today*, Heinemann, 1985

Umbach, K-H. *Moisture Transport and Wear Comfort in Microfibre Fabrics*. Clothing Physiology Institute of Hohenstein, Bönningheim

Acknowledgements and thanks:

Prof Subash Anand, Dr David Holmes, Bolton Institute, UK

David Bayliss, DuPont, Paris, France

Tom Beck, DuPont Dacron, Wilmington, USA

Julian Brown, Jockey, Gateshead, UK

Wendy Coffin, LL Bean, Freeport, Maine,USA

Rob Dewhurst, DuPont, Gloucester, UK

John Dyson, Akzo (Sympatex), Leicester, UK

Ian Gundle and Peter Wilson, Field and Trek, UK

Dr Roy Jeffries and Paul Holdstock, British Textile Technology Group

Robert Lomax, Baxenden Chemical Co, UK

Andrew Lotze, Clairant Chemicals (Sandatur HV)

Eileen Mockus and Sylvia Biasi, The North Face, San Leandro, USA

Bill Parker, 3M, Bracknell, UK

Susan Paton, WL Gore, Livingstone,UK

Angela Pendry, First Ascent, Matlock, UK

Andrea Pickard, Clark and Co for Malden Mills USA (Polartec)

Dr Richard Scott, Defence Clothing and Textile Agency, Colchester, UK

And special thanks to:
  Andrew Taylor, Coating Applications, Accrington,UK

Magazines:

World Sports Activewear

TGO (The Great Outdoors) – mthly

Section 2.4

Equipment planning:

Cooking and food

COVERAGE OF THIS SECTION

General philosophy. Something of a Cinderella among expedition skills, expeditions blessed with a capable and enthusiastic cook will know what an outstanding contribution this can be towards morale and the feeling of well-being among the team. Others will have experienced – usually at their own hand it must be added – the slightly 'can't be bothered' or minimalist approach to cooking – 'Twenty days, twenty tins of sardines, let's go!' Do beware of the tendency, during the comfort of the planning stage, to underestimate the importance of eating well – both in content and balance of diet. Whilst the actual food department is the area where the will to make things work well is most apparent, the attitude must also prevail in, and will affect, the choice of stove(s) and utensils too. And all must be given due attention at the planning and procurement stage first.

COOKING

Stoves

Fuel availability

Logistics rule. As we saw in Sections 1.1 and 2.1, local logistics totally shape an expedition, from the number and type of vehicles you take to the skills required in the team or the number of spare AA batteries you take. Fuel availability is thus the single most important factor in choosing what type of stove or cooking method you use. As a vehicle-dependent expedition you will have notable advantages over backpackers or logistically limited groups but will still have to consider:

• What, if any, cooking fuel is locally available?

• Will it be the same fuel as the vehicle uses?

• Will that fuel be available throughout the trip?

• What, with margins, is your take-along fuel requirement going to be?

• What are the implications in terms of bulk and weight of taking large amounts of cooking fuel with you?

Part of the problem in considering these points about fuel will be obtaining reliable information on local availability. Unlikely situations sometimes prevail; who would have expected difficulty in obtaining paraffin for stoves in Southern Africa?

Cooking fuel is the first, most fundamental decision. Affects what you eat and how you cook it. Know, accommodate fuel supply situation.

In remote areas you can never be sure about cooking fuel supplies until you get there. Often a weekly truck brings small gas cylinders, sometimes someone has a drum of kerosene in the yard. Plan your reserves and container sizes with care.

Fuel types: 1. Liquid fuels

Terminology. One of the first things to appreciate is the potential for misunderstanding over fuel nomenclature – the petrol /petrole /paraffin /gasoline /benzin imbroglio needs care in its resolution. (A well developed sense of smell is an invaluable asset as a final check.) Where 'petrol' in the UK means fuel to run cars on, 'petrole' in some countries means paraffin. It is best to use dual or triple terminology to be certain; thus when asking for petrol also use the terms 'gasoline' and 'benzin' and when seeking paraffin add the term 'kerosene'.

Petrol. Four fuels come under this heading as far as cooking stoves are concerned:

• **Coleman fuel.** This is petrol in its purest form, sometimes referred to as 'white gas(oline)' and is formulated specifically for stoves and lanterns. Nearly twice the price of car petrol, it burns very cleanly externally and also leaves no deposits in the stove fuel pipes ensuring the stove runs at maximum efficiency all the time. MSR White Gas is a similar type of fuel. White gas smells like car petrol but with a slightly 'sweet' smell.

• **Unleaded petrol.** Unleaded petrol, as sold in filling stations for cars, is not without additives; it's just that the additives are different from the leaded fuels'. Whilst suitable for engines, the additives do not always

fully disperse at stove temperatures and may clog the 'generator' pipe – the pipe that runs through the flame area to help evaporate the fuel – in some stoves.

• **Two-star petrol.** 'Normal', 'regular' or 'essence' (as opposed to 'super'), this low octane car petrol (usually 90-91 oct) has less lead than four-star and is the better fuel to use – on some stoves – if you cannot get Coleman fuel or unleaded. A stove will normally last a six-week expedition without much loss of performance on two-star vehicle petrol. Some stoves are more tolerant of leaded fuel than others. The cheaper petrol available in developing countries is a lower octane than European two-star and is better suited to petrol stoves.

• **Four-star petrol.** 'Super' or 'premium' petrol of around 96 octane has high quantities of lead additives to give it anti-knock qualities in a car engine but these additives clog up petrol stoves quickly. Loss of performance is obvious within a week or ten days and usually a new generator assembly has to be fitted to the stove.

Car fuels: _Warning._ Modern car fuels – leaded and unleaded – contain aromatics like benzene which give off particularly dangerous carcinogenic fumes. Benzene blends can also cause swelling of rubber washers in stove pumps etc.

Some multi-fuel capability worthwhile unless you're certain of en route fuel availability. Know which fuels degrade stove performance.

CAMPING STOVE FUEL – TERMINOLOGY ABROAD

Country	Paraffin	Petrol/unleaded	Coleman fuel	Meths
France	Petrole	Essence/ essence sans plomb	Essence blanche sans plomb	Alcool a bruler Alcool denature Alcool methylique
Germany	Petroleum, Paraffinol	Benzin	Katalytbenzin	Spiritus Brennspiritus
Spain	Parafina	Gasolina	Gasolina catalitica	Alcohol metillico
Mexico	Petroleo	Gasolina		
USA	Kerosene	Gasoline	White gas, naptha	Denatured alcohol

Pierceable gas cartridge and stove left, resealable types right. Bleuet 470 HPZ stove (right) has self ignition.

Paraffin (kerosene). A broad spectrum of fuel lies within this category:

• *Domestic paraffin/kerosene.* This is designed for stoves and lanterns.

• *Tractor fuel.* Some tractor fuels (kerosene type) can be suitable for use in stoves. Question the vendor and experiment at a safe distance first.

• *Jet aircraft fuel.* Aviation kerosene can be used for paraffin burning stoves.

Diesel fuel. There are many grades of diesel, some thin and paraffin-like, others crude and heavy. Though diesel fuel *can* be burned in multi-fuel stoves (see below), a clean blue flame is a rarity. In most cases the temperatures are not high enough to effect full vapourisation, a yellow flame dominates and glutinous soot and smoke result. Reckon cleaning time being about 150% of cooking time; regard diesel as a last resort.

Methylated spirits. The far end of the scale from diesel – clinically clean, easy to light and not needing the pressurisation that is necessary in petrol and paraffin stoves. Heat output tends to be low in comparison with the above (hence Optimus' special jet – see below), the flame is nearly invisible so care is needed. Often hard to obtain.

Fuel types: 2. Gas

Butane canisters. Well known worldwide as 'Camping Gaz' and other incarnations, the basic butane canister (or cartridge) stove is clean, lights instantly and is easy to control. Lightweight, these small disposable canisters suit short duration trips or backpack excursions from a base camp though supplies of canisters are bulky; spent cans should be retained for later proper disposal. Lately they are available with a 15% or 20% propane content that enhances cold weather performance. They are available as (1), pierceable or (2), resealable /valved types:

• *Pierceable cartridges* – once punctured on offering up to the appliance, the canister cannot be removed from the stove or lamp until the gas is exhausted. The classic Camping Gaz C206 pierceable cartridge (above) is one of the most widely distributed gas cartridges in the world, reputedly available in 129 countries; interchangeable with this is the EPI-gas 190 gm pierceable cartridge. A Camping Gaz 206 cartridge will operate a single 1300 watt burner stove for 2.5 hours on full power. (The 1300 watt output stove is the 'basic' Camping Gaz stove and equates to boiling a litre of water in about four minutes. The larger 3000 watt burners do not decrease the litre boiling time as much as might be expected.)

• *Resealable, valved cartridges* – the canister reseals when the stove or lamp 'top' is removed. This can be of considerable help when packing and the same canister can be changed from a stove to a lamp if required. However, unlike the interchangeable brands of pierceable canisters above, there are also two standards of resealable canister which are incompatible with each other:

• Camping Gaz 270/470 system (230 and 450 gm of gas mix). The burner top clips into the top of the canister and is then locked with a twist collar.

Liquid fuels are powerful, easy to carry in bulk. Gas is clean, controllable but bulky unless in the 2.72 kg exchangeable cylinders.

Master of the low simmer, Coleman stoves (white gas Peak 400 left, multi-fuel Apex II, right) epitomise the easy-light, high output, cleanliness and controllability of stoves running on white gas.

• EPI-gaz, now also known as – and equivalent to – Coleman. The burner top screws in on a metal thread.

A Camping Gaz CV270 will operate a 1300 watt burner at full power for three hours; a CV470 about double that time.

Pre-heater. Although a feature of the stove rather than the fuel type, an innovation that enhances cold climate (or low cylinder contents) fuel performance on some gas stoves is a pre-heater – the MSR Rapid Fire and Coleman 3093 Alpine HPX are two examples, early 1997. As well as overall enhancing the efficiency of burning, the pre-heater also confers an anti-flare characteristic in the event of the stove being knocked.

Two different types of disposable resealable propane canister exist – not interchangeable. Know resupply availability for longer trips.

Refillable gas cylinders. Designed for minor industrial applications or caravan cooking, exchangeable, refillable butane/propane cylinders around 25 cm high are available for use with more powerful single or twin burner stoves and would be suitable for longer trips. These cylinders (Camping Gaz 907) contain 2.72 kg of butane and are either screwed direct to the appliance or via a lower pressure regulator and tubing; if you are certain of resupply at the expedition site they can represent a very convenient solution to the cooking problem as well as being more cost effective. A typi-cal two burner (2 x 1300 watts burners) stove will operate up to 27 hours on a 907 cylinder with both burners alight.

Stove types

Selection criteria. The ideal expedition stove would have the ease of operation of the gas cooker in your kitchen at home and with this baseline the selection criteria for your trip stove would be:

- Ease of lighting.
- Cleanliness in operation.
- Heat output – gentle, fierce, needed for snow melting?
- Need for regular maintenance.
- Ease of maintenance – tools, parts.
- Weight and compactness.
- Need for dismantling to put away (add-on fuel bottles)?
- Need for dismantling to clean and maintain.
- Need for frequent cleaning.
- Number of burners.

The criteria are mostly common sense memory joggers for you to consider in relation to your particular project but one which perhaps needs further explanation is the fierceness and controllability of the heat. A powerful stove is a considerable asset but controllability is important too and certainly the simmer mode is one you will continually use; without a really low reliable simmer you will be forever burning food and spending time cleaning utensils.

Some multi-fuel stoves like the excellent MSR (Mountain Safety Research) X-GK pays for its extreme simplicity and versatility with a less than ideal low-power controllability and a slightly delayed-action control response (the latter in fact you soon get used to). It has a brutish heat output and with this and other high-output petrol stoves it is worth (see below) making at least one heavyweight, thick-bottom pan – paradoxical as it may seem for a weight conscious expedition – part of your kit to go with the stove.

Stove maintenance. While most of the other points above will become clear when reading the catalogues or examining the

Multi-fuel stoves are ideal for long distance expeditions where fuel supplies are uncertain: (l to r) MSR X-GK, Optimus 111 Hiker, Coleman Apex II. Separate fuel bottle designs are light for backpacking but messy to disassemble – but see photo next page. Easy to maintain MSR has great heat output (good for snow melting), crude flame, but needs jet change between petrol and kerosene, as does quiet, refined Coleman which would also need spare generator tubes for long trip. Optimus suits vehicle-based trip: strong, stable, boxed, windshielded, quadri-fuel, only needs jet change for meths.

hardware, the need or implications for maintenance access is less self-evident and this in turn will depend very much on the fuel used. In general, gas stoves will need next to no maintenance and the same will apply to a stove running exclusively on Coleman fuel (white gas).

Where you are operating in areas that demand you run your stove on vehicle petrol or paraffin you should put a high priority on the ease of maintenance of the stove – changing jets, cleaning or replacing generator lines. And with this necessity to dismantle, spare washers will be a necessary part of the spares pack. Some liquid fuel stoves do not permit the cleaning of these items and spare generator tubes must be taken – not such an elegant solution since it implies that a slow deterioration of performance is inevitable leading to expensive repair-by-replacement servicing at regular intervals.

The MSR X-GK multi-fuel stove and its smaller brother the Whisperlite are particularly notable for their ease of in-the-field maintenance even on the worst fuels. The fuel line and generator tube are one and the same and consists of a tube cored with a removable length of twisted steel wire cable to act as a restrictor. To clean the entire tube and generator the cable is pulled out and reinserted a few times thus scouring the inside of the tube of deposits.

Multi-fuel stoves. This is an appropriate point to mention multi-fuel stoves for they are likely to be a sensible solution to the cooking requirements on long trips in remote areas. The availability of small amounts of given fuels along a particular outback route will be the difference between being able to cook and not being able to cook if you have the wrong stove. Multi-fuel stoves break down into three types at the current technological state of play:

• *Dual-fuel stoves* such as the Coleman Peak Unleaded 442 that runs on Coleman fuel and unleaded petrol.

• *Triple-fuel stoves* such as the Coleman Apex that will run on Coleman white gas, unleaded petrol and, with the use of the supplied extra generator, paraffin. The Coleman's quietness, controllability and simmer makes it an attractive choice if your fuel supplies will permit.

• *True, run-on-anything* multi-fuel stoves like the MSR Whisperlite and X-GK trade a certain degree of controllability and ease of use for simplicity and the certainty that there is virtually nowhere in the world you will not be able to run these units. Alternative jets (supplied) are used for certain fuels. The Optimus 111 Hiker manages all this without a jet change – except for use with its fourth fuel (meths) – and is quiet.

Field maintainability of stoves as well as fuel availability affect choice. Don't walk into a 'degenerating generator' situation.

Remote fuel container can be large, stove dismantles small but at expense of spilled smelly fuel. For vehicle-based trip, consider leaving stove assembled – DIY biscuit-tin makes MSR X-GK ready to use, easy to pack – plus windshield.

The Hiker has no generator tube as such, heating incoming fuel by conduction, so sidesteps the clogged generator problem.

Both stoves have diesel in their repertoire but this should be regarded as a last ditch choice! (See under 'Fuels'.)

Paraffin stoves. Paraffin will always be more smoky than petrol and leaves more dirty deposits on the bottom of cooking utensils on a poor stove; once up and running, a good paraffin stove is as clean as any – the Optimus Hiker is excellent in this respect, especially considering it is multi-fuel. Paraffin is less volatile than gasoline and thus safer from the risk of flammable vapour but equally this means it does not evaporate away so quickly when spilled and can be smelly. (At the risk of stating the obvious, don't spill it! Don't regard spills and dirt as inevitable; it's surprising how little extra care it takes to keep everything clean and it really does pay off.) Paraffin as part of a good multi-fuel repertoire is a very sound choice.

Pre-heating of a paraffin stove is necessary prior to lighting; it can be pre-heated with its own paraffin but this does generate some soot. Sometimes a separate fuel (or a taper) can be used for this – methylated spirits, burning paste or solid fuel tablets.

Petrol stoves. Coleman exemplify elegant design of gasoline stoves – superbly controllable, quiet, clean and they do not even need a pre-lighting priming burn. Just turn on and hold the match. As with paraffin, a gasoline capability in a good, clean-burning multi-fuel stove makes good sense.

Stowage, compactness. Ease of stowage is no less important on a vehicle-based trip than it is for a backpacking trip and a fundamental divide occurs between:
- stoves with integral fuel tanks and
- those with fuel bottles remotely located at the end of a flexible or solid tube about 20 cm long.

The pros and cons of these two types of design usually break themselves down into:
- Fuel capacity
- Stowage problems
- Messiness
- Stability.

Remote fuel containers. Separate fuel containers joined via a pipe have the (sole?) advantage of usually being larger than the integral type so do not need refilling so often. On the other hand the remote-bottle stoves usually have to be dismantled to be stowed and the fuel left in the pipe has to be evacuated, albeit a bung is sometimes supplied (Coleman Apex). If this operation is not thorough, drip-back takes place and fuel drains into the packing area with attendant fire risk, smell and food flavour overtones. If it is running on petrol the fuel drips will at least evaporate relatively cleanly; if you are using paraffin evaporation is slower and the result smellier.

Remote-fuel container stoves sometimes fall into the design trap of having a small base (MSR X-GK) that makes them unstable compared with an integral tank item with fold-out legs. Being light they often do not 'settle' well on any but a firm solid surface.

One solution that retains the advantage of the larger remote-fuel bottle without any

Make stowage and compactness selection criteria too. Dismantling remote-fuel container stoves is an irritant. Consider stowing complete.

of the disadvantages is to leave the stove fully assembled when you pack it up and make your own stowage tin for the complete unit (photo opposite). This takes up a little more room (though not much) but makes life a lot easier.

Twin-burner stoves. Larger groups will require more cooking power but you may wish to compare the pros and cons of having two or more of the same types of stove vs having a twin-burner unit. Two separate stoves can be used one at a time for small cooking jobs, give you the safety fallback of completely independent items in the case of damage (plus the benefits of spares commonality) but twin-burner stoves are often packaged conveniently with built-in windshields and have the additional capacity for the large rectangular pans often favoured by group cooks.

Firewood. Inefficient, hard to control, unpredictably available (and often wet) firewood has its adherents – who are usually also expert enough in its use to make a nonsense of all the stated disadvantages! It is often popular with large group expeditions where the additional camp fire effect is specially welcome. If you plan to use this method of cooking, you will have to plan ahead with the extra equipment required – griddle, tripod pot supports, axes, machetes etc required for gathering the dead wood. It will all be heavy too but again, will probably be acceptable in the context of a truck-based group. Praised universally by all who have encountered it is the Volcano kettle; 'It'll boil a litre of water burning a few twigs and a sheet of A4. Well, almost..!'

Solid-fuel tablet stoves. Not as widely available as they once were and now unjustly regarded by some only as survival equipment, solid-fuel tablet cookers are worth considering for excursions from a base camp issued on a one-per-person basis. It is possible to use them for extended periods in warm climates where fuel requirements are modest. Their great benefit is their extraordinary lightness, compactness and surprising heat output. Often available with an

Large groups often need more stove capacity – twin burners or big pots on open fires. Fuel tablets cater for other extreme – featherweight catering.

Many find the smell of wood-smoke fails to outweigh hassle of wood cooking. Others make it a well-honed art form and can cook on almost anything. Volcano kettle (left) legendary in this respect. Not easy to locate but stocked by Safariquip, tel 01433.620.320.

Micro-minimalist cooking – where food takes second billing to reception of the BBC World Service! Hexamine fuel-tablets (Meta-fuel), here used with 'Hot-Pot' nesting stove/cup, are effective, exceptionally light for brew, soups, dehydrated foods for short periods. Or even longer periods.

accompanying pot which serves as a cup/bowl, boiling water for a cup of tea or an instant soup is quickly available. The hexamine fuel blocks should not be allowed to contact food and, alas, impart a sticky black deposit to the bottom of the utensils with which it is used. The ex-forces, folding, cigarette-packet-sized 'Tommy cooker' is a classic example but other brands are available. BSB International of Cardiff (tel 01222.464.463) stock these and many other survival-oriented equipments as well as a wider than normal range of foods.

Coolers

Need vs bulk, weight, cost

Coolboxes, coolers and 'proper refrigerators' (that make ice) – all different categories.

Application. It is easy at the planning stage to write a fridge or cooler into your equipment list as a sine qua non for any trip going south of Dover if you are UK based. Its advantages and applications are obvious – the cooling and preservation of:
- Perishable food supplies
- Cold drinks
- Bags of ice bought en route
- Film

The disadvantages of taking a coolbox, cooler or refrigerator – and these terms (see below) do represent three different categories of appliance – are the ever-present problems of:
- Bulk
- Weight
- Current drain
- Cost.

Short trips only. In overall terms of practicality, coolers are applicable to short trips only. Only on journeys straying not too far from shops and other facilities is it practical to stock up on supplies which need to be kept cool in a storage system of limited capacity. If you are on a journey with up to about 300 miles between replenishment points you will be able to carry enough fresh food or drinks for the intervening gap and then take on more stock. In some countries you can buy bags of ice cubes at en route shops and filling stations too and again the day or day-and-a-half gaps will not be too great. But only on short or logistically straightforward journeys are you likely to have the spare space and payload for a cooler of any kind.

Film. As an aside, and covered also in Section on 'Photography', it is worth noting

that even professional transparency film is
nowadays remarkably tolerant of extremes
of heat for quite long periods. Side-by-side
tests done on Fuji transparency film cooled
and not cooled on a four-week Sahara trip
with ambients up to 48°C revealed only the
smallest differences in colour rendition and
even those small changes were only apparent in side-by-side comparison. Without the
'control' film you would not have been able
to detect any deterioration.

Longer trips – the logistic crunch. A
double set of cons outweigh the pros when
you consider coolers in relation to longer
trips. Firstly you will soon be out of range of
resupply goods to put in the cooler and secondly the overruling needs of space and
weight make the cooler or fridge an unsus-
tainable luxury. On long trips in light 4x4s
with demanding logistics all space and payload will be taken up by equipment, supplies and cans of fuel and water. Unusually,
it is the bulk of even the simplest coolbox
that will be the main disadvantage.
Coolboxes and fridges run to around three
cubic feet of space – the floor space needed
for one or two fuel/water cans – and the
weight of an ice-making fridge can be of the
order of 16 kg. Coolers and fridges can take
up to 10 amps of current which means they
also have to revert to insulating box mode
when the vehicle engine is not running.

Types of cooler

Cool, cooler, ice. There are three types of
cooler used in and suitable for vehicles;
amongst other manufacturers, all three
types are made in a variety of sizes by
Coleman and Electrolux (UK addresses:
Coleman UK, Parish Wharf Estate, Harbour
Road, Portishead, Bristol BS20 9DA Tel
01275.845024 and Electrolux Leisure
Appliances, Oakley Road Luton LU4 9QQ
Tel 01582.491234). The three types are:

• *Coolbox.* This is no more than a simple
foam-insulated box with no 'mechanicals' or
active cooling which will reduce the rate of
warm-up of cold items put into it in summer
conditions. It consists of a shell with plastic
foam insulation and a tight-fitting lid and

*'Peltier effect', thermo-electric cooler is
not an ice-producer but keeps interior
around 20°C below ambient. Here used
for film, modern transparency film has
surprising tolerance of high temperatures.
Negative film even more tolerant.*

will obviously work best with bags of ice or
the more efficient 'freeze-packs' taken from
the ice compartment of a fridge before the
journey. Will gradually warm up to ambient
temperature in around 24 hours.

• *Coolers.* Sometimes called thermo-
electric coolers (in effect a coolbox with a
solid-state 'engine' operating on the little-
known Peltier effect) these coolers are just
that, coolers, not refrigerators. They will not
produce ice but will reduce the temperature
inside the coolbox by 15-20°C below external ambient when plugged into a 12 volt
supply. The cooling unit is actually a solid
state device that cools when current (about
3-5 amps) is passed one way through it and

*Even fridges
come in two
generic types –
the silent
'absorption' type
or domestic-type
with compressor
and pump.*

warms when it flows in the opposite direction; the box can thus be used as a 'warm box' too. A tiny fan is used also to move the heat from the Peltier device and free ventilation for this should be allowed when the unit is stowed. Coolers of this kind have the advantage of being relatively light – probably 5-6 kg – and cost between £80 and £160.

Ice-making refrigerators consume a lot of money, amps, space and payload.

• *Refrigerators.* 'Proper refrigerators' that make ice and keep things at about the same temperature as domestic units are obtainable and run off mains AC, 12 volt DC or butane or propane gas. These are usually absorption units that require external power only to provide the heat to evaporate the refrigerant; their multi-fuel capability is very convenient and their design means that they run in complete silence unlike the domestic fridge which has a motor and compressor. But the units are heavy and expensive – around £200 minimum; because of the weight they will also require special attention to being lashed down. Current drain on 12 v is around 6-8 amps but because of inherent design limitations these equipments cannot be relied upon to make ice when outside ambients are above about 30°C. Units running on domestic fridge principles with a DC driven compressor are also available but are a great deal more

expensive and even heavier; their benefit is that they are efficient ice-makers over a wider temperature range and usually offer a controllable thermostat too. Remember that a fridge is moving a lot more heat than a cooler so positive arrangements will have to be made to allow circulation of ambient air around the unit installation.

• *Solar-powered refrigerators.* It is possible to obtain solar-powered refrigerators for medical or domestic use but they are heavy and very expensive. See Section 2.7 'Electrical power'.

Usage tips. Take great care of the 'cold' you are producing in any cooler – or even the cold you have in a coolbox. Cold air is heavier than ambient air and (as in a supermarket deep-freeze) will pool in any upward facing vessel like a coolbox. Do not buy a fridge with a sideways opening door of the kind seen in hotel mini-bars or caravans; the moment you open the door all the cold air will cascade out invisibly and be replaced with warm ambient air that then has to be cooled down again.

Desert tricks. The special characteristics of deserts – very low humidity, clear radiation-enhancing night skies and often large diurnal temperature variations can be used to your advantage to make the most of your insulating box – or cool things even if you have no coolbox or cooler.

A tin of fruit or canned drink placed in a soup plate or small saucepan with a centimetre or so of water in it and draped with a Jcloth or absorptive cotton material will cool quickly if it is left in the desert wind on the shady side of the vehicle. The Jcloth wicks the water slowly and the wind evaporates it giving a very effective demonstration of evaporative cooling.

Anything you want to keep cool during the day such as your film supply or tins of fruit for lunch should be left out at night on the roof of the vehicle to benefit from diurnal and radiation cooling and then put into the coolbox (or in the depths of your hand baggage) at dawn; the subsequent insulation will keep them cool till the following evening if given enough insulation.

Despite appearances, not the place for a refrigerator or cooler. Logistics will likely demand payload allocated to fuel and water; resupply of perishables would be tenuous in this kind of region.

Utensils

Plan in detail

The principles. The overriding considerations in selecting your pots and pans are:
- Keeping things hot – lids, nesting pans, insulated mugs
- Keeping things clean – non-stick, easy clean or thick pans
- Keeping things to the minimum

Second only to the benefits of cross-country driving practice, pre-expedition training weekends are invaluable for establishing how much – or more important, how little – cooking gear you need to take. Avoid the temptation of grabbing a heap of pots pans and cutlery and hoping for the best. Pans are infuriatingly frustrating to pack – they take up lots of room, rattle and deposit soot on everything they touch – so keep them to the minimum. This minimum will only be arrived at by thinking-through the preparation of a typical meal and then practising it in the field before your trip.

Keeping things hot. School-book physics talked about heat loss through conduction, convection and radiation and to this is added, as we saw in the case of the human body in Section 2.3 'Clothing', the powerful effects of evaporative cooling where liquids – food and drink – are concerned. Even if your colleagues accuse you of becoming obsessive about it, develop till it becomes second nature, the habit of keeping lids on saucepans and keeping hot things out of the wind; there is always a wind when you are camping and even in the Sahara cooked or cooking food gets cold far quicker than you want it to.

Always cook with lids on pans, and when you take a pan off the stove (usually to put another one on temporarily) put it inside a larger saucepan if you have one or drape a tea-towel over it to act as an insulating blanket. If you have two pans of hot food while you are momentarily doing something else, stow them one on top of the other so the heat from the lower one is not wasted. With this sort of philosophy in mind the approach to utensils is simple:
- Only buy pans with lids.
- Your thick-bottomed 'luxury' pan apart (see below), buy pans that stow inside each other – save packing space and use them as double-walled heat insulators when you can.
- Always use double-walled insulated mugs – you can get them in stainless steel (Coleman and MSR) or plastic with clip-on lids (Aladdin). The metal ones are very durable and scratch resistant but don't usually come with lids; improvise with Tupperware tops or similar.
- A stainless steel vacuum flask is endlessly useful; two are even more so. Filled with boiling water the night before and stowed wrapped in a tea towel and a plastic carrier bag deep in the vehicle, you can have hot breakfast coffee without having to get the stove out. Or if you use the stove at breakfast flasks will give you stored boiling water for a coffee break or lunch-time soup and beverages. Use the flask for hot water only; don't make the beverage in the flask – you will never get rid of the stains or taste carry-over.

Keep things hot – lids, double-wall flasks, mugs. Keep things clean – a 'heavy' thick-bottom pan will resist burning and be easier to keep hygienic.

Judicious use of weight. Stainless steel double-skinned mug to keep drinks hot, heavyweight pans to spread heat and avoid food burning. Lighter pans can be nesters to save space and heat. Note lids.

Keeping things clean. Few things are worse than burned-on food stuck to the bottom of a thin aluminium pan, especially when you usually lack the facilities – notably limitless water – to properly clean it. As mentioned already it is worth investing a little extra weight in one thick-bottomed, stainless steel pan – a deep small (20 cm) frying pan will probably be the most useful format, having a large heat spreading base area which can be used for frying and heating tinned stews and the like; a top-quality non-stick coating will be worth getting too. Such heavyweight pans are usually very expensive but are about the only kind of utensil that can reliably cope with the ferocious heat of a petrol stove. For good measure they invariably have built-in handles and are difficult to pack ... but one is still an invaluable asset. A summary of points to consider, then, would be:

Minimise kitchen equipment and think through the packing so it does not clank as you drive

• Take one carefully selected thick-bottomed, non-stick stainless steel pan.

• Select your remaining pans to nest within this and each other – no handles, take at least one gripper-handle. A small kettle with folding handle that nests within the smallest pot can be useful despite its one-purpose format; the spout makes flask-filling easier.

• Use stainless steel pots; they are easier to clean.

• Consider non-stick but you may not need this if you have the one thick-bottomed pan. A non-coated pan can be scoured with fine sand if need be for a thorough river-bank cleaning session.

• When stowing nesting pots either to pack away or when using as an insulator for cooked food, a doubled over sheet of paper kitchen towel or dishcloth will keep the receiving pan from getting stove-soot from the upper pan. It will also prevent rattling when stowed en route.

• Carefully selected pan scrubbers and non-metal tools and stirrers for the coated pans are essential.

Keeping things to the minimum. Enough but no more applies to the kitchen department as to all others on an expedition and a clanking, chinking surplus of kitchen hardware, already difficult enough to pack compactly and without rattles, is not required. The only way to arrive at a definitive equipment list is first to think through preparation of meals in real detail and then try the equipment out in a pre-expedition training weekend or two; you will have such sessions (see Section 3, 'People, training') anyway so make sure all disciplines benefit. Your guiding principles, to which you may wish to make well-judged exceptions, are to ensure that everything is:

• Small
• Light
• Multi-purpose.

That said, the following are a few items you may wish to include on your list:

• Paper kitchen towels. Bulky to carry but light and invaluable if you have the space. Lightness sometimes enables them to be stowed high inside the vehicle in internal nets. If, much as you'd like them, you don't have the space, ensure you have enough cloth tea-towels to rotate and keep clean – see below 'Hygiene'.

• Lidded plastic food storage containers (Tupperware, Addis) are useful when you want to keep part-contents of an opened tin or cooked food to warm up later; 200 ml and 300 ml containers are a good size. A range of this kind of container can also be used – the dust and waterproof lids are what count – for de-canting foods in inappropriate packaging such as floppy boxes or heavy jars.

• Plastic reclosure lids for tins – available in supermarkets in pet-food section.

• Roll of tie-top pedal-bin liners for the daily refuse – see below 'Litter'.

• Small bottle of bleach. Keeps high hygiene standards and is the only thing that will remove tea and other stains from plastic mugs.

See list at the end of this Section for sample equipment list.

Table, fire extinguisher, light. Hard on the heels of an exhortation to keep things to the minimum – and against the ever present need to save weight – talk of tables may seem inappropriate. However, to save your aching back, creaking knees and to keep dust out of the food some form of raised table or surface on which cooking and food preparation may be done will be found to be invaluable. The solution, of course, is in some form of multi-purpose, minimalist utilisation of something you already have. Hingeing-out box lids, fold-down panels on the vehicle rear door, just using the top of a storage box – all bases for provision of a worthwhile facility at negligible weight.

Whatever solution you choose, bear in mind the fire risks, especially with a petrol-fuelled vehicle where you have jerry cans on board. The scenario of a flaring stove, a dropped pan and subsequent mayhem is not hard to conjure up (stability of your arrangements during gusty conditions is important) and two principles are worth bearing in mind:

- 'Sweep-off' capability and
- Instant-access fire extinguisher.

'Sweep-off' implies the ability to sweep a seriously misbehaving stove (saucepan and all) cleanly and at high speed, off the table and on to the ground away from the vehicle. An energetic sweep of the forearm should

be able to clear the table quickly rather than risk fire, possibly from spilled fuel during warm-up, spreading to the vehicle itself.

An instantly available fire extinguisher, stowed near to the cooking area – usually by the back door of the vehicle – is also an essential feature. Be sure you have the type that can be used on fuel fires and, an embarrassingly obvious reminder, be sure that you and your team are absolutely clear how to use it. Stopping to read which safety pin has to be removed is unlikely to be acceptable!

You will almost certainly find you need light for work in the evening and making positive, thought-through arrangements for this well in advance will be found to pay off. A low wattage (8 or 13 watt) fluorescent tube on an extension lead and attached to some part of the vehicle or a slide-out pole will position the light over the stove. Used with a Petzl head-torch, you will find you can use both hands for cooking.

Without bulk/weight of special table, plan some means of keeping food preparation off the ground and well lit at night.

Four times table. Lower right, food box lid opens to horizontal, supported by legs to form working surface. Sand ladders adapted to sleeping platform-cum-kitchen table; storage boxes (left) likewise. Special rear-door mod raises working height; note extinguisher.

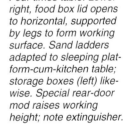

FOOD

Eating patterns

Workload, temperature, age, personal preference. Few areas of human behaviour are so subject to personal preference as food and no attempt will be made here to influence that. Broad advice on patterns of eating and a central core of acceptable food are worth noting down however. Appetite and the amount of food required – not always the same thing or accurately correlated – are greatly affected (and to varying degrees) by workload, fatigue, ambient temperature and age. Anyone who has seen scouts or cadets 'refuelling' during outdoor training camps will have been awestruck by the amount they can cheerfully consume; equally, many will have been in the presence of 'older persons' whose spartan abstinence can make you feel a glutton for wanting a cup a tea. Within broad limits that is the way people are, albeit they will, in a team – again within broad limits – almost invariably conform to the 'what's on offer' eating patterns that an expedition usually predicates.

There is a strong and predictable correlation between fatigue and susceptibility to cold. If you are tired you will feel the cold more and in many cases if you are cold you will get tired more easily; the circular interaction can be cut by the intercession of filling meals and hot drinks.

Hot climates do not switch off the appetite. Long hours, hot days with night temperatures that, subjectively, feel very cold characterise the desert expedition environment and contrary to what might initially be expected there is a requirement for substantial and filling meals - though not at the midday period.

What and when to eat. Because cooking is a time-consuming process that immobilises an expedition, many expeditions find it both desirable and convenient to use an eating pattern something like this, usually aiming to minimise disruption and unpacking during the lunch halt:

Light breakfast and lunch, main meal in evening. Diet very much as normal but keep an eye on adequate fibre and tinned fruit. Quantities vary person to person.

- *Breakfast*
  Cereal or porridge (powdered milk)
  Bread/biscuits with margarine/jam
  Tea/coffee
- *Lunch snack*
  Bread/biscuits with tinned savouries/jam.
  Tinned fruit
  Tea/coffee
- *Evening halt*
  Double mug of tea followed an hour later (after chores) by:
  Meat and veg main course
  Dessert
  Biscuits if required
  Tea/coffee

It is invariably best to start camp chores immediately you stop for the night – refuelling, vehicle inspection and the like – whilst the first brew is set up. This nectar – the best mug of the day – will boost you through your tasks which, with luck, will be done by the time the cook has had a chance to ponder on and prepare the evening meal.

An in-cab 'goodies bag' – sweets, biscuits, energy bars etc – for en-route morsels is always welcome and, for ease and speed can, with the inclusion of the vacuum flask and coffee, be made to contain the lunchtime snack to save getting all the kitchen equipment out at midday.

Diet

Oat cuisine. Commonsense plus fibre; no special changes of diet are called for or wanted on an expedition though there are pitfalls to be wary of in the quest to save weight or in adjusting to local availability of supplies. High protein, low residue foods such as tinned stews, especially when combined with the possibility of inadequate fluid intake associated with high ambient temperatures can lead to constipation so take care to include plenty of tinned fruits, and other palatable fibre/roughage such as All Bran breakfast cereal. Naturally bread

Local markets need practiced eye but often fruit and vegetables available. Heed oft-voiced warnings about washing produce thoroughly in chlorinated water and/or cook thoroughly as applicable. If you have any paranoia about flies, nurture it.

and fresh fruit and vegetables should be bought locally where possible en route.

Baking your own bread is feasible - a 30 cm cube metal box oven or biscuit tin (covered with cooking foil externally to cut heat loss) used over a petrol stove is effective; a collapsible device amounting to this and called 'The Outback Oven' is available in the UK market. For the bread, breadmix, dried yeast and water are the ingredients. Packets of Ryvita or similar crispbread are a suitable substitute for bread when it is not available. As well as common-sense considerations of what is nourishing and palatable, remember ease and speed of preparation are important in choice of diet as well as elimination of water-wasteful operations such as rinsing rice or elaborate washing-up.

Spices. The knowledgeable and the experienced expedition cook will often have a secret box of ingredients through whose magic the blandest of food can be brought to life. It will depend greatly on what the raw material is (see below) but it is an area where, again, the pre-expedition trial runs will prove invaluable. Of the food you know you will be taking find out what most needs 'help' and then determine the best methods of administering it.

Bought or brought. A very important part of the planning and supply sequence will be knowing how much food you have

to take and how much can be bought en route. In some regions such as southern Africa there is a small supermarket in virtually every small town from which you could buy everything you need yet in central Africa and even some parts of the Middle East the extreme opposite is the case.

In-between situations are the most prevalent and as on the diplomatic front where an advance recce trip will pay off so well, being there beforehand or being able to correspond with someone in the area will be your best intelligence about the supplies situation. In very few cases will you be able to take along all the rations you need for the whole trip.

Inevitably you will find yourself making inspired guesses, taking rare small volume items, hi-tech gap-fillers like cup-a-soups, beverages like Lift lemon tea, and maybe a week or ten days' 'float' of top quality tinned rations that will keep you going between local stock-ups. A good quality powdered milk and some Cadbury's 'Smash' dehydrated mashed potato are well qualified ingredients for the 'basics' pack. Dried vegetables such as peas, generously soaked and boiled with sugar are hard to tell from the real thing. The overall task will not be easy as you will be governed very much by the amount of space and payload available in the vehicle.

Local purchase situation usually unpredictable on both quantity and quality. Bring spices and add-ins to brighten menus and avoid blandness/ monotony.

Dehydrated or tinned

Weight and taste. Where you are operating in remote areas and local supplies cannot be bought you must consider the best way of taking your own food. The lightness of dehydrated foods has its attractions. In general, if water is readily available en route the weight saving can be considerable and provisioning for a whole expedition is feasible using dehydrated foods. However, over long waterless regions dehydrated food plus the water with which to reconstitute it weighs as much as fully constituted tinned rations which are usually a great deal more popular.

The other major consideration apart from weight is the palatability of dehydrated foods. Many past users describe them as all tasting the same and not very nice at that, but there are in fact considerable variations between brands and, more surprisingly, even within brands – ie variations in palatability between different meals provided by the same manufacturer.

The acceptability of such provender is enormously influenced by the prevailing conditions. It is unwise, for example, to try out camp food in the home; somehow – and it has been proven many times – that which is blissful in the field fails to impress among more civilised surroundings.

Two types. Remember there are two types of 'dehydrated' food – what may be termed 'ordinary dehydrated' and freeze dried which is still a dried food but is produced by a process that retains more of the shape and taste of the original as well as the vitamins and minerals. Look for the distinction on the labels before buying and look also for – and beware of – the 'textured soya' content which is often the source of a rubbery texture and an 'artificial' kind of taste.

Freeze drying is an expensive process and in the real world, to produce a food that is less expensive to buy, the freeze dried constituents are often mixed – severely diluted may be the more accurate phrase – with the soya pieces and the benefits and excellent potential of the process are lost. Some supermarket-available dehydrated foods are remarkably good to eat – the Vesta range in particular which are even better if you apply an extra hour's 'soak' period before cooking; the result can be hard to tell from the 'real thing' and is proof of the potential of the freeze-drying process.

Freeze-dried dehydration is potentially excellent but often diluted with 'texturised soya' (etc) which can spoil taste and texture

Tinned, dried or packeted. Wayfarer consistently well reported on (and Heinz, of course!) but many foods vary within brands – even the supermarket packeted foods seen here. Whilst it's usually difficult to assess foods in the home, packeted foods respond to the test quite well.

Dehydrated foods always benefit from extra cooking – the 'just add water' types are usually eclipsed by the 'simmer for 10 minutes' types. Optimus petrol stove here adds the requisite punch – as does the curry powder.

Bagged food. 'Real food' pre-cooked and bagged in plastic or foil bags is a tasty if sometimes expensive next step up from dehydrated food – often they will outclass (as well as outprice) tinned foods. Such food – the 'Wayfarer' brand in the UK is consistently popular and notable for its palatability – is worth considering at least for 'treats' if cost rules it out for the whole trip. It is available in camping shops and some supermarkets have their own products packed in this way too. The bags lack the awkward, space-hungry bulk of round tins and are very easy to pack as well as having a weight advantage over tins. Again, try some before departure as, particularly in the supermarket products, content varies considerably; some are moderately priced and excellent to eat. The really cheap ones should be avoided!

Military rations. Ex-UK Ministry of Defence ration packs are sometimes available – the well known 'Compo' (composite) rations. Main constituents are tinned and the ration packs are complete in every detail with all accessories; when available they are not cheap but quality is first class and they are worth obtaining if only on a 'treat' basis.

Incisive treatment. Dietetics – the matching of an expected workload calorie output with a balanced proposed food energy calorie intake – is a demanding process but well worth doing if your expedition is expected to encounter special energy, nutritional or workload/climatic problems. Specialist advice should be taken; the Royal Geographical Society's *Expedition Planners' Handbook* contains an incisive overview of the subject as well as a list of reference texts.

Hygiene

No compromises. Cooking and culinary hygiene must be uncompromisingly high. It is worth reading that sentence again. Always camp away from population centres if possible. Paranoia about flies on food – if you don't have it already – is worth cultivating. It takes a strong stomach to watch a medical school film on what flies get up to; in blunt terms they regurgitate or excrete on your food what they have last been on – and that, as often as not, will have been some form of excrement or a dead animal or bird.

More within your own control as cook/caterer will be:

• Washing hands before food preparation need not be a water-costly extravaganza; fingers in a half cup of chlorinated water

In general bagged food – 'tinned food in a bag' – is excellent. Easier to stow than tinned foods it is usually, alas, also a lot more expensive.

will usually do. Be especially meticulous if there is 'a bug doing the rounds'.

• Keep utensils pristine. Old de-composing food on inadequately cleaned utensils is a certain recipe for stomach infections.

• Tea-towels, dishcloths and washing-up brushes are the classic resting place for germs and must be regularly washed and kept hygienic; again the chlorine bleach is a certain way of ensuring all is well.

• Vegetables and soft-skinned fruit bought in markets en-route should be washed in heavily chlorinated water - and rinsed in normal water to remove the taste of chlorine.

• Be very sure, at the time of purchase, about fresh meat you may buy and then be certain to cook it thoroughly.

Despite all this there is some validity in the concept of 'gentle exposure' so that you get used to local bacteria. It is almost impossible to lay down precise guidelines but a measured and 'not over protective' policy is worth pursuing. For example, if a local water supply is pronounced, with reasonable authority, to be alright to drink, then it could be counterproductive to filter it again.

'Diplomatic eating'. Occasions will arise when local peoples whose standards of hygiene are different from your own – and whose digestive systems are well used to it – invite you to take tea, coffee or a meal. Their traditions and kindness are touching and you do not wish to offend by refusing ... but you do not wish to tempt fate and a stomach upset by accepting something you don't like to look of or have reason to suspect in terms of hygiene. There is no simple answer to the problem and each situation will have to be judged as it occurs. In most cases you will find yourself crossing your fingers and politely accepting and in most cases all will be well – including you; just occasionally this will not be the case.

Conditioned by our frenetic, 'civilised', compartmented and selfish way of life, we are sometimes shocked and humbled by the true generosity of poor people in foreign countries. Often when they offer a meal or even another round of mint tea they are

Don't let the rough and tumble of expedition life drop your guard on hygiene matters. 'Real men' are also careful enough not to get tummy bugs.

As a visitor you will often receive warm and generous hospitality. Tact and politeness are often required in the face of unfamiliar food and drink. To refuse is often to offend and there will be times when you just have to be brave.

using supplies already pared to the bone by sheer poverty and strained by the difficult logistics of resupply. Accepting enough hospitality for obligations to have been met and mutual host/visitor status to have been honoured will be tempered with a sensitivity to the size of the host's larder. Often such situations can be eased by a gift of tinned foods from your own supplies.

Litter

The problem will not go away. The responsibility to set an example in the minimising of and disposal of litter sits more squarely than ever before on the shoulders of any expedition. Take back what you brought in is the motto to remember wherever you are; it will not always be easy and will require some planning. There are few areas where this need pose a problem of insuperable scale.

Start with a daily on-vehicle litter bag – a tie-top pedal bin liner is usually ideal for this – and this can in very many cases be dropped off at filling station litter drums when you take on fuel. There are sometimes 'corporate' litter collection arrangements at game parks and reserves campsites but all too often these are infrequent and the local monkeys and baboons have long since worked out how the bins function and cause mayhem and danger to themselves and visitors.

Flatten and burn. When you buy tinned food stocks at supermarkets or shops get a cardboard carton to put them in within your own boxes, if possible. If you are not able to dispose of your bagged litter at filling stations or other 'official' outlets, then hygiene dictates you do some waste processing yourself.

In these cases, crush, burn and remove is

A funny thing happened on the way to...... Sesriem

The Sossusvlei Karos Lodge in Namibia is situated in the Namib-Naukluft Park in a pristine landscape. Up-market and low-impact, it is supplied from Windhoek 300 km away though it has its own water and generators. They also have their own crusher that processes all waste – which is then sent back to Windhoek! If *they* can do it ...

---

the key phrase. Tins can be flattened on a local rock by well aimed blows with a robust shovel, the whole refuse bundle can then be burned in a shallow pit with the aid of a cup of fuel and, when cool and hygienic the result can be put back into the cardboard box it came in and taken away with you. Retaining the cardboard box will keep the burned tins from dirtying the inside of the vehicle.

Problems arise in countries that themselves have not yet learned the proper disposal of rubbish and many developing countries fall into this category. Local rubbish disposal often consists of huge open tips without any attempt to bury or compact. In these cases, but only if you are out in the wilds away from routes trodden by visitors or locals, the better solution is probably to dig your burning pit deeper and bury the burned rubbish. Be sure the burning is thorough for remnants of food smells can attract wild or domestic animals which dig up buried refuse pits probably cutting themselves on tins or glass in the process and leaving the junk strewn about on the surface.

Litter and waste will not go away. Be positive and meticulous about how you dispose of it. Crush, burn and remove what you can. Bury biodegradables.

Acknowledgements and thanks:

BCB International, Cardiff, UK

Coleman UK plc, Portishead, Bristol, UK

Electrolux Leisure Appliances, Luton, UK

Graham Marsden, Alde International, (Optimus stoves) Northampton UK

Mountain Safety Research (MSR) Seattle, USA

Urban Petersen, Optimus, Stockholm, Sweden

Equipment planning:

Typical kitchen list

Example of food and kitchen equipment

Food, cooking gear

The following list is based on a two-man Algerian Sahara expedition in September and represents planned rations for 17 days plus a three day reserve. It would have been just sufficient for purpose. Higher-than-expected 'left over' amounts are because the trip was cut short to 14 days and 11 nights in the field. Considerable trouble was taken to achieve variety in menu and this more than paid off on the trip. For this trip, most food was tinned with little dehydrated or bagged food. Local purchases were restricted to bread, when available, and some fruit. The kitchen box list relates to a 6-week southern Africa trip.

Weight	Content	Taken	Left over	Comments for next time
Meats, main meal items				
Pkt	Waitrose 'Meals for two'	4	-	V good.
200 gm pkt	Hera Soya meal	1	1	
180 gm pkt	Holland Hutspot	1	1	
445 gm tin	Chunky steak	1	1	
445 gm tin	Chunky chick'n, white s'ce	2	1	
445 gm tin	Curried chicken	1	-	
445 gm tin	Beef in red wine	1	-	
445 gm tin	Beef carbonade	1	-	
445 gm tin	Sausages in beans	1	-	
300 gm tin	Corned beef	2	1	Try smaller size
445 gm tin	Minced beef	1	1	
425 gm tin	Steak and kidney pudding	1	1	Prep too long?
445 gm tin	Beans	2	1/2	
445 gm tin	Tomatoes	2	2	
340 gm tin	Ham	1	1	
225 gm tin	Pork and ham roll	2	2	
198 gm tin	Honey cured ham	1	-	
330 gm tin	Corn	1	1	
300 gm tin	Kidney beans	1	1	
700 gm box	Dried peas (12 servings)	1	2/3	
350 gm tin	Instant Smash potatoes	1	1/2	
1000 gm	Rice (20 servings)	1	2/3	
500 gm	Spaghetti (6 servings)	1	1	
Tinned fruit, puddings				
425 gm tin	Mandarin oranges	1	1	
454 gm tin	Pineapple cubes	1	-	
411 gm tin	Fresh fruit salad	2	-	
410 gm tin	Fruit cocktail in grape juice	1	-	
410 gm tin	Fruit cocktail in syrup	1	1	
411 gm tin	Seedless grapes	1	1	
439 gm tin	Tropical fruit cocktail	2	1	
440 gm tin	Pineapple slices	1	-	
300 gm tin	Chocolate sponge pudding	1	1	Prep too long?
300 gm tin	Treacle sponge pudding	1	1	Prep too long?
198 gm tin	Pancake mix (10 servings)	1	-	V good. Take more
170 ml tin	Nestles cream	2	-	Good
170 ml tin	Evaporated milk	4	1	Good
Pkt	Custard powder (20 servings)		5	4.5
Pkt	Mousses (9 servings)	3	2	V good

Cereals, biscuits, snacks, sweets

375 gm pkt	All Bran	2	1	Good mix
750 gm pkt	Muesli	2	3/4	with this
200 gm pkt	Ryvita	2	1	
200 gm pkts	Bran biscuits (42 bisc total)	3	-	V good. Another 2 pkts at least.
250 gm pkt	Crackerbread (56 total)	1	1/2	2 more pkts
300 gm pkt	Hobnobs	1	-	Excellent. 2 extra pkts
250 gm pkt	Disgestives	1	1	
200 gm pkt	Shortcake biscuits	1	-	1 more needed
200 gm pkt	Shortbread	2	-	V good
900 gm tin	Harrods fruit cake	1	-	V good
400 gm tin	Ginger cake	1	-	Crumbled in transit.
	Jordan crunchy bars	18	-	V good
225 gm	Raisins (20 Mini pkts)	(20)	6	
Bags	Opal fruits	2	1	V good
Tins	Travel sweets	2	1	
Bags	Fruit pastilles	4	1	
100 gm pkt	Nuts and tropical fruits	3	1	
Bag	Mint humbugs and Murray Mints	2	-	

Jams, spreads

113 gm jar	Marmite	1	1/2	
454 gm jar	Jam	2	1/4	Needed more
907 gm tin	Marmalade	1	1/2	V good
340 gm jar	Peanut butter	1	1/2	
35 gm jar	Savoury spreads	5	2	
95 gm jar	Savoury spreads	2	1	
125 gm tin	Sardines, makerel	9	1	Tomato sauce next time?
100 gm tin	Pate	2	1	Bad in heat
213 gm tin	Salmon	2	2	

Beverages, tea. coffee

500 gm box	Sugar cubes	4	3	Tuareg gift?
500 gm	Sugar in shaker	1	3/4	Shaker good
	Tea bags	160	120	
150 gm jar	Lift powdered lemon tea	3		V good. Take another jar Consider 'red top' sweetened
Sachet	Coffee (50/50 caff/decaff)	40	20	
Sachet	Hot chocolate, various	20	10	Choc-mint best
3 '5-pints'	Dried milk	15	6	Good
Pkts	Cup-a-soup	32	32	

Cooking ingredients, spices etc

300 gm box	Salt	1	1/2	Useful size
	Pepper pot	1	1/2	
250 ml	Vegetable cooking oil	1	1/2	
Tube	Tomato paste	1	1	
Pot	Mixed berbs	1	1	
	Tobasco sauce, small bottle	1	1	
	Piri-piri sauce	2/3	1/3	
	Vitamin C tabs	30	20	

Purchased en route

	Eggs	35		
Sticks	French bread	10		Tres bon!
	12 oranges, 4 lemons			Excellent
Pkt	Algerian biscuits	5	4	Mediocre
	Individual cakes	6		V good

Cooking gear – trip 1

Coleman Peak 1 stove. Fuel used (Coleman fuel) at rate of 440 ml per day.
Water consumption averaged 4.6 litres per head per day

Typical kitchen box – trip 2

1 x Optimus Hiker 111 multi-fuel stove with spares .. or ...
1 x MSR XGK II Shaker multi-fuel stove with spares

1 x fuel funnel
1 x small kettle
2 x pots – 1.5 and 2 pints with lid and pan holder
1 x small frying pan
3 x plates, 2 mugs,
Misc cutlery (inc tin/bottle-openers, plastic can lids, scissors,spatula, whisk)
Matches – 3 x std, 2 x waterproof boxes
2 x pan-scrubbers
5 x tea towels
1 x dish cloth
10 x Jeye-cloths
1 x sink brush
30 x pedal-bin liners (for refuse)
1 x roll dustbin bags
1 x roll 20 freezer bags
1 x box Kleenex
1 x jar moist tissues
1 x roll 4.5 m aluminium foil
1 x bottle 500 ml Fairy liquid
1 x bottle 227 ml Woolite cold water wash (30 handwashes)
1 x tent-tidy
1 x bottle 75 ml bleach
Clothes-line and pegs
Mosquito coils

Section 2.5

Equipment planning:

Water

COVERAGE OF THIS SECTION

Precise needs. One of the many miracles manifested by the human body, and indeed those of other animals, is its ability to derive and sustain life, abundant energy, work and intellect from the agglomeration of mush we group under the heading of food. It is amazingly tolerant not only of type but of quality and quantity of intake.

Regarding water, however, the body is far more particular. Quality is very important and the acceptable margins between what it needs and what it gets are very much narrower; if there is any shortfall at all, performance will be affected quickly and, before too long, terminally. Vehicles, of course, are even more intolerant; no fuel, no go. And the same goes for oil. As we shall see later, however, it would be an over-simplification to say that fuel is fuel and oil is oil and leave it at that; it is useful to know the implications of different grades and types and how we can give the vehicle the best chance of surviving the trials of the trip.

Such obvious-on-reflection facts are worth re-stating here since vulnerability and isolation from other human aid is an all-pervasive characteristic of expeditions and must be a constant incentive to put into practice the aims of thoroughness and detailed planning laid down at the start of this section on Equipment Planning.

How best to store and carry fuel, water and food has been touched on in Section 2.1 'Equipment basics' and is also referred to in Section 4.3 'Loading and lashing'.

Logistics

How much to take

Not like home. Weight is always the problem. Water is very heavy and self-sufficient expeditions will have to accept right from the start – day one – a dramatic change to the profligate habits of water usage prevalent in a typical 'Western' home environment. Even when travelling from one reliable supply to another, get the priorities right: the human body's need for fluid intake is fundamental, virtually irreducible and must be met in full but there are dozens of ingenious other ways in which the precious liquid can be saved. Get your brain into the algorithm; think before using water. Develop the ethos of water husbandry.

How much to carry ... ? Clearly water requirements will vary according to ambient temperature. The human body is in effect a machine – albeit an at times unfathomably advanced one – relying on the simple, unchangeable, laws of physics to maintain water-balance and ultimately, to maintain the performance of its thermo-regulatory apparatus, as indicated at the start of Section 2.3 'Clothing'. Maintaining constant body temperature is absolutely fundamental to the functioning of the human body.

The hot climate case is obviously the more demanding and the only way a 75 kg mass of this kind needing to hold a core temperature of 37°C can do so when ambi-

Water is far more important than food and the body far less tolerant of a shortage or of poor quality. In all other areas, make saving water a way of life.

A funny thing happened on the way to...... Muscat

Driving a topless Land Rover in summer in Oman (44°C) my colleague removed his shirt to keep cooler. Tut-tutting about Arab clothing micro-climates and excessive fluid loss, I suggested we keep tabs on our water intake and at the end of 24 hours Richard had used 1/2 gallon more than I had. Not a scientific test but it did seem to make the point.

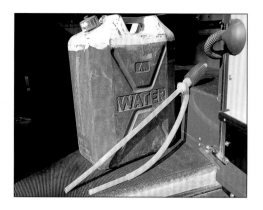

Military 20-litre hard plastic water can is the best and well worth searching for. Plastic squeezy-siphon (here with extended pipe to reach bottom of can) permits filling of water bottles, kettles, with can still lashed in place. Doubles as dip-stick. Periodically disinfect cans, pumps etc with strong chlorine or iodine, leave an hour, rinse.

Fluid intake can increase by up to 800% from sedentary temperate to high workload in hot deserts; add reserves. Use hard plastic water cans and a squeezy pump.

ents may be up around 40°C or when generating excess heat through work is to invoke some form of cooling. In the case of the human animal this is achieved by evaporative cooling, ie loss of moisture over the surface of the skin – sweat. Though it is slight over-simplification to say so, there is thus in broad terms no such thing as a tough person being able to do with less water than a sissy. Both respond to the same laws, like it or not, and the body-cooling apparatus will draw the water it needs from within the body to do its job. Both will only perform well if they have enough water each day.

A simple in-the-field check on 'enough water' is the frequency and colour of urination. Infrequent urination, passing dark urine (that sometimes stings), often accompanied by headaches and extreme fatigue are indications of insufficient water intake. Dizziness, nausea, cessation of sweating and a rise in body temperature indicate things have gone too far and the person is in danger.

A widely accepted basic daily water requirement for a person in temperate climates is 2.5 litres per day – sedentary, no work. This rises to a generalised 5.0 litres per day 'in the tropics'. Experience over a number of hot-climate expeditions and other known statistics show water required can rise to many times this figure. A rough daily consumption table would be:

- Temperate conditions: 2.5-5.0 litres per head per day
- Night/day temperatures 5/35°C: 5–10 litres per head per day
- Night/day temperatures 25/45°C: 8–15 litres per head per day.

The spread of the figures is accounted for mostly by differing workloads and body weight too will affect usage. The higher figures can, in extreme cases of combined high temperature and high workload, rise above 15 litres per day. The span is enough to make planning – particularly of your first trip – difficult but '7.5 litres per head' has been found it to be a safe amount at moderate workloads. At around 42°C demand takes a door-step leap and the figure should be raised to 11 litres per head per day. All the above figures include what is used for cooking and a small amount for personal washing – see opposite page.

... For how many days? Reserves.
Communications availability, rescue facilities, workload at regions of scientific study, replenishment potential must all be considered. Number of days' supply will depend

Few aspects of planning are as important as getting water and fuel logistics right. Rates of consumption times distance or days; plus reserves. Add too top quality containers and rock-solid lashing to stop them fretting.

on the particular trip or leg of the journey but a minimum of three extra days' worth is a prudent reserve to cover, say, time-consuming breakdown repair work. Thus a journey involving six days' travel should take nine days' water; that is, for a two-person vehicle:

2 x 7.5 = 15 litres per day
6 days + 3 days reserve = 9 x 15 = 135 litres
ie, 6.75 rounded to 7 x 20 litre jerry cans.

Carrying and dispensing

Jerry cans. Really robust hard plastic jerry cans iare the only satisfactory means of carrying water. Metal cans will impart rust and taste. 'Soft' polythene cans will impart taste too. Beware of plastic cans poorly made; check especially the lower corners of the moulding where the wall thickness may have suffered through poor manufacturing technique. Lifting, putting down, dragging, being stood on gravel or stones or concrete gives this part of the can a hard time anyway. Unquestionably the best water cans are ex-military UK items (see photo). Where the cans are lashed into the vehicle, put down a layer of felt or carpet to cushion the cans against chafing or small stones.

Vehicle water tanks. See under 'Bulk water', page 2.5 - 17.

Personal water bottles. Make sure each person has a personal water bottle – the robust hard plastic 1-litre type is best. These enable people to swig when they want to, are a natural means of keeping track of water intake and can be refilled together – say, lunch time, early evening and late – so that repeated access to the 'duty can' is unnecessary.

Container cleanliness. An 'empty' jerry can all too often has a cup of water swilling around in the bottom – a warm, wet, dark environment for breeding bacteria to re-infect the can. When a can has been used up, turn it upside down and empty the last drop out as soon as you can. All water containers, especially those liable to be refilled before they are completely empty (such as personal water bottles), should be disinfected period-

ically – see 'Vehicle water tanks', p 2.5 - 18.

Dispensing water. Lifting a 22 kg can every time you want to fill a water bottle or a kettle for a brew is tiring and will result in a lot of spilled water. Some means of dispensing from can to bottle without having to move or unlash the can is needed. In the UK a simple manual squeezy-siphon pump is obtainable from boat chandlers, caravan equipment depots and some camping shops and is worth its weight in gold – see photo left. Imported by Colley Nockolds Ltd of London SE18 (tel 0181.855.6593) in a wide range of sizes also suitable for decanting from 200 litre drums, the one shown is the Colley 'Spa'.

Electric pumps. Some may find an electric water pump convenient for transferring water from one container or source to another or to feed an on-line filter. Purpose-designed and built for mobile homes and small boats, the well-established US 'Shur-flo' 12 v DC pumps are imported into Europe by Leisure Accessories of Norwich (tel 01603.414551). Flow rates vary according to pressure required but the model range covers free-flow rates of 3.5, 7.0 and 10 litres per minute at equipment weights up to 2 kg using a current drain of around 2-6 amps. Prices (1997) are about £70 for mid-range models.

Water cans will be lashed down. Give thought to means of dispensing to water bottles, utensils etc. Manual plastic squeezy pump ideal; you may like electric pump.

In very high ambients, – bikes or open vehicles, body and thirst mechanism take time to acclimatise. Keep fluid intake up. This litre was downed in about two minutes – and sent sweat glands into over-drive.

When laundry is a luxury! Within sight of the next replenishment point and sure of resupply, reserve water can often be used for a general wash of clothes and their occupants. Nature's very own super-scale tumble-drier, the Sahara can usually do the necessary in the time taken to have a brew.

Using it

Thirst unreliable; monitor intake. Until it is acclimatised to hot climates, thirst will be an unreliable indicator of whether the body has taken on sufficient water. Remember this both from the point of view of expedition health and water logistics. This acclimatisation is particularly applicable to, say, university expeditions, pushed for time and new to an overseas area at the hot time of year during the start of summer vacation. Make a conscious effort to keep water intake up for the first week of the trip. By using the water-bottle-and-refill method of dispensing water (plus the communal tea brew), get each member of the team to monitor their own fluid intake. Allocate husbandry of water supplies as a specific task to one team member – numbered cans, use one can at a time, calibrated dipstick with a can-count and dip taken at a set time each day. This way a daily monitoring of consumption of the whole team can be carried out and, as with fuel (see Section 2.6), a how-goes-it chart can be kept.

Washing – personal hygiene. If you were wondering how feasible personal washing on a logistically demanding trip is, the good news is that unless or until you get

Thirst is unreliable indicator of water requirement until acclimatised. Personal hygiene need not suffer on expeditions. A mug of washing water works wonders.

to a survival situation, it is perfectly possible with a little ingenuity – not a Jacuzzi or a power-shower but the essentials may be addressed. A good mix of what might be called defensive and comfort washing need not use more than a mug per day and it will enormously benefit your own sense of well being (and the sensibilities of your neighbours!) to keep up the highest standards you can.

To come bluntly to the point, if the juxtaposed idiom may be excused, armpits and feet are most likely to be involved in troughs of personal popularity amongst the team. It is not just that Nature very reasonably equipped us with the necessary sweat glands to keep cool – eccrine all over (for 'thermal' sweating) and apocrine (for 'mental' or 'stress' sweating) in the regions where there are hair follicles such as (and especially) under the arms. The odour emanates not from the sweat – which poetic tradition regards always as 'honest' – but from bacteria that home-in on it with indecent haste, especially in the underarm area. (Incidentally, keep off anti-perspirants on expeditions. Anything that interferes with the sweating process is bad news and they can cause rashes when there is not enough water for showering.)

A very refreshing morning wake-up wash can be achieved with a wet square of paper kitchen towel or Kleenex. Most of your allocated single mug of water, a good bactericidal soap, a wash-cloth or face-flannel and a carefully chosen order of soaping, sponging and squeezing out the cloth, can be used for the 'main wash' in the evening after the day's work is done and will keep even the most weary expeditioner fresh and clean. Washing at the end of the day also means you do not take skin oils and dust into your sleeping bag. The remainder of the mug can be used to clean your teeth (maybe best to set it aside in a separate cup first!)

Environments differ. The desert, especially, is a very clean place helped by the fact that perspiration in such low humidities tends to evaporate at once without making you sticky or allowing dirt to stick to the sweat. To these benefits you should add (see page 2.3-37, 'Workwear') methodical use of overalls or thin gloves to keep you clean when doing dirty jobs. Just not getting dirty is half the battle. If you are encountering a lot of dust and cannot keep out of it then not much can be done; a shampoo of shortish hair can be achieved with a single water bottle but in most cases this blissful experience will have to be saved for a water resupply point such as used for washing clothes.

(Don't drive in dust – mainly for the benefit of your vehicle's engine air filter element!)

Washing clothes. Water for clothes washing obviously is not included in the main usage figures above but when clothes do need a wash, planning, as ever, helps. At the end of a long waterless leg, where known good water is available, your emergency water supply will no longer be needed and this, or water at the actual replenishment point, can be used to wash hair and clothes. Needless to say you must be certain of resupply before using water in this way. Given the choice and to avoid fouling the area with foaming suds, do your washing at some distance from the replenishment point.

Where water supplies can be relied on, an old trick, if you have room, is to take a 10 or 15 litre plastic lidded container with you. Put your washing, the washing powder and water in at the beginning of the day with the lid on; at the end of a day's bumping over rough roads the gentle washing-machine action will have worked wonders!

See also Section 2.3 'Clothing' regarding other washing and drying information.

Purification

Importance of clean water

Eliminate doubt. Ensuring the cleanliness of drinking water is unquestionably just as important as the water itself; if you drink infected water that causes stomach upsets such as diarrhoea and vomiting then the net result is overall fluid loss rather than fluid gain. If the illness is sustained and, as is often the case, is accompanied by an inability to keep water down, a serious and sometimes life-threatening dehydration problem can ensue. If in doubt purify. 'Doubt' includes any pipe and tap system that is not under constant high pressure and lacks a discernible chlorine smell. The danger here comes from low or intermittent mains pressure where, with leaking pipes and suction pumps, pollution can actually be sucked in to the main system from adjacent pools.

For the possible ruination of a trip, for the random chunks of time it takes out of your carefully planned schedule, for the serious consequences it can give rise to later, gambling with infected water is simply not worth the risk.

Clear streams – beware. It has been said many times before but is worth repeating that even the clearest most sparkling wild water can be heaving with infection. You

Don't take risks with water. Clean drinking water is of prime importance. Don't be taken in by 'sparkling clear' streams – often heaving with infection.

have only to wander in Britain's own Lake District or the Welsh hills, follow a clear stream and find, near the top of the hill, a dead sheep lying half in and half out of the water. Even without dead sheep, on terrain grazed by animals and littered with their droppings, rain will wash parasites into local water. In developing countries such streams are also used for washing and sewage disposal – an infallible hazard.

Prices. If you are not aware already, you will be when you come to the table of equipments on page 2.5 - 12. Good filters are, or will seem, expensive; even not-so-good filters are expensive. But they are worth it. Put clean water high enough on your list of priorities to warrant appropriate allocation of funds.

Bottled water, drinks. In a very few countries bottled water may be untreated but (monitored) still be safe to drink. Elsewhere such water will usually have been ultra violet irradiated (see p 2.5 - 16) and therefore be safe from bacteria and viruses. Get into the habit, however, of examining bottle seals carefully to ensure you are not the victim of local entrepreneurs who have been filling the bottle from the village tap.

International proprietary soft drink bottlers with famous names usually have excellent quality control and bottled beers are inherently sterilised of pathogens during brewing.

Processes. Which brings us to one or two definitions that should be got out of the way at this point:

• *Filtering* – is pretty much what it sounds like. Putting river water through a clean handkerchief is filtration but you will come across the term 'microfiltration' which implies a filter pore size of around 3 microns or less – see 'Filtration and pre-filtration' opposite.

• *Disinfection* – means just that; removal of infection, ie inactivation of harmful pathogens (bugs). There may be lots of others swimming around that won't harm you. Disinfection usually implies chemicals.

• *Sterilisation* – means destruction or

You don't have to know all the names. Divide them into 'big bugs', 'small bugs' and 'very small bugs' (viruses). Know how each category can be zapped.

removal of *all* life forms in the water.

• *Purification* – technically implies removal of smells and tastes. In common usage it usually implies this plus killing off of the very smallest bugs – viruses (see table next spread).

Purification – filtration, chemicals

Note: 'Purification – heat and ultraviolet' begins on page 2.5 -16.

The problem. Names of pathogens are liberally scattered through promotional literature. You don't have to know what they all are – albeit one or two names will keep cropping up (the giardia and cryptosporidia protozoa and E Coli bacterium). You do need to know that it is best to be rid of them. In knowing what you are up against, though, and what you can do about them, it helps to divide them into three categories – big bugs, small bugs and very small bugs – which, as we shall see, corresponds roughly to the steps in available equipments' filtration/purification capabilities:

• *Big bugs – parasites, protozoa.* Many UK citizens carry giardia protozoa to which they will have developed some immunity. It is when they encounter a new strain that they get ill. Protozoa, food and water borne, are nothing like as thick on the ground as bacteria but nonetheless just a few could spoil your trip. Their geographical distribution is unpredictable but worldwide. Originating in animal and human faeces, they are particularly resistant to chemicals – see opposite and table.

• *Small bugs – bacteria.* Far more prolific than protozoa, these are the main causes of stomach and gut infections. They are large enough to be filtered by a very fine filter and they can be killed chemically – see table on page 2.5 -10.

• *Very small bugs – viruses.* The more well-known viruses can be inoculated against. Though very small, they are not always free agents and tend to clump together or cling to mud, or larger microorganisms so that many, but not all, are removed by microfiltration. Like parasites, they need strong chemical treatment. Microfilters with no chemical second stage will take out 'attached' viruses. Where there is a chemical second stage the virus inactivation will be comprehensive but this is as much a side-effect of the chemical's use to eliminate bacteria as it is of dire necessity. Viruses, like protozoa (surprisingly), are not specifically monitored in public water supplies except in special cases – see p 2.5 -11.

Weapons to use. You can deal with all the 'bugs' problems using:
- Filters and purifiers
- Chemicals
- Heat/boiling – see p 2.5 -16
- Ultraviolet light – see p 2.5 -16

You can filter water very finely or you can filter it less finely and knock out the remaining micro-organisms chemically. You can also use chemicals on their own but this will leave many big bugs (protozoa) unscathed. Chemical disinfection needs clean-looking water for it to work.

Filtration and pre-filtration. A micron (SI unit: micro-metre, hence the abbreviation µm) is one thousandth of a millimetre yet, of the harmful bugs you must remove from water that you drink, the bigger ones are as small as 4-12 microns (4-12 µm) in diameter and the smaller ones are long and skinny – 3-8 microns long and probably half a micron thick. The good news, however, is that many modern filters have a micron rating of between 0.2 and 1.0, ie anything of that size or larger will not pass through – see table p 2.5 - 12. Pre-filtration by whatever method really is worthwhile; anything you can see would, of course, be filtered out by your microfilter but in the process clog up far more quickly than otherwise; get the visible material out first.
- Allow drawn water to settle in a container first or
- Use a fine-mesh fabric bag to remove visible particles and vegetation.

Microfiltration media. A fine micron-rating filter is, in effect, an exceptionally fine mesh sieve or 'solid' medium through which the water is drawn. In various promotional literature these are described as:

- Plastic membrane
- 'Matrix micro-strainer'
- Porous ceramic 'candle'
- Pre-coat candle filter used with kieselguhr powder.

The ceramic candle (do not use unglazed pottery) is so called because it is usually the shape and dimension of a fat candle; polluted water seeps through from the outside to the inside of the unit, leaving the 'bugs' behind in the process. (Getting the water to flow through the filtration medium is achieved either by pressure pumping or – slowly – by gravity.) This fine-grained filter develops a film of organisms on the surface which ultimately stops the water flow and must be cleaned periodically. A 'silvered' version incorporates silver particles within the ceramic (or in its hollow centre) to slow the growth of organisms and to help disinfect the filtered water.

Used in large-group trailer-borne filtration apparatus, pre-coat filter powder is like fullers earth and, in effect, forms its own filter medium around a metal mesh core – see 'Bulk filtration' page 2.5 - 17.

Chemical disinfection. First remember that disinfection should apply not just to the water you drink but to the containers, pumps, pipes and filters the water goes through (see also page 2.5-18 'Bulk storage'). It is vital to remember that all chemical disinfection requires a certain 'contact time' – usually 15 to 30 minutes. Chemical water disinfection is of three types:

1. Chlorine (eg, Puritabs, Aquatabs)
2. Silver-based products (eg, Micropur)
3. Iodine (eg, Potable Aqua)

They are listed in reverse order of efficacy – iodine is the most effective. A lot depends on the dilution but there are shortcomings to each method:

• *Tough protozoa.* Against protozoa – the tough giardia and even tougher cryptosporidia – chemical disinfection is ineffective or only partially effective. See table next spread, also under 'Emergencies'.

• *Chlorine.* Some of the Puritab type of pills are ineffective in developing countries unless used at up to five times 'normal'

'Big bugs' (giardia protozoa et al) unaffected by chemical treatment unless overnight soak. Keep this for emergencies. Use microfilter first.

strength and the resulting 'super-chlorination' then de-chlorinated with tablets.

• *Silver.* Despite reservations by some about use over extended periods, silver has been removed (1991) from the list of toxins by the US EPA and may be considered safe for long term use as a disinfectant. It can be used for stored water (see Tanks, p2.5 - 18.) Silver imparts no taste to water.

• *Iodine.* Iodine should not be taken over long periods of time – three to six months is the commonly quoted maximum. If using iodine for disinfection (see limitations in table below), use tincture of iodine drops:

• 2 drops per litre for drinking.
• 4-6 drops per litre for surface disinfection of fruit/salads (stronger if rinsing off – recommended).
• In tablet form as prescribed.
• Iodine in various proprietary filters will have a finite life – say 100 - 1000 litres – before exhaustion (see filters table).

• *Iodine – low temperatures.* Contact times or dosage should be increased when water contains dead leaves or when using iodine at low temperatures. As a guide, double Potable Aqua times below 20°C, then add a second tablet below 10°C.

Know the broad picture. Micro-filtration, chemical sterilisation, followed by carbon de-tasting is rule of thumb though other methods come very close.

De-tasting, activated carbon. Silver leaves no tastes. Both chlorine and iodine in appropriate strengths leave an unpleasant taste and can be used with a charcoal filter or de-tasting pills of some kind – sodium thiosulphate (in effect photographic 'Hypo', sometimes sold as 'Thio' tablets) in the case of chlorine and the Potable Aqua Plus kit in the case of iodine. Activated carbon filters have the special ability to remove tastes and smells but have a finite capacity to filter after which they must be discarded – otherwise the debris in the filter will act as a bacteria breeding ground.

Effect of water alkalinity. The presence of ammonia, organic matter and the like can affect the efficiency of chemical water disinfection and would warrant an increased dosage. Identifying this will be near impossible and local enquiry is the best approach if you have reason for doubts.

Combination – filtration and chemicals. Since certain filters have limitations and so do certain types of chemical disinfection, using the two processes in tandem is going to be the best solution in many cases. Summarised here is what you are up against in terms of size of micro-organism and their susceptibility to chemical disinfection:

'BUG' SIZES AND WHAT YOU CAN DO ABOUT THEM

	Big bugs (parasites, protozoa) eg: giardia, cryptosporidia, schistosoma, amoebic dysentery, worms	Small bugs (bacteria) eg: E Coli, bacillary dysentery, cholera, typhoid, leptospirosis	Very small bugs (viruses) eg: Polio, hepatitis, rotavirus	Tastes and smells eg: Residual iodine, and chlorine, pesticides, 'bad eggs', chemicals
Also see 'common usage' definitions next page				
Size: (1 µm is a micron: 1/1000th of one millimetre)	4 - 12 µm ie, well over 1 µm	0.5 - 3.0 µm ie, around 1 µm	0.02 - 0.08 µm ie, less than 1 µm	Dissolved
Can be filtered out by:	Virtually all micro-filters (see over)	The finest micro-filters	Too small to filter but may attach to larger impurities	Activated carbon granules or resin
Can be killed by:	Hot / boiling water. Resistant to chemicals (but see 'Emergencies' opposite)	Iodine, chlorine. silver in most cases	Iodine, chlorine. silver in most cases	n/a

Water purification hardware

Defining the risk – moving goalposts. It may come as a minor shock but developed countries' public supply water purification risks, standards, methods and pathogen detection disciplines, even in the late 1990s, are widely afflicted with the moving goalposts syndrome. By far the greatest risk – and main treatment target – are harmful bacteria. Most municipal systems cannot guarantee efficient removal of protozoa and these may be present in treated water from time to time. Similarly, no specific tests for viruses are carried out, their majority elimination being virtually a side effect of chemical treatment against bacteria.

Avoid complacency. The fact you have survived your home town water all these years confirms the validity of their priorities but hit the brakes hard before sliding into complacency. On an expedition the bugs will be a different strain. Bacteria will still be the greatest risk but, although protozoa are normally 'widely spaced', concentrations of them (different from the ones you're used to) can occur – the 'downstream of the refugee camp' scenario so evocatively described by the people at MSR!

Getting used to the water. Do not rely on 'getting used to the water'. Infection can be 'asymptomatic' (ie the infection is there but is giving no symptoms) or it can be 'symptomatic infection' – the bugs laying on the full fireworks of diarrhoea, cramps, nausea etc. The locals, who 'seem to be alright' very often have an asymptomatic infection – an immunity built up over a long period of time *after several bouts of very symptomatic illness.* You do not have time for this. Your hardware must eliminate the bugs.

Pros and cons. In order to do this effectively you may utilise a combination of filtration and disinfection for practical water treatment on an expedition.

- *The filter-only approach* calls for very small pore size (slow throughput, quicker clogging)
- *The filter-plus-chemicals* allows larger pore size but has the added complexity (and shorter life) of a chemical stage which may then also require de-tasting.

Definitions – 'filter-speak'. The promotional common-usage terms 'purifier' and 'microfilter' – terms you might till now have thought were interchangeable – turn the table on the previous page inside out, coming up with a 'definitions and what zaps what' list:

Common usage definitions. What zaps what

	Protozoa	Bacteria	Viruses
'Purifier'	✔	✔	✔
Microfilter	✔	✔	
Iodine / chlorine		✔	✔

Emergencies – 1. If you are ankle-deep in a voracious brew of Giardia and your pump has gone down or your filter element has clogged irrecoverably, a paper in the American *Journal of Public Health (1989, Vol 79, No 12,* 'Back country water treatment', Ongerth, JE et al) finds that the normally armour-plated giardia, though reduced by 90% after 30 minutes' exposure to Potable Aqua iodine tablets (not really good enough), are *all* inactivated after an overnight soak (eight hours) in this or a solution of 2% tincture of iodine (0.4 ml per litre). Cryptosporidia are tougher than this and are, on present information, likely to be reduced but not eliminated. Similar treatments with chlorine compounds left an unacceptably high proportion of active giardia even after an eight-hour soak – so use iodine, not chlorine. And give it plenty of 'contact time'.

Emergencies – 2. The ultimate and simplest fall-back is heat and boiling – note the two words. No ifs or buts. See 'Purification – heat and ultraviolet' on page 2.5 -16.

Marketing spiel. Each filter manufacturer understandably puts his own case most strongly, often with an unhelpful side-swipe at competitors to leave you further confused. Shorn of this, the following manufacturers' data (next page) indicates quantifiables on some current equipment:

Very small micron-rating and no chemicals can equal larger micron rating when used with chemicals. But check filter life and taste removal stage.

MANUFACTURERS' DATA ON SOME UK-AVAILABLE WATER FILTERS

Name	Filtering method	Pore size (µm)	Process rate (litres/ min)	Approx capacity of filter (litres)	Weight (kg) length (cm)	Guide 1997 price (£)	Remarks
Katadyn Combi	Ceramic/silver, (carbon)	0.2	1.2	50,000 (200)	0.55 26	190	Selectable carbon stage
Katadyn Mini	Ceramic/silver,	0.2	0.5	7,000	0.25 18	110	Ceramic or carbon option
Katadyn Pocket	Ceramic/silver,	0.2	1.0	50,000	0.65 26	235	Well known classic. 20 yr g'tee
Katadyn KFT Expedition	Ceramic/silver, (element No 4)	0.2	4.5	40,000	5.40 58	675	Stirrup-pump for jerrycans
Katadyn MF-3 and MF-7	Ceramic/silver, 3 and 7 element filters (No 4)	0.2	3 x 4.5 7 x 4.5	40,000			Home/industrial units (pressure supply) – base
Pre-Mac Model IWP	Iodine resin, carbon detasting	3.0	3.5	12,000	7.0 540	400	In-line, 20-80 psi mains. Two outlets, one de-tasted
Pur Hiker	Plastic membrane	0.5	1.0	900	0.31 19		Not a 'purifier'
Pur Traveller	Plastic membrane, iodine resin	1.0	< 1.0	450	0.34 17	54	'Cup-at-a-time', compact filter
Pur Scout	Plastic membrane, iodine resin	1.0	1.0	600	0.34 23	90	Carbon add-on option
Pur Explorer	Plastic membrane, iodine resin	1.0	1.5	1350	0.62 28	180	Carbon option, self-cleaning
First Need Trav-I-Pure	Structured matrix, carbon	0.1	>1.0	380	0.63 18±	80	Potable Aqua addable
First Need Deluxe	Structured matrix, carbon	0.1	1.2	380	0.42 30±	54	PotableAqua addable
First Need Base Camp	Structured matrix, carbon	0.1	>1.0	3800	2.8 30±	250	Potable Aqua addable
MSR Waterworks 2	Ceramic, carbon, plastic membrane	0.2	0.6	400±	0.54 23	130	0.6µm ceramic (scrubbable) acts as 'prefilter' to 0.2µm membrane.
PentaPure Oasis	Membrane, iodine resin, carbon	3.0	0.45	380	0.18 29	30	Filter cell in squeeze-sip bottle
Sweetwater Guardian	'labyrinth',carbon ('Viral guard' optn)	0.2	1.0	760 (340)	0.31 19	60	Iodine resin add-on + silt stopper

Work out filter capacity carefully if taking small 'personal filter' on a 3-4 person trip. Unless scrubbable, spare element may be necessary

Manufacturers' data on some UK-available filters – contd

Name	Filtering method	Pore size (µm)	Process rate (litres/ min)	Approx capacity of filter (litres)	Weight (kg) length (cm)	Guide 1997 price (£)	Remarks
Stella-Meta AB-1	Kieselguhr powder, chlorine	2.0	45.0	Very high	161.0 tare	12,000	Army, aid-agency 1-tonne trailer
Hanovia UVD-13	Ultraviolet light	No filter	13.0	Very high		400	230 v AC and 'mains' water
Pre-Mac SWP	Charcoal cloth, iodine resin. 3-5 ppm residual iodine	'90% proto-zoa'	0.2	50	0.06 13	14	Disposable, survival filter also sold as 'Pocket Travel Well'
Pre-Mac MWP	Charcoal cloth, iodine resin. 3-5 ppm residual iodine	'90% proto-zoa'	0.4	200	0.18 14	33	SAS issue pump filter; also sold as 'TrekkerTravel Well'
Pre-Mac PWP	Charcoal cloth, iodine resin. 3-5 ppm residual iodine	'90% proto-zoa'	0.2	1000	0.5 14	50	Gravity feed. De-tasting spout available
Pre-Mac JWP 4 or 8	Stepped 50µm to 3µm,carbon block, iodine resin	3.0	4.0	4000 or 8000	12-19 50-62	1200 - 2300	Available with hand and/or electric pump or, solar powered, as SW8
Aquarius 150	Fine sand, chlorine, activated carbon		11.0	Backwash 3-4 weeks	40 56	1100	10-60 psi mains pressure required
Aquarius 45	Fine sand, chlorine, activated carbon		3.5	Backwash 3-4 weeks		650	Backpackable unit

Even for a two-person, single vehicle trip go for the highest flow rate unit you can. Consider small 'hotel room' unit as well.

Notes to table :

1. Katadyn ceramic filters incorporate silver in their make-up to kill off trapped pathogens and prevent 'grow-through'.

2. Activated carbon, as well as removing the obvious bad tastes and smells of iodine and chlorine residue, reduces pesticides, herbicides etc.

A funny thing happened on the way to...... Laghouat

Stopping momentarily to put on a jacket, I noticed a nomad approaching. Greetings exchanged, his little lad brought coffee from the tent, poured with ceremony from an aged Berber pot. Hot beverages almost invariably kill infection so perhaps (I reflected later, and later again) it had been the flies, or the cups or, after all, the coffee. Some you win, some you lose!

Asking for trouble? If not from Omar Sharif riding out of the mirage, certainly from bugs in the water if gastronomic uses are planned. An obvious and extreme case this, but even 'clean' spring water in European countries is usually infected.

of 4 μm or more in size so all the listed filters except those showing '90% protozoa removal' will do this. Whilst elimination of protozoa is highly desirable, they are usually not too concentrated and it must be said, unhelpfully, that some armed services do operate on a 'balanced risk' basis (and for logistic reasons) using fairly coarse filtration and chlorination alone with remarkably low infection rates. This does emphasise the importance and effectiveness of *bacteria* inactivation but using this kind of treatment for a civilian vehicle-dependent expedition juggling even small risks from parasites in this way would seem to be pointless under normal circumstances.

• *Bacteria.* The highest risk area; elimination of harmful bacteria is essential. A large proportion of the 'small bugs' (bacteria, 0.5 - 3.0 μm) will also get filtered out by the above equipment but some of them – the long thin ones – may get through 'sideways' in the case of equipments with larger micron ratings. Note, though, that these units (Pur,

Flow-rate will be the starting point for filter selection depending on main camp or side-trip use. Go for 'all bugs' kill-off if you can.

Selecting your hardware

Using the tables. A roundup:

• *Parasites, protozoa.* It is clear from the first table that since some specially nasty bugs are untouched by chemical treatment they must be filtered out; do not rely on just a chlorine or iodine treatment on its own. Fortunately these are 'big bugs' (protozoa)

Four litres/min Pre-Mac JWP4H (top) can take electric pump but in manual form here compare size, bulk, cost, capacity with Katadyn KFT opposite. 3μm microfilter and iodine take care of all bugs, but 200 litre MWP (lower left) and 100 litre disposable SWP purifiers, whilst 100% on bacteria offer '90% protozoa' figure. Size and very low weight a great advantage for off-base hikes as is low cost for multi-person groups.

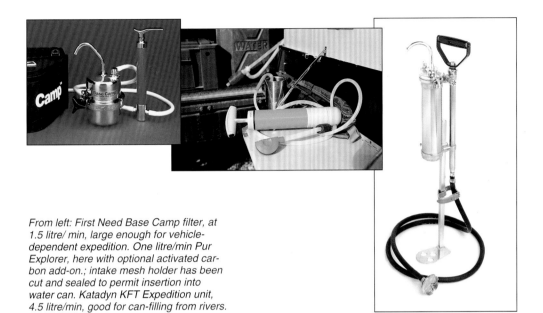

From left: First Need Base Camp filter, at 1.5 litre/ min, large enough for vehicle-dependent expedition. One litre/min Pur Explorer, here with optional activated carbon add-on.; intake mesh holder has been cut and sealed to permit insertion into water can. Katadyn KFT Expedition unit, 4.5 litre/min, good for can-filling from rivers.

with a 1.0 µm pore size or the mighty Stella-Meta at 2.0 µm for example and even those with no stated pore size) are invariably teamed with a chemical treatment to take care of the bacteria and many of the viruses as well.

Selection by flow rate. Look at flow rates when you are selecting units for your expedition. This will, for a vehicle-dependent trip, focus on the larger capacity equipments but bear in mind you may have backpacking forays away from a base camp or, more usually, have short stays in hotels with doubtful water supplies and you would be well advised also to carry a pocket sized filter for these occasions. With wretched regularity, expeditions report that 'in the field' health was fine but stays in hotels all too often brought on attacks of stomach and gut infection.

Care of ceramic filters. Any filter with a ceramic candle element will be vulnerable to being dropped on rock or stones. A cracked element will be useless as a filter. Take special care carrying and stowing the unit on the vehicle.

Standards. Nudged by a 90% surface water contamination of protozoa pathogens within North America – especially giardia, cryptosporidium – the US Environmental Protection Agency (EPA) produced 1986 standard for microbiological water purifiers:

Protozoa: giardia cysts –	99.9% removal
Bacteria: klebsiella terrigena –	99.9999% removal
Viruses: poliovirus and rotavirus –	99.99% removal

So at least you know where you stand with those that meet the EPA standard. The standard is being revised (1997).

Whatever purifier you use, prefilter to clear water first to enable chemicals to work. Observe contact times. Don't drop ceramic filters.

Water drums filled from ship's tanks yielded rich harvest of rust flakes (etc) in filter pump. Chemical disinfecion had been chlorine via 'WSP' – water sterilising powder, calcium hypochloride.

Purification – heat and ultra violet

Note: 'Purification – filtering, chemicals' is dealt with on p 2.5 -8.

Heat and boiling. Boiling is a reliable fall-back for any chemically safe water and will kill just about everything that could harm you. Boiling works; it kills everything but it is fuel hungry (1 kg wood boils 1 litre of water) and the water takes a long time to cool. The good thing compared with chemicals is that it imparts no additional taste (apart from an unattractive flatness); by the same token, however, it does not improve the taste, smell or appearance of poor quality water either.

Regarding its disinfection capability, a recently published roundup of information, in seeking to substantiate or challenge the 'boil for 10 minutes' tradition (the US *Journal of Travel Medicine, 1996; 3:1-4* Backer, HD, 'Effect of Heat on the Sterilization of Artificially Contaminated Water'), highlighted a collection of unconnected independent research on the subject (17 different references) accumulated by various authors over the past 25 years.

In summary the findings were that inactivation of micro-organisms *begins* at temperatures as low as 45°C. As you might expect, lowish temperatures for longish times equates to high temperatures for shorter times – thus the pop-bug giardia is 100% knocked out after 10 minutes at 70°C or instantly at 100°C.

A wide spectrum of bugs were found to be seriously inconvenienced around the 60°C for 10 minutes point. A few examples:

Without a thermometer, boiling is a safe way of assessing heat. Know the full story, though. Almost any heat above 55°C starts purification. Give it five minutes.

Lethal temperature-x-time combinations:

Giardia	55°C x 5 mins
	60°C x 10 mins (98%)
Worm eggs	50-55°C
Cryptosporidium	45°C x 5-20 min
	55°C x 20 min
	64°C x 2 min
Salmonella	65°C x 1 min
Cholera	62°C x 10 min
Viruses	60°C x 20-40 min
	70°C x 1 min
Hepatitis A (waterborne)	98°C x 1 min
	60°C x 19 min

What it means in the field. Firstly note the spread of findings, despite how little heating begins the inactivation process. Expeditioners will mostly not have a microscope or thermometer on hand but the implications of this information on relatively low temperature inactivation of micro-organisms are:

1. Almost any heating is better than no heating.

2. The real nasties – giardia, crypto, worms – start to keel over at 55°C.

3. In emergency situations use the time factor; heating to 60-65°C (too hot to hold your finger in it) and letting the water stand 10-15 minutes will help.

4. Just bringing to the boil will kill everything; no need to hold it on the boil. (Beware large containers/small heat sources that may boil at one end, not the other.)

5. Hotel hot water systems? Next.

Hotel hot water systems. A logical enough question: if 55°C starts to kill off bugs, what about hotel hot water systems? The simple answer is it works in most cases for most bugs and a heat-and-hold system could be safer than a cold tap as an emergency fall-back. Some limited research has covered this and, as may be expected from the list above, at 15 out of 17 West African hotels where the water temperatures ranged from 57-69°C no coliforms were found in cultures. All hot water systems are not the same though. It is important to remember that many hotels have gas-powered geyser systems that respond to water flow when you turn the tap on. This clearly would be ineffective since 'hot-soak' is important for killing the micro-organisms. However a system where a hot water tank holds a store of water at around 60°C or more is going to be, literally, a different kettle of fish. The two ingredients are therefore:

• Water too hot to touch

• A water tank held at that temperature.

Ultraviolet light disinfection. Widely used in the industrial, catering, soft-drinks and bottled water industries, strong UV light acts as a disinfection method against bacteria and viruses. (True to form, protozoa seem to be bulletproof and need massive doses of UV – way above standard water treatment levels – to be inactivated.) Unlike the chemical dosage methods inferred above with contact times of up to 60 minutes, process UV contact times – at the right intensity and in suitably confined treatment containers – can be from 0.5 to 5 seconds. The concept is simplicity itself and involves water entering a confined container in which a strong UV source is radiating and exiting at the far side. Although on an industrial scale well established, currently (mid-1996), there are no equipments available tailored specifically for expedition or remote area use.

However, electrical power consumption for small household units (Hanovia, Slough, UK; Katadyn, Switzerland) is no more than 18 watts for processing 13 litres per minute (much higher flow rate units are available). Such a unit could be used in a base camp scenario where electrical power – and clear water – was available. Such equipments need careful monitoring and are available with UV dosimeters (green, amber, red light sequence) built in. The finite sterilisation life of the UV tubes must be watched and adhered to strictly.

UV is a good disinfection process but needs clear water to work on so that UV can 'get around' the water as it flows through and 2-3 μm filtration if protozoa are to be kept out. As with virtually all other process-es, smells and tastes would have to be removed with an activated charcoal post-treatment filter. Salt or brackish water is not made drinkable.

Solar UV disinfection. If your lateral thinking extended to hotel hot water systems, the fact that the sun emanates a generous supply of UV and its possible potential for water disinfection will not have escaped your notice. As may be expected, it is a matter of intensity but the first broad answer is, yes it works. Published in *The Lancet* on 6 December 1980 was a report of work done in the Lebanon on oral rehydration solutions made with deliberately contaminated water.

In over 50 experiments a litre of the mixture, lying in a 2.5 litre polythene bag – ie thin and flat – was left in the sun for an hour and a zero coliform count achieved with one hour of solar radiation. With non-commercial items like free sunlight and polythene bags the 16 year pause pending huge publicity and exploitation is perhaps unsurprising but on the face of it the potential seems enormous, if only in the context of a survival situation. Putting kitchen foil on the ground under the polythene water bags would increase the UV intensity within the containers – just as the polished stainless steel interior of a Hanovia UV unit does.

Once again only bacteria were involved and high-angle, clear-skies sunshine would have yielded strong UV-C at germicidal wavelengths of 240-280 nm.

Ultraviolet is elegant way of inactivating bacteria and viruses but water must be clear. Be certain tubes are giving full output. Solar UV works in emergency.

Bulk water

Filtration and storage

Different approach. Large base-camp operations demand a different approach to water treatment since scale and flow rates will require a new kind of equipment and likely the decision to opt for a three-product approach:

1. Store/settle tank prior to filtration,
2. Washing-only water and
3. Drinking-only product.

For bulk water supplies pre-treatment by settlement is an important stage. Settlement means letting the water rest in a bulk storage. A minimum of four hours precipitates sand and detritus, 12 hours starts to precipitate colloidal matter and 48 hours removes bilharzia. Aluminium sulphate (alum) can be added as a flocculant to accelerate removal of colloids and to make the water transparent – a good start to the treatment.

Stella-Meta AB-1 2700 litre per hour large base-camp unit shown on table on previous spread. AB-1 is, in effect, 'one trailer's worth' of equipment and is totally self contained – pumping engine, filter unit and steriliser. Rail enclosures protect from damage, ease lifting.

The Stella-Meta military and aid agency filtration systems (see also 'Desalination'), the smallest unit of which (the AB-1) processes 2700 litres per hour, has its own engine, pump and ancillaries and inevitably is heavy – 161 kg tare; it is usually mounted on a small military-spec off-road trailer so as to be self-contained and to enable it to be detached from a towing vehicle and left in situ. The principle involved is that kiesel-guhr powder is mixed to a slurry and then, under pump suction, is drawn onto a filter element where the powder forms the filtering medium. This has a 'pore size' (equivalent) of 2.0 μm and the water then is 'super-chlorinated' for safe tank storage.

Bulk storage. This latter point highlights the potential problems associated with water storage where bacteria may otherwise breed in bulk water installations. UK tap water has a just perceptible chlorine content of up to 0.4 parts per million (ppm) of chlorine. Where water supplies for a large base camp are involved, it is customary to operate the filtration and purification unit to 'super-chlorinate' the water, ie to store water at chlorine levels above that of palatability (5 ppm) and then use de-tasting (sodium thiosulphate) tablets in individual water bottles before use.

Chlorination, super-chlorination. There is the chlorine that goes into the water and

'Super chlorination' and point-of-consumption de-tasting is elegant way of ensuring bulk storage tanks do not become a bug-fest. Not needed on emptied jerry cans.

the 'residual chlorine' left after it has combined with the foreign matter dissolved in the water. It might take 10-15 ppm added chlorine to result, after 30 minutes, in a residual chlorination level of >3.5 ppm – an adequate super-chlorination level. This would need to be reduced by de-chlorination to about <0.5 ppm for drinking.

'Storing' water at static or base camps implies use of large containers or tanks that seldom if ever get completely empty, ie part is used then it is topped up – hence the need for high chlorination levels to preclude bacterial growth within the storage tanks. This would not be the case in jerry cans in a vehicle; here the water in each can would be used up completely before going on to the next can so there would be no need for high-chlorination 'storage' treatment.

Similarly the problems associated with bulk storage seldom arise when hand held personal or small group purifiers are used since water usually goes straight from the unit, probably through a carbon de-taster of some kind, and into the in-use can.

Vehicle water tanks. If you have a built-in water tank in your vehicle (individual plastic cans are preferable), bacterial growth, especially in warm climates can be considerable – green slime that is also difficult to remove without contact scrubbing. Micropur silver tablets (normal dosage) can preserve water and is used for storage periods of up to six months.

In other words, treat *stored* water (tanks or jerry cans) in the same way as a base camp bulk storage system – super-chlorination, Micropur, or whatever. Some pumps – the Pre-Mac units for example – already provide residual chemical disinfection (iodine) but where this is not the case then treat the water in the tank with your own chemicals. You will then, as in the base camp case, need a point-of-use de-tasting system of some kind if iodine or chlorine are involved – de-tasting tablets or an activated carbon filter.

Make sure your tank has a 'last drop' drain cock on it so that you can periodically drain it dry, give it a super-strong chemical disinfection (filled to the brim, long contact time) then rinse before using it again.

Desalination

Water from the sea. Desalination – the production of drinking water from sea water – is a possible requirement for major remote area expeditions. This is a demanding process – primarily reverse osmosis –

and, not surprisingly, the equipment involved is heavy, bulky and expensive using presently available hardware. Stella-Meta (Whitchurch, Hants, tel 01256.895959) make a 2000 litres per hour equipment, based on defence services requirements, that is trailer mounted and grosses at 3 tonnes including a source engine/pumpset (ie to pump water from the shore to the desalination unit). Saline water is pumped through a pre-coat filter to remove suspended solids and bacteria before desalination by reverse osmosis to remove other substances such as the excess salt. The equipment adds super-chlorination so that tank storage will be safe. De-tasting at the dispensing point would then be carried out. Stella-Meta provide training, consumables packs, service kit.

Desalination of sea water for large group drinking is possible but equipment is heavy and expensive.

References:

Acra, A, et al, *Disinfection of oral rehydration solutions by sunlight*, Lancet, 6 Dec 1980.

Backer, HD, *Effect of heat on the sterilization of artificially contaminated water*, American J Travel Medicine 3(1), 1996.

Casemore, DP, *Enteric protozoa and water route transmission – Ch 10, Water and Public Health*, Ed Golding et al, 1994, published by Smith-Gordon. UK.

Jarroll, EL et al, *Giardia cyst destruction; effectiveness of six small-quantity water disinfection methods*, Am J Trop Med Hyg 29(1), American Society of Tropical Medicine and Hygiene, 1980.

Juranek, DD, *Cryptosporidiosis: sources of infection and guidelines for prevention.* Centers for Disease Control, Atlanta, Georgia, 1995.

Madore, MS, et al. *Occurrence of cryptosporidium oocyst in sewage effluents and selected surface waters*, J. Parasit. 73(4), 1987 American Society of Parasitologists.

Ongerth, JE, et al, *Backcountry water treatment to prevent giardiasis.* American J Public Health, 1989, 79(12).

Rose, J et al, *Survey of potable water supplies for cryptosporidium and giardia*, Environ Sci Technol, 25, No 8, 1991. American Chemical Society.

Book

Small water supplies, Cairncross and Feacham, Ross Institute 1986, London School of Hygiene and Tropical Medicine. (Booklet useful for rural health workers or aid agencies.)

Acknowledgements and thanks:

Robert Boesch, Katadyn, Wallisellin, Switzerland

Harold Charters, First Need Filters, General Ecology Europe Ltd, Crawley, UK

Tim Clark, Mountain Safety Research, Seattle, USA

David Dolphin, Hanovia Ltd. Slough, UK

Cameron Kiggell, Pre-Mac (Kent) ltd, UK

Kieth Parry, Colley Nockolds Ltd, London

Major Ken Roberts, Aldershot, UK

David Seaman, Pur Filters, Ibis Products Ltd, Stevenage, UK

Richard Simcox, Stella-Meta Filtration Systems, TM Products Ltd, Winchester, UK

Dr Richard Warburton, Lancs, UK

John Williams, London School of Hygiene and Tropical Medicine

David Zemlicka, Wisconsin Pharmacal Inc, Jackson, Wisc, USA

And special thanks to:

Eddie Potts, Liverpool School of Tropical Medicine

Stephen E Wright, Moredun Research Institute, Edinburgh

Section 2.6

Equipment planning:

Fuel, oil, fluids

COVERAGE OF THIS SECTION

FUEL

Logistics

Fuel types

OIL, FLUIDS

* **In a hurry?** Try these sections first and branch out from there as you need more information.

FUEL

Logistics

How much fuel to take

Doing the sums. When operating comfortably within the range of your normal fuel tank, fuel will not be a serious worry. Farther afield, it demands close and continuous attention. It is as vital to carry sufficient fuel and sensible, calculated, reserves on an expedition in remote areas as it is not to overload the vehicle – two potential incompatibles highlighted right at the start. Fuelling points in such regions are usually widely spaced; as you will see in Section 4.1 'Expedition vehicles', the distance between them is a major criterion in selection of the vehicle for your trip, determining total payload and payload left over for crew and other supplies after fuel and water load have been calculated. If D is the known distance between fuelling points (as opposed to a distance measured on a map scale), a safe planning formula for fuel to take is:

Total gallons required = D + 25% + 100 miles all divided by the expected mpg.

i.e. a reserve of 25% plus 100 miles to cover diversions and difficult going.

Fuel planning reserves – basic formula

Fuel for the <u>actual</u> distance ..   ... plus 25% ...   .. plus 100 miles

Remember, though, that this predicates D is the actual, known distance between fuel points.

Distances and 'terrain factor'. Where, more likely in off-tracks operations across

'Terrain factor' – map vs actual distance

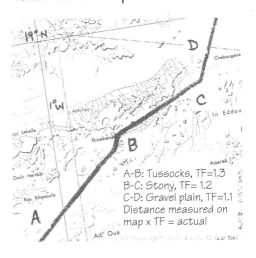

A-B: Tussocks, TF=1.3
B-C: Stony, TF= 1.2
C-D: Gravel plain, TF=1.1
Distance measured on map x TF = actual

untrodden desert or in some bush or jungle regions, the distance can only be measured on a map, you must make some allowance for the terrain and bends in the track or route by applying a 'terrain factor' (TF); this is what you multiply your measured distance by to get a more accurate estimate of the actual distance the vehicle will have to travel. Some figures for arid regions are as follows: on a large-area map (1:1m say) actual distance will be about 1.2 times measured distance (TF = 1.2), given reasonable going such as gravel and some stony regions. Savannah, slow going with much zig-zagging between grass tussocks will be 1.3; sand dunes 1.5 to 2; smooth sand / gravel plain 1.1. The revised version of the above formula then becomes:

Total fuel = (D x TF) + 25% + 100 miles all divided by expected mpg.

Allow ample fuel reserves for diversions round obstacles big and small. Also remember that a map-measured distance will not be a true distance: apply a 'terrain factor'.

Keeping track of mpg is especially important on long trips with long sectors. Calibrated dipstick yields accurate daily check. Where logistics are extra demanding a lightly laden trailer for the fuel is the answer, avoiding oveloading vehicle or resorting to unacceptable roof racks.

If you do not know what the local terrain factor is likely to be, make a sensible estimate based on the above and then compare estimated vs actual distances as you go along and devise your own for the next legs.

Using it

Fuel consumption. For reference, some fuel consumptions experienced in bush and desert regions in Africa:

SAMPLE FUEL CONSUMPTION

Keep daily check on fuel consumption and your total stock. Reaching for a can that turns out to be empty is bad for you. A half-laden trailer better than overloading vehicle.

Tracks and tarmac

Land Rover, 1-tonne military (V8)	14-18 mpg
Land Rover 110, 2.5 litre turbo diesel	23-27 mpg
Range Rover, V8 Europe touring	14-21 mpg
Range Rover, V8 7.50 x 16 Michelin XS tyres	
bad track:	12-15 mpg
fair track, tarmac:	15-20 mpg
Discovery Tdi (diesel)	26-35 mpg
Defender 90, 300 Tdi (diesel), bush, fair	
tracks, tarmac, moderate speeds	32-38 mpg
Range Rover V8 + 12 cwt Army trailer	
bush tracks, desert	9-19 mpg

Off-tracks, open desert (sand, rock, some dunes)

Land Rover, 1-tonne military (V8)	7-14 mpg
Land Rover, Srs 3, 109, 4 cyl petrol	10-12 mpg
Land Rover, 110 2.5 litre turbo diesel	22-25 mpg
Range Rover V8	10-15 mpg
Discovery Tdi 200	22-28 mpg
Bedford RL 4-tonne truck (petrol)	2-5 mpg

Fuel accounting. It is essential to do a nightly calculation of mpg and check on fuel remaining in tanks and cans. Know the exact number of gallons used to top up each night and divide it into distance covered since last top-up. Make an accurately cali-

brated jerrycan dipstick before departure and when, as will usually happen, you have put in, say, 'three-and-a-bit' cans to the same top-up point, use the dipstick to measure the part-can and accurately establish the total fuel put in. Monitoring your fuel consumption will enable you to work out a nightly 'how-goes-it' fuel state and range to compare with the distance to the next refuelling point. Your sums will indicate, if your planning has been correct, a consistent surplus of fuel in hand over that required to reach destination tanks-dry. The nightly check will also highlight any sudden change in consumption figures that, if valid, would require a change in plan.

Fuel carriers. A quick reminder is worthwhile here of what you will find in Section 4.1 'Expedition vehicles' and concerns the ability of vehicles to be self-supporting. In general, trucks, despite their much higher fuel consumption, have the ability to support themselves over far greater distances than light 4x4s – their payload capability is disproportionately higher still. (The down side to this is their poorer power/weight ratio which will make them less capable off-road.) Thus if you are working on some very demanding logistics, the inclusion of a single fuel carrier medium truck in the party may be the answer – so long as you have enough agile vehicles to assist in its recovery should it get bogged.

Another approach is a lightly laden trailer behind a light 4x4. Whilst this will reduce the 4x4's ultimate off-road performance, you will be spreading the payload over six wheels instead of four and at the same time keeping within the vehicle's own maximum gross vehicle weight (GVW). As indicated already, never exceed the maker's GVW; indeed, if possible, and to give the vehicle the best chance under demanding conditions, operate below max GVW if you can.

Aerodynamics. You may be surprised that fuel consumption off-road increases less than you expected. Particularly with the somewhat 'businesslike' aerodynamics of the typical expedition 4x4 such as the Defender (even more with roof racks and the like), it is an indication of how important speed-related air resistance is in consuming energy from the engine. Although the latest turbo diesels are very economical and feather-footed driving will always pay off, the remarkable Defender 90 Tdi figures in the table opposite are due to a considerable degree to the low speed at which the conditions demanded it be driven. The effect is difficult to predict so it is probably better to observe and be pleasantly surprised by this phenomenon than to bank on it too heavily!

Long-term storage. See next page.

Fuel types

Compression ratio

Heard it? Skip some of this if you are already familiar with the inter-relation of compression ratio and fuel octane; or just skim it to check we have it right!

Bicycle pumps – as usual. If you hadn't really wanted to get into compression ratios and engine design (it does help with the rest of the story on fuels) think about bicycle pumps. Bicycle pumps always get brought up on occasions like this. Car engines work by sucking fuel/air into a cylinder, compressing it, then setting it alight. The burning expands the gas, forcing the piston back down the cylinder at speed, turning the crankshaft and, eventually, your wheels.

Except for the burning (and a few other things), a bicycle pump does the same kind of thing – 'inhales' air, compresses it to force it past the valve and into the tyre. The ratio of the volume of air taken in and the volume of the air when it compressed, is the compression ratio.

The higher the compression ratio the better the economy you get from the engine – plus a little more power. In the '20s and '30s some engines had compression ratios as low as 6.5. Nowadays:

Fuels available overseas will be quite a bit different from those at home. Brush up on compression ratio, octane numbers etc and take action where appropriate.

Engine compression ratio

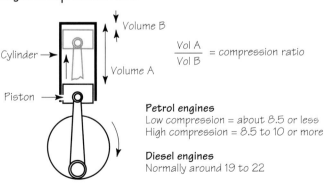

$$\frac{\text{Vol A}}{\text{Vol B}} = \text{compression ratio}$$

Petrol engines
Low compression = about 8.5 or less
High compression = 8.5 to 10 or more

Diesel engines
Normally around 19 to 22

- A 'low compression' engine is about 8 or 8.5 (though may be less) and
- A 'high compression' may be 9.5, 10 or even more.

Compression ratio and the grade of fuel used are closely related in petrol engines.

Diesels. Bicycle pumps again, but the heating you feel at the compressed air end of the pump is the heat of compression. Take that to extremes and, with the right fuel and injector, the fuel will self ignite due to this heat without the need for the spark plugs used in petrol engines. Diesels do have heater plugs but only for starting.

- Diesels have compression ratios around 19-22.

Compression ratio does not have much bearing on fuel used in diesels.

Climatic effects, oxidation

When in Rome ... . Fuel specified for the region will be what is on sale locally anyway. However, if you are having to ship bulk fuel for an expedition in especially cold conditions you will have to be sure, in the case of diesels particularly, to ship the right grade (see below 'Diesel engines – fuel grades'). It does pay to know what is going on climatically, especially with diesel fuels.

Storage stability. Regarding advance fuel dumps, anti-oxidants (etc) in fuels will keep gum and varnish (etc) at bay for up to 12 months. Oxidation rate doubles for every 10°C so 'store cool' as well as 'store short'. If organising shipped fuel tell the oil company the time scales and temperatures involved so that recent stock can be shipped.

Petrol engines – fuel grades

It's more than just '2-star' vs '4-star' petrol – 'Premium' in Burma is 80 octane. Low octane and high compression don't mix. A knocking engine is short-lived.

Octane etc – why it matters

Compression ratio and octane. Why bring up compression ratio? Because, as mentioned above, in a petrol engine it affects the type of fuel you need. Where a given fuel might work well in a low compression engine, another engine with a higher compression ratio will experience unusual combustion characteristics with it. Instead of a smooth burn outwards from the spark plug, the flame goes so far and then the remaining fuel/air mixture in effect explodes all at once which causes a sharp bang and pressure rise which makes your petrol engine sound like a diesel.

Referred to as 'pinking' (a good description of the way it sounds at first), it can get worse and is then described as 'knocking' or detonation. _It is very bad for the engine and if you allow it to continue will cause major internal damage._ When this high compression engine is run on petrol of a different kind with lead additives the burning characteristics are altered and the problem is cured. Highly refined fuels with lead additives

(enabling the highest compression ratios to be used) are called 'high octane' fuels. And vice versa – less exotically refined petrol with low amounts of lead additives are low octane fuels ('2-star') and can only be used in low compression engines.

There is more to it than lead; actual lead content in grammes per litre varies enormously, even for a similar octane of fuel. Papua New Guinea, Zimbabwe, Rwanda, West Sahara, Cuba and a dozen other countries have around six times the amount of actual lead in their premium grade petrol as we have in the UK. What we are really talking about, though, is compression ratio and octane number rather than actual lead content.

(See below regarding unleaded petrol.)

The octane numbers – RON etc. Though you will be familiar with the fuel you usually use in the UK and the look of the pumps used by your chosen oil company, few of us read much of the detail on them. When you get overseas the words 'Premium' and 'Super' are bandied about without much

regard for particular grades of fuel and you
will be unlikely to find the same kind of
pumps. Indeed in some areas you will find
fuel hand-cranked out of a 'pump' (dis-
penser) that may not have a front panel on it
at all; or it may come from a barrel. You
need to know more detail and this is it:
  • *Compression ratio* of your engine and
  • *Octane number* of the fuel available
      where you are going.
  Research Octane Number (RON) is the
unit used to denote octane and you may
recall '2-star' being about 90 and '4-star'
being about 97 RON. RON refers to low
speed knock. There is also the Motor Octane
Number method of denoting octane (MON)
which relates to high speed (high rpm)
knock. Usually they are inter-related; for a
given fuel, the MON is often 4-10 points
lower than its RON number.)

Octane: RON vs MON, approx

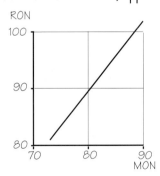

RON very roughly = MON + 10

  You will probably not need to remember
this – unless you are bound for China. Here,
among a large choice of fuel (country-wide –
not necessarily locally), 'regular' is listed
only as an eye-watering 70 octane; but it is

MON – equating to about 79 RON; low
enough but not as bad as it sounds at first.
One or two countries – Puerto Rico, Guam,
Samoa – quote an average (RON number
plus MON number divided by two) and you
may find this seemingly low average octane
number on the pumps in the USA too.

What can you do about it – gasoline?

  Climatic effects. Unlike diesel, gasoline
will in general perform anywhere on the
planet without special attention. Although
there are summer and winter grades with
different proportions of light and heavy
hydrocarbons to enhance starting and driveability, gasolines are not much affected by
extremes of climate from the point of view
of storage, flow and performance – although
at high ambients petrol's extreme volatility
and the danger from inflammable fumes
must of course be borne in mind. A jerry can
inadvertently left open can be dangerous.
  RON, MON: very interesting but ... ?
What can you actually do about the
RON/MON /compression ratio scenario
though? First of all take on board that it is
very important; getting it wrong can result
in catastrophic damage to your engine. *Run
your engine on too low a fuel grade with persis-
tent pinking and knocking and you do so at your
peril* in a remote area. Find out the available
fuel, relate it to your engine and take the
appropriate action – or buy a diesel! Look at
the table overleaf first which sums up the
engine/fuel relationship and supply scene.

*Find out in
advance the type
of fuel available
in the countries
your expedition
is visiting. Your
engine can be
tuned to accept
them – usually
but not always.*

GASOLINE ENGINES: HIGH OCTANE, LOW OCTANE, LOW GRADE LEADED FUELS

Engine type (CR = compression ratio)	Run on high octane petrol? ('4-star', 'premium', 'super', RON 95-97)	Run on low octane petrol? ('2-star', 'regular', 'normal', RON 91-92)	Run on low grade petrol? (RON below 90, down to 80 or lower)
1. Low compression engine (CR = around 8.5 or less)	Yes but needless expense. No damage.	Yes	Often yes, but if knocking retard ignition. See para opposite.
2. High compression engine (CR = 8.5 to around 10)	Yes	Rarely. If knocking retard ignition. See para opposite.	Almost certainly no.

Note:
1. Retarding ignition alone can only accommodate lower grade fuels to a certain extent. Fitting low compression pistons would be the next step – a major job and can be very expensive. Don't do this randomly or lightly; manufacturer's advice and approval should be sought plus specialist engineers. JE Engineering Ltd of Coventry, tel 01203 305018, well known for extra-power tuning of Rover engines is one company that could undertake such work in the UK.
2. See next table for countries with low grade fuels and how to obtain latest information.

Low octane petrol – where it is

Countries where 'normal/regular' petrol is under 90 RON but another higher grade is available (Source Octel '95).*

Oil company help-lines or Octel (contact address right, second column) can give you details of fuels available in the countries you are visiting.

Country	RON of 'regular'	RON of next grade
Africa		
Algeria	89	96
Benin	83	95
Botswana	87	93
Burundi	87-90	93-95
Central African Republic	83	95
Chad	83-85	93-95
Djibuti	83	95
Egypt	81-83	90
Gabon	85	93
Guinea Bissau	86	96
Côte d'Ivoire	87	95
Kenya	83	93
Madagascar	87	95
Mali	87-88	95-97
Mauritania	88	92
Morocco	87	95
Rwanda	83	95
Senegal	87	95
Sierra Leone	83-86	95
South Africa	87	93-97
Tanzania	83	93
Togo	83-91	93-95
Uganda	83	93
Zambia	87	93
Middle East		
Iran	82	95
Iraq	88	91
Jordan	87	95
Syria	76	90
Yemen	83	93
Asia		
Bangladesh	80	96
India	87	93
Laos	83	95
Phillipines	81	94-95
Thailand **	87	95
Vietnam	83	93

South America		
Argentina	85	95
Chile	81	93
Columbia**	84	93
Ecuador**	85	90
Paraguay	83	94
Peru	84	95
Uruguay	85	95
Venezuela	83	95
Cuba	84	96
Caribbean, North, Central America		
Trinidad	83	95
Belize	85	93
Costa Rica**	88	94
El Salvador	87	95
Guatemala	87	95
Honduras	87	95
Nicaragua	87	95
Mexico**	81	92

* Octel *'World-wide Gasoline and Diesel Survey, 1995'*, The Associated Octel Co Ltd. 23 Berkeley Square, London W1X 6DT Tel 0171.499.6030. For later information contact suppliers, eg Shell International for Africa
** Unleaded only

Low grade petrol – where it is

Countries where there is no petrol of 90 RON or over (Source Octel, 1995 – see above)

Country	RON of 'regular'	RON of next grade
Afghanistan	80	87
Burkina Faso	83	-
Comoros Islands	87	-
Equatorial Guinea	87	-
Ethiopia	80	-
Myanmar (Burma)	68-70	80
Pakistan	80	87
Somalia	79	-
Sudan	78-84	87
Western Sahara	83	-

Knocking (detonation) kills engines. If you have not experienced detonation before, the descriptive words – 'pinking', 'knock' – will tell you when it is happening. Low speed knock happens typically when you might be just struggling up a soft sand dune with not quite enough speed, in too high a gear and with too much throttle on. Ease off the throttle or quickly drop a gear and the engine will rev and stop knocking. This is low-speed knock which you can hear; it sounds awful but you can usually stop it as indicated. High speed knock is far more damaging as well as being hard to hear – you may catch it as a high 'tinkling' noise.

When to take action. How low is a too low an octane? Firstly remember that all engines are different and each will react differently to changes from optimum fuel grades. The following is given for general guidance only and you should *always consult your specialist dealer, or, more likely, the manufacturer.* Going to an area where only low octane gasolines are available, you will already have chosen an engine with a low compression ratio. Such an engine will usually have been tuned – workshop manual figures – for octanes of about 90-91. If you know that local fuel will be no better than 85-87 octane – that is the trigger – you will need to tune the engine accordingly.

First the engine types. There was a time when all petrol engines had moderate compression ratios and were fitted with carburetters and distributors for the spark plug ignition. There are now three categories of engine, the details of which affect the ease with which they can be tuned for poor fuel:

1. Distributors and carburetters. The simplest engines are configured like this but they will be a little less efficient or 'clean' than those in the other two categories. Ignition will be via either contact breakers or electronic ignition – both within the distributor. An example of this kind of engine is the 4-cyl, 2.5 L Land Rover petrol engine.

2. Distributors and fuel injection. Here there will likely be electronic ignition and fuel is delivered by 'EFI' (electronic fuel injection) as either single point injection into the manifold or a multi-point system (injecting for each cylinder). The EFI will be controlled by an ECU (electronic control unit) or engine management chip with various sensors; it is important to know if this is a 'closed loop' system with an oxygen sensor. If it is, and the engine was designed for unleaded fuel (see below), this sensor will be adversely affected if the engine is run on leaded fuel. Some models of Discovery had EFI engines with a distributor for ignition.

3. Engine management chips and fuel injection. In some engines there is no distributor; crankshaft position is established, in effect, by a tiny magnet within the flywheel. This information is sent to the engine management chip which controls ignition timing by electronics (ie retarding ignition – see below – cannot be achieved by rotating the distributor!) An example of this kind of engine is in the new Range Rover.

Tuning for poor fuel. So 'tuning' an engine stricken with low grade fuel will mean one or more of the courses of action shown below. It is assumed you will have first chosen, where there is a choice, a 'low compression' version of the engine – a compression ratio around or less than 8:1 rather than 9:1 or higher. The graph on the next page sums up the following:

1. Retarding the ignition – delaying the point at which the spark plug fires by anything up to 10° of crankshaft rotation. This is usually done by rotating the distributor and checking the timing by timing light. Any octane shortfall requiring more than this is likely to be a major job involving considerable expense – next paras.

2. Reducing the compression ratio – usually by the fitment of low compression pistons, if these are available. This is a major job requiring the engine to be completely dismantled. *Only manufacturer-approved schemes should be used.*

3. Revised engine management. Where an engine's fuel injection and ignition timing are controlled by engine management chips, the chip has only limited capacity for accomodating lower octane fuels and very specialist (costly) tuning would be needed.

Sustained knock kills engines. Modern engines less easy to tune for low octane fuels. Poor-petrol countries list small, area vast, eg Egypt, Sudan, Ethiopia, Somalia.

Compression ratio vs minimum required fuel octane – conceptual guidance only

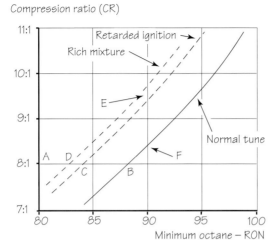

Compression ratio (CR)

Examples:

1. Engine with 8:1 CR (A) in normal tune requires 88 RON fuel (B). With retarded ignition it can make do on 84 RON (C). If mixture can be richened it will run on 83 RON (D).

2. Or, if your engine has 9.5:1 CR (E), and you'll only have 90 RON fuel, then low compression pistons to achieve 8.4:1 CR (F) will be needed – or max retard and richening.

Note: This is conceptual only. Take the manufacturer's advice. Engines vary a lot and CRs of 10:1 or 11:1 routinely use 95 RON. At the lower end, however, poorer fuels do demand lower compression ratios.

The graph above, based around test engine data from Ricardo in Sussex, high priests of the art, sums up the *general* situation in a single picture very well indeed. Retarding the ignition may be good for 3-4 octane numbers, richening the mixture, if you can (best not to meddle), another one.

Unleaded petrol

Unleaded: low compression only? A presumption might be that without lead additives unleaded is only suitable for low compression engines. This is not so. The advent of lead-free petrol does not necessarily mean it can only be used in low compression engines. The technicians have achieved the 'high octane' characteristics using different processes and additives so an *unleaded petrol still has an octane number*. Unleaded is available in RONs spanning 89 to 98 or 100 in various countries; *only* unleaded gasoline is available (1997) in Austria, Korea, Malaysia, New Zealand, Sweden, Thailand and the USA. Elsewhere, labelling as Premium or Super Premium is not always consistent. As before, RON is what matters.

Unleaded: valves and CATs. Lead-free petrol was introduced primarily to eliminate the harmful lead content of exhaust emis-

Petrol engines are designed exclusively for use with leaded or exclusively for unleaded with only small overlap. Be sure to know the table (right) or expect damage.

sions. You should be aware, though, of two other effects on petrol engines stemming from the use of leaded or unleaded petrol. They concern:

• *Valve seats – old engines.* Lead in old-style leaded fuels also has the effect of inhibiting damage to cylinder head valves and seats that would otherwise occur. Engines designed to run on unleaded petrol use specially selected materials for cylinder heads to preclude this problem. If you have to run an older engine on unleaded petrol you may experience damage to valve seats. In these cases you can sometimes use an additive yourself (such as Valve Master); one or two countries' unleaded fuels already incorporate a valve seat recession (VSR) additive (Sweden, Denmark).

• *Catalytic converters – new engines.* Exhaust systems in recent vehicles designed to run on unleaded fuels will often (though not always) be equipped with catalytic converters to further reduce noxious exhaust emissions. *These devices are very expensive and can be damaged when the engine is run on a leaded fuel*. If the vehicle has no 'cat', it can be run on leaded fuel of appropriate octane rating without damage to the engine.

The table here sums it up:

WHAT WILL RUN ON WHAT – PETROL ENGINES: LEADED AND UNLEADED FUELS

Engine	Run it on leaded fuels? (2-star, 4-star etc)	Run it on unleaded fuels?
1. Older engine designed for leaded fuels (2-star, 4-star etc)	Yes	Normally no; valve seat damage likely. Additives such as Valve Master may help. A few unleaded fuels have Valve Seat Recession additive (VSR) – Sweden, Denmark
2. Modern engine designed for unleaded fuel. Simple exhaust.	Possible. May damage oxygen sensor in engine management system.	Yes
3. Modern engine designed for unleaded fuel but with CAT (catalytic converter in exhaust system)	Possible but will damage the CAT and may harm oxygen sensor.	Yes

Diesel engines – fuel grades

The variables

Diesel specification; relevance. If you are running a diesel-engined expedition vehicle worldwide you will encounter far fewer fuel quality-related problems than with a highly strung petrol engine. Though none is likely to have such immediate and harmful implications as running a petrol engine on the wrong fuel, be aware of what is involved in a diesel fuel's specification since some aspects will need attention:

- *Cetane number* – starting, power
- *Sulphur content* – lubricants, lubricity
- *'Cloud point'* – waxing at low temperatures
- *Water contamination* – sedimenters, filters.

Cetane number

What it is. In as much as a high cetane number attaches to a 'better' fuel (and the number is arrived at in a roughly similar manner), there are some parallels to the octane rating of a gasoline. Cetane number in a diesel fuel indicates the rapidity with which the fuel will ignite spontaneously under high compression in the engine.

Does it matter? A high cetane fuel ignites readily under high compression –

starts better. A low cetane fuel ignites less readily, your engine may sound harsh, noisy or rough, may smoke, lose some power, use more fuel or be less easy to start – a worst case being low temperatures and high altitude. Modern diesel engines are best suited to fuels around 50 cetane (roughly the European norm) but will tolerate lower quality fuels. Large, slow revving marine diesels run on much heavier fuels of very low cetane value; such fuels would not be suitable for vehicles – so don't be tempted to borrow fuel from the ship you came out on!

Unlike high quality gasolines, diesel cetane is not 'first-world / third-world' related. Some economically disadvantaged countries have quite high cetane diesel because they are distilling less gasoline from their crude; Egypt with a rather sporty 56 cetane diesel (with a similarly high sulphur content!), has one of the highest cetane fuels around.

LOW CETANE DIESEL

Countries with diesel of 45 cetane or lower (Not all countries' data available) Source Octel '95.

Brazil	40
Canada	40
India	42

Diesels are less touchy about fuel than petrol engines. Not much you can do about cetane, sulphur spoils the oil, cloud point very important in cold weather.

When taking expeditions – large or small – overseas, check specs of en route fuels. Relating petrol octane to your engines' compression ratio is fundamental. Diesels usually more tolerant but high sulphur will damage engines; wrong cloud point will stop you dead in very cold conditions.

Cetane: what to do. You are unlikely to encounter serious problems attributable to low cetane diesel fuels and these will not be of a damaging nature. 'Ignition delay period' – the time between injecting the fuel and it actually igniting – is a little longer with low cetane fuels and if you were operating on such fuel permanently there may be a case for advancing the injection timing a whisker – consult the engine manufacturers. However this would increase the noise and would be a little harder on the engine (rather like advancing the ignition in a petrol engine too much) and for operations of a few weeks or a few thousand miles through an area of poorer fuel it is better to accept the slight loss of power, put in ear plugs and be kind to your engine.

'The wrong diesel' fuel is unlikely to have such dire consequences as the wrong petrol but though effects less immediate the welfare of your engine is still at stake.

Sulphur content

What it is. Sulphur content is what it sounds like and is expressed as a percentage of fuel weight. Less sulphur equals less exhaust pollution (less particulates) and is thus a cleaner, 'better' fuel. Low sulphur fuel (ie below 0.05%) has been mandatory in the US since 1993 and in EU countries since

October 1996 as part of 'Euro 2' regulations. Such fuels require more sophisticated refining than the higher sulphur diesels. Diesels in many countries average a sulphur content of 0.20 to a maximum of 0.50% but some are in the range 0.50 to 1.20% – listed opposite.

Does it matter? Sulphur matters quite a lot. There are two aspects to be aware of – related to high sulphur and low sulphur content. Sulphur content affects:

• *Lubricant contamination.* Engine lubricating oil deterioration results from the use of a high sulphur content fuel. Take anything over 0.50% as the danger level in terms of engine protection. The contamination takes the form of sulphuric acid (the sulphur combining with the water which is a product of combustion) and can cause engine corrosion, wear and eventual breakdown of the lubricant. What to do – see 'Sulphur content: what to do' opposite.

• *Lubricity of the fuel.* Low sulphur fuel can have its problems too; read on for a 'just be aware' warning. The lubricity or lubricating properties of the diesel fuel is important because the fuel injector pump needs constant lubrication of its sliding parts which it derives from the fuel itself. Early users of fuels of the low sulphur kind now mandatory in Europe and North America experienced (c. 1991) catastrophic rates of pump wear. Injector pumps are very expensive indeed. The low lubricity of low sulphur fuel was not due to the lack of sulphur but the method of its removal and currently (mid 1997), with the overdue agreement on a common test method for measuring lubricity (!), lubricity additives have rescued the situation and restored lubricity to that of 'normal' diesel fuels. If you are tempted to say, 'So it's OK then?', note the lesson anyway as it could apply (below) in the case of cold-weather diesel fuels based around aviation kerosene.

Sulphur content: what to do. As above, consider the two aspects:

• *Lubricant contamination.* Three headings spring forth under the 'What to do' section:

1. Use high 'service category' lubricant.
2. Use high 'TBN' lubricant.
3. Reduced oil drain intervals.

This is covered fully under 'Oils for diesel engines' on page 2.6 - 24.

• *Lubricity of the fuel.* This will very rarely happen but if confronted with a low lubricity problem or the suspicion of one, the obvious answer is the right one – add oil. Surprisingly little will suffice. Shell Canada recommend 0.1% – that is 5 ml for a 50 litre fill of the tank – of a simple additive-free mineral oil or engine oil. Other experts suggest that up to 1.0% of ordinary engine oil will do no harm. If you are going to add lubricant to your fuel tank, estimate how much you need to add and put it in immediately before putting in the fuel. The swirl of the incoming fuel to the tank will ensure the lubricant is thoroughly mixed. For preference wait till you have at least a half tank of fuel to put in so that the mixing

is thorough. As US and European fuel suppliers have addressed the lubricity of low sulphur fuels with some vigour you are unlikely to experience a problem; the treatment, however, is worth remembering for the case of low-lubricity arctic diesel fuels – see p 2.6 - 16.

HIGH SULPHUR DIESEL FUELS

1. *The following countries are listed as having diesel fuels with a* <u>*sulphur content of '0.50% max':*</u> *(Not all countries' data available) Source Octel '95.*

Croatia D1, UAE, Qatar, Oman, India, Sri Lanka D1, Indonesia, Macao, Malaysia, Philippines, Vietnam D1, China D1, Russia D2, Reunion, South Africa, Zambia D1, Caribbean countries, Mexico D2, all Central American countries except Panama and Nicaragua (0.33%)

2. *Countries in which diesels of* <u>*0.50 -0.75% sulphur*</u> *content are available. (Not all countries' data available) Source Octel '95. See note on p 2.6 - 8.*

Country	Sulphur content % weight
Jordan D1	0.45 - 0.59
Syria	0.70
Turkey	0.70
Cyprus	0.60
Malawi	0.55
Mozambique	0.55
Zimbabwe	0.55
Costa Rica	0.70

3. *Countries in which diesels of* <u>*0.75% or higher sulphur*</u> *content are available. (Not all countries' data available) Source Octel '95. See note on p 2.6 - 8.*

Country	Sulphur content % weight
Croatia	1.00
Cameroon	1.00
Egypt	0.88
Jordan D2	0.74 - 1.00
Lebanon	1.25
Iran	1.00
Bahrain	1.00
Kuwait	1.00
Morocco	0.65 - 1.00
Mauritius	1.00
Tanzania	1.00
Gabon	0.80
Zambia D2	1.00
Zaire	1.00
Bangladesh	1.00
Pakistan	0.85 - 1.00
Sri Lanka	1.10
China D3	1.00
Vietnam D2	1.00
Taiwan	1.00
Brazil D2	0.50 - 1.00
El Salvador	0.90
Uruguay	0.75
Venezuela	1.00

High sulphur diesel causes engine corrosion, lubricant deterioration; use right oils, reduce drain intervals – p 24 et seq. New extra low-sulphur fuels – lubricity OK?

Cloud point – waxing, CFPP

What it is. This is essentially a cold climates problem. Cloud point in diesel fuels is an indication of when waxing begins to occur at low temperatures. Waxing takes place when the temperature of the fuel drops below the point at which the dissolved wax in the fuel can remain in solution. As the temperature drops, the wax slowly forms plates or crystals which can block filters and this results in power loss or can cause the engine to stop altogether. You may hear reference to CFPP (cold filter plug point) – the temperature at which, with a given fuel, a filter will clog due to waxing. Seasonal variations in fuel formulation – the fuel at the pumps – mean the summer/winter span of CFPPs varies; they also vary considerably according to the country in which the fuel is sold. Australian diesels might have CFPPs of +1°C to -4°C in summer and winter; Finland might span -25°C to -40°C.

Blending it right. The cloud point of a diesel fuel can be manipulated in the distilling and blending process by the use of special additives and blending of other fuels – typically straight aviation kerosene, otherwise known as 'Jet A'. As indicated in the preamble to this section, if you are visiting an area where the climate is expected to be exceptionally cold, you can rely on the normal fuel suppliers to supply fuel of appropriate grades.

Buying fuel to ship. Be on your guard, however, if you have to ship your own fuel in drums though you will often find that oil companies are aware of special requirements already – for example, extreme winter grade diesel fuels are available for shipping from Cape Town or in Southern Argentina for operations in Antarctica.

In arranging shipping of fuel supplies, however, be sure that the pursuit of low waxing does not involve other problems such as an unusually low cetane number which can cause noisy rough running and poor starting – already likely to be a problem with the cold. The oil companies will have the full story even if your initial contact does not.

Diesel blends vary enormously – an Australian summer fuel might wax solid on an autumn evening in UK. 'Local' fuels for local use should be OK. Beware if shipping drums.

Cloud point – does it matter? Clearly, from the above, cloud point and the likelihood of waxing matters in that the engine is likely to stop if there is a mismatch between the ambient temperature and the fuel. The potential danger lies firstly in a vendor having old stocks of summer fuel and secondly from an unseasonal cold snap that catches everyone by surprise and finds most people with the wrong fuel in their tanks.

Seasonal or not, by consensus -40°C seems to be about the level where Nature starts winning over technology and the whole vehicle – when not running – starts to need protection from cold. In Siberia, truck convoys shelter overnight in big hangars to keep batteries, oil, fuel and seals from succumbing to the cold. Shelter or, in its absence, applied heat of some kind is the solution.

However, if you are above -40°C and the fuel has wrong-footed you, a stopping engine is not a damaged engine and a waxing fuel can be warmed and/or treated: see below.

Waxing: what to do. When you do encounter a fuel / ambient temperatures mismatch or when you know you will be in on-the-limits conditions, two approaches that can be adopted are:

- Adding heat
- Adding kerosene.

1. Adding heat. Unless it is tackled properly and with foresight it can be a bit like nailing a jelly to the wall – as soon as you put heat in, it leaks away somewhere else. Built-in heaters and insulation for fuel lines, tanks and water separators (sedimenters) are a thorough solution but heaters come in two types:

- Overnight, block or sump heaters running off mains voltages
- 12/24 volt heaters for en-route use.

Whichever solution you opt for be sure that the heat you put in cannot easily leak away; insulated jackets round tanks, fuel lines and filters is an obvious adjunct to the main item. Magnetic heaters that clamp to a sump are another crude solution that is better than nothing or as an emergency fix where a system is not plumbed, but a heater is far more effective if it is immersed, ie surrounded by the medium it is heating.

Two well known US suppliers are:
• Peter Hamilton Corporation, Racor Division, PO Box 3208, 3400 Finch Road, Modesto, CA 95353 USA Tel (209).521.7860, Fax (209). 529.3278
• Kim Hotstart Mfg Co Ltd, PO Box 11245, Spokane, WA 992311-0245 USA. Tel (509).534.6171, Fax (509).534.4216

Both the above companies are represented in UK by BSC Contracts Ltd of Tipton, West Midlands DY4 9HB. Tel 0121.557.4651.

Heaters of this kind are otherwise not easy to locate in the UK. Neither Lucas not Bosch make them any longer though Raychem, essentially a US firm, can sometimes obtain US supplies.

2. Adding kerosene. Adding kerosene to diesel fuel lowers the cloud point but can bring lubricity problems. <u>Warning</u>: Lack of lubricity may damage fuel injection pump.

Waxing – lowering cloud point with Jet-A mix

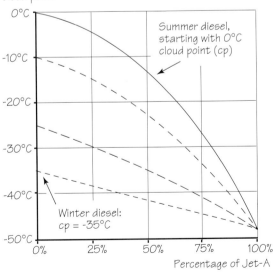

Four different fuels with basic cloud points of 0°, -10°, -25° and -35°C have cloud points lowered by mixing with Jet A kerosene.

Cloud point

Summer diesel, starting with 0°C cloud point (cp)

Winter diesel: cp = -35°C

Percentage of Jet-A

• *Lowering the cloud point.* Pure 'Jet A' (aviation kerosene) with a cloud point of -48°C is marketed in northern Canada as Arctic Diesel so in some of the worst conditions of cold 100% kerosene will avoid waxing and run diesel engines. It follows that blends of less than 100% will help in less demanding cases. As indicated above, usually the fuel available locally will have been selected and distributed according to local conditions but where you are dealing with unseasonal conditions or the wrong base fuel you can add kerosene yourself to lower the cloud point and CFPP.

Percentages of added kerosene have to be quite high to drop the cloud point, as you might imagine; 25, 50, 75% will give you around 5°, 15° and 25°C improvement depending on the fuel you start with. As you may expect, it is more effective on a summer fuel. Shell Canada, blending Jet-A with fuels of various basic cloud points, produced the graph on the left based on tests they did at their refinery ('Use with caution elsewhere', they say).

Of course it's bound to happen, isn't it, that when you don't have a fuel that will run your engine because of the cold you can also finish up having equal difficulty finding some 'Jet A' to make the appropriate cocktail that will make it flow down the pipes. Alongside the yurt behind the derelict building on the edge of the vast Mongolian plain, though, there is a drum of something that smells like domestic paraffin and that the locals fill their lamps with. Is it OK?

Highly qualified people who would know but would not dream of being quoted indicate that in general, the spectrum of fuels embraced by the term 'kerosene' – stretching from fuel for hurricane lamps right up to the most

Unseasonal cold or old summer fuel stocks can lead to surprise waxing – blocked filters, stopped engine. Adding heat and/or kerosene in moderation will cure.

highly specified aviation kerosene – will do for in-the-field, do-it-yourself fuel blending in emergencies. The problem is always to know what the fuel actually is but the *ones to avoid* in such an exercise – both aviation designations, *JP4 and Jet-B* – will for sure be labelled as such at source (that source, for aircraft, being sealed drums, a tanker or a major storage installation). It may be wise not to go above a dilution of 75% with fuels selected 'by smell'.

• *Maintaining the lubricity.* To ensure the safety of your diesel injector pump, it is worth considering adding lubricant in the quantities shown on p 2.6 - 13 once the added kerosene exceeds 50%. If this is too much or not needed, the worst that can happen is that the injectors will get fouled a bit by the excess lubricant and a high power blast or resumption of proper fuel diet will cure that in due course. All the above is offered in good faith on best current advice as an emergency 'get you to the next settlement' measure; it is better to let the professionals do the fuel blending if at all possible!

Winter diesel fuels can raise the same doubts. When sold at garage or refuelling station pumps such fuels can be relied on to be non-damaging. Some injector pump manufacturers such as the US Stanadyne make 'Arctic' pumps with specially hardened internal parts but Lucas and Bosch in Europe do not consider this necessary and their pumps are cleared for operation on any fuel likely to be encountered down to -40°C. At and below this temperature waxing and lubricity are joined by O-ring brittleness as potential problems – and fuel pumps are not the only items with neoprene seals in a vehicle! See above under 'Cloud point – does it matter?'.

Most kerosenes will do for DIY cold weather 'blending' (not JP4 or Jet-B). Adding lube may be advisable. Before -40°C , whole vehicle will need overnight heat.

Water contamination

Extra protection. Water contamination in diesel fuel storages is a risk in remote areas where inspection and sampling standards may be low. The best way round this problem is a two-pronged attack:

• *Preparation* – sedimenter, filtration
• *En route check*s – filter contents.

1. Preparation. A sedimenter is a device that may be fitted between the vehicle's diesel fuel tank and the fuel filter that precedes the fuel injection pump. The sedimenter permits any water in the fuel to settle out and avoids the risk of it reaching the filter and pump where it could cause serious damage; the unit has a drain cock for draining off contaminants. On many vehicles a sedimenter is an optional extra fitment mounted on the side of the chassis near the fuel tank at the lowest point in the fuel system. It is well worth installing one even if it is not a standard extra.

2. En route checks. Establish an en route routine of draining the sedimenter regularly to check for water contamination in the effluent. You can also do this with the fuel filter itself, releasing the securing bolt and catching the contents of the bowl carefully in another clean container which may then be examined for the presence of water at the bottom of the fuel.

References:

Paramins (Exxon Chemical Ltd, Abingdon, UK), *Autotrends 96*

Caterpillar. *Diesel Fuels and Your Engine*, Version 02, 1997

Acknowledgements and thanks:

Robert Bosch gmbh, Germany

Jonathan Douglas, JE Engineering, Coventry

Shell UK Limited, London

Dr Matthew Vincent, Associated Octel Co Ltd, Milton Keynes

Les Wilkins, Land Rover, Solihull

And special thanks to:

Cameron Bailley, Shell Canada Products Ltd, Calgary

Paul Jarrad, Land Rover, Solihull

John Stokes, Ricardo Consulting Engineers Ltd, Shoreham

OIL, FLUIDS

Introduction

Macaws shrieked in the darkening rain forest twilight. Grizzled explorer Jake Adair, veteran of a hundred forays into trackless desert and impenetrable jungle, planted a Timberland on the bumper of his battered truck crushing an eight inch centipede as he did so, tipped his hat to the back of his head, struck a match on the seat of his Wranglers and lit a thin sheroot from his discreet supplier in Havana. The subject was oil for expedition vehicles. Inhaling deeply, he paused and addressed the tyro adventurers before him.

'Take the oldest oil you can find – black, sooty, sludgy – and how does it feel?'

The steady glare through narrowed eyes, the lop-sided grin and the wait told young Quentin an answer was expected. Glancing at Fiona for an instant he stammered, 'Er, well, it feels slippery. Oily, sort of; rather like ..'

The big man cut him off. 'Right. Oil is oil. Period. If it moves it's doing its job. So don't get all fired up about oil change intervals when you're out here doing a man's work. Why, I remember ...'

'But ...'

Er, excuse us, Jake. It might be a good exchange for that sort of film but we all know how horribly, metal-grindingly, engine torturingly wrong and bull-headed the good Mr Adair is – though we have heard the view a few times.

Oils — the job and the definition

Essential additives – that get used up. If you haven't seen Jake already, you probably will. Once the smoke – from his engine, not his sheroot – clears. But to deal with that last point before going on, oil does feel slippery all the time, right up until you pour it into the waste drum but the additives that do the clever bit – combating the acids, soot, varnish, gum, water, rust, corrosion – get 'used up' over a period of time; just as a single squirt of washing-up liquid will only cope with so much grease before you need fresh water and have to start again.

What oil does. You know all this but let's recap what it does anyway:

- Lubricate metal sliding over metal
- Prevent wear
- Counter corrosion
- Keep the engine clean
- Prevent sludge, varnish, gum
- Cool the engine
- Permit easy starting

Clever oils. Not all of these tasks can routinely be performed by straight mineral oils and they are achieved by ever more precisely targeted additives. It is trite but true to say that modern engines operate under far more strenuous conditions than their forebears but they are at the same time far better designed and longer lasting. Their durability is due in very great degree to the quality of the modern lubricants available and, as we shall see, that quality is rising all the time. Remember the philosophy quoted many times in this book; your vehicle is your life-blood on an expedition. Take the very best care of it; give it the best maintenance, the greatest consideration and the best oils.

Follow the book, know some theory – you'll need it. The baseline starting point is following the vehicle handbook in terms of matching the oil you put in to the specifications laid down and then sticking to the oil change intervals. These latter may have to be reduced, for very valid reasons, when operating overseas on poor fuels or with other hazards to engine health. It is not only fuel that will be unusual on an expedition. It is unlikely you will to be able to take complete oil change supplies with you so you will be well served to learn the rudiments of what oils do, what you should choose and what you should avoid when topping up with unfamiliar products.

Oils have more to do beside feeling slippery. Neutralising contaminants that will otherwise damage the engine is achieved by additives – with a finite life.

Defining an oil – 1. Viscosity

More than just SAE. It is not everyone that gets beyond a maker's name and an SAE viscosity number in specifying the oil they use. This is by no means a complete definition and every manufacturers' vehicle handbook quotes a variety of specifications such as API, CCMC, ACEA, US MIL or ILSAC as well. Some are alternative means of defining the performance of an oil but all are essential adjuncts to the simple SAE viscosity figure. There are other defining characteristics too such as mineral or synthetic content or blend. The full gamut could be:

- Maker's name
- Engine or transmission oil
- Gasoline or diesel engine
- Mineral or synthetic base
- Viscosity – eg SAE 15W-40
- Other designations – eg API SH/CF
- EC or EC II – economy rating

There are two types of classification in this list:

- One merely describes the oil – thick or thin, engine or transmission
- The other shows how good it is – performance rating

So SAE viscosity, for instance, is simply a description like knowing you need a size 9 shoe – a question of matching an oil to climatic operating conditions; a higher number

There's a lot more to defining an oil than just the maker's name and the viscosity. Remaining spec contains essential performance parameters.

Choosing the right viscosity – for extremes of heat or cold – is only the start of selecting the right oil for your trip. Base oil and 'service category' (next spread) are very important for the welfare of your engine.

is not necessarily a better oil. Some of the other designations, however, denote performance capability so an API-SG oil is better than an -SF oil; here a 'higher' or later letter is better than a lower or earlier one. Just to spoil things, another designation is both a description and an indication of how good an oil is – a synthetic based oil is invariably better than a mineral base. Before asking 'So why use mineral oils ... ?', the familiar picture of cost emerges (graph, lower left):

The customer interface with an automotive oil – especially if it is an unfamiliar make such as you would find on an expedition – is the viscosity number and all the other (mostly obscure) designations written on the little label beneath the marketing blurb. That is what you have to go on.

Reading the label. From above, first remember the difference between a straight description and a performance indicator. Then look at the label. This – facing page – is what you will probably see:

Engine oils – the broad picture

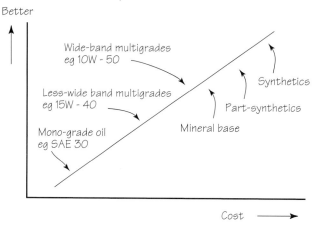

Better

Wide-band multigrades
eg 10W - 50

Less-wide band multigrades
eg 15W - 40

Synthetics

Part-synthetics

Mineral base

Mono-grade oil
eg SAE 30

Cost ⟶

WHAT THE LABEL MEANS

'Mobil' you know. The branding is seldom obvious; no manufacturer will say 'this isn't our top grade of oil' or 'this is our cheapest'. In this case **'super'** means that this oil is mineral-based, not 'super S' (semi-synthetic) or 'Mobil 1' (all-synthetic). Base should be indicated elsewhere on the label: look for it and for performance specs, especially if you don't know the maker – overseas you may be staring at a label that says something like 'Brastava Eco-lube 40'. Look for whether it's an **engine oil or a gear oil** – most important. This example is an 'old' label (not Mobil's latest) to show typical markings.

Viscosity; how 'thick' the oil is. **SAE** = the US Society of Automotive Engineers' system, accepted world-wide. High numbers mean thick oil, low numbers thin. Two together like this is a multi-grade: when cold the **10W-40** behaves like an SAE 10 oil, when hot like an SAE 40. The W? See text.

API (American Petroleum Institute) oil performance standards for gasoline engines (**S + letter suffix**) or diesels (**C + letter suffix**). See table below, right. Suffix denotes ascending standards of control of deposits, oxidation, wear and corrosion. So 'H' (1992) is better than 'G' (1989) etc. Category SJ introduced in 1996/97. Similarly for diesels: 'CD' is obsolete, so is 'CE' (example here is a petrol engine oil), 'CF' is better; 'CG-4' is the 1994 API Severe Duty Diesel Engine category ('-4' for 4-stroke).

CCMC superceded (Jan 96) by **ACEA** (*Association des Constructeurs Européens d'Automobiles* – of which Rolls-Royce, Rover, Mercedes, BMW *et al* are members). Lays down European oil category test standards. Here, G4 (relating to SAE 10W-, 15W- and 20W- multigrades) is less 'good' than G5 which relates to 5W- multigrades. **ACEA equivalents are A2-96 and A3-96.** Likewise PD-2 (passenger diesel) replaced by **ACEA B2-96.** See table, far right.

Viscosity description of the oil – like saying a shoe is a size 9. Has nothing to do with how 'good' it is.

How good the oil is. These are service suitability or performance indicators listed against various national or international oil classification systems – **API, CCMC, ACEA, US MIL, ILSAC.** Some manufacturers have their own test schedules too – VW (here), BMW Mercedes etc.

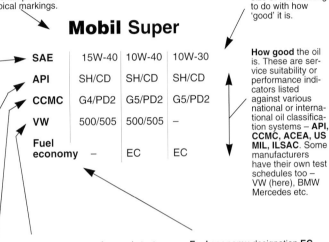

Mobil Super

SAE	15W-40	10W-40	10W-30
API	SH/CD	SH/CD	SH/CD
CCMC	G4/PD2	G5/PD2	G5/PD2
VW	500/505	500/505	–
Fuel economy	–	EC	EC

VW, or other manufacturer's test designation, is just that – particular manufacturers have their own tests which sometimes differ a little from the API , CCMC or ACEA equivalent.

Fuel economy designation **EC** (energy conserving) indicates a 1.5% fuel economy improvement on a standard Reference Oil. Designation **EC II** indicates a 2.7% improvement.

Read the label – all of it, not just the viscosity. Wide-band multigrades are best. A low left-hand figure means oil will get all round your engine quickly.

ILSAC SERVICE CATEGORIES
Japan/US System
Gasoline engine oil categories
GF-1 – roughly equal to API-SH
GF-2 – Introduced late 1996. More severe specification than GF-1.
GF-3 – 1999?

ILSAC specs only evolved for gasoline engines. Incorporate catalyst compatibility; also economy criteria along lines of EC II – see above.

API SERVICE CATEGORIES
US System
Gasoline engine oil categories
SA	
SB	
SC	
SD	Tests obsolete
SE	
SF	
SG	
SH	1992, active category
SJ	1996/97 introduction

Diesel engine oil categories
CA	
CB	
CC	Tests obsolete
CD	
CE	
CF	1994, active category
CF-2	2-stroke diesels only
CF-4	Hi performance diesel
CG-4	Severe duty diesel
'PC-7'	(Provn'l name) 1998?

CCMC/ACEA CATEGORIES
European system
NB: ACEA categories replaced CCMC categories in Jan 1996. ACEA categories and tests (see text):
'A' – gasoline engines
'B' – 'light duty' diesels (see text)
'E' – 'heavy duty' diesels (see text)
A3, B3, E3 more severe than '2' tests

Gasoline engine oil categories
CCMC	ACEA
G1-G3 – obsolete	–
G4 – Jan 96 →	ACEA A2-96
G5 – Jan 96 →	ACEA A3-96

Diesel engine oil categories
CCMC	ACEA
D1-D3, PD1 – obsolete	–
PD2 – Jan 96 →	ACEA B2-96
–	ACEA B3-96
D4 – Jan 96 →	ACEA E1-96
–	ACEA E2-96
D5 – Jan 96 →	ACEA E3-96

Viscosity and multigrades. Viscosity is a measure of how 'thick' or 'thin' a fluid is. Treacle is thick, cooking oil less so; both get thinner and flow more easily as they get hotter. Pre-electric shave lotion is very thin already and flows very well and quickly. Engine oil viscosity is quantified by using the US Society of Automotive Engineers' J300 system of 'SAE numbers'. The lower the number the thinner the oil and the more suitable it is for cold climates – and vice versa with high numbers and hot climates. Low numbers like 0, 5, 10 and 15 are applied to thin oils; high numbers like 30, 40 and 50 apply to thicker oils. The SAE number(s) thus represent a description of the oil – rather as you would describe a size 9 shoe; a size 9 is not better than a size 8, it is merely different. All these oils, be they thin or relatively thick, get thinner when they are hot.

Most often these days you will find oil viscosity defined by a combination of these numbers such as 15W-40 or a 20W-50. These are multigrade oils that combine the low-temperature viscosity of the thin oil (SAE 15, say) with the high temperature viscosity of a thick oil (SAE 40, say). The oil still gets thinner as temperature rises, but not as much as if it were a mono-grade oil of SAE 15.

Viscosity only describes the oil. Know the 'service category' specs too. Even on familiar brands this tells you a lot. On foreign brands it's all you've got to go on.

Why viscosity matters. Eighty percent of damage and wear to engines occurs in the first 20 seconds of use – yes, 80%! A thin, free flowing oil that can be pumped very quickly to all the wearing parts of an engine immediately after start-up is thus extremely important. After the previous run, when the engine is switched off the oil (aided by the engine's high temperature) will have drained down into the sump leaving a minimal coating on the metal surfaces. Whilst a thin low viscosity oil will circulate quickly and permit brisk cold cranking for a quick start, it lacks the film strength and protective ability of a high viscosity oil.

The benefits of combining – in a multi-grade oil – the characteristics of a thin quick-flowing oil at low temperature with the strength of a thicker one at high temperatures are easy to see; it benefits engine life and reduces oil consumption too. The 'W"

suffix of the lower viscosity designation (think of this as Winter) implies that the test for low viscosity was actually done at low temperatures; thus a SAE 20W oil will be thinner than a SAE 20.

Viscosity Index improvers are the magic additives that enable oil engineers to achieve this viscosity span in a multigrade. As we shall see, synthetic based (as opposed to mineral based) oils are less prone to viscosity change with temperature so can achieve this even better.

It is important to have the optimum viscosity (or viscosity span) oil in your engine – winter grades or summer grades – even when using multi-grade oils albeit the span of the latest oils is usually enough to enable one product to be used year-round in most parts of the world. The handbook for your vehicle will indicate which viscosity oils to use; in most cases this will be dictated by the requirements of the higher viscosity – say a SAE 40 grade – and will take as a bonus the benefits that the oil engineers may have achieved in lowering the left hand figure to 10W, 5W or even 0W. Shell claim that their 5W-40 Helix Ultra all-synthetic oil will reach the top of your engine in a third of the time taken by a non-synthetic 15W-40. Mobil 1 (all synthetic), now appearing as a 0W-40, will presumably get there even quicker.

Defining an oil – 2. Service categories

Oil service categories – better and better. Technology rarely stands still and the part of your oil specification written so incomprehensibly (until the advent of the chart on the previous page!) covers the ability of the oil to protect the engine from wear, corrosion and the oil's own otherwise relentless degradation from contaminants – acids, gums, varnish, sludge and emulsions with water. The 'service categories' cover an oil's capability to combat all these things.

Service category – what is it? 'Service category', if you are not an oil engineer, is not a self-explanatory term and something like 'test capability' is perhaps more helpful. As the requirements of engine designers get more demanding (typically, smaller sumps so less oil has to do more work and neutralising of contamination) and as the capability of the oil engineers expands, so the test or 'service category' capabilities in terms of engine protection go higher and higher. This usually happens on a three- or five-yearly basis so that the 'top spec' for a gasoline engine in 1989 might have been SG (on the API system – see below) but, by 1992, SH was the latest thing. At the time of writing 'SJ' has just been introduced (1996/7) indicating further pinnacles of torture that the oil is able to survive and worse horrors from which it will protect your engine.

Says who? API and ACEA are the organisations whose service category systems are in most general use – see below. Member manufacturers contribute to establishing and raising standards of lubricants and in devising tests to establish compliance. Long-suffering engines from Mercedes, Cummins, Mack, Peugeot, VW, Buick and many others are regularly torn down, examined and photographed to establish standards of bore polishing, piston ring sticking, cam wear, oil sludge, oil viscosity increase, evaporative loss, foaming stability, varnish and half a dozen other criteria.

Watch the specs. So watch the specifications or 'service categories' all the time. Note:

• They change every few years to a later letter suffix or number though sometimes two successive categories can be current at the same time indicating two levels of oil performance, eg ACEA B2-96 and B3-96. (ACEA's year suffix makes it easier to keep track of what is going on. API's evolutionary 'SH' or 'SJ' is not exactly self-explanatory!).

• A later Service Category oil will always benefit your engine.

• They are different for gasoline and diesel engines though many oils will have a dual category such as SH/CD meaning that the oil is up to spec SH if used on a gasoline engine and spec CD if used on a diesel.

Oil service categories – different systems. The main engine oil service categories

(two US, one European and one US/Japanese – API, US MIL, ACEA [ex CCMC] and ILSAC) are covered below, in addition to the information on the chart on the previous spread. Though they overlap, they all aim at the same thing – establishing the most precisely detailed lubricant standards. To the bewildered customer the newly established European ACEA system will seem the most incisive and comprehensible.

• **API service categories.** See also chart on p 2.6 - 19. The American Petroleum Institute have oil classifications for petrol engines (S + suffix letter) and for diesels (C + suffix letter). To help remember which is which think of them as being S for spark ignition and C for compression ignition (even though that was not the origin of the letters). Starting in the 1930s and '40s with SA and CA, the specifications have progressed to SJ in 1997 and CG-4 in 1994 – the '-4' denoting 4-stroke diesels as opposed to 'CF-2'. (Beware, CF-2 isn't the next progression from CF, it's the oil for 2-stroke diesels.) Provisionally named PC-7, a new API heavy-duty diesel category is due about 1999. API also have gear oil specification categories of GL-1 up to GL-4 and GL-5. These last two (manual gearboxes and axles) are the latest – see below under 'Gear oils' – but not for long; MT-1 (manual transmission) will be replacing GL-4 for gearboxes and there will likely be an upgrade of GL-5 axle oils. It hardly needs pointing out that the API system is getting more and more difficult to follow.

• **EC – energy conservation.** Oils which in addition to the normal API category carry an 'EC' or ECII' category have passed standard tests showing respectively a 1.5% and 2.7% (or greater) fuel economy improvement when compared with a standard reference oil. Such an oil might carry the designation API SJ/CF/ECII indicating compliance with petrol engine standard SJ, diesel standard CF and energy conservation standard EC II.

• **US MIL service category.** The US armed forces evolved their own standards

API, US Mil, CCMC, ACEA, ILSAC are just different sytems for achieving the same thing – an oil performance category for all types of operation. Use them carefully.

denoted by 'MIL-L-' followed by a four or five digit number and then a letter, eg MIL-L-46152E. In case you are wondering, the numbers here are totally non-self-explanatory. The designations in some cases reflect the need for multi-engine-type use. MIL specifications are not always quoted but some current ones and their approximate API equivalents are:

- MIL-L-46152E (so-called 'light duty' gasoline and diesel engines) = API SG/CC/ECII
- MIL-L-2104F (so-called 'heavy duty' diesel engines) = API CF/CF-4. See below under 'Truck oils' for the 'light duty' and 'heavy duty'.
- MIL-L-2105 gear oil that equates roughly to API GL-4 and '2105D that equates to API GL-5 – see below under 'Gear oils'.
- MIL-PRF-2105E (PRF stands for performance) supercedes 2105-D and combines the axle performance of API GL-5 with the gearbox performance of the new API MT-1 – see above, below 'Multi-purpose oils'.

- **ACEA service categories.** See also chart on p 2.6 - 19. European service categories are reflected in the ACEA (*Association des Constructeurs Europeéns d'Automobiles*) specifications. These superceded in January 1996 those from the previous European organisation CCMC whose various oil designations can sometimes still be seen on oil cans. ACEA use the following prefixes to denote engine type tested:

'A' – gasoline engines
'B' – 'light duty' diesel engines
'E' – 'heavy duty' diesels (trucks)

To avoid confusion over which is a current category they have a final suffix indicating the year of the test spec, eg ACEA A3-96 and they may have two or three test categories current at the same time, such as B2-96 and B3-96 – the first for 'passenger car and light duty diesels' and the second for 'high performance oils for severe duty / longer drain intervals' .. etc. Incidentally, beware the 'light duty' / 'heavy duty' distinction inferred by 'B' and 'E' categories –

ACEA system of oil performance codes easiest to understand and arguably more incisive than API. Synthetic-based lubricants more expensive but well worth it – for all vehicles.

see below under 'Truck oils'.

Another useful aspect of the ACEA system is that test categories will be maintained – eg ACEA B2-96 will likely be superceded by ACEA B2-98 and ACEA B3-96 could be supplanted by ACEA B3-99 or whatever year the new test comes in.

(In case you are wondering there <u>are</u> A1-96 and B1-96 categories – low viscosity economy oils – but these are not widely available at the time of writing.)

- **ILSAC service categories.** See also chart on p 2.6 - 19. ILSAC (International Lubricant Standardisation and Approval Committee) is a relatively recent (1990) organisation among Japanese and US automobile manufacturers and has established a GF-1 and (in 1996) GF-2 service category. The standards appear to be based around the API categories (GF-1 = API SH) with additonal requirements relating to catalytic converter compatibility and fuel efficiency of the kind addressed by EC and ECII (see below and on chart). You will see this standard quoted on some oil can packaging.

Defining an oil – 3. Synthetics

Synthetics are special. It will be clear by now, if not before, that synthetic base stocks for engine lubricants are a bit special. Oil company advertising, pricing and the little graph on p 2.6 - 18, interpreted on the basis of 'if it's expensive it must be good' indicate synthetics are in the Ray-Ban/501s/Cartier category among lubricants. In a short list a synthetic compared to a mineral-based oil:

- Flows better at cold temperatures
- Can operate at higher temperatures
- Has a much stronger film strength so gives more wear protection
- Is less volatile so consumption due to volatility is less.

In a synthetic oil, most of the clever additives are retained but the oil is built around a synthetic base-stock instead of a mineral one. Viscosity indexes are inherently much wider (the multi-gradeness, if you like), the pour-point – how well it pours in extreme low temperatures – is far lower so you will get a far faster gush of oil to the most distant parts of the engine on start-up (minimising cold-start wear) and the stability at higher temperatures is better too. Engine life will be considerably enhanced as wear on a carefully run-in engine is virtually halted using a first class synthetic. There are at least five different 'synthetics', of which the poly-alpha-olefins are the best known. Frequently blends of synthetics are put together to optimise the various characteristics for automotive use.

They add up to being a pretty smart oil. All brands are not the same, albeit, alas, you would have to be a clever oil chemist to be able to distinguish the good brands from the less good. Take something of a leap of faith, though, and choose the really well-known names, check out the service category information on the label carefully and the SAE span and – reach for your wallet. Synthetics are more expensive but if you hold your well prepared engine in the high regard you should when embarking on an expedition, it is hard to justify not giving it the benefit of a fill of top quality synthetic lubricant.

Any vehicle of any age will benefit from a wide-band multigrade – so long as the upper figure of the multi-grade SAE viscosity is in accordance with the figure in the handbook. And any vehicle will benefit from using a synthetic – provided it is fully run-in (see p 2.6 - 29, 'Running-in').

Even semi-synthetic would be better than straight mineral in terms of engine protection. See also below under 'Topping up'.

Synthetics – low oil pressure. On older engines, if equipped with a quantitative oil pressure gauge, there may be a slight drop in oil pressure on changing to a synthetic oil. This will be a feature of its easier pumping characteristics and better flow rate and should not cause alarm. It is 'thinner' so inevitably there will be less back-pressure – which is what oil pressure is.

Synthetics – oil changes. Retain the same oil change intervals with a synthetic as you would normally use; and change the filter too. Whilst synthetics are remarkably robust and efficient they are, as other oils, still heavily reliant on additives to combat

incipient oil degradation. It is these additives that become depleted in engine oils and to maintain engine protection the oil must be changed at the right intervals.

'Best oil' – the 'Mark 2' syndrome

Promotional double-talk. Be aware of the marketing man's problem – and how it affects you. People buy what they can afford so price is a marketing factor. A range of products can be put on the market varying between the 'cheap but reasonably satisfactory' and the 'expensive and a lot better'. Whilst hopefully the readers of this book will stop eating for a week in order to devote the budget to the best synthetic oil in the world, the marketing man still has to sell his range of products and do so without making the cheapest one seem shoddy. He is faced with manifestations of the 'Mark 2 syndrome' – an improved product tends to put the old one in the shade.

So the carefully worded promotional information put out by manufacturers on each product in the range will reflect considerable effort made to stop someone feeling bad just because they don't want to buy the most expensive oil. The write-ups therefore make all oils sound equally good. Only on the third reading (and knowing what you are looking for) can you detect the subtle difference in the wording ... !

It gets worse; to the extent that sometimes the full cross-qualifying gasoline/ diesel service categories which the oil is capable of fulfilling are *left off the label* to channel buyers to a given product. At least three recently launched products are sold that way – one of which meets ACEA A3 <u>and</u> B3-96 so has nothing to be ashamed of. There is little you can do about this kind of thing and you are best advised to concentrate on the technical information that *is* available on the label.

Empathise with the marketing man; he has his job to do. Then be hard-nosed and read the oil spec and service category with precision. Look at mineral / semi-synthetic / full synthetic; look at the service categories – etc. Think of your vehicle.

Diesels demand special oils. Watch for diesel service specs on package. Pack language like 'Turbo', 'Sport' or 'Rally' usually misleading. Protection is what matters.

Oils for diesel engines

Spec, not pack. Oils for diesel engines have to address problems of soot and acidity that are more severe than is the case for petrol engines. This would normally demand additives to effect greater detergency, dispersancy (separation and reduced size of soot particles) and an alkalinity to neutralise the often stronger acids resulting from combustion of diesel fuels. Note the word 'normally' because many oils cross-qualify to very respectable service categories as both petrol engine and diesel engine oils.

There is a certain amount of naughtiness going on among the manufacturers in making people think a particular oil is tailored specifically for diesel engines. This is not always the deception it sounds but identical or very similar oils may be packaged in petrol and diesel engine oil containers leaving you with the impression that there is a Chanel No 5 and a Chanel No 5D specially tailored for your diesel. Thus Mobil 1 0W-40 for petrol and turbo diesel engines is the same oil and performing very nicely thank you for both types of engine by meeting ACEA A3 and B3-96 as well as API SJ/EC and API SH/CF/EC II. To repeat, the API or ACEA service category designation is what counts – ACEA is clearer, more incisive.

That said, – wouldn't you know it – there is more to consider in the context of oils for expedition diesels; like TBN.

Oils for diesel engines – TBN. This may be something of a Holy Grail to mention since oil packaging rarely mentions it but Base Number or Total Base Number (TBN) is a measure of an oil's ability to combat acid contamination formed when a high-sulphur diesel fuel is used – important to know about if you are taking your vehicle on an expedition to operate in areas where fuel of that kind is the norm – see page 2.6 - 13. Such acids will cause corrosion and excessive wear in the engine if not neutralised. Moreover they will accumulate and the state of the oil will become worse. TBN is good to have lots of (10-12 or more) but it is not laid down *per se* in the service categories that, in effect, are the only other indication you have

Oils for diesels see more soot, acidity, varnish. A few oils cross-qualify petrol/ diesel but rarely to high enough standards especially with high sulphur fuel. Go by service cat.

of an oil's performance.

Does TBN really matter? After all you don't see fleets of bulldozers and graders being wet-nursed over poor fuel, do you? Yes, you do. Caterpillar, who know a thing or two about diesels and lubricants for diesels, have a rule of thumb regarding fuel sulphur content and required TBN:

• *'The 20x rule'* – oil TBN should be 20 times the sulphur content when used on an *indirect-injection* diesel engine (eg the old 2.25 litre Land Rover diesel and the 6-cylinder BMW unit fitted in the new Range Rover).

• *'The 10x rule'* – oil TBN should be 10 times the sulphur content when used on a *direct-injection* diesel engine (eg the 2.5 litre Land Rover 200 Tdi and 300 Tdi engines).

For example, a fuel with a 0.75% sulphur content requires a lubricant TBN of 15 on an indirect-injection engine, and a TBN of 7.5 on a direct-injection diesel. (See page 2.6 - 12 and 13 for more detail on sulphur in diesel fuel in general. Whilst the world fuel companies are trying to reduce it – and Europe and the US have just enacted a 0.05% sulphur maximum – there are still countries, as listed on page 2.6 - 13, where sulphur content is 1.0% or higher.)

Caterpillar have, recommend and use portable fuel sulphur analysers and residual TBN test kits – not practical for a small expedition but an indication that the problem is real and that you must do something about it. They regard 0.5% as the red light figure.

All very well, you say, but if I am in Outer Bogdanistan with crummy diesel fuel and running out of top grade oil for changes and top-ups to counter its bad effects, what do I do? See 'Engine oils – what to actually do' (next spread), para 8.

Truck oils. Engine oil for trucks are usually used for a significantly different sort of operation compared with light 4x4s and vans. Very long drain intervals are achieved (45000 km or more is not uncommon) but this is due to fewer cold starts, longer journeys, big oil sumps and oil top-ups of the order of 1 litre per 2000 miles – plus some characteristics of the oil formulation itself.

The pumps may not always be labelled – or powered-up. Knowing in advance the fuel grades and specifications generally available where you are going will enable you to prepare engine and lubricants accordingly. Watch out for high-sulphur diesel – as do down-to-earth professionals like Caterpillar.

Such extended drain intervals are achieved *only* with long distance truck operations and usually only after oil sampling tests to establish trends so do not feel that a truck oil (ACEA E2 or E3 – see below) confers the same benefits on expedition type operations. Drain intervals apart, however, these oils are of interest.

Recall the ACEA service categories:
ACEA 'A' – for gasoline engines
ACEA 'B' – for light duty (including passenger car) diesels
ACEA 'E' – for heavy duty diesel engines

Although, to quote Castrol, a truck is 'easier to lubricate', truck oils are in fact very highly specified, some aspects of that specification are ideally suited to certain expedition or outback diesel applications. Alas, as if the subject were not complex enough, it is regrettable, or maybe inevitable, that the test procedure for an

ACEA 'B' oil is not the same as a test schedule for an ACEA 'E' oil. You are therefore not considering a single parameter where you can say X is bigger than Y but a series of different parameters ascertained by different tests on different engines.

Thus an ACEA E3-96 oil is 'higher specified' than an ACEA B3-96 oil in many respects but not all. And few E3 oils have been put to (or quote) the B3 small engine test procedure – but see Mobil Delvac, p 28.

Why the interest in truck oils? Because they could be just what you are looking for; nearly all truck oils, as well as being higher than average in dispersants to keep soot small and in suspension, have a very high TBN and this, as we have seen, is of considerable relevance to the welfare of your engine when you are operating – as you will be in many areas overseas – on high-sulphur fuels.

The ACEA 'B' test requirements are important for a smaller engine, though, and an oil meeting B2 (or the markedly better B3) test *as well as* an E3 rating will be close to the ideal for an expedition diesel. So, keep your eye on the service categories, as already advised, and see 'Engine oils – what to actually do' overleaf.

Overseas you'll likely encounter high sulphur diesel (where? – p 13) demanding a high TBN oil. 'Domestic' oils rarely have enough TBN for this so try ACEA 'E' oils.

Engine oil – what to actually do

Making your choice. After all this background information and theory, what to do? Check the oil recommended in your handbook and do not use a less well-specified product. So:

1. Viscosity 1. Check handbook recommendation on viscosity. This may be a simple figure like 15W-40 or may be listed as different oils against ambient temperatures. If so, select the one covering the widest ambient temperature range and make sure that temperature range covers your proposed operations. Use this viscosity as your baseline.

2. Viscosity 2. You can tweak this choice to the benefit of your engine. Where the baseline figure is, say, 15W-40, don't go below, or normally above, the right-hand figure but you can beneficially lower the left- hand figure by using a 10W-40 or a 5W-40 or even a 0W-40. As well as extending the span of operating ambients, this will, more importantly, give you better cold-start oil pumping and reduce engine wear. If your engine is very old or worn (but still fit enough for an expedition!) you can push the right-hand figure up from 40 to 50 to, as a senior oil technician once said, 'help fill the spaces'.

3. Service category. Ascertain the minimum service category of the required oil as indicated in the handbook. Oil service categories may well have advanced since your handbook was written and using a high spec – an API SJ instead of an API SH – will always benefit your engine in terms of protection. Don't let the label-talk of 'racing' or 'super high performance' cars put you off; such activities will be helped by high spec oils but your 4x4 will also reap enhanced protection.

4. Base oil. Then refer to 'non service category' items like oil base. Oil service categories lay down performance capability but do not refer to base oils – for example Mobil Super Diesel (mineral base) and Mobil Super S Diesel (semi-synthetic) both meet CCMC-PD-2 (now ACEA B2-96). A mineral base oil will have a good many of the additives available in more expensive oils but a semi-synthetic or full synthetic will have very much better cold-pumping attributes and will be much better at reducing engine wear – to almost zero with a full synthetic.

5. Aim high. Combining 3 and 4 above, go for the highest service category and cleverest base oil you can – in the example quoted, Mobil 1 0W-40 Turbo Diesel is a full synthetic meeting the highest (present) category of ACEA A3-96 (petrol engines) and B3-96 (diesel) and would do exceptionally well in a petrol engine or where low sulphur diesel fuels are used. With its '0W-40' SAE it will probably pump – to every corner of your engine on a cold start-up – quicker than after-shave when compared with a 15W-40 mineral-base.

6. High-sulphur diesel fuel? Truck oils? The classic expedition situation is a vehicle prepared in the UK and then shipped or driven to an area where local diesel fuel has a high sulphur content – 0.5% or higher. The 'best' oils as determined by service category and base oil (3, 4 and 5 above) are not usually formulated to deal with high-sulphur diesel fuels but truck oils are (albeit the nascent API CG-4 oils, of which there is at present still something of a scarcity, are formulated primarily for fuels up to 0.5%). ACEA E3-96 'heavy duty' service category oils will encompass nearly every aspect of the highest 'light duty' categories but also, if you choose right, sock in with very high TBN (16 or 17) to counter high-sulphur diesel acidity as well. Just what an expedition or remote-area diesel needs. So think about truck oils – see table p 2.6 - 28.

7. Drain intervals normal. Don't step outside your normal drain intervals, whatever oil you use. As already mentioned, however good the base oil, it is the additives that will be depleted with time and hard work and when they are 'used up' the oil is no longer protecting your engine properly. If you have a diesel and are on truck oils, do not be tempted to emulate truck drain intervals. Trucks do huge distances between drains because they have enormous oil sumps, liberal topping up with fresh oil,

Choosing multigrades, right hand figure should be manufacturer's advised but left figure can be as low as affordable. Go for highest service category.

tend to run at low rpm so cope with viscosity increase and have far fewer cold starts.

8. Drain intervals reduced. There is a need to *reduce* drain intervals if you have a diesel operating on high sulphur fuels and do not have high TBN oils to use – another classic expedition case when you are operating in remote areas where special oils are not available. If your oil TBN fails the Caterpillar '20x' or '10x' test (see p 2.6 - 24) reduce your engine oil change intervals. The US diesel doyens Cummins have a beautifully elegant formula for assessing this but, reduced to expedition vehicle terms, it amounts to:

- Diesel fuel sulphur content 0.05%-0.50% – reduce drain intervals to 75%.
- Diesel fuel sulphur content over 0.5% – reduce drain intervals to 50%.

9. Buying it. Try very hard to consider engine oil as a part of your spares pack. In other words take enough for an en route change. If you cannot take a complete change or would finish up with a can and two fifths, just taking a 5 litre can of the right stuff topped up with 'local' will help the engine in its hour of need. Buying the best oils is not cheap. Sometimes the top brands of truck oils are only available in 25 litre drums. Decide what you need and stick

to it; then shop around. Ring the manufacturers, open an account for your project and get supplied at trade rates through manufacturers' local distributors (see table).

10. Topping-up – mixing oils en route. People who care about engines sometimes worry about not being able to top-up with the same oil they originally filled with. So long as there is not a mix of mineral/synthetics with a vegetable oil such as a castor-oil based lubricant (very rare these days anyway), you can mix oils without doing harm though naturally topping up with the original type oil is best. You can top up with a better oil or a less good one though it will pay you, if you are in the running-in period (first 3000 miles) not to put in synthetic.

As mentioned below, never top up an engine with a gear oil – though the other way round is safe and preferable to running low on oil.

11. Keep a good used oil or change it ...? If faced with the dilemma of having a sump full of a once-very-good oil that has done its mileage and having only a less exotic oil to replace it with, do the oil change, if necessary reducing the oil change intervals you use with the replacement oil.

12. New engine and vehicle. See next spread under 'Running-in'.

See p 2.6 - 24 re high TBN oil for diesels. Keep to or reduce drain intervals; take oil change if at all possible. Buy at trade rates by opening account with local distributor.

Get the best and cleverest oil you can and take enough for a change too. Stick to, or reduce, oil drain intervals – see text. Where the oil you buy is only available in 25 or 205 litre drums you will have to carry it in your own cans, maybe, as here, using a squeezy pump (see page 2.5-4). Cleanliness is vital. Don't use galvanised containers.

ENGINE OIL MARKET SNAPSHOT – WINTER 1997

Four representative companies listed, alphabetically. Oils listed: gasoline engine oils first, then 'for diesel', then 'truck' oils; all in descending service category order – shown gasoline first, then / diesel, then / EC if applicable.

Make and brand	Viscosity	Base oil	Service category API	ACEA	TBN	Min qty	Price band	Notes
Castrol								
RS	10W-60	Synthetic	SJ/CF	A3/B3	11.0	1.0 L	A	
SLX	0W-30	Synthetic	SH/CF/ECII	A3/B3	8.9	1.0 L	A	
GTX Magnatec	10W-40	Synthetic base	SJ/CF	A3/B3	10.7	1.0 L	C	
GTX Protection Plus	15W-40	Mineral	SJ/CF	A2/B2	9.5	1.0 L	D	
GTX	15W-50	Mineral	SH/CF	A2/B2	9.3	0.5 L	D	
GTD	15W-40	Mineral	CE/CF-4	B2/E2	12.0	1.0 L	D	
Syntruck	5W-40	Synthetic	– /CF	– /E3	15.9	25.0 L	A	
Esso								
Ultron	5W-40	Synthetic	SJ/CF	A3/B3	11.3	1.0 L	B	
Ultra	10W-40	Synthetic blend	SJ/CF	A3/B2	8.3	1.0 L	C	
Uniflo	15W-40	Mineral	SJ/CF	A2/B2	8.3	1.0 L	D	
Ultra diesel	10W-40	Synthetic blend	CD	–/B3	11.0	1.0L	C	
Uniflo diesel	15W-40	Mineral	CF	–/B2	10.0	1.0L	D	
Essolube XTS501	10W-40	Semi-synthetic	CF	– /E3	17.0	25.0L	B	
Essolube XT401	15W-40	Mineral	CF	B2/E3	15.0	25.0L	D	
Essolube XT301	15W-40	Mineral	SG/CG-4	A2/B2/E2	11.0	25.0L	D	
Mobil								
Mobil 1	0W-40	Synthetic	SJ/CF/EC	A3/B3	9.0	1.0 L	A	Delvac 1 SHC and XHP are the only listed B3/E3 dual qualified oils.
Super S	10W-40	Semi-synthetic	SJ/CF	A3/B3	10.2	1.0 L	C	
Super	15W-40	Mineral	SJ/CD	A3/B3	10.3	1.0 L	C	
Mobil 1 Turbo Diesel	0W-40	Synthetic	SJ/CF/EC	A3/B3	9.0	1.0 L	A	
Super S Diesel	10W-40	Semi-synthetic	SJ/CF	A3/B3	10.0	1.0 L	C	
Delvac 1 SHC	5W-40	Synthetic	– /CE	B3/E3	16.3	25.0 L	B	
Delvac XHP	10W-40	Special min'l	– /CF	B3/E3	16.3	5.0 L	D	Also 15/40, 10/30
Delvac MX	15W-40	Mineral	SH/CG-4	A2/B3/E2	10.0	5.0 L	D	
Shell								
Helix Ultra	5W-30	Synthetic	SJ/CF	A3/B3		1.0 L	B	
Helix Plus	10W-40	Semi-synthetic	SH/CF	A3/B3		1.0 L	C	
Helix Standard	15W-40	Mineral	SG/CD	A2/B2		1.0 L	C	
Helix Diesel Plus	10W-40	Semi-synthetic	– /CF	– /B3		1.0 L	B	
Rimula Ultra	5W-30	Synthetic	– /CF	– /E3	16.6	25.0 L	B	
Rimula Super	15W-40	Mineral	– /CG-4	– /E3	11.5	5.0 L	C	
Rimula X	15W-40	Mineral	– /CF-4	– /E2	8.0	5.0 L	C	6 grades available
Rimula TX	15W-40	Mineral	SG/CF-4	– /E2	10.0	5.0 L	D	

Expedition usage is niche in oil market. Seek the most advanced grades capable of also dealing with the worst climates, stress and fuels. Look first at the service category.

Notes:

1. If need be, recap Service Category meanings on chart at p 2.6 - 19 or text on 2.6 -21/22. In general the ACEA system is the easier to follow: A = petrol, B = diesel, E= diesel trucks. API on petrol oils is simple progression to SJ (1996/97) but diesel oil categories (C + suffix) get ragged. The ECII is energy conservation rating – see p 2.6 - 21. The obsolete CCMC ratings (replaced by ACEA 1996) are shown when manufacturers have not yet appended an ACEA category.

2. TBN number indicative of ability to neutralise lubricant degradation through acid from high sulphur diesel fuels.

3. Price banding shown to indicate that the best oils cost more and by roughly how much; trade rate shown, excluding UK VAT when bought as a 4-pack of 4 or 5-litre cans or as 25.0 L drum if that is only source. The single-litre rate can be up to 35% higher. See previous page, para 9, on how to buy.

Band A	£4.50 - 5.50 per litre
Band B	£3.50 - 4.50 per litre
Band C	£2.50 - 3.50 per litre
Band D	Under £2.50 per litre

4. Re-read 'Engine oils – what to actually do', on previous spread if you need reminding of where to start!

5. There is still some reading between the lines to be done. Oil service category tests are very expensive for manufacturers to carry out. The ACEA A, B, and E tests are all different despite the B and E both being for diesels – albeit B is more demanding on cam wear than E (so go for B3 if running a 'light 4x4' diesel). It is almost inconceivable that Rimula Ultra – as an all-synthetic – would not pass the B3 test if it was carried out. But because the marketing people decided to sell it in 25 litre drums to commercial vehicle operators, the B3 test was not quoted. A B3/E3 would be nectar for expedition diesel.

5. Gasoline/diesel oils (eg in ACEA, a high 'A' and 'B' number together) are useful for mixed-fleet expeditions.

RUNNING-IN A NEW ENGINE

Carefully does it. If you have a new vehicle your driver's handbook will cover the manufacturer's recommended running-in procedure which you should adhere to in most cases. On the other hand some of these procedures seem to have been written by an accountant or a lawyer with impossibly impractical limitations laid down simply to cover the maker from warranty claims and without much understanding of what engines need. If you find yourself faced with this or, possibly, have had a reconditioned or re-engineered engine fitted in an old vehicle for your expedition the wisdom and sensitivity of the running-in instructions for Yamaha motorcycles could hardly be bettered. A slightly summarised version using percentage of red-line rpm instead of actual rpm figures is:

There is never a more important period in the life of your engine than between zero and 1000 km. Because the engine is brand new you must not put an excessive load on it for the first 1000 km. The various parts of the engine wear and polish themselves to the correct operating clearances. During this period prolonged full throttle operation or any condition which might result in excessive heating of the engine must be avoided.

1. 0-150 km. (0-90 miles)
Avoid operation above 55% rpm. Stop and let the engine cool for 5-10 minutes after every hour of operation. Vary the speed of the machine; do not operate it at one set throttle position.
2. 150-500 km (90-300 miles)
Avoid prolonged operation above 70% rpm. Rev the engine freely through the gears but do not use full throttle at any time.
3. 500-1000 km (300-600 miles)
Avoid full throttle operation. Avoid cruising speeds in excess of 85% rpm.

This procedure has the ring of people who know engines and how to be kind to them. The bit about 'revving freely through the gears' with its overtones of low engine loads – the quick vroom up and down again when you are changing gear – is particularly appropriate.

If you don't have a tachometer – get one fitted (see pages 4.2 - 5 and 6)! Engine welfare apart, you will find it an invaluable driving aid – as often as not useful for avoiding too low an rpm rather than an excessively high one. If you do not have a laid down 'red line' (never-exceed rpm) for your engine, a sensible guide to the kind of engines fitted to expedition vehicles might be:
* Older small diesels – 4000 rpm
* Older large diesels – 3250 rpm
* New or recent diesels – 4500 rpm
* Older petrol engines – 4750 rpm
* New or recent petrol engines – 5500 rpm

Running-in oils. Initial-fill oils for running-in should be something like a 10W-40 mineral-based multi-grade – not a synthetic or semi-synthetic. The first service at 600 miles should be done and the engine refilled with the same type of mineral 10W-40 oil. You will be wise to continue the running-in procedure philosophy (Items 2 and 3 above) until around 2500 miles. Only then, or even later at, say 3000 miles, think about a synthetic content to the oil. A synthetic oil will virtually arrest the wear in an engine from the time you put it in. Do not put a synthetic oil into a new engine; if you do you will never achieve a proper bedding in and you will be in danger of achieving bore polishing instead.

Bore polishing is, in effect, a polished area on the cylinder bore that because of its lack of surface texture will not 'hold' an oil film as well as a micro-textured surface would. Such a film will be thinner than optimum and the results can be serious local overheating, engine tightness and even scuffing.

Let the engine reach 2500-3000 miles of carefully monitored driving and then give it its first fill of a full synthetic oil – and keep it on it thereafter.

Running-in is crucial with a new or re-engineered engine – the first 90 miles especially so. Fit tachometer if you do not have one. Save synthetic oils for after 3000 miles.

'There is never a more important time in the life of your engine than between zero and 1000 km' – part of Yamaha's matchless advice on running-in a new engine; they even single out the first 90 miles for special treatment. Never run-in an engine on a synthetic or part-synthetic oil. Give it 2500-3000 miles of measured and considerate use before using a synthetic base oil.

Tractor fluids

Multi-purpose fall-back. If all else fails when you are seeking en route supplies, you may come across something mysteriously called a 'tractor fluid'. These are oils used by farmers and industrial users who have to try to minimise the number of lubricants they keep in the store so 'tractor fluids' are multi-purpose. Some are more multi-purpose than others and to distinguish them they are classified as (specs are examples only):

For mixed fleet of vehicles tractor fluids can help reduce number of oils to carry but performance categories tend to be low. Refill gearboxes, and axles before departure.

• UTTO – Universal Tractor Transmission Oils for use in all transmissions and hydraulics sytems. This can be SAE 10W-30 (summer) or SAE 5W-20 (winter) and equates to API GL-4 specification as a gear oil. There is also:

• STOU – Super Tractor Oil Universal – an 'everything oil' – which is formulated to be used in engines, transmissions and hydraulic systems of many farm tractors. STOU is SAE 10W-30, conforms to API SF/CE engine use classifications and also CCMC D-4. As a gear oil it meets API GL-4.

Gear oils

Fill and forget – not quite. Gear oils are far less of a problem in an expedition context since transmission oil change periods are very extended in comparison to engines' – typically 24000 miles or even more in some cases. This enables all transmission oils to be fresh-filled, using the correct grade, at your home base before the trip and little further action will be needed. 'Little further action', of course, does not mean 'no further action' as we shall see on the daily inspection schedule which includes checking for leaks. Where there are leaks – possibly through weeping oil seals or gaskets – top-up oils must be available. Amounts are likely to be small but they must still be the right oils – but see opposite 'Multi-purpose oils'. A few points should be taken on board:

• **Engine/gearbox units.** Vehicles where the engine and gearbox are built in the same unit such as the Toyota RAV4 or the Land Rover Freelander share the same oil. In general the loads on an engine oil are much more demanding than those on a gearbox oil – high temperatures, contaminants, high pressure points such as cam-shaft lobes – so use of a common lubricant is not a problem especially as the gearbox will have been designed for a shared lubricant operation.

• **SAE viscosity scales.** A different SAE viscosity scale (J306) is used for gear oils so an SAE 80 gear oil is not twice as thick as an SAE 40 engine oil. Actually it is thinner. This is worth remembering if you have to use engine oil to top up gearboxes (see below). You can do this in small quantities but never

For most trips it will be possible to fresh-fill axles and gearboxes before starting out and thereafter only inspection for leaks will be necessary. Not to be confused with tractor fluids above, multi-purpose gear oils (facing page) can be used for top-ups. Be sure axle and gearbox breather pipes are extended and vent high in engine bay to avoid ingestion of water when wading.

the other way round – never put gear oil into an engine.

• **'EP' oils – final drive.** Vehicle handbooks often stipulate oils with an 'extreme pressure' additive (such as an SAE 90EP). EP oils should only ever be used where they are specified – axle differentials, some transfer boxes in Land Rover vehicles. Do not routinely use an EP oil in a normal synchromesh gearbox unless specified as it may interfere with operation of the synchro cones. Never put an EP oil in an engine as it can cause damage to some of the metal surfaces at high engine temperatures.

• **Gearbox oils.** Looking at a span of maintenance manuals it would appear that manual gearboxes are very pernickity about their lubricants. The reason for this is seldom the basic lubricant requirement and has more to do with the manufacturer's tweaking the quality of the gear change and how the synchromesh works and feels to the driver. Nevertheless pay careful attention to what the maintenance manual says and the oils laid down. As mentioned above, oils with EP additives (or the wrong amounts of EP additive) can be bad for the gearbox. In broad terms oil specification minimum performance requirements are covered by:

- *Manual gearboxes.* API GL-4 – or MIL-L-2105 (90W EP). API GL-4 spec is soon to be replaced by the new API MT-1 specification for manual transmissions.
- *Axles (and some transfer boxes).* API GL-5 or MIL-L-2105D (80W EP). An update of API GL-5 is under development – provisionally called API PG-2.

Some gearboxes are specified to run on ATF (see below) and some do require an EP-additive oil. Check the handbook carefully.

• **Manual gearboxes – ATF.** Some manual gearboxes are specified to run on ATF oils (Automatic Transmission Fluids – see below) which make the synchromesh feel smoother. Top-ups for such gearboxes can be in engine oils if necessary.

• **Multi-purpose gear oils.** Where an expedition needs to cut down on the number of top-up oils taken – won't you always? – an oil like the part-synthetic SAE 75W-90 Castrol Syntrax which has a unique additive can be used in EP and non-EP gear oil situations. In other words it can be used as a top-up for an axle differential as well as for a manual gearbox. Another very high grade multi-purpose gear oil is the SAE 75W-90 all-synthetic Mobilube 1 SHC which meets API GL-4 and GL-5 as well as MIL-L-2105D and the new API specification MT-1. As mentioned above, a new specification for a multi-purpose oil is the US MIL-PRF-2105E which combines the axle performance of API GL-5 with API MT-1 oil for manual transmission gearboxes.

Automatic transmission fluids (ATF). Like motorcycles which have 'wet' clutches, ie multi-plate clutches that actually run in the same oil that lubricates the engine and gearbox, automatic gearboxes are quite particular about the fluids used in them. In general terms the 'friction modifiers' that cause fuel economy oil to be 'super slippery' would upset the action of the clutches and brake bands within an automatic gearbox so the formulation of the oil (which also doubles as a hydraulic fluid for good measure) has to be fairly precise. Pre-1981, or thereabouts, things were even worse in that the two main manufacturers, GM and Ford, specified different and incompatible ATFs.

Dexron and Mercon are the respective spec trademarks for GM and Ford ATFs and ATF that you buy will be signified as complying to one or other specification – or both. They have now come very close to each other and most ATFs will now comply with both – eg Castrol's latest ATF is actually called 'TQ Dexron III', complies with GM Dexron III (F30520) and Ford Mercon (M941009) and is 'backwards-compatible' with the earlier Dexron II. Mobil ATF SHC is another 'all specs' ATF.

Apart from its carefully tuned friction profile, an ATF's wide-temperature flow characteristics are what make it special. Nevertheless Mercedes commerical vehicles equipped with Allison transmission may be filled with engine oils of 10W-30 or 15W-40

Gear oil with 'EP' additives must be used only where specified – and never in engines. Manual synchro boxes are particular about oil fill to retain optimum feel.

for ambient temperatures up to 35°C or 45°C respectively so it is likely that such oils could be used in an emergency for other transmissions. Naturally you should watch for leaks in the same way as for any other part of the vehicle in your nightly inspection but the cleanliness of any top-up operation is really critical.

Brake fluids

Compatibility. One area where you absolutely cannot mix oils is with brake/clutch fluids. What is at stake, in the case of an incorrect brake fluid, is the seals on the brake master and slave cylinders. Nearly all these systems are designed to work with a synthetic brake fluid (ie not derived from mineral oils) and will thus be compatible with particular types of seal. If you use a mineral oil where you should be using a synthetic-based fluid there is a risk that the seals will swell, deteriorate quickly and in time *a sudden brake failure will result*.

Check in your handbook what kind of brake fluid is required. Land Rover and most – but not all – other manufacturers specify a brake and clutch fluid meeting the US specifications DOT 4, FMVSS 116, SAE 1703 (this is a spec, not a viscosity here) or the European ISO4925. Currently, so far as is known, only Rolls-Royce and Citroen specify mineral-based hydraulic fluids so be sure not to re-stock from these dealerships if you are among the great majority of 'DOT 4' users. DOT 4, incidentally, supercedes DOT

Use of the wrong brake fluid or of a mineral oil where a synthetic 'DOT 3' or 'DOT 4' fluid is specified <u>could lead to complete brake failure</u>.

3 so if you have an older vehicle specifying DOT 3, then DOT 4 will do nicely. DOT 5, however, is <u>not</u> compatible where DOT 3 or 4 are specified.

If you should experience a major loss of brake fluid for whatever reason in the back of beyond (see below left for one of the more bizarre!) it is better to use water drained from the engine coolant system than to use mineral oil. (The anti-freeze will not attack seals and will have rust inhibitors in it; the radiator can be topped up with ordinary water.) Needless to say you should undertake a replacement with the correct fluid after a thorough flush-through as soon as you reach appropriate facilities.

Wash it off. Spilled brake fluid will ruin any paintwork – even the enamelling on the outside of the brake servo; wash it off quickly with a petrol soaked rag – but don't let the petrol anywhere near the reservoir.

Engine coolant – anti-freeze

Change, don't mix. Drain and recharge your engine coolant system before your trip. Anti-freeze mixture is more than just a means of stopping the radiator and cylinder block freezing. It also raises the boiling point of the coolant to up to 135°C with a radiator pressure of 1.5 bar. Anti-freeze to BS 6580:1992 is the minimum standard to accept. It contains corrosion inhibitors which will protect iron, steel, copper and aluminium alloys. Avoid <u>mixing</u> types and brands of anti-freeze; hard water, phosphate types and mixed metal engines can result in radiator sludge. Drain, flush, refill anew.

Just enough. Paradoxically, there is an optimum dilution for anti-freeze to obtain protection to the lowest temperature. Though you would expect the most protection the higher the percentage of anti-freeze liquid used, in fact the most protection (down to about -40°C) is obtained at a concentration of 55%. Any higher concentration actually raises the freezing point of the mix.

Wash it off. Anti-freeze, neat or diluted, can damage paintwork and if spilled should be washed off with copious amounts of clean water.

A funny thing happened on the way to...... Chobe

Lying on my back beneath the engine doing the evening inspection in Chobe reserve, a sudden cascade of hydraulic fluid rained down. Spluttering out from under, I was amazed to find a monkey sitting at the raised bonnet yanking at the white nylon brake fluid reservoir thinking it was a binned milk carton. My bellow scared him off but I was glad I had a full can of brake fluid for a top-up.

Final thoughts on fuel practicalities. Clockwise from above: When carrying a large built-in or strapped-down tank, decant into a jerry can to refuel so you can count the cans and dip the part-cans and calculate an accurate mpg. To refuel from a can, many vehicles require a spout extension. Defender has telescopic fuel tank orifice extension as available option; with its mesh filter, worth its weight in gold.

Anti-freeze coolant mix offers greatest protection against low temperature at 50-60% dilution – not 100% as you might expect. Use a fresh mix before expedition

References:

API (American Petroleum Institute), *Motor Oil Guide*, 1988

Bunting, A, *Quantum Leap or a Question of Terminology*, *Transport Engineer*, Oct 1996, pp 12-13

Castrol, *A guide to Automobile Engine Oil Specifications*, April 1996

Caterpillar, Illinois, USA. *Caterpillar Machine Lubricant Recommendations*, 1997

Cummins Engine Company, *Service Bulltetin 3810340-2*, May 1996

Lubrizol, *Ready Reference for Lubricant and Fuel Performance*, 1996

Paramins (Exxon Chemical Ltd, Abingdon, UK), *Autotrends '96*

Acknowledgements and thanks:

Graham Clarke, Cummins Engine Co, Daventry, UK

Les Dash, Shell Oils, Manchester, UK

Exxon Chemicals Ltd, Abingdon, UK

Mike Frost, Mobil Oil Company Ltd, Berkshire, UK

Emma Nichols, Castrol, Swindon, UK

Dave Nycz, Caterpillar, Illinois, USA

Roger Perkins, Caterpillar, Leicester, UK

And special thanks to:

John Allan, Mobil Oil Company Ltd, Coryton, UK

Stewart Arkley, Castrol, Swindon, UK

John May, Rover Group, Gaydon, UK

Dr Mike Wharton, Esso Lubricants, Abingdon, UK

Section 2.7

Equipment planning:

Communications

COVERAGE OF THIS SECTION

Planning and theory – what is going on

Practicalities – what to use for what

The need – who talks to whom?

Who talks to whom and why

Types of communications. There will not always be the need for radio or satellite communications on an expedition. The requirement will arise depending on your aims, project, number of vehicles, schedule and the type of country you are traversing. Depending on all these, communications can be classified, by 'traffic', into the categories shown below. In all cases except a MAYDAY call or short-wave reception, the communication will be two-way.

- *Emergency calls*
  - Distress MAYDAY call – see SARSAT beacons, Section 5.6.
  - Summoning specific help – spares, medical, from:
    - Home-country base
    - Field or in-country base
    - Other parties in group.
- *'Safety calls'* – position, revised ETA, passing project data, warning of re-supply requirements to:
  - Home-country base
  - Field or in-country base
- *Vehicle to vehicle* communications, short range.
- *Reception of short wave* broadcasts – BBC World Service.

Classification by equipment function. Whatever the nature of the 'traffic' or messages passed, the above list will self categorise by equipment function since the range of the transmission is what affects the type of equipment you will need. So if you have decided you do need some form of communication, it will fall into one of three categories for two way traffic and one for receive only:

- Vehicle to vehicle, short range.
- Vehicle to local base, short-medium.
- Vehicle to home base, long range.
- UK to vehicle – short wave broadcasts.

Advance planning. A decision on the need for and extent of expedition communications capability – base camp and/or mobile, on-vehicle – needs to be made at an early stage since there will be considerable cost, space, weight, bureaucratic and possibly training implications that will need to be accommodated across a wide spectrum of the expedition planning. Consult specialists early to get a broad picture of equipment, official permission and licensing requirements. And keep in the back of your mind that equipment can be hired for expedition use. There is also the buy, use, and resell path to consider.

Get it very clear that you really do need radio comms – and who needs to talk to whom. Sticking to the regulations is absolutely essential.

The regulations and the medium

Regulations

Rules rule. Electromagnetic radiation is evident in so many forms – of which 'radio' is just one – the notable part about regulations regarding its utilisation is that they are so well co-ordinated in concept and so few in number. And there is a noticeable and laudable tendency towards deregulation wherever possible. Worldwide, the International Telecommunications Union (ITU) is the governing body to which each nation belongs and legislates according to

agreements of member nations. In the UK the legislating body is the Radio-communications Agency (RA), an executive agency of the Government's Department of Trade and Industry (DTI). The legislation covers a huge spread of devices which we all, as ever, take for granted and includes everything from ingestible radio pills and other medical applications to car alarm remotes, garage doors, model aircraft, Citizens' Band radio, aircraft, marine, hobby radio, broadcasting and use of satellites. The RA pro-

Mobile communications centre. Camel Trophy communications requirements are exceptionally demanding – inter-vehicle, vehicle to local base, vehicle and local base to UK and on-site journalists to UK by satellite phone, fax and/or HF. Aerials carried by this Defender are (from the right) telescopic HF with inverted-V dipole, Inmarsat-A dish, Inmarsat-C stub, and (being adjusted) VHF whip aerials for vehicle to vehicle and vehicle to relay station.

All expedition-relevant comms equipment will have to be licensed – in the country of origin and in the country of operation.

duce a very informative range of leaflets about equipment specifications and licensing. The Agency General Enquiry point switchboard number in London is 0171.211.0211.

Licences, power. In very broad terms – and understandably if this miraculous natural phenomenon is to be most effectively utilised – operating licences are required for a large proportion of the above applications. Surprisingly, many come under the heading of 'short range devices' and are exempt from licensing of any kind. The aim, of course, is

to ensure that 'the airwaves' are equably and effectively allocated to particular purposes and that their use is such as to maximise effectiveness and eliminate interference between one device and another. On this basis, therefore – and as a moment's thought would lead you to expect – licences become important above certain levels of transmitted power and, as in life, power equals sphere of influence – and potential interference (!).

Transmitted power is expressed in watts and there are huge variations. The BBC's FM transmitter at Wrotham south of London transmits 250,000 watts (250 kW) , BBC's 'long wave' 198 kHz transmitter at Droitwich puts out double that at 500 kW (and covers the whole country on it – see below), a vehicle remote locking key transmits 10 milli-watts (10 mW – ten one-thousandths of one watt), model aircraft 100 mW, a PMR (personal mobile radio, see below) about 4 watts. Though it varies a little according to the frequency the device is operating on, around 2 watts is the rough transmitting power threshold above which licences and/or certificates of competence become necessary. Where 'power' is mentioned, the term ERP is assumed (effective radiated power) as this takes into account any 'clever' aerials which have the effect of boosting effective power over and above that which leaves the transmitter.

Long distance short wave (HF) radio transmit/receive communications is a bit of a special case and here a short course will generally be necessary to gain a long range operators certificate – see 'Vehicle to home country communications – radio' below.

That said, an exception is that not all satellite communications require licences; the reason for this is that in many cases (see Inmarsat below) control of the satellite and subsequent stages in relaying the transmission is charged independently and controlled by specialist organisations – usually the owners of the satellite.

The message from the regulations is, rightly, very clear: the regulations are there for a purpose, stick to the equipment specifications and operating rules absolutely.

The medium

Frequencies, modulation. A quick round up of the salient principles of radio wave propagation might be appropriate if you are not that familiar with it. As well as transmitted power mentioned above (which in fact ought to come last), particular radio transmissions are actually defined by their frequency – the long wave, medium wave and VHF on your domestic radio – and, worth mentioning, their method of modula-

tion: AM (amplitude modulation) or FM (frequency modulation).

Transmitting a straight radio frequency or carrier wave would result in a single mono-tone; modulating it is what enables to you to turn it into music or speech. More easy to grasp in the case of AM, you need a certain amount of 'bandwidth' – ie a little section of the medium waveband, and there's only a finite amount available to share around – to give 'room' for your modulation. This bandwidth requirement (and behaviour of the ionosphere – see below) is part of what gives interference and fading on medium and short-wave broadcasts and communications. VHF may be AM or FM, though broadcast transmissions are invariably the latter these days. A narrower bandwidth (relatively) will suffice, hence the clearer reception. Digital transmissions are, if the purists will forgive so simplistic a visualisation, lots of 0s and 1s defining a signal, as it were 'in line astern' and take up an even smaller bandwidth, particularly in non-hi-fi applications like (see below) C-Sat.

CW – Morse code transmissions, telex. When ionospheric conditions and local interference are difficult enough to prevent good legibility of the voice modulated signal, resorting to 'CW' – carrier wave only – will often save the day. As mentioned above, voice takes quite a lot more bandwidth as well as needing conditions in which the various modulations will be clearly audible. Using carrier wave only and signalling by turning it on and off for different lengths of time – Morse code – will get through when voice is unintelligible. It is slower, of course, and, as already indicated will need a qualified, skilled and practised operator. With the right facilities each end, a lap-top computer and a telex modem can achieve 'bolt-on' telex, based on CW transmissions and reception from an HF transceiver.

Line-of-sight, ground wave and ionosphere. Radio transmissions radiate from the aerial in all directions and in a straight line. The 'all directions' bit can be modified by making the aerial directional with reflectors

Getting down to brass tacks and skipping theory is actually counter-productive. Know a little bit about how and why it works. You'll need to for your HF licence.

Radio wave propagation

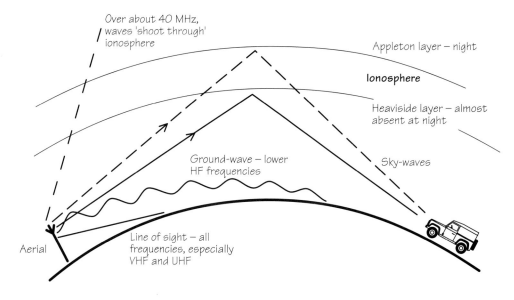

Over about 40 MHz, waves 'shoot through' ionosphere

Appleton layer – night

Ionosphere

Heaviside layer – almost absent at night

Ground-wave – lower HF frequencies

Sky-waves

Aerial

Line of sight – all frequencies, especially VHF and UHF

and thus more effective but the energy still leaves in a straight line. The earth though is curved and, helpfully, what we could call 'AM' these days, ie long and medium waves, have the characteristic and ability to follow the curve of the earth – the 'ground wave' – and 'flow' round hills to a certain degree. In doing this there is quite a bit of attenuation (loss of power with distance) so pretty high transmitting power is needed to make it work over a good range – hence the BBC long wave using 500 kW and some of the medium wave transmitters (Talk Radio UK) using 400 kW or Virgin 200 kW. This kind of 'long wave' will have a range, at that power, of 1000 miles or so, the medium wave transmission will reach around 100-200 miles depending on terrain; the medium wave 'stations' have transmitters dotted round the country whereas the long wave broadcast is achieved just using Droitwich.

Now the clever bit starts. The frequency of Virgin Radio (medium wave, AM) , for instance, is 1215 kHz or 1.215 MHz. Frequencies of around 3 MHz to 40 MHz have a reduced ground wave (because the frequency is going up) but can be reflected off the ionosphere, the relevant lower surface of which ('F' or Heaviside layer) is about 200 km above the earth's surface. Reflection back down to the earth's surface from the ionosphere (and sometimes back up to it and down again) gives the opportunity for hugely increased range so, surprise, this is where the 'short wave' band of long range broadcast frequencies is placed.

Like a flat stone bounced across a duck pond, radio waves reflect off the ionosphere only when the angle is right; again, just like a duck pond there is 'skip distance' between you and the first bounce which may give you problems (see below) on short/medium distance comms as in vehicle-to-local-base situations. You are sitting between the finish of the 'ground wave' and the start of the first bounce-down from the ionosphere, the sky wave. The duck pond analogy could be extended; certain types of stone skip better than others. Thus high frequencies above 40 MHz sometimes 'punch through' the ionosphere so there is no reflection. The additional complication is that the ionosphere's characteristics (level of the duck pond, if you like) change during the hours of darkness which is why, when listening to short wave broadcasts from UK in, say, Kenya or Ethiopia, you have to use around 17-21 MHz during the day and drop to maybe 6-9 MHz frequencies at night.

Frequency vs distance

Optimum frequencies for the job. The relevance of all this? The relevance, and it is fundamental to an understanding of communications as it might apply to an expedition, is that certain frequency bands (and thus types of equipment) are suited to certain ranges between transmitter and receiver – and no other. So you have to choose your working frequency (and thus your equipment) according to the required range of the transmission. It is worth noting, in terms of expedition practicality, that low frequencies usually need large cumbersome aerials and high frequencies can make do with smaller, lighter ones. Looking at frequency vs distance, a rough breakdown would be:

• *VLF (very low frequency)* has the ultimate ground wave and thus enormous range – given enough power. This can actually penetrate water which is why it is the basis of a navigation fixing system originally commissioned for submarines but (as VLF/Omega) usable on land. Of no relevance in the context of this Section – communications. Huge aerial arrays, very long range.

• *LF (low frequency)* – 3-300 kHz (BBC 'long wave' sits at 198 kHz). Very good ground wave. Very large aerials required and, with enough power, ranges of 1000 miles or so.

• *MF (medium frequency)* – 300 kHz to 3 MHz. The bottom end of this, up to around 1.50 MHz comprise the 'medium wave band' of AM broadcasting – the BBC's Radio 5 Live is on 909 kHz (0.909 MHz). Big aerials needed, 100 to 500 kW power to achieve up to about 200 miles range depending on terrain.

• *HF (high frequency)* – roughly the 2-30 MHz range – is the start of expedition-rele-

vant frequencies. The classic long range communications (and short wave broadcasting) span of frequencies and, for longer ranges, relies on 'sky wave' reflectance from the ionosphere. This long range comm is greatly helped by using Single Side Band (SSB) transmissions – conceptually the upper or lower half of the wave. SSB uses less bandwidth so yields clearer reception on HF. Long range, quite large aerials ('clothes line' with height or maybe a 10 ft vertical whip aerial on a 'ground mat'). Practical for vehicle-mounted equipment – probably 20 kg of equipment running off 12 volts DC. Transmitting 30 watts on 18 MHz will reach from the Sahara to the UK, two way – see below 'Vehicle to home base comms'.

The lower end of the HF band, around 2-3.5 MHz, has a good ground wave and will achieve excellent ranges in this mode – up to 300-500 miles in daylight and 6000 or more at night. Propagation conditions are more important than sheer power. This frequency band will, of course, also work line-of-sight – short ranges depending on frequency – with smaller aerials.

• *VHF (very high frequency)* – 30-300 MHz. Broadcast band VHF is around 76 to 108 MHz with a range of 50-100 miles from elevated aerials. UK/Europe/overseas legislative sub-divisions put communications VHF into a number of compartments with outputs of 0.5 watts up to 25 watts giving ranges of a few hundred metres up to 60-70 miles depending on aerial type and height. Generally low band (around 70 MHz will give better range than mid and high (140-170 MHz). Small aerials (under a metre), line of sight. (See below under 'Vehicle to vehicle' and 'Vehicle to field base' PMR – Private Mobile Radio).

• *UHF (ultra high frequency)* – 300 MHz-3 GHz. Communications application around 420-470 MHz. Very small aerials (under 30 cm), line-of-sight, not quite such good range as VHF but better penetration in, say, built up areas. PMR uses UHF as well as VHF.

• *SHF (super high frequency)* 3-30 GHz. Frequencies (giga-hertz, ie, thousands of

Every comms application has an optimum frequency – VHF/UHF for line-of-sight, HF for long range and giga-hertz to zap satellites.

MHz) are used to communicate to and from satellites.

The above gives a broad overview of what kind of equipment you need for what type of communications and the ensuing sections will be clearer for your having the basics. There is a potential problem area, as the duck-pond skip distance analogy above indicates, in the vehicle-to-local-base kind of communications ranges around 30-80 miles – too far for VHF or UHF line of sight and not far enough for an HF to get a good sky wave; the lower HF frequencies , given enough power, will produce an earth hugging 'ground-wave' to get over the problem.

What to ask for. You will be starting to get a feel for where, in the field of frequen-cies and equipment, your communications requirements are going to lie. The diagram and preceding text make the requirements for vehicle to vehicle comms pretty clear – line of sight, VHF, UHF or low frequency HF (see next section). Vehicle to field base is less clear cut, sitting sometimes between (or in both) line of sight low band VHF and ground wave for HF. Sometimes it is worth setting up a hill-top relay station for VHF. As we see below ('Use/licensing overseas') you have to have as clear a picture as possi-ble – knowing the distances, terrain and time of day – of what band of frequency you are going to need. Knowing what to ask for and why will help in getting authority to use the frequency bands you want.

Vehicle to vehicle communications

Contrary to gen-eral belief, 'they' are trying to ease regulations and easy-to-use-and-licence SRBR could have many short range expedition applications.

Wide choice. Since the application of vehicle to vehicle comms is likely to be vehi-cles in a convoy where the lead vehicle can warn of hazards or a tail-end vehicle can inform of a flat tyre or other problem, a line-of-sight or essentially short range operating situation exists. And since just about any-thing will work line-of-sight, the choice of equipment is considerable – albeit the high-er frequencies such as VHF/UHF usually favour more compact installations from the point of view of aerials. Cost and complexi-ty rises in direct proportion to the range required. In ascending order of cost and UK/European licensing complexity (but see final section 'Use/licensing overseas'), the following equipment would fulfil the vehi-cle-to-vehicle comms requirement:

1. 'General purpose' categorised, deregu-lated (ie no licence required) ultra-low power 'toy shop' walkie talkie gear avail-able in consumer electronics shops, some-times available as motor cycle intercom or bike-to-bike comms. Equipment must con-form to DTI Spec MPT1336. 49 MHz, extremely low power (0.1 watt) nominal range under 100 metres and inevitably sus-ceptible to interference, A two-set kit with headphones and voice-activated mics can be around £100 or less. Try before you buy!

2. Short Range Business Radio (SRBR), semi deregulated (£30 licence for three years) for quarries, building sites, sports sta-dia etc. Equipment must conform to DTI 'type approval' spec. 460 MHz UHF (likely to change c.1999 but will remain in the 450-470 MHz band). Very low power (0.5 to 2.0 watts), nominal range 400 metres on hand held set, probably up to 2 miles with a roof aerial or very clear line-of-sight; up to 15 channels. This is a new category of comms introduced by European legislation and the Radiocommunications Agency in March 1996 aimed at freeing-up the airwaves with minimum regulation. Short range minimises chance of interference so a frequency free-for-all is inherent in, say, towns or busy sports events but there is unlikely to be any congestion problem on expeditions; one-way at a time comms, check 'channel busy' indicator before transmitting, identify your-self and who you are calling, keep calls brief, conclude with 'Over' if expecting reply or 'Out' if exchange concluded.

3. Citizens' Band radio (CB). Long established HF, 40 channel system (of 'Breaker one-nine this is Pig Pen, come on' fame – the 'Convoy' hit song of the '80s) originated in the US; 26.965 to 27.405 MHz using latest spec. £15 per year licence required. Equipment must comply with DTI spec and bear mark CEPT PR 27 GB followed by ETS 300 135; this ETS will eventually replace current MPT 1333 or MPT 1320 DTI specs. 4 watts max power, range 1-2 miles on short 'rubber duck' aerial, 4-5 miles if larger external aerial used. Relatively inexpensive equipment. Close to ideal for vehicle convoys with fixed installations (smaller than car radio sized). UK CB licence valid in certain European countries. Hand-held versions available but heavy and less compact compared with SRBR or PMR (see below)

4. Personal Mobile Radio (PMR). The next step up from SRBR in VHF/UHF with allocated frequency bands (as opposed to free-for-all) and more power. Latest DTI/Eurospec for equipment is ETS.300.086. Operating licence required (£140 per year for up to 10 sets) using, optionally, the following frequency bands:

VHF low – 68.0-87.5 MHz
VHF mid – 138-165.0375 MHz
VHF high – 165.05-174 MHz
UHF1 – 420-450 MHz
UHF2 – 450-470 MHz

Frequency allocation is centrally regulated to minimise interference in particular regions of the country. For a UK licence your area of operation must be defined and, if there is danger of interference or congestion, a frequency band other than that opted for may have to be allocated. Up to 5 watts max power mobile to mobile within nominal 3 km radius of nominated permanent location; actual max range will probably be 2-4 miles if clear of obstacles. Up to 25 watts permitted operating from a fixed base which, with a high aerial, may yield 10-20 or even 40-50 miles range. No choice of channels; use allocated frequency only. Small unit, small aerial. Line-of-sight; use of VHF optimises range, UHF optimises penetration.

Typical equipment. Lists showing typical vehicle equipments and approximate costs, including rental, are appended at the end of this Section.

PMR has more power and versatility to step between already allocated frequencies in your area of operation.

Examples of vehicle to vehicle communications equipment. From the left, an SRBR (short range business radio) – very low power, cheap to buy and licence; then a typical hand held PMR (personal mobile radio), the Maxon SL70, VHF/UHF up to 5 watts power, licensing more complex. Third from left another VHF/UHF PMR (Maxon PM150) for mobile or fixed installation up to 25 watts pep. Right is Citizens Band (CB), HF or VHF radio; max power 4 watts

Vehicle to field base communication

Difficult sector – HF/VHF. Vehicle to field base communication usually encompasses a difficult range bracket of 50-150 miles – far enough not to be line-of-sight, far enough to be falling off the end of the ground wave at some frequencies and transmitted power, and much too close to be getting a decent skywave. The solution at the 100-150 miles end of the scale is in the choice of a low enough HF frequency – probably around 2 MHz – to hang on to a good ground wave propagation. Quite a bit of power will be needed – up to 100 watts – and, since low frequency equals large aerial and vice versa, something like a 3 metre whip or a directional dipole aerial as high off the ground as possible will be needed. In clear conditions of flat ground and no obstructions, low band VHF (around 70 MHz) can reach up to around 50 miles, or a little more if there is a hill to stand on. See 'Personal Mobile Radio' above. The VHF solution has much to recommend it for the simpler aerials required.

Relays, aerials. Larger expeditions with advance knowledge of the area they will

Vehicle to field base is the awkward one – often too far for VHF and not far enough for HF to work properly. Homework pays off.

operate in might consider installing a small self-contained solar-powered relay that could be put on a hill – not a complicated thing to do technically nor an especially heavy piece of equipment but cost and accessibility to hilltops usually has budget implications – extra equipment, helicopter access etc. This would assist any struggling VHF signals to 'get down into the dips' and extend their range as well.

Regarding normal aerials in these marginal conditions, some users have found that even a makeshift dipole is better than a whip aerial. A dipole aerial is a piece of wire of a length appropriate to the frequency you are using, cut in the middle and attached to a feeder cable to the radio; the tip-to-tip run of the wire (not the feeder) should be at right angles to a line between the base and the vehicle, ie it should 'face the target'. Passable results can be obtained even with the wire at head height but the farther off the ground it is the better it will work; poles mounted on the roof of two vehicles would

Self-powered hilltop VHF relay. For major expeditions operating beyond VHF range for lengthy periods of time and automatic relay can be established on a hill visible to both parties. Here extensive solar cells are used to power the equipment and a high aerial mast is used.

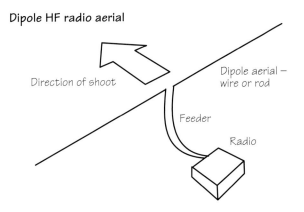

Dipole HF radio aerial

Direction of shoot

Dipole aerial – wire or rod

Feeder

Radio

be a reliable set-up.

When in Rome... There will be a lot to learn from what 'the locals' do, if there are any and they use radio, since geographical terrain, position in the sunspot cycle, forests and any climatic influences will all have

been taken into consideration. As you will be proposing transmitters and receivers in the same approximate location you will be in touch with the local authorities anyway in seeking authorisation to use comms equipment. Do this well in advance so you are sure about what frequencies, aerials and equipment are best suited to your chosen operating area and conditions.

Typical equipment. Lists showing typical vehicle equipments and approximate costs are appended at the end of this Section.

In terms of help in the field just communications is not enough – a ready-to-implement 'what-if' infrastructure is essential to go with it.

Vehicle to home country communication

Uses? Radio and satellite. Think quite hard about the exact uses of any vehicle to home country communications and how necessary it is. Radio is sometimes a glib supposed solution to any rescue problem but first bear in mind that a radio call is not itself a doctor, a new alternator or a barrel of fuel; in other words in the rescue context it is only the start of a procedure that may, you hope, yield these items in the very near future *if such an infrastructure has been thoroughly and reliably organised in advance.* It is preferable to organise your rescue procedures with more immediate resources if you can; better yet to be self-sufficient. In practice long range communications must, of course, be part of a network – either already established, or yet to be set up.

Safety or information calls, the passing of data or staying in touch with business or families is a different matter. Position, how-

goes-it messages, tee-ing up team replacements or film supplies would be likely traffic to a small, even one-man, home base group but even this can sometimes – and in certain areas of the world that really does mean sometimes – be achieved by using telephone or telex from local centres of habitation.

Satellite is more expensive for equipment and for the cost of calls but in terms of infrastructure required may be simpler, surprising as that may sound. Satellite is already set up to interface routinely with land lines whereas special arrangements may have to be made using a radio network – one of the exceptions being the UK where British Telecom has the services of the ubiquitous Portishead Radio ready and able to put HF radio calls through to any telephone in the land; automatic accounting services are thrown in.

Concentrated comms in Camel vehicle.Top left of the stack is a Trimble GPS and Yaesu FTL2011 4/40 watt VHF set; the right stack, from the top is a Yaesu FT757GXII with a FT890 beneath it (both HF). The black box is an aerial tuner on top of an an air-band VHF transceiver, and a public address amplifier – to lend punch to team briefings! 'Suitcase' behind right hand seat houses C-satellite equipment – next spreads.

Terrestrial radio

Base facility required. If radio is to be used then, your very first step – and possible stumbling block – will be to establish who you will be transmitting to. Unlike vehicle-to-vehicle or vehicle to field base operations you will here almost certainly be transmitting to an outside organisation that has agreed to help or is set up to do so routinely; setting up your own transmit/receive base in the UK would be a major undertaking and would also require licensing under the Wireless Telegraphy Act 1949. Looking elsewhere, large, up-and-running radio transmit/receive stations with the right aerials, equipment, operators, listening watch schedules and time to help are few and far between and your most likely source of assistance will be the military or some aeronautical or marine station such as, in the UK, Portishead Radio.

Portishead (01278.772200) used to be marine only but in recent years British Telecom (BT) have enterprisingly opened up the facilities to all under the marketing brand name of 'Gateway' and, as well as help and advice from some extremely experienced hands-on radio people, will, bottom line, put calls from your HF transmitter in the field through to any UK telephone number at (1996) around £3.10 per minute billed to your own home number or, in effect, as a 'reverse charge' to the number called. Callsign, frequencies, schedule and account details would all, naturally, be pre-arranged with BT.

Operating schedule and frequencies. As in every other aspect of expedition planning, the details count, even when taking an initial look at the big picture. As we have seen, the ionosphere changes according to whether it is day or night and this dictates appropriate frequencies should be used – lower frequencies at night, higher during the day. Transmitting across a day/night time zone, ie east-west or west-east where one party is in daylight and the other in night will make radio conditions more difficult, especially at certain parts of the 11-year sunspot activity cycle which affects reception conditions; take detailed advice early in this case as satellite may be the better solution. Transmitting north-south – say from UK to West Africa – both parties are in near enough the same time zone and there will be little problem. Whatever your in-the-field location, therefore, you will have to consider at the planning stage when your radio schedule will be most convenient from the expedition point of view and then check

With long range HF comms your frequencies will have to be carefully chosen for the time of day your transmit. Pre-planned schedule is essential.

with the radio propagation experts that this is feasible.

In the UK Portishead can advise on frequencies for particular times of the day and also indicate when conditions are likely to be best. Let us say you were operating from Somalia. You would choose a schedule (ie a time of day at which you would make your regular call) such that both Somalia and UK were in full daylight or full night – probably the former for convenience and propagation conditions. From the expedition point of view the most convenient time for the radio call might be early evening when you are pitching camp but technically this would be the worst time with ionospheric changes taking place. You will probably find the lunch-time break will be the optimum time from the propagation conditions viewpoint.

Having made this decision, Portishead could allocate exact frequencies for you to use – frequencies in the optimum band for propagation which were also allocated to 'Gateway' and on which they maintain a listening watch. A callsign would be agreed plus a time for the schedule – say from 1200 to 1215 GMT – and this would enable Portishead to listen out on the allocated frequencies if they were not already covered.

You could at this point also make account arrangements with Portishead – fix how the calls would be paid for or to which telephone number they would be billed.

Equipment. Inevitably, HF, SSB (single sideband) equipment capable of transmitting in the 2-30 MHz kind of range will be required. Likely power will be 30-100 watts and this, operating from a vehicle power source, will limit the time on call – if cost of call doesn't already. As mentioned above, aerials for HF will be a fundamental consideration. For best performance such frequencies demand large directional aerials – as much height as possible, long aerial wires

Getting the aerial right is hugely important in long range HF comms. Condition of ground – dry desert or wet jungle – affects aerial performance.

Different approaches. Australian Defender has 100 watt Codan X-2 HF transceiver (right-hand aerial) tuned to Flying Doctor frequencies (4-7 Mhz) and 12 watt Uniden AX144 SSB CB for short range work. Below, a Siemens-Plessey PRC320 'Clansman' 30 watt HF radio with hand-generator-charged ni-cad battery and whip aerial (left, background) sending position report from mid-Sahara to UK on CW (morse). 18 MHz worked well for this midday schedule. Two-way voice worked most of the time too.

Long range HF sets, the 150 watt marine IC-M710 left , and the100 watt IC-M800 with a separate front panel for dash mounting. The M710 costs £1600 (late 1996). Both sets feature programmable presets for quick mid-schedule frequency changes.

If tight for budget, bulk and weight, special-to-frequency cut aerials can be used instead of an aerial tuner but changing frequency will mean changing aerials.

aligned according to the direction of 'shoot' – but, in many cases, a vertical whip aerial with a 'ground mat' of earth wires or using the vehicle itself as earth will work to voice standards of legibility provided frequency prediction has been good. Either way the aerial equipment alone will be cumbersome and heavy and will need up to 15 minutes to erect. (A main base could afford to erect a high and properly aligned aerial or even a beam aerial with directional reflectors.)

A typical general equipment list would be:

• Slung dipole wire aerial with light poles or whip aerial with cable and ground mat (or vehicle mounted and removable).

• Aerial tuner – about the size of an A4 box file.

• HF radio and hand-microphone. Radio will probably be about the size of two A4 box files stacked on top of each other and may have a separate front panel for dash mounting.

• Additional equipment/lap-top/software to provide a teletype facility.

Such a radio will probably require about 20 amps of 12 battery current during transmit and about 1 or 2 amps whilst on receive.

Current drain on transmit is thus very high and a second and discrete high capacity battery for the vehicle will be essential to ensure safeguarding the vehicle's own battery. On a brief schedule you will probably be able to get your traffic through without the engine running but this may not be the case and you will have to be sure there is no radio interference resulting from vehicle electrics.

Typical equipment. Lists showing typical vehicle equipments and approximate costs are appended at the end of this Section.

Certificate of competence, training, testing. As we have seen, operating PMRs or SRBRs on VHF/UHF requires only the most basic licensing arrangements since they are pretty foolproof to operate, being set for given frequencies allocated exclusively for that purpose. HF is different in that your equipment is tuneable, ie will be capable of transmitting on a wide range of frequencies only a very few of which will be legal for you to use. More than mere legality is involved; there are life-dependent safety implications. Certain frequencies, for instance, are reserved for air traffic, marine, amateur and, most important of all, safety and rescue emergency use.

It is not unreasonable, therefore, that people using HF equipment should have to undergo some basic training and acquire a certificate of competence. It is essential that operators are fully aware of the implications of frequency allocation and the traffic for which each may be used. The only framework of legislation presently in place in the UK relates to Marine Radio Operators' Certificates, though even as this book goes to press the Radiocommunications Agency of the Department of Trade and Industry are working on how the land-mobile case may be covered more precisely.

In the meantime the acquisition of a marine Long Range Radiotelephone Operator's Certificate (LRC) – the simplest of those currently being examined (and these will have changed somewhat by 1999) – will ensure an appropriate knowledge of radio procedures and the Radio Regulations of the International Telecommunications Union. No CW (morse code) training is necessary. With an LRC you will have acquired the right degree of professionalism to operate your equipment properly, safeguard your expedition and not hazard other users.

Training for all marine radio certificates is undertaken by colleges or training establishments of the Association of Marine Electronics and Radio Colleges (AMERC) [National Administration Centre 015394.32255]. A dozen or so such establishments exist within the UK and training for an LRC would take about three days on a full-time course though home-study distant-learning packages are currently being prepared (these would involve a one-day attendance for practical work). Cost of the intensive course would be of the order of £175 plus an exam fee; the home-course would be about half that.

Whilst theoretically you could take your Land Rover to the bush with an HF radio subject only to local (foreign country) approval to use it, the advantages of an LRC are three-fold:

A funny thing happened on the way to...... El Adem

It was early days and it wasn't much of a radio, more an emergency system with a hydrogen generator and balloon for an aerial. On the last night in the desert we thought we'd try it; it didn't work. Next day, dust covered, we presented ourselves to the Adjutant whom we assumed was watching our ETA. He looked up. 'Who are you?', he said. Try not to rely on outside authorities!

• Like taking a driving test before driving a car, you will know how to get the best out of your equipment to the benefit of your expedition and without hazard to others.

• Preparing and setting up your vehicle radio equipment properly in the UK before departure will require test transmissions with Portishead and it would be illegal to do this without a certificate of competence of some kind.

• Of pivotal importance, obtaining permission from the overseas country in which you intend to operate will be critically enhanced if you are able to wave an accredited operator's certificate that attests to proper training.

Take a short training course at an AMERC establishment to obtain an HF certificate – Long-range RT Operators Certificate (LRC).

For best performance every aerial, especially on HF, must be correctly 'loaded' or tuned for the frequency in use. An automatic antenna tuner, bulky but light, is invaluable when rapid change of frequencies is required.

Satellite communications

Powering-up the ionosphere. Satellite communications developments do make the practicalities of radio a lot simpler. Equipment is small, aerials are either flat and roughly A4-sized or no taller than a Coke bottle. Power requirements are well within the capabilities of a vehicle 12 volt battery and no special skills are required.

Normal AM and long distance HF radio communication is dependent on transmitted radio waves passively reflecting off the ionosphere, a process that can take a lot of transmitter power and a need to change frequencies according to the time of day to prevent radio beams shooting through the reflecting layer.

Satellite communication works by positioning a space relay station, self-powered by solar cells, that boost and re-transmit incoming signals; these signals are then monitored by Land Earth Stations (LES – such as British Telecom's Goonhilly Down) with very large and well-directed aerials. A Mobile Earth Station (MES) – or 'land-mobile' – is you in your Land Rover or truck or boat out there in the back of beyond. Lower mobile station power outputs are possible using satellites as opposed to HF terrestrial radio.

The immediate future for satellite communications is very exciting. Presently available, on the horizon or just over the horizon are:

• *Inmarsat.* Long established, operating now with a wide variety of services from cheap data-only transmissions or 'pagers' to full video.

• *Iridium.* Motorola-backed, low-orbit, 66-satellite constellation operating on cell-phone principle for voice, data, fax. Projected operational date, late 1998.

Satellite comms is a simple, day or night procedure but equipment and airtime is more expensive than HF. Inmarsat is the only current operator (1996).

Inmarsat 2 relay satellite coverage

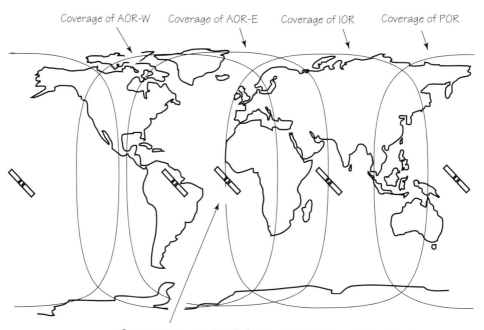

Coverage of AOR-W   Coverage of AOR-E   Coverage of IOR   Coverage of POR

Geostationary satellite (AOR-E) – Atlantic Ocean Relay, East.
Other three: Atlantic West, Indian Ocean, Pacific Ocean Relay

Inmarsat-A satellite equipment package operating outside vehicle from an auxiliary power unit (see Sec 2.8 'Electrical power'). Aerial azimuth (compass heading) and elevation are simply determined from a map – see opposite. Equipment here is the Nera Compact T A-sat package. C-sat more compact, less capability, aerial much smaller, omni-directional – see Defender at beginning of Section.

• *Orbcom.* Low orbit, store-and-forward data-only (as opposed to voice) 36-satellite system expected to be operational early 1998.

• *Globalstar.* Low-orbit, 48-satellite system expected to be operational early 1999.

Inmarsat. Inmarsat is an internationally owned co-operative established in 1979. It is at the moment (late 1996) the only provider of global mobile satellite communications.

The Inmarsat satellites comprise a constellation of four high-orbit geostationary satellites. Current Inmarsat-2 satellites each weigh about 1000 kg and have a power rating of around 1200 watts to amplify and re-transmit incoming signals at extremely high frequencies (satellite-to-mobile 1.5-1.6 GHz, satellite to LES 3.6-6.4 GHz; domestic FM is 88-108 MHz!).

The geostationary satellite positions are over the equator as indicated on the map. Note there is no polar coverage, the satellites cannot see further than 76°N and 76°S. The application of the map is commonsense; an MES in the field will have to aim its aerial at the closest satellite – from Congo you would point it just about due west at the Atlantic Ocean Relay – East (AOR-E) satellite, from Madagascar north-east towards the Indian Ocean (IOR) satellite. The closer you are to the satellite's position, the higher your aerial angle must be. The extremely high frequencies involved mean aerials can be physically small, usually flat, from a metre across down to not much bigger than a piece of A4 paper.

Inmarsat services. With these satellites Inmarsat can provide (summer 1996) a wide range of services:

• *Inmarsat-A.* Voice, fax, telex, high-speed data transmission and even low-resolution video conferencing. Top-end, power-hungry, expensive, industry-standard facility used by seismic/geophysical and shipping industries. Around 100-150 kg including antenna, plus peripherals; cost $US20,000-30,000.

• *Inmarsat-B.* Same facilities and application as Inmarsat-A but digitally carried, uses less power and bandwidth, lower costs – ultimately the long term replacement for A-Sat and still in the high end cost bracket unlikely to suit expeditions. Around 35 kg and $US30,000-40,000. $US3-7 per minute

• *Inmarsat-C.* C-Sat is a two-way, store-and-forward network for telex and data (not voice) using less power (and time) at satellite and on the ground than A-Sat or B-Sat. Messages up to 32 kilobits (about 800 words) are transmitted in data packages, reassembled and land-lined on by the LES usually within minutes. Some equipment is integrated with GPS (see p 5.2 - 24) to give automatic position reporting. Mobile stations (MES) available to interface with laptop PC. Many use 150 mm high conical omni-directional antennas. Cheapest of all the services at present and with most application for vehicle-based expeditions; 'Coke

Prices, facilities, bulk and weight vary enormously with Sat-A, B, C, D or M. Voice is seldom best utilisation of air time and Sat-C provides sensible solution for expeditions.

C-sat message being prepared on lap-top computer with suitable software. Message rates for C-sat significantly lower than for A or B; transmissions use less air time too. Combined with GPS (Trimble Galaxy, see Sec 5.2, p 5.2 - 24), automatic position reporting valuable for remote expeditions.

When speech really is needed, M-sat extremely impressive for its compactness, simplicity. Air time can be bought in advance and dispensed by smart card.

bottle' or A4-sized aerial. Cost $US3,000 to $US12,000 depending on features; weight around 5 kg. Calls cost around $US1-1.50 per kilobit (about 25 words).

• *Inmarsat-D.* Currently a one-way messaging system (see also next para) available through pocket-sized receivers like terrestrial pagers. Up to 40 messages of up to 128 alpha-numeric characters are time-stamped, numbered and stored. Mobile equipment costs presently vary from $US500 to $US700.

• *Inmarsat-D+.* A new generation of satellites (Inmarsat-3) will be launched

1996/7 eight times more powerful than the current Inmarsat-2 constellation. More directional 'spot-beam' technology will concentrate satellite 'power' on areas of highest traffic potential. As well as enabling smaller, lower-powered C-Sat equipments to work in these regions, Inmarsat-D+ will permit limited two-way communication in brief data bursts – responses from the land-mobile that could include acknowledgement, requests or position information.

• *Inmarsat-M.* M-Sat is a smaller, more portable and more economical version of Inmarsat-B offering voice, fax and slow-speed data transmission in 'briefcase' format with A4-sized fold-out aerial, most weighing 3-12 kg. Mobile equipment cost can range from $US13,000 to $US25,000. Calls (more power, greater bandwidth than C-Sat) cost around $US3-6 per minute.

From the above summary typical expedition mobile equipment can be selected. In most cases real-time two-way voice will not be necessary – hard-copy or stored messages such as provided by C-Sat will be more use. Costs of both equipment and transmission time are likely to come down in future years

M-sat is 'satellite phone' – exceptionally light and compact, power efficient. Nera unit (left) has similar face-the-satellite flat aerial as the Magellan Micro-Comm M whose aerial folds. Unless speech essential, C-sat probably best for expeditions.

but will likely, as now, still favour C-Sat and Inmarsat-D+ when it comes on line. M-Sat equipment is a little heavier (but the smallest is less than briefcase-sized) and more expensive to buy and in cost-of-call. But if voice really is important it is still a technological miracle.

Land Earth Stations (LES) – service providers. Land Earth Stations are the stations to whom messages sent to the satellite are relayed for further relay by land line.

In the UK British Telecom is the principal service provider. They run the satellite tracking dish at Goonhilly Down and offer land-line services from there – and also from Norwegian and Singapore partners across the world. Between them they have direct view of all four Inmarsat satellites.

Inmarsat equipment guide. Inmarsat at 99 City Road, London EC1Y 1AX, Tel 0171.728.1000 produce an informative and invaluable collection of publications on the above services. Amongst these publications is a two-monthly magazine *Transat* and an annual equipment buyer's guide giving full specifications and contact addresses for all type-approved equipment in each of the above categories.

Buying or renting equipment. British Telecom publish a Mobile Satellite Services dealer list of all UK dealers together with an indication of the equipment (A-Sat, B, C, M etc) and whether the dealer is an agent, distributor or manufacturer. Some will sell, some will rent – often the latter will be for a full retail price deposit and, typically (for an M-sat phone) £35 per day. Such equipments will usually be UK-ready, ie cleared for operation in UK with a starter kit of credit and other formalities. You can, for example, buy a Magellan Micro Comm-M from Next Destination in the UK, take it out of the shop and operate it straight away because it has been registered in the supplier's name and transfer to the new operator is then all that is necessary.

Commissioning, formalities. A land-mobile or Mobile Earth Station (MES) in the back of your vehicle is still in effect a radio transmitter/receiver and, as with terrestrial radio equipment, appropriate licences and check-outs have to be made before you may operate it. In concept, four aspects must be addressed in the context of initial commissioning:

• *Financial.* Pre-payment or account arrangements for cost of calls.

• *Legal.* National licences and Routing Organisation rules must be met.

• *Contractual.* Agreement to rules governing use of the Space Segment.

• *Technical.* The land-mobile equipment must be type-approved and pass commissioning tests.

All the above can be more easily accommodated in the tighter-regulated world of marine operations for which sat-comm was originally designed than for 'little one-offs' like expeditions. See next spread..

Inmarsat can point you to overseas countries' telecom authorities; also publish two-monthly 'Transat' listing latest equipments and manufacturers.

Satellite propagation

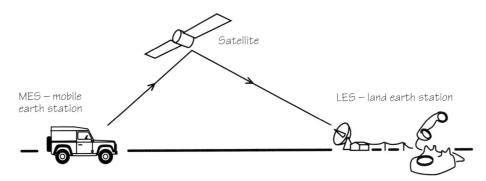

Satellite

MES – mobile earth station

LES – land earth station

Use/licensing overseas

Overseas regulations. All radio transmitting equipment, be it terrestrial or satellite, will need approval to operate overseas. A sad but all too familiar tale in the context of organising expeditions is that the man-made obstacles often outweigh the physical or technical problems. Be prepared for three alternatives to present themselves:

• Without the right paperwork, arriving at a border with radio transmitting equipment will probably lead to straight confiscation without recourse.

• Importing and use of such equipment without proper clearance is illegal and extremely risky if caught.

• Attempting to obtain prior clearance is likely in most cases to result in unanswered letters and a bureaucratic stalemate.

Despite this, the effort must be made. Approaching the appropriate embassy in the UK is an optimistic starting point but in some cases will meet with a lack of knowledge of regulations. Approach the appropriate communications authorities in the prospect country direct if you can, naturally using any local contacts you may have – especially other operators. Problems, if there are any, will vary according to the use for which you have the equipment – business, recreation, safety – and the times of transmission. Short range low power vehicle to vehicle equipment is likely to cause far less problems than long range transmitters; HF is easier to monitor than satellite so may be easier to get clearance for.

Advance clearance to operate really is essential before attempting to import and use any radio equipment in a foreign country.

In all cases, however, the country's authorities will have to know the frequencies to be used (they may have to allocate different ones to avoid clashing with local services), and the power of the transmitter; it will help to know the DTI or European spec type approval to which the equipment conforms.

Inmarsat, amongst others, keep a current directory, as accurately updated as they can, of the regulations and relevant authorities in all foreign countries – a huge document. Most dealers in such equipment will also likely have access to such information too. You can also refer to the International Telecommunications Union in Geneva who will have a list of telecommunications authorities worldwide.

As with many other aspects of the expedition preliminary organisation, clearance for use of radio can be best obtained during a preliminary recce visit to the country.

In the field, reactions will vary; from instant confiscation, suspicion bordering on paranoia or a natural acceptance of the equipment as a sensible safety aid.

Satellite equipment. The core problem is that you will be taking a land-mobile station out of the country in which it was bought and commissioned – probably using BT's Goonhilly LES as a service provider for good measure – and into another country where permission to use it has to be obtained and where you might be required to use their own service provider. Again, a patient approach with and visit to (preferably) the appropriate authorities is the only way forward.

Emergencies

See Section 5.6. etc re rescue plan, SARSAT beacons etc

C-sat terminal – lap-top, 'suitcase' and aerial – operating in field base facility overseas.

Broadcast reception

Keeping in touch. Wherever you go, be it the hills 200 miles away or the plains a couple of continents and an ocean away, it is nice to be in touch with home and world news. Held in justified and peerless regard throughout the world by people of all nationalities, the BBC World Service is the broadcast station to be in touch with for solid, reliable, bedrock information – larded with a sprinkling of entertainment as well. Fundamental to its reception is knowing what frequencies will apply at what time of the day in what parts of the world and what programmes are being broadcast.

BBC World Service publish a monthly publication, *London Calling* (available free from BBC Bush House, World Service Publicity, PO Box 76, Strand, London WC2B 4PH Tel 0171.257.2878) that lists all this

information concisely enough for it be fold ed up and kept with your personal radio in the padded recesses of your bag.

Equipment

Short wave receivers. You will need a short wave radio to pick up the BBC World Service. Even the shops that sell short wave radios in the UK appear, in general, to be chronically ignorant about what they do and what features are good so it pays to hold out for a comprehensive brochure even if it means writing to the makers. Most SW radios are available as multi-wave sets capable of tuning in to local VHF (FM) and medium wave (AM) broadcasts as well so you might as well get one of those. Such sets are available in very small compact size, some as small as a pack of cards; prices (mid 1996) will vary up to £400 for the 'best' (ie the most knobs and switches and capable of accurately picking up HF SSB too) but competently performing ones for broadcast reception will be available for £100 – £200.

Frequencies: buttons, not knobs. Buy a radio with PLL (phase locked loop) frequency synthesisers, ie those in which you tune by punching the frequency you want into some buttons. If you want 15.070 MHz (World Service, daylight hours, Algeria, Libya, Egypt, Sudan), you press the buttons in the right order and that is what you get on the LCD display. Ever more crowded frequency bands mean that stations are far too close together for you to be able to tune reliably by the analogue method using a rotating knob and a pointer moving across a scale. If your radio has half a dozen or more frequency presets you can set it up with day, evening and night frequencies; as we

News bulletins from home are welcome, sometimes heighten feeling of being 'on expedition'. Get top quality PLL set (not dial and pointer) and advance info on frequencies.

Frequency-synthesised (PLL) push button short wave radio is a must for reliable overseas broadcast reception – as is the BBC's irreplaceable 'London Calling' which gives World Service frequencies, timings.

have seen above, the day/night changes in the ionosphere which cause you to have to swing down from midday around 17-21 MHz to 11 or 9 or even 6 MHz later on, mean that dawn and dusk are the most difficult times for reception. Weak signals and fading will mean you have to change frequencies quite a lot at these times of the day.

Other specification points. A small point on frequencies. Some sets, even with PLL frequency synthesisers, limit available frequencies to those sections of the spectrum concerned only with broadcasting. Thus your radio may cover 7100 to 7300 kHz (the 41 metre band) and then jump to the bottom of the 31 metre band at 9400 kHz. More comprehensively specified radios will give continuous cover all the way up the HF band and thus, as well as broadcasting, include amateur, marine and aeronautical frequencies as well. It is conceivable that this could be of interest in some expedition contexts where rendezvous with aircraft or ships is involved, albeit on receive only. Some sets also give synthesised short wave frequency steps of 100 Hz or even 50 Hz so that frequencies having '.10' or a '.15' at the end of a four figure frequency can be tuned precisely – useful if you are on standby listening for a call.

Power, speakers. PLL synthesisers tend to be battery hungry (not as bad as they once were) so get a radio with a 12 volt car adapter add-on if you can. Also head-

Shops seldom know details of SW sets they sell. Homework with manufacturer's brochure pays. For any electronic equipment, know operating temperature limits.

phones; you will get better audibility and, however nostalgic the BBC's Lilibulero signature tune and news is to you, it may not always be to everyone's taste in a campsite! It is possible also to obtain an audio cassette shaped device which accepts output from your radio's 'line-out' or tape recorder output and, when inserted into the vehicle's radio-cassette machine, will amplify the output of your SW radio through the vehicle's own audio system.

If you can prise it out of them, the shop people should have a full technical specification for the SW receivers they sell – not always very informative – but a radio with a speaker large enough (7-8 cm diam) to be rated at 400 mW or more output will be more audible (for longer, for they usually have more battery capacity too) than the tiny 250 mW ones.

Few manufacturers cover this rather specialised market. Sony started it all a long time ago and usually seem to have the edge over the competition spec-wise as well as producing indestructibly reliable radios for this kind of trip. Their paper-back sized ICF-SW 7600 series that covers the above points (but 1 kHz steps) at around 600 gm is a robust, sensible expedition radio; their minuscule, demi-Walkman sized ICF-SW 100 (220 gm), with smaller speaker and less battery power, would be for mountain climbers. There are others to choose from between and above these sizes.

Climatic conditions

Extreme temperatures. Electronic equipment does not like extremes of temperature. The most usual application of this will be in guarding against excessively high temperatures. Check specifications and data sheets with equipment you use and note maximum 'storage' and 'in use' temperatures. Matt black boxes exposed to direct sunlight through vehicle windows or windscreen can get extremely hot as can those subject to

heat soak through the floor from engine, radiator and exhaust system air blow-back. This can be enough to render a unit nonfunctional. LCD display screens can also sometimes be affected by extremes of heat.

Less widely known is that radio oscillators can malfunction in exceptionally cold conditions. Minus 20°C is the danger mark. Below this temperature instability can be experienced and co-axial aerial feeder cable can crack. Foreknowledge of the conditions, however, will enable you to take appropriate action by obtaining the right cabling; it is possible for specialists to cold soak the radio units and 'tweak' the oscillators so that they are optimised for the very low temperatures you will encounter.

Military ('MilSpec') units are usually equipped with components immune to temperature extremes but these – and the generally 'boot-proof' build – are what make the units extremely expensive.

A vehicle-borne expedition in the broadest interpretation of the phrase and an indication of an HF dipole – here strung between skis – in operation in extreme conditions (hence suitably grainy photograph!) Aerial performance considerably affected by nature of the 'ground'.

Acknowlegements and thanks:

BT Networks and Systems, Portishead Radio, Highbridge, Somerset, UK

Inmarsat, City Road, London EC1Y 1AX

Radiocommunications Agency, Dept of Trade and Industry, London SE1 9SA

And special thanks to:

Kerry Cahill, Communications Centre (Photo Accoustics Ltd), Newport Pagnell, UK

Richard Mumford, South Midlands Communications, Eastleigh, Hants, UK

Section 2.8

Equipment planning:

Electrical power

COVERAGE OF THIS SECTION

Electrical power sources

First assess the need. Certainly in the context of the high current drain associated with prolonged radio transmissions on HF but also in a host of other expedition applications – base camp facilities included – the question of electrical power should be considered well in advance. Hardware is costly and needs to be tailored as precisely to requirements as possible if unnecessary cost is to be avoided. Don't buy a 1500 watt generator unit if a 550 watt item will cover the need; don't buy a 750 watt, sine-wave inverter if a 'modified sine-wave' 300 watt unit will suffice. Only with a clear idea of the electrical equipment you will be operating and when it will be used – static, mobile, separately or simultaneously – can you formulate the requirement for power with sufficient accuracy .

Many electrical power solutions will bring other problems in their wake – special fuel for generators (petrol supplies on an all-diesel expedition), selection of correct operating voltages for specialist equipment (12 volt, 24 volt DC and AC mains equipment – are alternatives available so can you select a common voltage?).

There are a number of ways of tackling the need and, as with many aspects of expedition equipment acquisition, the world of small scale marine operations is one way in. Small sailing boats, power boats and even quite big boats often have the same needs as a remote-area expedition so ships chandlers and associated traders may well be able to help you at the early stages of your enquiries. Quite a lot of gear is made for remote-area on-land operation too but is often less easy to track down.

Extra batteries

More of the same. Multiple high capacity vehicle batteries (connected in parallel to reduce the current load on an individual battery) can often provide the power reservoir required for extended communications schedules and operation of other ancillary electrics. They would, however, be extremely heavy and you would have to judge whether they could be adequately recharged by the vehicle even if a high-output alternator (120 watt) is fitted.

As covered under Sec 4.2 'Vehicle modifications', often you will need no more than a single extra vehicle battery together with a split-charge system whereby the vehicle electrical system senses which battery needs charging and directs charging current accordingly. The main point here is that you must at all costs safeguard the battery required for starting the engine; it is all too easy with a long night's work using lighting and other electrical equipment, to find that you have dropped below the critical voltage needed to start the engine. As covered below, portable engine-driven generators are obtainable configured specially for charging 12 and 24 volt batteries at high charge rates.

Know exactly what units you will need to run before deciding on format of extra electrical power. Second 12 v battery will often suffice – but protect main battery.

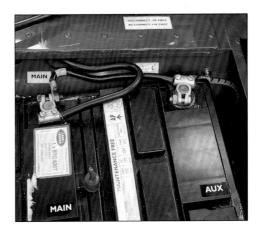

Second 12 v battery fitted in Land Rover Defender 90 with split charge system to safeguard main vehicle battery used for starting the engine. Labelling a useful safeguard. See detail Sec 4.2, page 4.2 - 11.

Portable generators

A size for every need, DC and AC.
Portable electrical generators can provide
not only a means of charging the radio and
vehicle batteries but also power for camp
lighting, small refrigerators, computers and
domestic AC devices such as the nickel-cadmium battery re-chargers for the small electronic devices with which every expedition
will find itself surrounded. Though there are
many generators on the market, the name of
Honda jumps inevitably to mind with the
picture of one throbbing away behind every
mud hut, outback shop or garage on the
planet.

An extensive range of sizes and power
outputs are available and, for once, the
small expedition seems to have been catered
for almost perfectly. At the lower end of the
range, for example, the 300 watt EX350B
unit provides 240v AC or 12v DC at 6 amps.
Just over a foot long, a foot high with a dry
weight of only 8.5 kg, cost, mid 1996 is £419
plus VAT. A 750/1000 watt model EX1000B
weighs 26 kg (£675 plus VAT) and other
models for base camp use go right up the
range to 5 kW or more. Among a huge

*Portable genera-
tors come in
very wide range
of power outputs
and voltages. Be
aware of special
fuel require-
ments if any and
keep an eye on
noise output fig-
ures too.*

range, models are available designed specifically for 12/24v battery charging (ED400 –
£550 plus VAT) at rates up to 17.5 amps.
Honda UK are at 4 Power Road, Chiswick,
London W4 5YT and have a freephone
number 0800.378.086 or on 0181.747.1400.

Take note of the noise output which is
covered in the specification sheets. Some of
the smaller engines, designed for close-in
camp use, are remarkably quiet whilst others, designed for industrial and building-site
applications where ambient noise is already
high, are less so.

These engines run on unleaded gasoline
but can use the leaded variety available
overseas too; the two-stroke engines need
oil pre-mixed with the petrol before use.
Honda make two diesel-engined portable
generators but they are 4 kW and 10 kW
models (weight 100 kg or so) more suited to
base-camp requirements.

Solar panels

Nature's module. Just as the unit cell in
a vehicle battery is 'Nature's module' of a
nominal 2 volts (six 2-volt cells put in series
gives you a 12 volt battery) so solar photo
voltaic cells will each produce a voltage of
0.7 to 0.45 volt according to the load put
across them. Comprising a thin upper layer
and thicker lower layer of slightly different
types of crystalline silicon (or, modern-tech,
cheaper 'thin film' amorphous silicon sput-
tered onto a substrate), a 'solar panel' thus
usually takes the form of 30-or-so cells connected in series to provide a nominal 12 volt
DC module. The whole thing looks like a
sheet of large postage stamps encapsulated
behind glass with a thick plastic edging.
Man's module – and accessories.
Similarly any number of these 12 volt modules can be put in series to produce higher
nominal voltages (12, 24, 48 etc) at the same

*Well packaged, compact, quiet – portable
generators cover expedition field requirements well. This Honda EX350 outputs 300
watts of 240 v AC or 12 v DC at 6 amps.*

BP solar cells used during the day for charging camp lighting modules. A wide range of lighting sets are available and BP can offer comprehensive advice on usage.

current output – or connected in parallel to produce a greater current output at the standard 12 volts DC. Because output will vary according to the strength of the light falling upon it – sunny/cloudy, summer/winter, north/south/tropical conditions – such cell panels do not run electrical devices directly but invariably feed as a top-up charge into a 12 volt battery from which the working load is taken.

In an optimised static system aimed at long life installations such as a radio relay, special batteries should be used which have been designed specifically to take the repeated charge/discharge cycling and occasional deep-discharge events inherent in such a set-up. These batteries are tubular plate, heavyweight units with minimum maintenance requirements and a life expectancy of up to 10 years. Such batteries would be applicable more to base-camp or static installations than to vehicles with a small radio transmitter.

To get the best out of the solar cells and the batteries a charge regulator would also be required if the charge current is between 5 and 20 amps – representative of a moderately powerful static set up. In the smaller ranges, self-regulating units are available so that a separate regulator would not be need-ed. A typical fairly large solar installation would therefore comprise:

- Solar modules
- Mounting structure to ensure pointing at the sun*
- Charge controller*
- Special batteries*
- Cabling
- Inverter if DC to AC conversion required (see below)*
- *– probably not required for a vehicle installation.*

Practicalities, vehicle use. Solar modules are large, fairly heavy and expensive. BP Solar (at PO Box 191, Chertsey Road, Sunbury-on-Thames. Middlesex TW16 7XA, Tel 01932.779.543 – part of the British Petroleum BP) produce a wide range of equipments which are in use all round the world. As at mid 1996, they produce two modules aimed at 'activity' use – caravans, boats, vehicles: the BP210SRU – the type is BP2, the '10' means a 10 watt typical peak power, and the 'SRU' means self-regulating unit – and is what might be regarded as the entry-level unit. It will provide a maximum power of 0.66 amp at 15 volts for a trickle-charge set up. Size is roughly a foot by a foot and a half by an inch thick; weight/cost is 2 kg/£105 trade for this panel. The more

Soler panels in small sizes are inherently fairly heavy, low-power trickle charge items. Could be ideal for continuous-monitoring scientific instruments.

powerful 20 watt BP220SRU is twice the size (534 mm square), twice the weight and would cost £143 trade; the doubled 1.3 amp charge rate is going to be more use even in a small-battery trickle charge configuration. Non self-regulating solar modules are available in 55 watt, 75 watt and 85 watt capacities (ie up to nearly 5 amps) at around a metre by half a metre in size and weighing up to 7.5 kg. A BP585 module would cost £357 and the GCR500 control unit that will handle up to 5 amps, £40.

Special applications. With base camps, aid agencies, remote hospitals in mind, BP Solar also make solar-powered medical and domestic refrigerators as well as a solar lantern and small domestic lighting sets (BP LK4 set uses 2 x 8 watt tubes, 2 x 13 watt). Self-contained solar-powered water pump sets are made too. BP offer a comprehensive and user-oriented advice service with a firm grip on the realities of cost: 'Anything over 1 kilowatt continuously is likely to mean the system is too expensive' is part of their advice.

DC to AC mains – inverters

AC convenience. If you have 'domestic AC' requirements and will not be using a portable generator as mentioned above, another way of obtaining AC current is by the use of a compact solid state inverter that takes DC from the vehicle battery and turns it into 230 volt AC, 50 Hz supply. There will be many AC devices you will find it invaluable to have operational on a trip and, so long as the power involved is low, an inverter can be a most convenient solution. But think carefully before embarking on this path.

Power requirements – DC equivalents. In the home we rarely even think what the actual wattage of an appliance is unless it is something obviously power-hungry like an electric fire or a cooking stove where the unit of our awareness is seldom smaller than a kilowatt. Who could quote the power requirements in watts of their TV set, computer, electric drill, hi-fi or toaster? Wattage requirements here are in the region of 70-700

Getting 'domestic AC' from DC-to-AC inverters is possible but at high wattages it starts to become very expensive and also require extra-heavy-duty wiring.

watts; compare this with the combined power of both vehicle headlamps being about 120 watts. You would not be happy to leave both headlights on full beam for more than a minute or two without the engine running so think hard about what you would be running if you decided to have a DC to AC inverter. There may be certain ni-cad battery chargers for which you might need an AC source but in this case, if the current requirement is high, you will probably be able to organise it so that the device is in use only when the vehicle is in motion and the engine running.

Again marketed by BP Solar, 'PRO-watt' DC to AC inverters (simple 'quasi sine-wave' units – see below 'Sine-wave AC?') are available in power ratings from 140 to 1500 watts continuous output and priced from £76 to nearly £600 trade (mid 1996). Dividing the wattage by 12 you find the 1500 watt unit would be running away with a harness-melting 125 amps or more. Smaller units with 140 or 225 watt continuous outputs make more sense once the need has been clearly established but even these will have to be used on appropriately fused and loomed DC outlets on the vehicle – preferably from a separate battery with a split-charge facility as described above.

Other manufacturers of inverters include Victron Energie (used on and survived the Camel Trophy) and Mass, both of Netherlands origin and distributed in the UK through Geko Power of Pixon Court, Pixon Lane, Tavistock, Devon PL19 8DH, tel 01822.616.060. Both the Victron 300 watt and the Mass 400 watt inverters ('modified sine-wave' – see below) cost a little under £400 plus VAT.

Remember that most inverters incur a small current drain on the vehicle battery even when not operating if they have been hard-wired into the system. Put a master switch into the circuit to cut the inverter off completely when not in use and/or when the vehicle is 'resting'.

Overall efficiency. The '125 amps or more' wording above was deliberate since inverters are not 100% efficient, especially on part load, and you will probably be using at least 10% more current from the vehicle than the calculations indicate. The BP 'PRO-watt' range of inverters are quoted as 'approximately 90%' efficient (the Mass units 92-97% on full load) which, although unprecedentedly high in comparison with the agricultural rotary inverters of yore (DC motor coupled to an alternator!), still needs to be taken into account.

Sine-wave AC? Again, whilst modern solid state units are far better than they used to be, pay careful attention to the kind of AC they produce – is it close enough to a true sine-waveform that you get from a domestic AC mains socket? It is cheaper to produce the relatively crude, 'quasi sine-wave' or 'modified sine-wave' inverters than to reproduce mains electricity exactly. Such 'cheap AC', of course is perfectly adequate for something like a filament bulb or a toaster and there is no benefit in paying more for the true sine-wave inverter.

However, and alas it is not possible here to be any more precise since there are great variations, some equipment is sensitive to the AC it uses and will malfunction without 'the real thing'. Get advice from your equipment and inverter manufacturer (and try to be patient with all the intermediaries who say 'Ooh, I'm not very technical'!), check the specification and/or do a real live test if in any doubt. Some devices will not function on a crude or jaggy wave-form AC – the ni-cad battery charger for a particular upmarket cine-film camera jumps to mind as but one example. Surprisingly there seems to be no ISO or British Standard for what may be labelled 'AC' and equally no spec definition that lays down how near a true sine-wave the AC for your particular device should be. It would appear that you have to investigate each case separately.

Victron Energie make a sine-wave AC inverter and, as expected, it is more expensive than the 'quasi sine-wave' variety.

Named the Phoenix, the sine-wave 350 watt version costs £790 (mid 1996, excluding VAT). A 12 volt 750 watt version and several high output 24 volt versions are also available.

There are also regulations regarding electro-magnetic compatibility (EMC – in effect electrical interference with other equipment such as TV sets or computers) and late updates have resulted in some product lines having been dropped or rigorously redesigned. Whilst you are checking the specification of the inverter, check its temperature operating limits and be sure to mount it in the vehicle where it will be reasonably cool and have sufficient circulating air around it.

The more elegant approach. A further check before going the inverter route is to consider the fact that much of your electrical equipment in all probability runs internally at a low voltage anyway. Stepping your DC up to 230 v AC through a 10% loss inverter and then re-converting it back down within the electrical appliance in a similarly inefficient way is wasteful of power (and money) and the more elegant approach is to obtain the device in a low voltage DC form in the first place if you can. It sounds very obvious but is worth checking availabilities.

DC to DC converters

24 volt to 12 volt. You may find your expedition vehicle is an ex-military 24 volt machine. Should you require it, conversion to 12 volt can be done but is complex, time consuming and very expensive. If you have such a vehicle and have equipment that needs to run on 12 volts, DC/DC converters are available. Victron Energie (see above, contact via Geko Power) do a range of converters with capacities of 6 to 20 amps and efficiencies of 82-93%. The 20 amp model weighs 1.5 kg and costs £238 (mid 1996, excluding VAT).

Most inverters use some power when not in use and conversion efficiencies are around 90%. Check carefully if your AC application requires sine-wave AC.

Section 3
People, training

Section 3.1   Team selection

NB Driver training is dealt with at Section 5.3.1

People, training

Team selection

COVERAGE OF THIS SECTION

Types of trip and team

Perspectives

Team sources. There will be considerable differences – and significant similarities – between the handling of small and large expeditions when it comes to leadership, personnel selection and training. If the use of these terms already make the trip sound like a military exercise, be patient. The threads of these aspects will run through the smallest closest group (the similarities) but the way they are addressed will vary enormously according to the size and experience of the team (the differences). The kind of trip you are planning will dictate the size, source and qualifications of your team:

1. Friends. People who know each other will have done a mutual and unconscious team selection already. Compatibility, strengths and weaknesses will be known and the mix will be – must be – acceptable to those taking part. The leader will usually be the person who has the idea to organise the trip.

2. Call for volunteers. There will be projects where you need to assemble specialist skills and this will mean calling for volunteers. Be clear, unless you are exceptionally lucky, this will be a huge and onerous job. Indeed it could be asked, only slightly tongue in cheek, that if you don't find it huge and onerous are you being careful enough, or are you sensitive enough? Team selection of this kind is dealt with in the case study below 'Selecting and training the team'.

3. Group development. This kind of trip, typically, in which you may be taking a youth group on an expedition to give them experience, will call for a different approach to selection, training and leadership from those above. By definition, your team – if they are ripe for 'development' – will not be the fully qualified people you would want for category 2 above. At the same time, there will have to be some degree of selection before the trip and you will have to judge how far up the ladder your volunteers must

be and what their potential is before you take them on.

Gut feel. It will be said again later but is worth consideration now: trust gut feeling when it comes to personnel selection – something you probably had a gut feel about anyway! Even if the skill qualifications are there, if you think there is going to be a problem of compatibility with either the other people or the conditions, don't select. The degree to which this applies in a developmental group will be slightly different but many leaders are reluctant to give in to subjective feelings about potential team members and all too often finish the trip shaking their head slowly and wishing they had trusted their sixth sense.

Teams can be formed from friends, 'going out to tender' or from clients. Each will require its own selection method and criteria and type of lead.

Group development expeditions will call for a special kind of leadership if all are to benefit and be given a feeling of responsibility and achievement. Here the group are paying adventure travellers but the leader's problem has similarities – the numbers and the challenge to encourage individuality to come through.

Leadership – the leader

Leadership

A compound of optima. Epigram, paradox, oxymoron; some of the phrases to describe good leadership often have a whimsical self-contradictory oddness about them. 'A good leader should have the absolute maximum ... of moderation.' Or ' ... be uncompromisingly ... even handed.' In truth good leadership is not a package of maxima but a compound of optima. The absolutes, where there are any, usually apply to the leader rather than leadership; and in the realms of personal qualities like integrity and moral courage.

The latest stuff. The deafening noise of rolling bandwagons in the last decade or two denotes that industry, psychologists and sociologists have 'discovered' leadership. Whole libraries are available on the subject, the wheel is reinvented annually, and terms like 'Interpersonal group dynamics motivational scenario model' are bandied around to leave you slack jawed in your feeling of ignorance and inadequacy. Do not let it overwhelm you; and do not be too defensively cynical either. A few people make money with fancy courses on this stuff; big deal. The news is good. At least people care. Look at industrial relations and management methods in the best companies nowadays – the teams, the participation schemes, the 'cascades' of information and responsibility, the feeling of contributing and belonging.

But do not feel it is all getting too technical. The names and labels are new – those are the only things that spring up each year, bright and shiny – but the ideas and concepts are well established, old, and reassuringly simple: mutual respect. The recognition that people do best under a leader they respect; a leader who respects and values them. Opening his short tract on Expedition Leadership in the Royal Geographical Society *Expedition Planners' Handbook*, (which nicely covers group development) Chris Loyne quotes Lao Tzu:

Good leadership is a compound of optima, not maxima. Despite plethora of modern psychobabble, tenets of good leadership are well established and well known.

A leader is best
when people barely know he exists,
not so good when people obey and proclaim
*   him,*
worst when they despise him.
Fail to honour people,
they fail to honour you.

Lao Tzu is not a behavioural psychologist at Shanghai University; he lived around 450 BC.

Distilling to basics. So the old truths keep coming through and their basis is always the same – common sense and a regard for people's feelings. People like to be led (helped), shown (taught), trusted (delegated to) and appreciated (valued) at the end. Don't let experience foster complacency. Read the new stuff, overlay it with what, deep down, you know was there all along, and note any useful new angles on how to distil it to make it more memorable.

Types of leadership. The military taught leadership long before it became 'fashionable' in industry and they used to classify it as three types:

1. Passive

2. Autocratic

3. Permissive.

The passive leader is an averaging device – a role for which there can still be a place if it is accompanied by integrity and moral courage to ensure the averaging is not just an easy way out; but too often passive leadership just lets it all happen and doesn't lead at all. The autocratic 'sergeant major', roughshod and insensitive, probably regarding himself as a go-getter is often lacking in real perception; he usually gets instant obedience, surreptitious scorn and is in most respects a dinosaur. That said, there are rare moments in emergencies when the do-now-ask-later approach really is needed.

The permissive lead – since leadership is a counsel of optima not maxima – lies somewhere in between, but well clear of, the two types mentioned above. Whilst having firmness of purpose, the permissive leader is yet a good listener; he recognises truth and the ability of his team, combining their efforts with his own to achieve the aim. He does not succumb to the 'not invented here' syndrome that declines all ideas but his own! He has the moral courage to make the hard decision – straight down the middle.

The leader – characteristics

Familiar ground. Again, libraries and a hundred biographies have been written on the components of leadership and the best leaders and the compilation of a list of attributes brings unsurprising results; slippery, blustering loudmouths tend to score low, 'good guys' (and ladies) score the most. Ordinary decent people with integrity and unselfishness and professionalism and enough confidence – not too much, not too little; if there is a sprinkling of charisma and flair then so much the better but these come after the basic qualities. Extra stature will derive from the fire in the belly of the leader – the enthusiasm of the man who is putting his dream and plan into actuality. Deep down we all know exactly what works and what doesn't and the list below is thus no more than an aide memoir and reminder that it all applies to expeditions – especially expeditions where there is 24 hour contact between team and leader and where getting it wrong can be very serious.

- Professionalism – knowing the project and your job
- Delegation vs supervision – the right balance
- Personal qualities
  - Enthusiasm
  - Sincerity
  - Integrity
  - Humility
  - Moral courage
  - Sense of humour
  - Listening
- Planning, detail
- Communication

Getting it right. Professionalism and planning in detail are already vital for mere survival, or certainly for the efficient discharge of the project and a leader who has thought things through and generally knows what he is about will gain considerable respect and support from the team. The balance of delegation vs supervision is a delicate one. Many of the tasks will be very important to the safety of the whole group and double-checking on such matters is no more than common sense. A pilot setting an aircraft up on the approach will not regard double checking by the co-pilot as an insult to his capability, just a sensible confirmation of safety. It is useful for a leader to cover this point in briefings before the trip so that people are not over-sensitive to him 'breathing down their neck' later.

Communication. The addition of 'communication' seems almost unnecessary but a short briefing session every morning before setting off or in the evening does pay off. It is really surprising how the 'No one ever tells me anything!' bug can take hold in even the smallest group. Communication must, of course be two way, and the team must (if necessary) be bludgeoned into coming out with beefs so small problems are not allowed to fester.

Consulting on courses of action is important and does not amount to abdication of leadership; 'This is the problem and this is how I think we could tackle it. What's the general view?' will foster involvement – and come up with good ideas too.

For leader no substitute for 'knowing your stuff' but this must be teamed with sensitivity and personal qualities of a high order. No surprises really.

In a two-person or friends group leadership must be delicate, low profile and in the best Lao Tzu category (see text).

Selecting the team, training

Selection and training go together. Leader has huge responsibility. Interview marking sheet (p 13) distils aims but give 'gut feel' the power of veto.

Aim. The aim of all personnel selection and training prior to an expedition is to make that expedition effective – not so self-evident as it may at first appear since the effectiveness and team effort from an expedition are influenced by many subjective and intangible factors outside the apparently cut-and-dried business of recruiting say, one mechanic, two cooks and four geologists – the mere filling of vacancies.

Inextricably tied in with the quantifiable such as age, paper qualifications and number of previous expeditions a candidate has done are a person's adaptability, cheerfulness, practicality, sensitivity, compatibility with others and motivation for the project. All these are qualities that affect the achievement of an expedition to a great degree since they have a critical effect upon its morale and team spirit. That hard-to-define quality in people 'practicality' is one to look

out for in training; the sort of person who can produce a brew in the teeth of a howling gale when jaws are clenched and morale is flagging; or who has the willpower to get out of a warm sleeping bag when a guy rope is flapping rather too loosely.

In selecting his team the leader must assume a god-like role and enormous responsibility lies with him. If the lessons of the past 20 years had to be crystallised, two main points come out:

' ... one leg of over 1000 miles off tracks ... not previously traversed ...'. That first-man on earth feeling in the Ijafene dunes of Mauritania. Logistics ruled – fuel and water, so vehicle crews had to be kept to two persons. This meant multi-role personnel and cross qualifications – a demanding team selection task.

• Motivation - keenness to be on the expedition - is the most important single factor in the selection of the candidate. It is not enough on its own but it is very important.

• Always trust your own judgement and 'gut feeling' about a candidate and never take anyone you are unhappy about.

Case study

How it was – for real. The report that follows is on the actual personnel selection, training and in-the-field routine for an eight-man, 100-day Joint Services expedition in the Sahara combining science and exploration. The emphasis on infallibility at the selection – and subsequent – stages must be seen against the background of the expedition's route (the first west-east crossing of the Sahara from the Atlantic to the Red Sea) which included one leg of over 1000 miles and another of 650 miles, each completely off tracks – not just off tarmac – devoid of habitation and not previously traversed by vehicles.

Case study: Report – team selection, training, expedition routine

Personnel selection

Infallibility the aim. The ultimate aim in personnel selection and training was the same as the philosophy of the whole expedition - infallibility. The problem faced was very akin to that of flying an aircraft: a human being on its own at 30,000ft is in a potentially very dangerous position but with adequate training and teamwork in the right machine the situation can be made safe and routine. Likewise in a desert expedition there is no room for error; the consequences of error or failure are so serious as to be unacceptable - hence infallibility must be the aim. Most failed expeditions or enterprises fail through human error - either directly through insufficient training or indirectly through poor planning, i.e. failure to appreciate dangerous contingencies or potential natural hazards.

In this expedition the keynote was proper operation of the vehicles up to, but not beyond, their limits. These limitations vary according to terrain, load, speed etc, and a prime requirement in all candidates was 'mechanical sympathy'. From this, with training, would stem good driving and, with perception and sensitivity, driving as nearly infallible as it was possible to get. On top of 'mechanical sympathy' had to be motivation - the next most important quality. Sheer keenness on the project would breed

resilience and tenacity, lend motivation to train, to perfect skills, to overcome obstacles and, in an environment of similar motivation from others, go far along the road to establish compatibility with the team.

The trawl. A great deal of individual expertise was required to achieve the aim of the project in addition to the qualities common to all team members mentioned above. The overall requirement on the personnel side was summed up in the original call for volunteers:

"Expedition conditions are likely to be demanding. Extremes of temperature (hot and cold), long periods of travel over rough, bleak, uninhabited terrain, and repeated physical activity will be the background against which very high standards of human reliability will be essential, manifested in care of vehicles and equipment, the highest standards of cross-country driving and general attention to detail in the discharge of often routine tasks. If the expedition is to achieve its aims and the necessary harmony within the team maintained, fitness, stamina, sense of humour and above all the strongest motivation towards this kind of project will be essential in all team members. The optimum amalgam of the following qualifications will be required within the team and many may apply to each team member:

Report covers very demanding expedition. You may not need this 'SAS selection' mind-set but scanning skill requirements and training done could yield benefit.

*Previous expedition, hot climate or
    desert experience
Cross-country driving experience on
    Land Rover or Bedford
Mechanical aptitude or sympathy
Radio operator/fitter experience (HF)
Use of theodolite for astro fixing
Geological qualifications or knowledge
Medical qualifications
Knowledge of French or Arabic".*

Selection by training. Some skills were more difficult to find than others and the choice was sometimes limited. Nevertheless the criteria mentioned, reinforced by hindsight experience on the expedition, remain valid and precisely to the point. 155 volunteers were forthcoming initially. The requirements above and the additional problem of location and availability for training whittled this three months later to about 40 for interview. To make interview selection as objective and quantitative as possible, candidates were marked in accordance with Annex A and a 'short list' of about 20 went on to cross country driving tests at Aldershot. This was very time consuming but was aimed at choice not so much according to overall competence at that time but according to mechanical sensitivity and training potential. A group of about 12 then went on to regular driver training from March/April until October/November. This was combined with camping-out at the rough-terrain training areas near Aldershot and Bordon in Hants and was used as a familiarisation on expedition procedures for the future.

Selection of the eight man team from the 12 then depended upon the results of the training set out below and upon the degree to which the criteria above could be met by various combinations of personnel from within the group. The inevitable Service commitments such as postings, availability of replacements etc, had a further effect on the selection. Selection of prime team and reserves from the group of 12 was made late in October. Two of the three reserves subsequently withdrew.

*Put 'mechanical
sympathy' highest on list of driver attributes.
Particular skills,
techniques can
be trained in but
an uncaring driver is a disaster
waiting to happen.*

Training

Driver training. Driver training was allocated highest priority in the training programme since cross-country driving is not widely practised and is very rarely taught in such a survival orientated context. The training notes used angled towards proficiency on the 109 inch (.75 ton) long wheelbase four cylinder Land Rover (Series II) with synchromesh on 3rd gear only. This vehicle is a good training vehicle since it has an unforgiving ride, relatively poor axle articulation and limited underbelly ground clearance and steering lock. Accent was on meticulously careful driving, on-foot recce before an obstacle and marshalling through hazards where clearance was in doubt or where tyre damage might result. 'Tyre consciousness' was also emphasised – different pressures for road, track and soft going, different pressures for rock and sand, the effect of weight on recommended pressures and the vulnerability of radial tyre sidewalls to rock damage. The team also practised removal of tyres without damage. In the driving sessions deliberately 'impossible' traverses were attempted so that precise marshalling, 'landscaping' (removing obstacles by shovelling), and single and tandem towed recovery could be practised. Trailer towing cross country, reversing and de-coupling for recovery as well as extreme climbs and descents were all practised in the roles of the driver, marshaller, and supervisor. All vehicles were driven where possible without side windows or canvas roofs (as on the expedition) in order that optimum visibility could be obtained. Each team member had a 2-4 hour familiarisation/assessment drive during the personnel selection stage. Weekend training, of which each team member had about six sessions, began in June and was invariably combined with at least one night camping out – without tents. Naturally some feel for compatibility within the team was possible during the training.

Servicing. In addition to basic knowledge taken into consideration during selection, a familiarisation visit to Land Rover

Solihull and a Servicing School session of four days at British Leyland Allesley was arranged.

Astro navigation. A two-week course at the School of Military Survey on desert navigation and astro fixing using a theodolite was arranged for four of the group.

Language training. The leader took a nine-week part-time refresher course in French prior to leaving on a diplomatic recce visit to Mali and Mauritania in June.

Cinematography. Three members of the group attended a week's course on cinematography at the Fleet Photographic School at HMS Excellent. The actual 16 mm professional quality cine-cameras to be used on the expedition were available to practise on; this was considered essential to achieve the requisite familiarity.

Parascending. Weather continually forced cancellation of projected training sessions but one was achieved. There were experienced parachutists in the team.

Medical training. No doctor was available to include in the team but there was in any case a need to have all members familiar with the most common contingencies. The RAF Institute of Health and Medical Training at Halton arranged a two-day briefing for the team and included practice at the administration of intravenous saline drips in cases of heat exhaustion and severe dehydration. Emphasis was laid on water purification procedures, treatment of gastroenteritis, precautions against endemic diseases, inoculations and the use of various drugs.

Fitness training. This had for the most part to be left to the individuals but the limitations of both the concept and method of administration were appreciated. It was impossible to say with certainty that a given type of training would produce a given result on the expedition since, as mentioned above, motivation was far more important. It could be said, however, that for a given motivation better stamina and tenacity would come from a fit man than an unfit man. The type of fitness and training required was

open to considerable discussion but aerobic training (1.5 mile run) offered an easily quantifiable criterion to work against. Whilst this was good for CVR development and tone, circuit training was used as a more general fittening process.

All this training, done in the candidate's own time and as a result of his own willpower, is also a useful indication of his general motivation and as such is an aid to the final selection process. The training was generally unpopular and it was necessary to run a test weekend to establish standards; training was also continued again on an individual, voluntary, and not very effective basis during the pre-departure phase. One potential team member of the 12 was rejected as a result of not taking the training seriously. Hindsight dictates that stricter supervision and go/no-go tests (with due allowance for the widely different types of fitness for different people) at regular intervals could have been more advisable. But against this, the self-discipline required to meet the requirement without close supervision was a very significant indicator of candidate motivation and calibre. Eventual standards by the aerobic training criteria were good or excellent.

Miscellaneous training. Other training carried out came under less formal categories but covered familiarisation with the radio equipment, camping gear, gravimeter, vehicle servicing and tuning gear and preparation of lizard collection/preservation equipment.

En route routine

Ordered procedure. En route routine was important to establish, particularly in relation to job allocation so that all the tasks were adequately covered and evenly spread amongst the team. In general, camp was set up away from centres of population or villages since this presented least hazard to health or from potential thieves. Lightness being of prime importance since most of the vehicle payload was allocated fuel and water, full-sized tents were discouraged though lightweight units were produced and

'In the field' is not the place to learn. Know what you don't know, prepare and train before departure – part and parcel of overall need for thoroughness in planning.

used by some members.

The team rose just before dawn and aimed to be on the move about 60-75 minutes after getting up. Breakfast was eaten, tyre pressure and vehicle coolant water checked (engines/tyres cold); sun compass settings were checked (Local Apparent Time calculation and latitude setting as well as alignment compared with a magnetic compass). Set convoy order for the four vehicle team was maintained and was as follows:

• *Lead vehicle.* Leader and navigator/co-driver. Prime navigation gear, cine sound and still photographic gear. Green expedition flag on pole to aid identification by following vehicles.

• *Second vehicle* with trailer. Geophysicist and deputy leader/French interpreter. Gravimeter and aneroids, medical kit, spares and tools.

• *Third vehicle* with trailer. Radio operator and Arabic translator. Radio gear.

• *Fourth vehicle* without trailer. Cook, 3rd mechanic. All cooking gear, water pump and filter. Red ensign on pole to aid identification by lead vehicle.

Route information and DR log was kept by the lead vehicle co-driver (see Section 5.2) and stops were made normally every 20 km for gravity, aneroid and temperature readings. Water bottles could be refilled during gravity stops. Stops were also necessary for filming and where possible these coincided with gravity stops though inevitably they could not always be predicted either in location, time or time taken. The timing of the radio-call at 12.00 GMT was made the basis of the lunch halt. Normally a stop 10 minutes before 12.00 GMT was enough time to get the aerial erected and whilst this and the radio call were going on the lunch snack and tea were being prepared. It was seldom possible to achieve the combined lunch stop and radio call in less than one hour and frequently where there was a lot of signals traffic it took longer. Water bottles were refilled at lunch time and sometimes cine camera film changing was carried out.

Change of drivers. Afternoon routine was similar except that drivers and co-dri-

Set routine and designated jobs and chores for each team member is framework to hang an efficient expedition on. Jobs get done and there's still time to enjoy the trip.

vers exchanged seats at lunch time. This gave each man 24 hours driving broken by a night's rest. The expedition halted about 1.5 hours before sunset in order that the majority of the evening workload could be achieved during daylight. In particular any vehicle maintenance or repairs could be done before dark. The camp was set up in an open ended square formation, the two trailers forming the up-wind side, the lead vehicle the western side and the cook vehicle the eastern side with cooking being done a safe distance away from petrol containers the vehicles carried. Each vehicle had a 12v fluorescent light which could be clipped where required for evening work.

Evening chores. Particular tasks to be done at the evening camp halt were:

• Vehicle daily inspections
• Remedy any vehicle unservicability
• Refuelling and calculation of mpg. Refilling cans
• Prepare initial brew of tea and main meal later
• Begin reduction of gravity data
• Calculate DR position and gravity station positions.
• Set up theodolite for subsequent after dark astro shot
• Refill (and if necessary purify) water jerry cans
• Mark and preserve any lizard collections
• Mark and pack any rock collections
• Catalogue still film shots
• Catalogue cine film sequences
• Clean and reload still and cine cameras
• Monitor and log any cine sound recorded
• Write up daily log
• Enter any expenditure in accounts
• Re-stock rations from main boxes
• Lay out bedding and personal kit, wash and shave (.5 pint)

Normally one or two members of the team were working until 10 or 11 pm every evening. Guards were not routinely mounted but when this was done (in populous areas) a roster of 1 hour per man was adhered to since this way there was not too much dis-

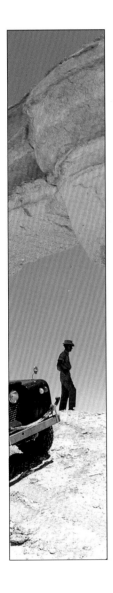

ruption of sleep. The cook, who always had early duty, was given the last position on the guard roster 5 to 6 am.

Rest houses. Staying in hotels and rest houses when it was necessary was found to be more trouble than it was worth – albeit the showering and clothes washing facilities were welcome. It was invariably after such stays in towns that gastro-enteritis infections struck the team; the desert and open country together with the team's own cooking was always cleaner and more healthy.

Summary. A small expedition such as this demanding a multi-skilled team all imbued with a common feeling for mechanical things and a love of the desert is probably one of the most difficult selection problems it is possible to find. The most important single selection criterion is keenness since it leads to the drive to attain the high standards required, provides at the same time the enjoyment of the environment that lessens stress which in turn produces the team spirit that overcomes unforeseen difficulties.

Together with thorough planning, the training – especially the driver training – was one of the major factors leading to the success of the expedition. Care in the operation of the vehicles whilst stationary or on the move was the theme of the training and thoroughness and attention to detail the keynote.

For demanding trip, pre-training is greatest asset. Even for less edge-of-the-seat trips preparation and planning are bedrock ingredients of success.

The expedition team is probably its most valuable asset – when chosen with the thoroughness that the task demands. The leader has to be satisfied that all the professional qualifications are there as well as the all important question of compatibility. Be very sure you are not seeing just a thin slice of your candidate ...

Comment on report

Lasting lessons. Despite the above report being on a major expedition (in concept if not size) – and one that took place some years ago – the read-across of principles outlined here are completely valid (still) for smaller, less ambitious schemes. Especially noteworthy are the importance of motivation in team selection and the vital importance of pre-expedition training in the skills required, especially driving. The team was a tight one with, for payload reasons, only two persons per vehicle. It followed that cross qualification in expedition tasks was essential. The driving was common to all members in this case but specialist skills were also tested – the cook cooked, the radio operator operated a radio.

Navigation training would now include thorough familiarisation with GPS and other satellite equipment (immeasurably simpler than taking star shots and carrying out the subsequent calculations). The cine training would take place on broadcast-quality video cameras if those were to be used – again far easier with 30 minutes-plus record time and instant shot playback. Apart from that the near-20 year gap between the above expedition and the present day has little effect on validity of the detailed selection and training methods used.

Multi-role team members. Selection and training were complementary and inseparable – all members had to be masters of their specialisation – but for the logistics/payload/skill requirements reasons already stated, no single-skill prima donnas could be entertained. Not all expeditions will be this demanding but the concept of all members 'mucking in' on all jobs and the ethos of mutual assistance at all times is worth making the bedrock of your trip for the team spirit it engenders.

... be sure to see the whole picture.

Team selection and training need not be difficult. Having the confidence to follow what, deep down we all know are the right standards is the key.

TEAM CANDIDATE INTERVIEW MARKING SCHEDULE

CANDIDATE'S NAME									
ATTRIBUTE	**Max**								
Personal qualities									
Motivation	9								
Rapport	9								
Intelligence / sensitivity	9								
Practicality	9								
Present fitness	6								
Experience									
Hot climates	3								
Outdoor life	6								
Desert expeditions	5								
'Land Rovering'	5								
Survival etc	4								
Specialisation									
Radio operator	7								
Navigation / survey	7								
Doctor	6								
Geologist	6								
Rock climber	4								
Photographer	5								
Mechanic	6								
French / Arabic	6/5								

Carefully weighted marking schedule distils expedition requirements in advance, helps quantify candidate. Note high weighting given to personal qualities.

1. Note the weighting given to attributes and the very high store set by the first four personal qualities.

This was the actual marking schedule used for team selection in the expedition for which the report appears on the preceding few pages. Such a procedure is highly recommended for any project for which you must call for volunteers. Establish your criteria and weighting in advance of seeing any candidates. It will clarify in your own mind exactly what you are looking for.

Section 4
Vehicles

Section 4.1

Vehicles:

Expedition vehicles

COVERAGE OF THIS SECTION

Probably the most important and (often, thanks to the dealers – confusing) aspect of your chosen expedition vehicle. Take your time with this; it will be worth it.

What for?

The task

The chicken and the egg. In the case of expeditions and the acquisition of vehicles there is often a third option to the 'Which came first ... ?' conundrum.

- We have this vehicle, is it OK for that trip?
- We want to do that trip, what vehicle should we get? and
- We want to do that trip what vehicle can we afford?

It is absolutely essential – because your vehicle is your life-blood – that you stick within its limitations in terms of load and

terrain so it does matter what vehicle you choose. Scan the following and you will see how to gauge what you need. Even if you already have your vehicle, go through the procedure and you will get an idea of how far you can go – in both senses.

Puddleton or Patagonia. There will be a huge span of trips that you might be contemplating, from the simplest and most local to the most distant and ambitious. Realising now that this could mean just as wide a span of vehicle specifications will help you match your vehicle to your trip and your trip to your vehicle.

Know the task in order to select the right vehicle; or know the vehicle's capabilities so you limit your task – or divide it into practicable legs – accordingly. The criteria are:

- Vehicle maximum payload
- Terrain you will encounter.

Payload and range. It has been flagged-up twice already but learn, here on the first page, that you must stick to load limits. Your vehicle will have enough on its plate on a demanding expedition without having to cope with overloading as well. GVW, or 'Gross Vehicle Weight', is the 'never exceed' or maximum permitted weight of a vehicle. It is made up of the empty (or 'kerb') weight and the load. In general a big vehicle can carry more cargo for a much longer distance than a small one – a Shogun vs a Fiat Panda or a Defender 130 vs a Bedford Rascal?

Kerb weight is the empty weight of the vehicle but includes driver and a full tank of fuel. The difference between this and GVW is what else it can carry – see diagram left. If there are great distances between replenishment points, a vehicle with a given difference between kerb weight and maximum weight will have to devote a great deal of that weight to extra fuel. As the next diagram shows, this will leave little payload to devote to other things like kit, food, water and passengers. If the distances between replenishment stops are short, easily within

Match your vehicle to your trip – or vice versa. Distance between replenishment points, payload you need to carry and the kind of terrain dictate the vehicle.

Gross weight, kerb weight – Defender 90

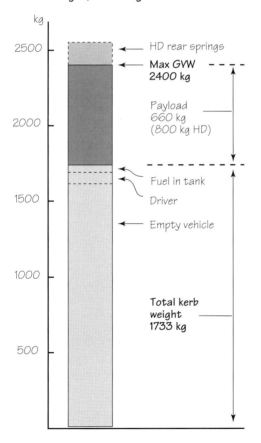

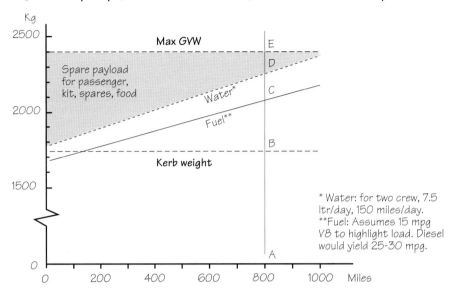

Logistics – spare payload dwindles with range. V8 Defender 90 example

the capacity of a single fuel tank (with reserves) and there is easy resupply at the end of the run, then the majority of your payload can be given over to people and kit.

So for a given vehicle and crew, distance (and days) between replenishment points dictate the load of essentials like fuel and water you need to carry. The weight of other kit such as food, spares and camping gear follow from there.

The diagram above gives an example – a worst-case big-engine scenario is shown to accentuate the point; a diesel engine provides more than enough power-weight ratio and the fuel required would be far less. Every vehicle will have a graph of this kind reflecting its maximum practical range between replenishment points. There are many ways around the sums if they come out wrong – fewer passengers, less kit, shorter legs, more economical engine, larger payload vehicle or even a trailer.

Kerb weights – warning. Some manufacturers (eg Land Rover and Mitsubishi) include a 75 kg driver in the kerb weight of the vehicle ('EC kerb') so that subsequent payload figures truly represent what extra

Correlation between replenishment point spacing, payload and vehicle size/type is absolute. Don't fudge it; do all the sums realistically – including reserves.

Rough sums will do just as well but graph shows vividly how range erodes spare payload. In a fairly extreme case, on an 800 mile leg, A-B is kerb wt, B-C is fuel load, C-D is water required, only leaving 150 kg (D-E) for a 75 kg passenger and remaining kit. In real life you'd go diesel, shorten legs and/or get bigger vehicle like Defender 110 or 130. Fuel and water calculations (including reserves) as at Sec 2.5. Bigger vehicle equals more payload but less power/weight ratio. (See diagram page 4.1 - 11.)

can be carried. Many other makers quote unmanned kerb weights so payload is affected; be sure you know the basis of your vehicle's quoted payload. 75 kg is three 20 litre jerry cans of water – so it matters!

Terrain. The kind of tracks or terrain you have to traverse is a dominating factor too in defining the task, though less easy to quantify. There could well be routes straightforward enough to cover in a normal two-wheel drive (4x2) van or station wagon. If the terrain is more demanding or is uncertain you will want more ground clearance or off-road capability to use or have in reserve. The table on p 4.1 - 9 will give you the detail

It's in the genes all over the world and it starts young – fascination with vehicles. Bashful enthusiasts' concept model opts for rear loading platform and separate chassis.

ingredients of a strong expedition vehicle starting from a simple 4x2 van or pick-up.

Function vs fun and luxury

Not all vehicles are the same. The span of machinery encompassed these days by the descriptive but uniquely apposite American term 'sport utility vehicle' (SUV) is large. Within it are lightweight SUVs aimed at two-seater days on the beach, there are heavyweights most of whose payload is devoted to luxury appointments and there are the more spartan vehicles with high payload ratings that can handle a large expedition load more easily.

There is no law against having fun in a functional vehicle or against being luxuriously comfortable when logistics permit but, whilst the divisions are not hard and fast, it is worth having in the back of your mind the following categories:
- Lightweight 'fun' vehicles
- Luxury vehicles with not much payload
- Luxury vehicles with payload but high GVW
- 'Working' vehicles, no frills, plenty of payload.

How many vehicles, load, type?

Spreading the load – and the risk. One big vehicle or two small ones is the simplistically stated decision you may wish to consider at the task definition stage. Some trips will naturally be multi-vehicle, for others there may be a choice. Influences will be:
- Degree of sub-group mobility required
- Cost of multi-vehicle ferry fares, etc
- Difficulty of terrain – large vehicles tend to be less athletic than small ones (see 'Power/weight ratio')
- Reliability fall-back in case of breakdown of a single vehicle.

Do not let this last consideration stem from a feeling that breakdown and damage are inevitable. Rather take the opposite view – as we shall see under 'Driving' and have already noted under team selection – that the implications of breakdown or damage on an expedition can be so dire or so expensive that they must not be allowed to occur. Driving, general care, and maintenance standards must be that good.

Nevertheless, random mechanical failures do occur and a back-up vehicle and one to help in towing out a stuck vehicle will be invaluable. The payoff in peace of mind is high. If you can, never take less than two vehicles - three is best since all the load from one incapacitated vehicle can in many cases be transferred and spread without overloading the other two.

Overloading – excuses. As we have just seen, overloading cannot be considered. 'Ah, but there are margins ...' say some. And

Though divisions are blurring more and more, be aware of the different market sectors covered by modern sport-utility vehicles – not all are aimed at hard-nosed trips.

A second or third vehicle is an invaluable safety back-up for mutual assistance. Never exceed the manufacturer's gross vehicle weight.

margins are exactly what you want on an expedition over difficult terrain in foreign parts. 'Ah, but I've seen vehicles with roof racks up to here ... ', say some; and they will also likely have seen the same vehicles rolled onto their sides due to the high centre of gravity or with cracked pillars because of the fatigue loads on elements not designed for the stress. 'Ah, but you can fit stronger springs .. ', say some; and in doing so merely transfer more road shocks into an already overladen chassis.

And if you are thinking of Camel Trophy and the like, vehicles used there are subject to very special re-engineering. Roll cages anchored to the chassis that help to transfer roof rack loads back down to the chassis rather than through the body structure. Huge back-up organisation goes into events of this kind. Cut your finger on the Paris-Dakar and you would almost expect a helicopter to come pattering over the dune with a plaster.

Born for expeditions with its tough build, lightweight body and exceptional off-road performance, Defender (top) is here on roads where vans could cope. Toyota's huge luxury Landcruiser VX is surprisingly capable off-road but, like Range Rover, has high gross weight and small payload.

Ordinary expeditions are not like this and ordinary expeditions are for doing with maximum safety and maximum margins. So when considering matching the task and the hardware, do not let the idea of upping the load even enter your head.

Big and small together. As we shall see below, the concept of a large less athletic load carrier teamed with one or two smaller vehicles can work since they can recce ahead for the best route and also attach tow ropes with power to spare at times if needed.

Trailers

50% more axles. In trying to work out your load and vehicle count at this stage, you will very likely encounter the problem of having a greater load and bulk than the vehicle's size and payload maxima. A trailer can offer a practical solution. It is not a solution that should be entered into lightly since it will affect everything from ferry costs to spare tyre commonality. There is also the serious shortcoming that you will be unlikely to be able to reverse out of a bogging. A vehicle with a trailer is less agile than one without; however, a given load may be spread over six instead of four wheels and, so long as two or three people are available to manhandle it, a trailer can be invaluable.

The right stuff. Firstly the only trailer robust enough to be recommended for inclusion on a light 4x4 expedition would be an ex-British military three-quarter-ton trailer such as are used behind army Land Rovers. They are fitted with 16 inch wheels and tyres of the same kind as the towing vehicle so could share the same spare tyre. Towing arrangements will have to be similarly upgraded and a NATO towing pintle must be fitted to the tug vehicle to match up with the 7-tonne ring hitch on the trailer. Be

sure that the trailer's shock dampers are in first rate condition when you purchase; they will keep lateral roll in check.

Keep it light – and low. It is important that the trailer load be kept light – not more than 50-60% of the rated load is the secret of trouble-free expedition trailering. This will not only put the trailer under less mechanical stress but it will enable lower tyre pressures to be used thus reducing sinkage, drag and load on the tug in soft going. Importantly, running light will also reduce the ratio of gross weights between tug and trailer which has considerable effect on the stability and agility of the ensemble. Keep the centre of gravity of the load in the trailer low down, keep the high-mass items close to the trailer axle and central to reduce moment of inertia and ensure that there is a down-load at the trailer tow bar of about 50-75 kg. Remember that this 'nose-weight' is bearing down on the towing vehicle's rear end and will result in a reduction in the tug's payload.

Nose-weight, tug payload. Actually, for reasons that schoolboy maths and mechanics can confirm, since the tow hitch is some way aft of the tug's axle, the rear axle load on the tug will increase by more than the 50-75 kg tow bar download. To accommodate this – rule of thumb – remove twice this figure from the towing vehicle's payload. Thus if the download is 50 kg, take 100 kg off the listed maximum payload of the tug when

A really robust (military) off-road trailer, part-loaded, can be an effective solution to the excess payload problem. It also spreads the load over six wheels instead of four.

Exemplary combination for a small group – supremely capable truck (Mercedes Unimog) lightly loaded, featherweight roof load, baggage trailer sensibly smaller and lighter than tug riding on wheels and tyres of similar size for interchangeability.

Next stop Reggan – 900 miles north, all off-tracks. Thirsty V8, 17 day transit, posed major logistics problem neatly solved by use of 3/4 ton military trailer. Loaded to only about 60% payload, riding on high flotation tyres, trailer was minimal problem to high power/weight ratio tug. But team of man-handlers would have been useful!

working out how much else you can carry in the towing vehicle.

Brakes, tyre pressures. Be sure that the trailer overrun brakes are working properly, evenly side to side and not grabbing. Never allow yourself to get into a position of having to brake when the vehicle and trailer are on a curve since this is a basically unstable condition. Be aware that, off-road, or on rough tracks trailers betray their inherently poor lateral damping and are prone to tipping over in surprisingly mild situations. (Your tow hook, and/or the towing neck on the trailer, should be of the 360°-freedom

Take twice the trailer's actual nose-weight off the tug's payload. Ensure swivel hook allows trailer roll-over without rolling the tug too.

type that permits a trailer roll-over without communicating the roll to the towing vehicle.)

Be constantly vigilant on trailer tyre pressure. The lower trailer tyre pressures you use to lessen sinkage and drag off-road can induce lateral oscillations at higher speeds on-road so, as with tyre pressures on the main vehicles, tyres should be re-inflated to road pressures when out of the soft going.

See also *THE LAND ROVER EXPERI-ENCE* chapters on towing trailers on and off road.

Vehicles – general criteria

What to consider. With a broad overview done, plus a quick look at the possibilities of trailers, the criteria below help define your prospective vehicles in their operational roles. Certainly for larger projects where a mix of vehicles may be indicated, the more analytical approach is essential. It is worth, for any trip, being aware of the ingredients of a competent off-road vehicle – what ingredient yields what reward and at what cost – and so bring together a ghost specification that you can template on to what the market is offering at any given time. Just as a recap to get the value of par-

ticular attributes clear in your own mind, these are dealt with first:
- Ingredients
- Size/power-weight ratio/payload
- 4x4 or 4x2
- Types of 4x4 (four-wheel drive)
- Controlling wheel-spin
- Auto or manual gearbox
- Ground clearance, suspension
- Weight distribution
- Petrol or diesel
- Hard top, station wagon, crew cab
- Servicing, inspection, preparation
- Modifications, tyres (see Section 4.2)

EXPEDITION VEHICLE ATTRIBUTES – IN ORDER OF PROGRESSION FROM SIMPLE 4X2 PICK-UP

Feature	Benefits	Disadvantages
Leaf springs	Low cost, simplicity, easy replacement. Springs act as means of locating axles.	Inter-leaf friction gives stiff ride, poor traction; limited wheel movement. If springs very long and 1- or 2-leaf (Land Rover 101), these problems are lessened.
Large diameter wheels	Improved under-axle ground clearance. Goes *over* pot-holes rather than into them.	No functional disadvantage.
Torsion-bar front springs	Smoother ride than leaf springs. Better traction and braking. More wheel movement.	Usually associated with independent front suspension so less ground clearance.
Beam axles	Good under-axle clearance, wheels always perpendicular to ground.	Clearance above axle needed for wheel movement makes vehicle tall. High unsprung weight difficult to damp.
Coil springs all round. (See page 4.1 - 28.)	Smoother ride than leaf springs. Better traction and braking. Usually a lot more wheel movement so best off-road capability; best traction on uneven ground.	More expensive than leaf springs due to need for alternative axle location links. If too short and stiff, ride is still poor.
No anti-roll bars	Permits full axle articulation – twist relative to body – off-road wheel movement enhanced.	Body roll. Designer's nightmare to balance on- and off-road performance.
Short wheelbase	Improved off-road capability but only noticeable in worst conditions.	Usually associated with lower max payload than long wheelbase versions.
Large approach, departure, ramp angles, 'high stance' (See p 4.1 - 26)	Off-road agility without danger of grounding body parts. Short tail overhang specially valuable exiting ditches.	High centre of gravity can cause body roll.
High payload	Obvious advantage when there are long distances between provisioning points.	Stiffer springs give less pliant ride.
Automatic transmission. (See p 4.1 - 25.)	Helps driver. Smoothest gear changes safeguard driveshafts, precludes lost traction through jerkiness. Very good.	Cost mainly, some weight. Perceived loss of manhood by some.
'Part-time' (selectable) four-wheel drive (4x4). (See p 4.1 - 19.)	Huge improvement over two-wheel drive (4x2) in soft sand, mud, snow etc.	Compared with 4x2, cost. Must be selected when needed and de-selected on hard surfaces. Full-time 4x4 better.
Part time pseudo (or 'automatic') 4x4. (See p 4.1 - 19.)	As above but speed differences between front and rear axles have to be sensed before 4x4 is engaged with viscous coupling.	As above but things have to get bad before they get better, ie some wheel-spin. Not totally positive drive.
2-speed transfer box. (See page 4.1 - 24.)	In effect a 2nd set of extra-low gears for off-road use. Highly desirable for expeditons.	Cost.
On-the-move range change (Lo to Hi range) (See Sec 5.3)	Invaluable when you have to start in Lo and need to change to Hi without stopping. Can't be done with 'electronic' range changes.	No real disadvantage except some skill / technique required to do it.
'Full-time' (permanent) 4x4 with centre differential. (See p 4.1 - 19.)	Much better than part-time 4x4 or 'automatic 4x4' because it is there all the time, ready for anything. Best kind has manually lockable centre differential.	Compared with part-time 4x4, more cost since centre differential needed. Must remember to unlock diff if on hard ground unless VC controlled. (Panel p 4.1 - 20)
Locking axle differentials. (See p 4.1 - 22.)	Overcomes those 'one spinning wheel' situations superbly to preclude getting stuck.	Cost. Risk to half-shafts if not properly engineered. Must remember to de-select.
Forward-control cab	Ideal for expeditions – enhanced visibility for off-road obstacles, permits load bed to stretch forward to distribute cargo weight front / rear.	Impractical for consumer vehicles, gives high vehicle with athletic entry to cab over front wheels.
Portal axles (centre of wheel below axle; hub reduction gears. See p 27)	Dramatic increase in under-axle clearance for rough ground and deep ruts. Very good for the worst off-road conditions.	Very expensive to produce, high centre of gravity, higher unsprung weight but lighter transmission shafts.

Know the progression of features that take a vehicle from a high-street load carrier to an expedition star. All the time match this to your trip requirements.

Ingredients

The features mix. With a broad indication of the kind of trip you are going on and an initial feel for the number of vehicles you will want, examine the table on the previous page that goes over the ingredients of an expedition vehicle. Bearing in mind that you could start off looking at 4x2 vans and pickups, scan the table of attributes and get a feel for what features are to your advantage and why. When looking at specifications try not to make rapid judgements – 'terrific' or 'terrible' when looking at various combinations of features manifested in particular vehicles. Most manufacturers could make a vehicle that combined *all* the features in the table but it would probably turn out to be a capability overkill – certainly a cost overkill – and would have compromised handling and comfort levels.

A lot of the features have trade-offs in terms of cost or on-road handling characteristics and a lot of manufacturers have chosen quite deliberately to go for certain design feature combinations because they feel these will meet the requirements of the majority of the particular sector of the market they are looking at, be it the customers that go off road a lot, those that don't, those that want more roll control than off-road axle articulation, those that want a comfortable soft ride, those that want high payload capability and don't mind the firm springs

'Best' expedition vehicle features have cost, road handling, comfort trade-off. Manufacturers judge best mix for markets. You can sometimes add – with care.

this will entail – and those that perhaps don't want to pay too much money for facilities they would seldom use.

Some customers want a 4x4 only for the safety it gives on snow and slippery surfaces without having the need for extra low gears – some even find these 'confusing'. Hence special specs for special markets evolve without a two-speed transfer box – the Toyota RAV4 and Land Rover Freelander being cases in point.

Most of the people most of the time. So manufacturers have to please most of the people most of the time. This way sales volume is achieved so that prices can be more attractive – so that more vehicles sell. Depending on where your expedition sits in the 'Puddleton or Patagonia' spectrum you will find a large group of acceptable vehicles or a diminishing one as you are backed into the logistical and bad terrain corner labelled 'hard expeditions territory'.

At the extreme recesses of this corner are vehicles like the Steyr-Daimler-Puch Pinzgauer – very specialised and capable, thus made in small numbers and, because of this and its huge engineering content, very expensive. The mighty Mercedes Unimog in its wide range of variants is a similar class of vehicle – albeit starting to fall off the power-weight ratio curve – and you will find it costs you a lot of money. Faced with this and the mountain of machinery you are getting, some would say, 'Yes, that's the one'

Rare combination of Pinzgauer's exceptional off-road 6x6 capability and camper body would make ideal, if costly, expedition base vehicle. Such bodies can take up alarming proportion of gross weight leaving little for payload. Often made by caravan constructors more used to smooth roads, watch for structural robustness and ability to take vibration and off-road torsion. Mercedes Unimog chassis offers three-point body mount to accommodate this.

for an extreme trip – or reflect that maybe it's overkill and that, well, they do need to be able to go down to the shops in it occasionally too and, for the trip, 'normal' 4x4 will do quite well!

In this league it can be argued that only one vehicle really bridged this payload/performance/engineering-content/cost chasm and that was the forward control military Land Rover 1-Tonne 101 – alas, no longer made, but it showed what could be done at (despite its limited production run) reasonable cost; the 101 was an extraordinary combination of conceptual simplicity and outstanding off-road/expedition performance.

Look again at the list on p 4.1 - 9 and then, heading by heading, at the material to follow within this Section 4.1.

Size, power-weight ratio, payload

Swings and roundabouts. In general a medium truck (say 4-tonne) can support itself and a team over a greater distance and/or longer time than a 'light 4x4', such as a Discovery or a Shogun. It is a direct function of payload (the fuel or supplies it can carry) and there is no substitute for detailed and accurate calculations of requirements in this area. These calculations would be based on the number of people to keep in the field for how long at given consumption rates, how far between resupply points and whether there are basics such as water close to the worksite or along the route. The general picture looks like this:

The size trade-offs

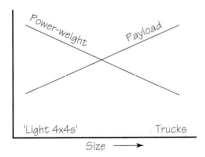

Power-weight – where it matters. If payload is what gets you long distances then, all other things being equal (note that and see next page ' ... perspective'), power-to-weight ratio is what gets you up a sand dune, a steep loose slope or through a boggy patch that you might have to use speed for. Power-weight ratio is the number of bhp per tonne of laden weight the vehicle has; as the little graph (left) shows, small vehicles with big engines have lots of it (4.0 litre Jeep Wrangler, RAV4, even 4.6 Range Rover); trucks don't. So long as there is grip – which there isn't on a sand dune, a loose slope or a sticky mud patch – a vehicle with a *low* power-weight ratio will, by sheer low gearing, crawl over rocks or slowly up a steep climb. All those brochure pictures you see of vehicles doing their 45° slope climbing act have been taken on a reinforced concrete slope with a good roughened surface!

Power-to-weight ratio equals dynamic off-road capability and is usually, as the diagram implies, a direct trade-off for size and carrying capacity. If this is all so, you may be wondering, and with all this talk about sand dunes, how do the oil exploration trucks get around? With some understatement, these vehicles could be described as gargantuan and though their engines are big, it would probably take nuclear power to push their power-weight ratio up to the 35 bhp/tonne-plus of the most agile off-roaders. If you have ever been close to such machines, the answer will be staring you in the face; indeed until your upward gaze exceeds about 45°, staring you in the face will be huge tyres of a very generous cross section – see photo next page.

Tyres. High flotation tyres are, if not a direct substitute for power-weight ratio, certainly a means of lessening the effects of its lack. Steep, loose, shortish inclines are still going to need power to get the momentum with which to 'ballistic' to the brow without too much reliance on the poor supply of grip, but on the level or with moderate slopes wide, sometimes deflated, tyres can help a low powered vehicle 'soft shoe' without sinkage or excessive demands on torque.

Power-weight ratio is what makes a vehicle sprightly in difficult off-road conditions. 'Light 4x4s' have high power-weight, big load carriers have far less.

Power-weight ratio vs flotation. Bedfords bravely pushing their luck backed by multi-vehicle, multi-person assistance. Mighty Kenworth, here freed from the sands, hints at what (very) large tyres could do.

Keep power-weight ratio in perspective. Anything above 35-40 bhp/tonne usually goes on tarmac performance. Off-road, tyres and drive line affect end results.

Power-weight – perspective. Don't let power-weight concerns get out of proportion. Above a certain figure you will have more than enough for expedition purposes and the surplus will go on sizzling on-road performance – this is the case with many of the 'high end' vehicles in the list on p 4.1 - 14. In truth *torque* per tonne probably matters more (together with knowing what sort of rpm the peak torque occurs at) but either one should be regarded in the context of the whole vehicle. For instance both Pinzgauers have the same 115 bhp engine; one has a GVW of 4850 kg, the other 3850 kg. That's 24 vs 30 bhp/tonne; but the heavier vehicle is a 6x6 (808 kg per tyre) and the lighter is a 4x4 (962 kg per tyre). Depending on terrain, you'd probably find the 6x6 is the better expedition vehicle for extreme conditions and the extra payload would certainly come in handy. And both vehicles have cross axle diff locks; how would they compare with a vehicle with more power per tonne and free differentials? (There's more on these features later – see p 4.1 - 22.) Then again there's cost, they're fairly spartan inside ... Decisions, decisions!

Big and small together. Large load carriers will often be involved when a field research programme is to take place in a remote area for a number of weeks or months since only they can move the equipment needed. The remoteness of the area and the state and condition of tracks to and from it will dictate whether a large load carrier can get through or not. As already mentioned, it may be that a mixed fleet is necessary – say a 4-tonne load carrier with two or three light 4x4s to scout and/or assist with tow ropes should the truck become stuck. Again, though, note the type of terrain; this kind of solution can work well in patchy mud but not pulling up long sandy slopes or dunes.

Case study. As a case study it is worth noting that such a set-up was tried during the recce for the Joint Services West East Sahara expedition – mainly to assess the Bedford 4-tonner's suitability for the job. The logistics of this trip were extremely demanding – the first lateral crossing of the thousand-mile Mauritanian Empty Quarter, all off-tracks, inevitably without external support. The Bedford's fuel carrying capaci-

ty was required but it was not known if the dunes would be too difficult for it. A 250-mile recce into the dunes was carried out using a Range Rover, a Series 3 Land Rover and a Bedford – photos this page. After a few days it became clear the Bedford was struggling in repeated tandem-tows and laying of sand tracks. Nor did the smaller vehicles have the fuel carrying capacity to support such a long crossing without replenishment. The result was the choice of

an in-between vehicle, the military 1-tonne forward-control Land Rover – a vehicle having more carrying capacity than its smaller siblings but a better power-weight ratio than the Bedford. In the event, because the logistics sums were still too tight, two of the four 1-tonne Land Rovers in the team were used with power-driven trailers, leaving two less-encumbered vehicles to come to their rescue should it be necessary.

Load carriers teamed with light 4x4s can be a way round the logistics vs agility problems of a long hard route but there could be lots of towing and digging.

Selection process – top. Left to right: ascending load carrying capability and descending power-weight ratio – the latter broadly determines limits of off-road agility. Combination shown here can work well, smaller vehicles route-finding and towing-out as needed. For this requirement, solution was 1-tonne Land Rovers (left), some using trailers as fuel and water carriers; logistics demanded 1000 miles-plus, off-tracks.

Payloads and power. The payloads of a sprinkling of UK-available vehicles are shown in the table in the next column to give you a feel for how many jerry cans, boxes and the like can be carried and keep within GVW. Note the earlier warning about quoted kerb weights. Discussed in more detail below under 'Weight distribution', bear in mind too which vehicles have their payload sitting mainly over the back wheels (most of them); it makes a difference when flotation is on the limit. As we shall see in Section 4.3, 'Loading', taking out back seats and positioning high-density cargo as far forward as possible helps.

What to do with this information? An interesting table. With these primary expedition-critical parameters listed – and remember there are other factors that affect even the validity of these – there are a few surprises. Of course, as already mentioned, on easier trips not everyone will be pushing the logistic and off-road limits. What is clear from the list is that for a trip that is logistically and track/terrain-wise fairly straightforward, you do have a great deal of choice of vehicles from the luxury heavyweights to the nippy lightweights. With a fair sprinkling of fuel stations, resupply shops and not too much kit to carry you can go in sybaritic luxury or in compact sporting mode. As things get more demanding logistically, however, you will not have the spare payload for moving all that leather and walnut around the world. So:

1. Look at the payload/GVW ratio.

(Column 3) Is the vehicle a 'worker'? The higher this value the more of a no-frills working vehicle it is. Then look at actual payload and see if you can carry your first-calculations kit list. Next, after logistics – payload percentage and payload itself – look at terrain. If terrain is going to be tough you will need power; not to scar tarmac but enough to be nimble when required. So:

2. Look at power-weight ratio.

(Right-hand column) Don't decide yet. Go through to the end of this Section. Do you *need* 4x4? Geometry? Weight distribution? And so on. Then re-check.

Primary, 'ballpark' selection criteria are listed in the table (right) – most important of which will usually be payload.

PAYLOAD, POWER-WEIGHT RATIO – 1997

Payload kg**	Vehicle	Payload as % of GVW	GVW kg	BHP per tonne of GVW
334	Honda CR-V 2.0L auto	17	1900	66.32
315	Toyota RAV4 3dr	20	1565	80.51
345	Jeep Wrangler TJ ('97) 2.5 L	18	1925	60.78
447	Ford Explorer	18	2530	79.23
455	Vitara 2.0D 5dr	23	1945	35.98
486	Freelander petrol	26	1900	62.28
560	Range Rover 4.6 L	20	2780	79.49
565	Toyota Landcruiser VX	19	2960	56.75
589	Nissan Patrol GR 2.8 TDi 5dr	20	2920	43.89
585	Toyota Colorado TD 5dr	22	2680	45.89
590	Jeep Cherokee 2.5TD	26	2230	51.12
598	Frontera Sport 2.5TD	24	2510	45.82
603	Frontera Estate 2.5TD	23	2600	44.23
620	Shogun 3.0V6 5dr	23	2650	65.66
630	Nissan Terrano II 2.7TD 5dr	24	2580	47.77
635	Shogun 2.8TD 5dr	23	2720	45.22
640	Discovery Tdi 5dr	24	2720	40.80
660	Defender 90 HT, 2.5Tdi	28	2400	46.25
665	Range Rover 2.5D	24	2780	48.20
676	Daihatsu Fourtrak TDL 2.7TD	27	2510	40.07
694	Mercedes ML320	25	2727	78.84
700	Shogun 2.5TD 3dr	28	2510	39.04
705	Ford Maverick 2.7D 5dr	22	2655	47.67
715	Toyota Colorado TD 3dr	28	2510	49.00
755	Toyota Hilux DC PU 2.5D	30	2515	31.01
800	Defender 90 HT Tdi HD	31	2550	43.51
834	Ford Expedition (US)	26	3243	70.90
925	VW Caravelle Synchro 2.5 pet	35	2650	43.02
960	Vauxhalll Brava DC PU	36	2650	28.28
1030	Defender 110 SW Tdi	34	3050	36.39
1139	Defender 110 HiCap PU	37	3050	36.39
1414	Defender 130 DC PU Tdi	40	3500	31.71
1425	Pinzgauer 4x4 (soft top)	37	3850	29.87
1925	Pinzgauer 6x6 (soft top)	40	4850	23.71
2200*	Mercedes Unimog U100L	40	5500	17.82
2940*	Mercedes Unimog U1550L	39	7500	20.67
3570*	Mercedes Unimog U140L	48	7500	17.73
4715	Leyland 4 tonne truck 4x4	44	10800	13.42

Notes:
All the above are 4x4
**'EC kerb weight' = empty vehicle plus driver plus full fuel tank. This has been used and manufacturers' data adjusted where necessary in all the above figures. 'Payload' thus represents what extra the vehicle (with driver) can carry.
DC = Double cab on pick-up
PU = pick-up
HT = Hard top
TD = turbo diesel
D = Diesel
3dr = 3-door, generally shorter wheelbase
HD = Heavy-duty springs
SW = Station wagon
Tdi = Land Rover 2.5 litre turbo diesel
* = Unimog kerb weight given for chassis/cab. 500 kg body assumed. Resulting payload shown.

Defender 110 Tdi – all-time classic? One-Ten quietly emerges from the list (left) as benchmark all-round expedition vehicle – simple concept, light body, generous payload, moderate cost, full time 4x4, excellent off-road performance. But different circumstances and needs may determine different choice.

Transmission systems

Two-wheel drive or four-wheel drive

Two will do? All the vehicles in the facing table are four-wheel drive vehicles – 4x4s. Will 4x2 do? A robust 4x2 with big wheels and a couple of willing crew to push is surprisingly capable so the cost of a 4x4 may not always be absolutely necessary if firm roads – surfaced or unsurfaced – are available. A classic vehicle frequently seen in Africa in appalling conditions, is the Peugeot 504 pick-up as well as many Japanese vehicles of a similar concept. The Toyota Hilux (also made as a 4x4) can boast

a jaw-dropping worldwide production count over literally decades and its standard simple configuration of independent front end, leaf springs aft (a 'firm' ride when lightly laden!), long pick-up bed and payload of a ton or so helps keep appeal wide, production figures up and price down.

'Dual cabs' or 'crew cabs' (pick-ups with two rows of seats and four doors ahead of a smaller load bed) are a popular solution where families or small groups are concerned and are frequently used with a lock-

Rewarding trips can be done in simple 4x2 pick-ups or vans. But be sure of your terrain and driving skills must be high – gentle off-road practice helps.

Classic surprise. What starts as a good tarmac road, suitable for 4x2s (or 2x1s) can sometimes be found to have succumbed to the forces of Nature and challenging off-road diversions are required.

Whilst 4x2s are seen in the most surprising places, this is almost invariably due to drivers who know the tracks well and know how to coax a 4x2 through them.

able rear-end cover – a sensible expedition set-up. If considering this approach in a 4x2 (or even in the 4x4 versions), check carefully the payloads, ground clearance, wheel size and wheelbase before making your choice. A 15 inch rim size should be regarded as the minimum to provide adequate ground clearance and tyre footprint; it will also be an indication of the vehicle's design philosophy in regard to rough ground.

Driving standards. Some well-known marques of expedition 4x2 such as the VW Microbus have performed heroically in Africa in the past but too often with frightening risks in remote areas requiring tow-outs from other vehicles in deep sand. Off-tracks or on known tracks with much soft sand 4x4 is desirable to the point of being essential; but remember, equally, that the wrong tyres, tyre pressure and driving tech-

nique can see a bogged 4x4 passed by a well operated 4x2 whose driver is picking his micro-route and throttle setting with care and expertise.

Having said that, a novice in a 4x4 will do better than a novice in a 4x2. So will an expert. It is clear, therefore, that existing and potential driving skills come into the list of parameters to assess when considering vehicle choice. It almost goes without saying that such skills amount to something more subtle than a heavy right foot and white knuckles – see Section 5.3, 'Driving'. A 4x2/4x4 mix in a multi-vehicle team might

Clockwise from below: 4x2 'high street' Leyland with twin rear wheels and expert driver beat the Zaire mud – albeit with much toil. (Company plans to re-equip with 4x4!) Tombouctou 4x2 boards its 'self-recovery system'; note long leaf springs. Mitsubishi L200 4x4 and 4x2 pick-ups highlight on/off road geometry. 4x4 has 16 inch wheels, 4x2 makes do with 14 inch. Consider 15 inch minimum for expeditions.

Typical 4x4 transmission

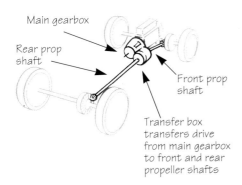

Main gearbox

Rear prop
shaft

Front prop
shaft

Transfer box
transfers drive
from main gearbox
to front and rear
propeller shafts

be considered despite the problems of
spares commonality.

More from four. For a full and detailed
explanation of four-wheel drive and permanent 4x4, see the appropriate section in the
companion book to this, *THE LAND
ROVER EXPERIENCE*. A quick recap here,
though, will do no harm. Four-wheel drive
does not, as some people say, 'double the
power on the road'. It takes the power you
have and spreads it between four wheels
instead of two. In doing so, and for a given
amount of required grip or forward push,
the 4x4 set-up asks less of the ground (half
as much) and so the margins of grip are
greater. Safety is enhanced under all conditions. So when there isn't much grip
around, a 4x4 will get through where a 4x2
might sit spinning its wheels; this is what
matters.

So 4x2 or 4x4? The temptation is to dismiss this question as almost rhetorical – not
least because once you have driven a good
4x4 on an expedition the tendency is to
think nothing else will do.

There is already quite a strong case for
4x4 instead of 4x2 for ordinary road cars,
bearing the full spectrum of European driving conditions in mind. That this case
should be stronger still for expedition conditions – unsurfaced roads, mud, deep
sand, *unpredictable* conditions – is not surprising.

There will be many trips that can quite

satisfactorily be done in a stout 4x2 but the
final message, where there is any doubt
about the conditions (or even, some would
say, if there is not) has to be go for 4x4 if you
can. Cost could well be the deciding factor
but even this can be accommodated to some
extent in the various types of 4x4 available
today – read on.

Types of four-wheel drive

Different approaches. Driving all four
wheels all the time but in a way that accommodates the slight differences in distance
travelled by left and right wheels, front axle
and rear axle is the ideal. From the design-
engineering point of view this is easy to
achieve. The 'differentials' (see p 4.1 - 20)
that have sat between the left and right
wheels of a normal car's driven back axle for
over a hundred years enabling the outside
wheel to go further when it turns a corner
can be installed between the front and rear
prop shafts of a four-wheel drive vehicle.

The bean counters, marketing, costs,
profits, and genuine 'do-we-need-it '
philosophers enter at this point arguing that
a centre differential adds cost and if you
make 4x4 selectable – for use only when
needed – then you can do away with the
centre diff. Some argue – shakily – that 4x4
uses more fuel so the facility should be used
only when needed. The result is a bunch of
different design philosophies – and termi-
nologies – when looking at 4x4 vehicles:

• 'Part-time' 4x4 (selectable)
• Part-time 4x4 with freewheeling hubs
• 'Auto' (pseudo) 4x4
• 'Full-time' (permanent) 4x4
• Full-time 4x4 with viscous centre diff
• Combinations of the above
• A blizzard of trade names such as
Selectrac, Super Select, Quadra-trac, Control
Trac to cause you further confusion.
• All of the above are usually – but not
always (VW Synchro, RAV4, Honda CR-V,
Freelander) – combined with a two-speed
transfer gearbox that gears the final drive
down by a factor of around two giving you
a 'second set' of extra low gears (p.4.1 -24).

*If you decide you
need 4x4, manu-
facturers have a
number of ways
of providing the
facility. Often
the main barrier
is finding a deal-
er who under-
stands the vehi-
cle he is selling!*

Sort it out, once and for all. You really do need to know the various systems if you are to make any kind of sensible choice of vehicles for an expedition and operate them properly. Hacking your way through the marketing obfuscation and sales staff ignorance is the start. Take on board first that there are really only three basic types of 4x4 system. That's them on the page opposite. From now on it will all get clearer ... promise!

Four-wheel drive systems. A quick round-up:

1. Selectable 4x4 – part-time. A four-wheel drive vehicle in which the shafting for the front axle drive remains disengaged from the gearbox until 4x4 is selected by the driver, usually by a lever in the cab, is deemed to have selectable or 'part-time 4x4'– see upper diagram opposite. When so selected, the front shaft and rear shaft are locked together and always turn at the same speed as each other; there is no centre differential. This latter causes some 'fight' between front and rear axles which would normally have slight speed differences on corners. If you are off-road or on a loose surface this can be accommodated by small amounts of wheel slippage. On hard, dry surfaces, however, this slippage does not happen and transmission 'wind-up' occurs causing tyre wear, transmission stress and stiff steering. With part-time 4x4 you must not engage 4x4 on hard surfaces. When leaving dirt tracks, snow or other potentially slippery surfaces for hard grippy road you must disengage 4x4 if you have no centre differential.

To confuse things a little, one US interpretaion of the term 'part-time 4x4' is not, as above, to describe the *system* but to describe the *usage*. Part-time in the latter case meaning you can only use it part of the time, ie not on hard surfaces.

2. Pseudo ('auto') 4x4. In this type of 4x4, the vehicle is in effect a part-time 4x4 (ie a 4x2 most of the time, usually with drive to the front axle) and the 'selection' of 4x4 is done automatically when a viscous coupling (VC – see panel above) or other

Part time or selectable 4x4 requires you to know in advance when you are going to need it – not always too much of a problem but you do get taken by surprise sometimes.

> ### WHAT IS A VISCOUS COUPLING?
>
> **Paradoxical goo.** A classic viscous coupling (VC) between two shafts consists of interleaved vanes, alternate vanes being splined to each shaft. Special silicone fluid takes up the space between the vanes. A VC has the unusual – indeed paradoxical – characteristic that, although there is a small degree of freedom for each shaft to rotate relative to the other, when that rotation becomes excessive, ie when one shaft moves at a markedly different speed to its neighbour, the viscous fluid is 'stirred' and very soon locks the vanes together, inhibiting relative movement and causing both shafts to move at the same speed. You would expect that when the fluid is stirred or gets warm it would get thinner and freer but the opposite is the case.
>
> **Distinctly different uses.** There are different uses of a viscous coupling between front and rear propeller shafts and they should not be confused:
>
> 1. Sometimes – see 'Pseudo 4x4' opposite – a VC is used. through prop shaft speed difference, to bring in 4x4 to an essentially 4x2 system. Here the VC is a link in the drive system and is, so to speak, *in series* with it.
>
> 2. Similar but quite different use is to inhibit relative motion between two halves of a differential in a permanent or 'full-time' 4x4 system as in the Range Rover, Grand Cherokee, RAV-4 auto. Here the VC *controls* a 'shafts-and-gears' drive system rather than being a link in that drive system. It may be considered as being *in parallel* with it.
>
> **Pre-load in pseudo 4x4.** As soon as a VC locks up there ceases to be relative shaft motion and it will thus unlock again and a 'pseudo 4x4' quickly reverts to 4x2. A clever way round the problem is 'pre-load'. By installing slightly different axle ratios in front and rear axles, the prop shafts will turn at slightly different speeds even without wheel spin so the VC is in a part-locked condition all the time and transferring power to the rear axle. Neat. Take a bow, designers of Fiat Ducato and Land Rover Freelander.
>
> **Hydraulic VC?** A contradiction in terms but Honda's CR-V does what a VC does hydraulically. Hydraulic pumps on front and rear prop shafts compare shaft speed-related outputs and when they differ an inter-shaft clutch begins to lock up.

---

device (as in the Honda CR-V) senses a speed difference between front and rear prop shafts. In other words when one axle begins to spin due to lack of grip or traction the VC will begin to lock up and bind front and rear prop shafts together, making the vehicle a 4x4 for the time being.

Front and rear prop shafts are connected, not by a differential or any 'shafts-and-gears' arrangement but *solely* by a viscous

Four-wheel drive systems – general

NB. *These diagrams do not show hi/lo ratio. See page 4.1 -24 top diagram.*

1. Selectable 4x4 – 'part-time'

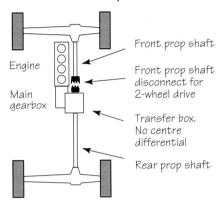

Front prop shaft

Engine

Front prop shaft disconnect for 2-wheel drive

Main gearbox

Transfer box. No centre differential

Rear prop shaft

2. Pseudo 4x4 (or 'auto' 4x4)

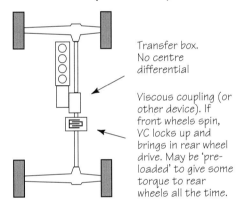

Transfer box. No centre differential

Viscous coupling (or other device). If front wheels spin, VC locks up and brings in rear wheel drive. May be 'pre-loaded' to give some torque to rear wheels all the time.

3. Permanent 4x4 – 'full-time'

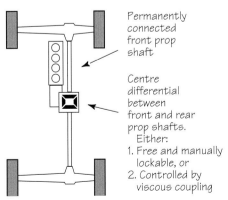

Permanently connected front prop shaft

Centre differential between front and rear prop shafts.
Either:
1. Free and manually lockable, or
2. Controlled by viscous coupling

coupling. On straight main roads with ample grip the two axles are revolving at virtually the same speed – one driving and the other 'trailing' – so the VC remains 'slack'; the vehicle is virtually in two-wheel drive only. However, should the front axle encounter poor traction and spin so that there is a speed difference between it and the rear axle, the VC, sensing the speed difference, locks up and gradually introduces four-wheel drive to get the vehicle out of trouble – see centre diagram, left.

The concept is elegant in that the entire cycle of sensing spin, needing, engaging and disengaging 4x4 is completely automatic. Moreover it is gentle with no shock loading of drive shafts either. On the other hand, the VC has to experience wheel-spin to some degree before it will engage at all – a disadvantage if serious off-road operation is envisaged (classically a static, poor-traction hill restart where you want to avoid wheel-spin at all costs or a long muddy track).

By definition, this kind of 4x4 'lets go' the moment the two prop shafts are once more revolving at the same speed so it cannot be recommended for expeditions where prolonged difficult conditions may be encountered.

A partial exception is a 'pre-loaded' VC that feeds *some* torque to the rear axle all the time and boosts it when conditions get really bad – see panel opposite 'Pre-load in pseudo 4x4'.

3. Permanent 4x4 – 'full time'. In full time 4x4 – the system adopted for vehicles such as Defender, Discovery, Range Rover, Grand Cherokee – there is positive drive to front and rear axles at all times: 'shafts and gears' – lower diagram, left. Such a set up always has a 'centre diff' between the front and rear prop shafts that accommodates the small differences in axle speeds inevitable on cornering and off-road manoeuvring. This central differential is normally 'free' so in extreme conditions there is the possibility that if the front axle had poor traction and the rear was on dry concrete, then the front axle would spin endlessly while the rear axle stayed stationary – see panel on differ-

Know the basic three types of 4x4 system – 'part-time', 'pseudo' and 'full-time'. Everything out there is a variation or combination of these.

entials below – 'The basic thing'.

To preclude this kind of situation, the centre differential is usually lockable. This locking can either be done manually (Defender and Discovery) or automatically as in the Range Rover, RAV4 auto, Grand Cherokee. (See panel on page 4.1 - 18 'VCs, Distinctly different uses', item 2. Also see panel below 'Inhibiting wheel spin'.) In this viscous coupling application the centre diff lock is virtually foolproof; automatically engaged and disengaged, albeit in extreme torque conditions (1st gear low range) the lock-up is not as 100% positive as the manual lock of Defender and Discovery.

There is little doubt that for an arduous expedition the concept of full-time 4x4 is

'Automatic 4x4' is a way of providing 4x4 quickly when required. It disengages at once when traction regained – a two-edged weapon when tackling long soft stretches.

best of all in that as well as giving best on- and off-road traction with least call upon the road or track surface for strength, firm grip or traction, it is ready for anything at any time – the sudden icy patch, the wet leaves on the corner, the sudden soft sandy area in the track. With part time 4x4 you have to know in advance that you will need it – life is not like that – and with 'automatic' 4x4, despite its elegance, you have to experience slip before you get full 4x4. As with selectable 4x4 above, with a manually locked centre differential on a full-time or permanent 4x4 vehicle it is essential to unlock it on firm grippy surfaces.

Once again, as with part-time 4x4, one US interpretaion of the term 'full-time 4x4'

FAMILIAR WITH DIFFERENTIALS? ... ER, YES, OF COURSE ...

The basic thing. We are so familiar with differentials just through usage that we seldom stop to think exactly what is going on inside. Only one pinion is shown here but there are usually two or four. The whole group of bevel gears is attached to the 'carrier' which is almost invariably another wheel which is itself driven to rotate – the gearwheel in the diagram on p 4.1 - 24 marked 'A'. The differential takes this rotational 'power' (P) and passes it on to the two output shafts (two times 50%P) – be they front/rear prop shafts or the half-shafts of an axle. Where the loads

on each shaft are equal they will go at the same speed. When one, due to increased load slows down, the diff action makes the other one speed up. The most usual occurrence of this in transmission is when one shaft, due to *reduction* in load or resistance to rotation (slippery mud or ice) spins, then the other shaft stops: *voila* wheel spin on one wheel. There are degrees of this and the 'grip' wheel may not actually stop.

Inhibiting wheel spin. What is done to stop or inhibit this wheel spin is to make some other connection between the two shafts which prevents excessive speed difference. This device can be:

1. Diff lock. A sliding dog clutch between the two big bevel gears in the diagram (big clonk unless there is no speed difference at moment of engagement). This is the principle of a simple manual, pneumatically or hydraulically operated diff lock.

2. Viscous coupling. A viscous coupling (VC) sitting between the two gears is 'free' when there is little or very small speed differences between the shafts. When the relative rotational speed increases, the viscous fluid stiffens and finally 'locks up', binding one shaft to the other. The reaction time of VCs these days is very quick and the whole thing is automatic and progressive in operation – no big clonk – but lock up may not be absolutely total. For this reason a manual, mechanical diff lock as above has its followers for really serious off-road conditions.

3. Limited slip diff. This is a clutch between the two big bevel gears that limits the slip. A nice idea and better than nothing but the function is a matter of degree and durability depends on usage and design. Most usually associated with axles rather than centre diffs. There are numerous variations of this theme.

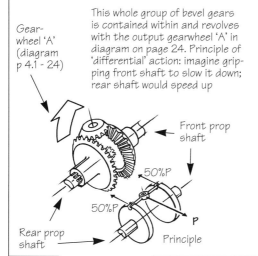

Gearwheel 'A' (diagram p 4.1 - 24)

This whole group of bevel gears is contained within and revolves with the output gearwheel 'A' in diagram on page 24. Principle of 'differential' action: imagine gripping front shaft to slow it down; rear shaft would speed up

Front prop shaft

50%P

50%P

P

Rear prop shaft

Principle

Jeep's 1997 Wrangler TJ, direct descendent of the WW2 'Jeep' of 50 years ago (plus), has finally gone coil spring, transforming ride and articulation. Like Land Rover's Defender, and as befits its senior heritage, designers have retained 'the look' but here held out for its traditional part-time (selectable) 4x4. To make the point unambiguously the brochure says: 'Centre diff: none.' (though refrains from adding, 'OK?!')

is not, as above, to describe the *system* but to describe the *usage,* 'full-time' in the latter case meaning you can use it all of the time, even on hard surfaces. (Hence apparently odd Jeep Cherokee transfer lever, Section 5.3.)

Part-time 4x4 with freewheeling hubs. Ah, freewheeling hubs. A body of opinion holds that freewheeling hubs on the front wheels when in 4x2 will allow the wheels to rotate without the transmission parts revolving and thus save fuel. Whilst the theory of this is undeniable, the practical effect on mpg is often undetectable and, as the saying goes, 'within the bounds of experimental error'.

Freewheeling hubs vary in their operation – manual or automatic – and you should consult your instruction booklet very carefully indeed about procedures and limitations – engaging, disengaging, whether you can use reverse in 4x4. (Consult the booklet; the salesman will rarely know!)

Combinations of features; names. Various tunes are played on the 4x4 sytems categorised into three types on page 4.1 - 19 to accommodate what the market is perceived to want – even if this amounts to little more than the need to be different! Jeep and Mitsubishi currently (1996/7) offer transmission systems (respectively 'Select-Trac' and 'Super-Select' that provide the

Full time (permanent) 4x4 spreads drive loads between all four wheels all the time. You are ready for anything – all the time. Functionally the best.

Land Rover Freelander (right) has what may be termed 'biased' automatic 4x4 (a VC with 400 NM preload) with a degree of drive going to the rear wheels all the time and a final boost later. Honda CR-V has quick-acting 'pseudo 4x4' but like Freelander, no low ratio transfer gears (see p 4.1 - 24). For the most demanding expeditions, two-speed transfer box and 'shafts and gears' 4x4 are best.

If there is a 'best', this is probably it – full-time 4x4 with centre diff lock. Leyland 4x4, in service with British army since early 1990s, has manually selectable, pneumatically activated centre diff lock. Range Rover has permanent 4x4 (shafts and gears) but diff lock effected by automatic viscous coupling lock-up.

Diff locks are an effective solution to wheel spin but conceptually crude, adversely affecting handling. Must be engaged in advance, disengaged when not essential.

selectable option of 4x2 <u>and</u> full-time 4x4 with centre diff. It is hard to imagine anyone opting for 4x2 if they have the alternative of 4x4 with an elegantly equipped VC centre diff (lockable too) but the marketing men may well have it right in a few cases, if only to appease the 'bells and whistles' demand. The plethora of registered trade marks from which the above were taken also includes 'Command-Trac', 'Control-Trac', 'Quadra-Trac'. No harm done, but if you are in the market for such a vehicle satisfy yourself, despite the fast talking salesmen and woolly brochures, what it all really amounts to. Go back to page 4.1 - 19 and start from there.

Controlling left/right wheel spin

Axle diff locks. Any, all or none of the above 4x4 set-ups may be had, according to manufacturer, with cross-axle diff locks, ie a diff lock that locks the right wheel to the left wheel for those embarrassing one-wheel spinning situations – usually a 'diagonal suspension' situation; see Section 5.3 and *The Land Rover Experience.* Stepping back one pace to recap what the overall aim is, there are, even here, different approaches to the problem which is simply that of maintaining traction. In some ways, long wheel travel and diff locks can be considered an

either/or design solution. If that sounds obscure, consider this: spinning wheels tend to occur when one wheel is offloaded. Offloading occurs when the axle cannot follow the contour of the ground well enough. Ensure long axle travel, the wheels will stay in contact with uneven ground and the situation will be less likely to arise in the first place – a lower cost plus simplicity approach favoured by Land Rover for many years, fitting in as it does with a design philosophy of long travel coil springs anyway.

The other approach (photos opposite) is for a designer to say, 'Well lots of wheel movement equals lots of body roll so we'll go for inhibiting body roll and install cross axle diff locks instead (and hang the expense).' Pinzgauer have a high body anyway because of (see p 4.1 - 27) portal axles, plus these axles are short-length swing axles which should not be provoked too much on corners if you want a quiet life. The designers have opted in this case for a limited amount of (all-independent) wheel movement plus diff locks all round, even on the 6x6 – a solution strongly focused on off-road performance and on a driver who will know when to use (and disengage) the system.

Diff lock caution, traction control. Axle diff locks, like centre diff locks, have to be used with caution – and that means not on hard grippy surfaces. Rule of thumb is to select axle diff lock only when you really need it and then de-select; the cab usually has a fairly unambiguous warning light (or lights) to remind you! One way of getting the advantage of an axle diff lock without its disadvantages and operating limitations is to use traction control (eg Range Rover, Mercedes ML320). Traction control involves slight braking of the spinning wheel (or throttling back, sometimes both). The individual wheel speed sensors employed for the anti-lock braking system can be utilised to pass rpm information to a control unit which compares left wheel speed with right wheel speed and then applies a touch of brake to the spinning wheel. This is an elegant approach since it uses equipment already in place, can function on or off-road, is fully automatic and, unlike a diff lock, has the advantage of no handling problems. **Diff locks or not?** For difficult or extreme conditions opt for axle diff locks. This is a very general statement since, as we have seen the requirement will itself vary according to the vehicle you are using. If you are fitting diff locks to a vehicle that was not originally designed for them, remember that

you could well be increasing the torque load on the axle half shafts and these should be up-rated at the same time. Most of all, if you take diff locks on board, temper your driving accordingly:

- Use only when definitely required.
- Engage when the shafts are stationary – not in the middle of a hectic wheel spinning bout.
- Disengage at once when not needed.
- Never use on hard roads.
- Be doubly cautious in the case of front axle diff lock which can make the steering feel as if it has 'frozen'.

The human element. As we shall see in Section 5.3, the main way to conquer wheel spin is gentle use of the throttle foot! Don't let it happen in the first place; even if you *are* only human!

Wheel spin on one wheel can be controlled by not letting it happen (keep axle on ground), locking the differential or stopping it when it happens (traction control).

The task is the same – to maintain traction. Discovery uses articulation to keep wheels on the ground. Pinzgauer, with short half-axles and high C of G, opts for locking cross-axle differentials. Somewhere between, Range Rover's rear wheel, about to lift and spin, will be quenched by traction control braking. Results? Similar.

Two-speed transfer box – high and low ratio (range)

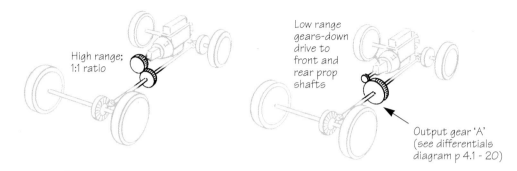

High range; 1:1 ratio

Low range gears-down drive to front and rear prop shafts

Output gear 'A' (see differentials diagram p 4.1 - 20)

Two-speed transfer gearbox

Not always there. With a new type of 4x4 joining the market optimised for on-road or only mild off-road conditions, a two-speed transfer box is no longer standard fit. This new breed of 4x4 – RAV-4, Freelander, Honda CR-V – is capable of a wide range of adventurous activity but for the most demanding off-tracks conditions where heavy going, repeated recovery and extreme gradients are envisaged, a vehicle with a two-speed transfer gearbox would be essential.

As the diagram above shows, its function is to gear-down the drive leaving the

Some 4x4s don't have a two-speed transfer box – so no low ratio gears. No problem for 'activity' sports trips etc but intrepid bush or jungle explorers likely to need one.

main gearbox at the point it joins the propeller shafts, thus providing a low range version of *all* the gears in the main gearbox. An indication of this, as manifested by speed in the gears in both high and low range is shown below.

Transfer lever – or button. Most transfer gearboxes' range change is effected by moving a transfer gear lever from a number of 'Hi' positions to a single 'Lo' position. This is a good deal more positive than electrically actuated range change and, as we shall see in Section 5.3 'Driving', there are other advantages too. Almost invariably the manufacturer's recommendation is to effect range changes with the vehicle stationary.

Speed in the gears – two-speed transfer box

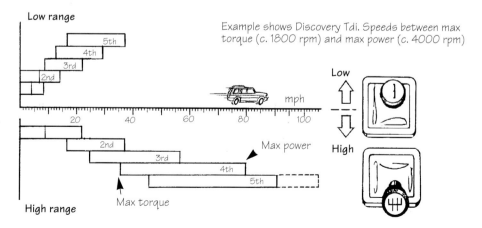

Low range

5th
4th
3rd
2nd

Example shows Discovery Tdi. Speeds between max torque (c. 1800 rpm) and max power (c. 4000 rpm)

mph

20   40   60   80   100

Low

High

2nd
3rd
4th
5th

Max power

Max torque

High range

Auto or manual

Elegant and gentle. The idea of automatic transmission for off-road or expedition use usually takes people by surprise. Automatic transmissions are neither a sissy option nor the passports to high fuel consumption they once were considered. Looking at the rpm an automatic transmission asks of the engine on a given off-road section in comparison to a white-knuckle manual driver it is easy to see that the opposite is sometimes the case.

On a track where a soft patch takes you by surprise, the down change can be lightning-quick and in rough-track 'forest floor' situations the auto really shines, reliably exciting countless gentle gear changes in long-day conditions where, with a manual, driver fatigue may rear its head.

An automatic will make immaculate UP-changes on steep loose inclines when you are in danger of provoking wheel spin, indeed it will pay to select low range '3' (or '2' in a 3-speed) to limit the extent to which it can do this. An automatic will also reduce shock loading on drive shafts.

What do the toughies use? Many vehicles used as standard in the armed forces worldwide are equipped with automatic transmission – the operational advantages in terms of driver workload and vehicle durability are seen to win over costs. Cost is about the only disadvantage that an individual expedition will find in opting for an automatic transmission vehicle. There may be a slight increase in fuel consumption although, with lock-up (ie no slip) on 4th in most boxes now, the increase will be small or insignificant; even the usual increase in weight is down to a few kg – or in some cases is in favour of the automatic.

Test your prejudices. Satisfy yourself if you have doubts about automatics. Take a day's course at an off-road school if you are not sure; most people become instant converts for the sheer ease of driving in demanding conditions and for the gentle treatment of the vehicle.

Do use low range. Be sure to get into low ratio when required or you will be using the torque converter like a slipping clutch and will induce overheating of the transmission fluid. Remember also to select '1' for steep descents; indeed the latest Range Rover has an automatic 1st gear hold if lift-off takes place at 2000 rpm or more.

Reliability, service. The reliability of automatics is , if anything, better than that of a manual box – partly because they are difficult to mis-handle. One expert summed it up: 'If an auto is OK for the first year, it'll live forever.' (Land Rover design specification centres on 120,000 miles and 10 year service life.) Because vehicle dealers encounter so few faults with autos and may lack experience, go to a specialist automatic gearbox engineer for a pre-expedition service or if you want a second-hand vehicle checked; they are working on them every day. Have the fluid changed, a check for leaks and functional checks monitored pre-trip.

Coolers. Be sure your vehicle has a transmission oil cooler (mounted up front where the engine fan is) and that the fluid overheat light works – about the only in-the-field point to keep an eye on. (All Land Rover auto vehicles are configured this way, with a fluid overheat warning light too.)

Not all the same. Some automatics have clunky changes; clunks are not why you opt for an auto. The Discovery and Range Rover in petrol or diesel forms are very well matched to the ZF auto box; the effect is like driving behind a great big electric motor.

Automatic transmission is a beautiful and gentle way to handle power, especially effective off-road. Only disadvantage is cost. Start saving!

New Range Rover's H-gate is a simple, single-lever way of controlling automatic transmission, low transfer gears and a 'sport/normal' selection of gear change points. Cognoscenti will notice inability to do often useful low-to-high range change on the move.

Suspension, weight distribution

Geometry, suspension

Let the wheels do their job. Just as four-wheel drive is about getting the most of your engine's power turned into forward push or traction without wheel spin, so vehicle geometry is about ensuring that the wheels – and only the wheels – are in contact with the ground to enable this to happen. On rough terrain, deeply rutted tracks, when crossing ditches or other obstacles, 'grounding' the front, rear, underbelly or the centre part of the axle can cause damage to the vehicle and probably stop you altogether too. Many trips, by their aim, nature and their route along roads and reasonable tracks, will be immune from such problems but if your expedition vehicle is destined for some rough tracks or a lot of off-tracks work you will be looking for:

Even long travel coil springs get you hung up if you provoke them enough – and afford chauvinist instructor opportunity for the ultimate in back-seat driving! Tail bumping is the most common form of grounding, especially, if, as here, a low-trailer hitch is fitted. Easier to dig out of than bellying.

Big wheels, small overhangs, under-axle and underbelly clearance are things to look for in vehicle geometry. Short wheelbase helps. Portal axles too; high but costly.

- Big wheels – under-axle clearance
- Small overhangs front and rear
- Plenty of underbelly clearance

This latter will point toward a shortish wheelbase but this may itself conflict with optimum load distribution or the carriage of bulky loads where a long load bed is required. As we shall see under 'Weight distribution' on p 4.1 - 29, a forward control layout is a way of overcoming the two potentially incompatible attributes.

The above headings, as shown in the diagrams, relate to an absolute standard of off-road vehicle capability. In day-to-day expedition work some, such as under-axle ground clearance and rear overhang, will be invoked more frequently than others.

Together and in optimum quantities, however, they contribute to an effortlessly competent off-road vehicle.

Portal axles – etc. Mention of some mild exotica is appropriate at this stage. Conceptually brave and hugely effective as an approach to maximising under-axle clearance is to use portal axles. Here, by using reduction gears within each wheel hub of the vehicle, the centre line of the axle is raised above that of the wheel by 10 cm or more by the offset of the gears. The geometry and ensuring the stability of such a device would cause many an engineer's

'Grounding' geometry

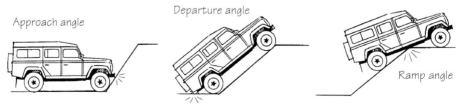

Approach angle

Departure angle

Ramp angle

Under-axle clearance

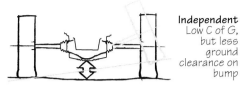

Independent
Low C of G,
but less
ground
clearance on
bump

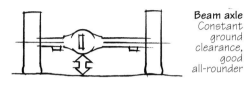

Beam axle
Constant
ground
clearance,
good
all-rounder

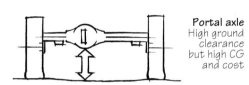

Portal axle
High ground
clearance
but high CG
and cost

palms to become moist and its cost reduce an accountant to apoplexy. Nevertheless Pinzgauer use the concept, achieving with a 16 inch wheel the kind of under-axle clearance you would associate with a wheel four to six inches greater in diameter. In the Pinzgauer's case a little of the advantage is lost by use of independent suspension but Mercedes' mighty Unimog (20 inch rims) straps downward-offset reduction gears on the end of a *beam axle* with appropriately Wagnerian results.

The deeper ruts of Africa's bush tracks would respectfully admit defeat by such engineering; along with off-road agility, however, unsprung weight, centre of gravity and cost all go up too, so it will not be a solution for all. Needless to say, portal axle layouts are found on vehicles whose role is heavily biased toward off-road extreme-conditions operation.

Articulation, anti-roll bars. The other half of seeing that the wheels can do their job is ensuring that they can 'reach down' to the ground when it is uneven. That is 'articulation' and we have briefly touched on it already (photo: Discovery p 4.1 - 23):

• As much wheel movement or axle articulation as possible.

Really supple but well damped suspension contributes to optimum traction in soft or poor-grip conditions. If you are wondering why all off-road vehicles are not designed this way it is because there is a disadvantage in the shape of body roll on corners when driving on roads at brisk speeds. The early Range Rover (Classic as it is now called) had very long-travel coil springs and no anti-roll bar in order to obtain maximum axle articulation. Whilst it was hailed as the best off-road vehicle ever, those who used it

Axle design, articulation, anti-roll bars all part of designer's agonising juggling act mixing on- and off-road performance while still keeping accountants happy.

Discovery and Pinzgauer both use 16 inch wheel rims but Pinzgauer (right) opts for portal axles' high ground clearance and centre of gravity in a very off-road focused configuration. Discovery aims for well judged on/off-road compromise.

Defender 110 showing off extreme articulation in realistic conditions approaches wheel lift off. Articulation is the means of maintaining wheels-on traction under the most demanding off-road conditions. Ride enhanced too.

Pliant, long-travel springs – usually coil springs – are the means of keeping wheels on the ground to do their job of providing traction. Leaf springs' friction jars.

mainly on-road – for the Range Rover's other well known attributes – opted for less body roll. The designers had a knife edge to tread when they fitted anti-roll bars taming on-road cornering roll yet still maintaining off-road performance; the same development sequence has applied to the Discovery.

In the great cosmic order of things there is, once again, no 'best'. Body roll and free articulation are in general terms simple either/or attributes; maximise one and you compromise the other. Each manufacturer makes their own judgement on where the optimum lies.

Having your cake ... . Exceptional articulation is still one of the cornerstones of Land Rover chassis design but the Freelander targets a slightly more road-oriented market sector with *four-wheel* independent suspension and lower centre of gavity. Provision of four-wheel traction control (anti-wheel spin) is a great on-road safety feature but, as the group of pictures on p 4.1 - 23 shows, it also elegantly overcomes the potential disadvantages of this more limited articulation by precluding wheel spin from a lifted wheel in extreme off-road conditions as well.

Suspension – leaf springs. A legacy from the days of horse-drawn carriages, leaf springs are a simple way of effecting springing; they also have the advantage of locating the axle as well, in effect forming a pair of trailing radius arms to position the axle relative to the chassis. In nearly every case they are also the means of lateral location. Multi-leaf springs, however, thanks to their diet of corrosion, grit and dust, suffer from high inter-leaf friction so there is a high 'break-out' force before they will start flexing at all and the result is a stiff ride, especially in an unladen vehicle. Wheel travel is usually limited too. There are ways round these problems – very long springs will give better wheel movement (albeit bringing lateral location problems in their wake due to flexing) and if the spring is made as a single or two-leaf unit, bowed so that the leaves are not touching too much, then the break-out 'stiction' is reduced too. Making such leaves wide will give the designer firm lateral location of the axle but there is a balancing act to be done. Once again the 101 inch wheelbase forward control '1-tonne' military Land Rover must be quoted as exemplar for such a layout.

Suspension – coil springs. Coil springs, of course, have no 'stiction' so give an inherently more compliant ride – in the case of an

Trucks of this size achieve effective articulation by use of torsionally pliant chassis. Despite rigid leaf springs, Bedfords have legendary chassis twist to keep wheels from spinning. Leyland 4x4 (twin taper-leaf springs) and Unimog have open-channel chassis too. Weight distribution is ideal.

off-road expedition vehicle this enables the wheels to stay in responsive contact with the ground better than with leaf springs and thus yield better traction. But like the wobbly head of a jack-in-the-box the axle will need both longitudinal and lateral locating bars since it is getting no help from the spring itself. These are invariably some kind of longitudinal radius arm, lateral Panhard rod or swing wishbone. These, with their associated rubber bushings, add to cost which, of course, is why they have been a long time gaining widespread acceptance.

Suspension – mixtures. For many years the Japanese made off-roaders with torsion bar independent front suspension and leaf sprung rear ends. In their view at the time the benefits of lower centre of gravity at the front outweighed the off-road ground clearance penalty on bump and, at the back, the simplicity and lower costs of 'cart springs' outweighing their less supple ride. Such vehicles were reliable and sold well – the result of clear design engineering decisions (wrong in the eyes of some!) and precise targeting of perceived needs in particular sectors. The public (and most designers) are

now leaning towards better ride so many of these vehicles are appearing with coil springs and more comprehensive transmission features and the customers are accepting the engineering cost increases involved. As always, the vehicles are blending with the demand trends – but still there are different approaches.

All coil springs are not the same. For over a decade the Range Rover was the only all-coil sprung vehicle. Because, like any 'non-commercial' vehicle, it had a lowish payload-to-GVW ratio and because it had exceptional axle articulation, many people have associated coil springs with this kind of very large wheel movement and pliant ride. This is not always the case. All manufacturers do not make coil suspension the same way and by making the springs short and stiff to resist body roll produce vehicles with mediocre ride, limited articulation and thus less fluent off-road performance. The Lada Niva is a case in point; conceptually the Niva suspension is very similar to the Range Rover but, partly due to it being a smaller vehicle, the execution is different and the result is a terrier-like approach to obstacles rather than the Range Rover's wolf hound.

Weight distribution

Spreading the load. Weight distribution ideally should be 50/50 front/rear so that both axles and each tyre carry an equal load. The relevance of this becomes clear in soft going where it is analogous to walking on weak thin ice – the heavier foot will go through, ie the back end bogs down. This ideal weight distribution is rarely achieved except with forward-control vehicles such as the 1 tonne (military) Land Rover, the Bedford and Leyland 4-tonners and the Pinzgauer. Laden long wheelbase light 4x4s and pick-ups tend to be tail heavy (exacerbated by excessive rear overhang), especially when at max GVW, so it is important when, loading, to keep high-density items well ahead of the rear axle in order to do what you can to redress the unequal axle loading – see Section 4.3 'Loading'.

In general coil springs are best for ride, off-road traction and braking on- and off-road. Early Range Rovers set standard but coil springs don't always feel like that.

Engine, configuration, service

Petrol or diesel

Fuel: availability. First know your route. If use of a petrol engine is a real possibility, know its generic type (p 2.6 - 9) and consult the tables in Section 2.6 'Fuel, oil, fluids' or the latest Octel survey to find out the grade of fuels available en route. As covered in that section, petrol engines have to be tuned to the fuels available and some kinds of modern engine cannot be tuned to use very low grade gasolines; they will destroy themselves if you try. The list of countries in which only low octane fuels are available is not large but the areas affected are. Egypt, Sudan, Ethiopia and Somalia, for instance, have no fuel above 90 octane.

Fuel load, cost. So your route may rule out some petrol engines on grounds of fuel grade. Or it may not. The relative economy of petrol vs diesel must be considered next; the distance between refuelling points will influence your choice of engine. The fuel economy of diesels means a smaller fuel load (maybe a smaller vehicle) – the diagram on p 4.1 - 4 hammers home what fuel load does to residual payload. There is often also a substantial price advantage to buying

Choice of petrol or diesel engine greatly influenced by fuel availability, type, grade and cost in expedition area. Diesel usually a lot cheaper, more widely available.

diesel fuel overseas compared with petrol and it is well worth making specific advance enquiries at an early stage in your planning.

If all things are equal. Generally, petrol engines are lighter, more powerful, more thirsty, and cheaper (to buy) than diesels. Diesels, however, have advanced dramatically in recent years in terms of power, responsiveness and efficiency. Despite the folk-lore depicting all diesels as sloggers with flat torque curves over a wide engine rpm band, they often have quite a peaky torque curve demanding frequent and rapid use of the gearbox – albeit no more or less than for a petrol engine. The peak torque, however, is usually at 1800-2200 rpm – low compared with a petrol engine but not as low as it sounds since most diesels will not rev above about 4500 rpm anyway.

Turbo diesels. Turbo-charged and inter-cooled diesels cost more than a simple diesel but offer improved *efficiency* – improved power and fuel consumption, the very essence of the expedition requirement. (Turbo-charging is a way of supercharging the engine. Exhaust gases spin a turbine driving a compressor which gets more air into

Benefits of turbo diesel economy are often very important indeed – this particular leg having a 380 mile gap between fuelling points. At the speeds that wildlife and track difficulties demanded, aerodynamic drag was greatly reduced and 37-39 mpg was regular figure on this Defender 90 with 2.5 litre Tdi.

the engine so that more fuel can be injected and the power enhanced. But compression makes the air hot which makes it expand so it is hard to get as much *weight* of air into the cylinder as if it were cold. The intercooler is a heat exchanger which uses ambient air to cool the compressed air going to the cylinders.) Not all turbo-charged diesels are intercooled – a cost compromise again.

High power conversions. Beware of 'performance conversions'. On expeditions durability and reliability is all and high power conversions will usually compromise the structural margins of an engine.

Reputations; assessing reliability. This is a difficult and surprisingly subjective matter. Getting a clear story from the 'experts' is half the battle. Many will recount a second-hand story from someone whose engine 'blew up' – an over-used term that seldom if ever means what it sounds like and equally rarely yields to more incisive enquiry.

Solid repairable simplicity has an attractive ring – the 2.5 litre, 4 cylinder Land Rover petrol engine, for example. Certainly there are parts of some modern engines that cannot be repaired in the field and electronic control units (ECUs), engine management chips, fuel injection pumps and injectors are among them. Repair-by-replacement is often the order of the day even in maintenance centres and then sometimes accompanied by electronic analysis or facilitated by the use of special tools. That said, the reliability of such components is generally very high.

You have to make the difficult assessment about reliability before you make your vehicle and engine choice. In that they *don't* rely on spark plugs and contact breakers, diesels look a good bet if running without routine checks is your aim which of course it shouldn't be. Traditionally diesels 'have a long life' since we all think back to trucks that go on for ever. Modern but not too modern is probably the best phrase to have in your mind. Modern engines are far more reliable than they used to be but the very newest sometimes have teething troubles, remedies for which are quietly incorporated in production nine months to a year after

launch.

The choice. All things being equal, a modern, *established* turbo diesel is probably the best engine for an expedition vehicle – especially where distances are large. Diesels tolerate poor fuel better than petrol engines. Vehicle power-weight ratios (table p 4.1 - 14) show that the days of diesel vehicles being underpowered are gone. In an older vehicle (the old diesel era), the 2.5 litre Land Rover petrol engine (*et al*) takes some beating.

Configuration

Hard-top, station wagon, crew cab. If you are seeking the quintessential expedition experience, nothing encapsulates the feeling of space and freedom so well as driving a screen-down, open-top vehicle off tracks across open desert. If you are seeking practicality and want to justify it, a vehicle in this trim is also probably 100-150 kg lighter than a hard-top equivalent and that, in logistically demanding conditions, means more payload; this was the case in the 'topless' 101 Land Rovers used in the West East Sahara Expedition (photo p 4.1 -13) where hood rails, screen, windows and canvas were dispensed with.

A soft-top is not as light as a no-top, especially if fitted with a robust roll-over

Diesel engines for light 4x4s have been transformed since early '80s. Power, driveability enhanced, mpg around 25% better than petrol equivalent.

Leaving screen, windows, and top off yields valuable payload. Driving is exhilarating.

Removing aft seats considerably enhances payload and space available when a long-range expedition is planned. It also enables high-density cargo to be placed further forward to improve fore-and-aft weight distribution.

bar, but a Land Rover of this kind with built-in lockable compartments can be made reasonably pilfer-proof – not really thief proof – and, as well as being lighter, is less of a tin oven than a hard-top in hot climates. It also fortuitously precludes the temptation to fit outsize roof-racks which should in any case be avoided. Regrettably, unless vehicles in a group are never left unattended the increased worldwide incidence of crime demands that in most cases a hard-top vehicle be used and equipped with comprehensive anti-theft devices and alarms.

Which hard-top? The choice, if there is one in the vehicle range you select, really is between types of hard-top:
- Windowless van-type
- Station wagon with doors, windows
- Crew cab.

Much will be dictated, again, by the length of trip, logistics and thus how many people you will carry in the vehicle. Inevitably the longer trips seem to gravitate towards two persons per vehicle with the remainder of the room devoted to cargo. In this case the van-type hard-top has the advantages of less weight albeit you should fit internal roof trim and side panel insulation to reduce noise and heat in hot climates.

Despite this the weight will still be lower than a station wagon type of vehicle – in a

Need for thief-proofing makes hard top virtually essential. 'Van' type yields more payload. Two persons per vehicle is best on long trips; residual payload is enhanced.

Defender 110 you will gain 105 kg of payload by using a hard-top. Of course a station wagon (as a 4-door) will have the advantage of easier access to cargo and the windows permit better all-round vision. A crew cab – four doors on a pick-up with a reduced cargo bed length – is a most practical solution where more than two people are to be carried such as a family trip. Where children are small it is an idea to raise the back seats so that they can take better advantage of the view on long sectors and you may also find this enables you to install underseat storage at the same time. If you are modifying seats in this way, though, be certain that seat security and seat belt attachments are fully up to the standards required.

Seats out. In a station wagon or any three- or four-door vehicle carrying only two persons remove the rear seat(s) to save weight. This will reduce your kerb weight and increase your available payload considerably – you will be aghast at the weight of the hardware you remove and can revel in the additional fuel or water cans that it represents, especially if the vehicle is in the 'luxury' class. As we shall see in Section 4.2 'Modifications', seat anchorages can be used as the basis for cargo lashing points.

'Van' side windows, roof-racks. See Section 4.2 'Vehicle modifications'.

Simplicity, service, spares

Keep it simple. All things are relative and what is considered simple now in terms of an ideal expedition vehicle would have been regarded as complex not long ago – power steering and electronic ignition, for example, now being taken for granted. To further confuse and confound the easy pigeon-holing of vehicles and their characteristics, reliability as a whole of any given component is improving. So what to do? As with engines a couple of pages back, automatic this, electronic that, say the traditionalists, 'Why, I can remember ... '. What most of us remember is that things actually went wrong a lot more often than they do now but when they did they were easier to fix yourself. Standards of reliability these days – in general – are off the graph compared with those of thirty years ago.

There is, alas, no easy answer to this question of reliability – doubly important in the context of an expedition where the implications of failure are so high.

Keeping the specification simple will certainly be a good start. Air conditioning is a case in point where hot climates are concerned; a lot of cost, climatic shock every time you get in and out of the vehicle, a lot of weight, a lot of complexity. Strike it from your list and you will benefit in most cases.

Service, spares. All this agreed – verging on platitudes – you will still have to make your own assessment of the reliability record of your chosen vehicle. Is the design 'bedded in' or a brand new model; what if there really is a problem; are there dealers in the area you are visiting – or the country or even the continent? Is there a course you can go on before departure? Are there good service manuals? What is a sensible spares pack? What about the need for special tools?

Operation – mechanical sympathy. Better than no answer at all, though, is the enjoinder to ponder the fact that very rarely do things break of their own accord. Far more usually they are broken by people; usually through insensitive operation, driving, overloading, inattention. You will read it elsewhere in this book but the acquisition of mechanical sympathy, that sensitivity to the operation of equipment, especially in conditions of stress, is an attribute almost beyond price when it comes to keeping going on an expedition. Of course there will come times when you must operate the vehicle to its full potential but even here it can be done with sensitivity – feel for it, care for it, don't break it. Prepare the vehicle impeccably; drive impeccably too.

Inspection, preparation

New or second-hand. Just as the above selection criteria will apply to *any* vehicle in matching it to the task ahead, so pre-purchase and/or pre-departure inspections of a very demanding nature must precede the expedition, be it on a new vehicle, one you already have, or – most importantly since you do not yet 'know' it – a second-hand vehicle bought specially for the trip.

'The garage at home is the place to do the servicing, not out in the field.' 'With thorough preparation you can almost leave the spares pack at home.' These are but two of the pearls of wisdom encapsulating the need for the most painstaking inspection, servicing and preparation, whatever vehicle you decide to take on your journey.

New buy? Independent inspection. The seller of any prospective expedition vehicle should have no objection to your having an independent inspection carried out before purchase. Be there, if possible, when it is done. Be sure it includes a drive in which steering, transmission and suspension clonks are felt and listened for. Play or wear in steering, transmission or suspension bushes will get rapidly worse on a demanding trip.

Since you will be doing it nightly on the trip and will have to get to know the parts anyway, carry out the 'on-your-back' inspection schedule outlined in Section 5.5.1 as a start – yourself, and before committing yourself to purchase. Any oil leak matters but some are absolute no-go faults – on a Land Rover product, leakage where either of the wading plugs are inserted. The aft one means the danger of oil on the clutch, the forward one hazards the camshaft drive belt; either can be an expedition stopper.

Major service. Depending on your vehicle and its servicing intervals, have a major service done (be there if possible) before leaving – a 12000 or 24000 mile check, for example. As well as all-round oil changes with carefully chosen oils (Section 2.6) hoses, accessory drive belts, camshaft drive belt (if applicable) brake shoes or pads, batterie(s) and tyres should be renewed.

Assessing reliability of your chosen vehicles requires mature advice, fastidious pre-expedition overhaul and maintenance. There's no substitute for taking care.

Section 4.2

Vehicles:

Vehicle modifications

COVERAGE OF THIS SECTION

Why modify?

If it ain't broke, don't fix it. To those who question, from their high horse, why there should even be a section on modifications to vehicles – the 'height of the horse' being proportional to how much they may have just paid for their 'go-anywhere' 4x4 – it must be said that many vehicles can lope, unmodified, through a dozen expedition outings of a fairly routine nature just as they left the showroom. A fishing trip, a day on reasonable hill tracks, a week-end's climbing or camping can usually be accomplished on a 'bung it in and go' basis albeit you are beginning to get ideas about how you will do the next trip by the time you get back.

The back of the vehicle looks like a tip by the time you get home, somebody's muddy boots landed in the kitchen box on that big bump you went over, the shovel wore a hole into the side of someone's bag with the vibration, you really could have done with more light last night, the water can fell over on the bends – regularly ...

The hazards ahead. Cargo tie downs, compartments, racks, and a bit more light are the usual starting points for modifications. There is only so much a production vehicle can provide and that, by the disciplines of commercial viability, will be aimed at the majority of users, few of whom will welcome the additional cost of features that they themselves will not use. Think in any depth about more demanding trips to distant destinations and you quickly come up with a list of possible hazards for which it would be nice to be prepared:

    Dust
    Extreme heat
    Extreme cold
    Getting stuck
    Tracks with deep ruts
    Cargo bumping around
    Camping lights
    Deep wading
    Rocks in the track
    Carrying recovery gear

What's designed-in already? Depending on the state of your selected vehicle when you acquire it you should consider what, if any, modifications are needed to suit it to the particular tasks of the expedition. In terms of climatic extremes most modern vehicles are already designed to accommodate ambient temperatures down to around -30°C or up to 45-50°C for normal operation though even here the situation is different in the case of cold soak or desert conditions of repeated boggings in soft sand with high engine output and little forward speed so there is no oncoming breeze to cool the sump or transmission oils.

You will be seeking to safeguard and enhance the performance of the vehicle, protect it from damage, secure it and your equipment, tailor the ensemble into a package that will make expedition life easier and smoother.

Modifications – the spectrum

The categories. Most modifications fall into three categories and it helps to consider them in this light when deciding what, if anything, needs to be done to the vehicles on which an expedition is based. Not all of the following are 'do' mods; some are 'don't do' or 'think very hard first' headings. They are dealt with in this section in the order shown below.

1. Vehicle function – engine and electrics.
 • *Engine and fuel system*
High level air intake, filter
Radiator fan – electrical
Electronic contact breakers
Tachometer
Diesel tachometers
Oil temperature gauge, cooler
Long range fuel tank
Fuel sedimenter/filter
Fuel filler extension
Fuel system/block heaters
 • *Electrical system*
Heavy duty battery
Second battery, split charge system
Battery master switches
Battery warmer
Accessory power points
De-activate the courtesy lights.
Extra interior lighting
Moveable hand spotlight

Not all vehicles and not all expeditions require modifications to be done. However, matching your specification to your trip brings huge benefits to safety, convenience.

- *Vehicle security alarm*
- *Navigation system*

2. General and expedition function.
Special fitments related to the role of the
expedition, protection of the vehicle, tie-
downs for equipment, lockable compartments etc.

   Tyres
   Speedometer calibration
   Roof-rack
   Roll-over bars
   Roof tent
   Steering gear protection
   Fuel tank protection
   Bull bars, side bars
   Underbelly protection

   Tow hooks and rings
   HiLift jack sockets
   Sand ladder and shovel racks
   Winch
   Seats out
   Internal tie-downs
   Special equipment mountings
   DIBS mirrors of desert

3. Crew function. Modifications that
affect crew comfort:

   Vehicle upholstery
   Extra ventilation
   Floor insulation
   Roof and body-side insulation
   'Van' side windows
   Audio

VEHICLE FUNCTION MODIFICATIONS
Engine and fuel system

Engine function improvements

High level air intake, filter. The main
criteria to think about are the adequacy of
the built-in air filter system and then give
thought to the source of the air feeding it.
All vehicles will have engine intake air filters adequate for normal operations. Every
filter is designed for use in a particular
engine so 'adding a filter' is not an option
unless you are an engine designer and can
tune the carburation as well.

There is scope for improvement however, in where the air comes from. Look at
your vehicle to see the source of the air
going into the filter; some surprising design
weakness do get through into production,
an historical hiccup being the standard 1-
tonne military Land Rover that, incredibly,
drew its engine air from the one place guaranteed to be dusty – the wheel arch (easily
modified to inhale via the battery compartment).

Even the early diesel engined Discovery
(200 Tdi), in all other respects ideal for
desert or bush use, takes engine air from
inside the double skin of the left wing which

*Don't let engine
breathe dust.
Check source of
engine air; a
raised intake
also enhances
wading capabili-
ty. Beware add-
on electric fans
and rickety
mountings.*

in turn gets it from the door shut-line (ie the
gap between the door and bodywork)
immediately aft of the left front wheel arch;
again a reliable source of dust swirl.

It is possible to modify this and many
other vehicles by fitting a raised intake pipe
to ensure a clean air source. Many vehicles
take air from within the under-bonnet area
which frequently is turbulent with dust
sucked up by the fan or from preceding
vehicles. A raised intake overcomes this
problem. Such an intake also permits deeper
wading should floods be encountered.

Radiator fan – electrical. Add-on – as
opposed to original design – electrical cooling fans are not always the good idea they
may seem at first. A properly cowled
engine-driven fan with a viscous coupling
will be adequate for virtually every condition you are likely to find. When not part of
the original design, an electrical fan's large
'dead' central area not covered by blades
can give rise to doubts on whether it is
doing more harm than good. Be manically
particular about the mountings. These are
often 'designed' with inadequate pinch-

Dust is the constant enemy. Get behind this vehicle, or even have it come towards you and your engine inhales dust. Air filters and ignition points suffer. Know where the engine air comes from (note dust round wheel arches and doors above) and fit a raised intake if possible.

clamps on round shafts; almost beyond belief, one actually clings to the radiator face itself with nylon straps! Such mountings would be cause for unease on the velvety roads of suburbia, never mind the stresses and vibration involved with remote-area driving on corrugated tracks for weeks on end. In one recorded expedition incident an electric add-on fan, mounted in the way the vendor intended, vibrated loose and, blades whirring, hit the radiator matrix. Not recommended.

Electronic contact breakers. Mechanical 'make-and-break' ignition systems fitted to older and some current petrol engines do not hold their adjustment or last long in dusty conditions because the rate of wear on the nylon heel of the contact breaker is rapid and excessive. On the early Rover V8 engine, for example, the contact breakers were short lived even in the UK. With powdered dust on desert tracks they are much worse due to the attraction of the dust into

the distributor head though static electricity; the same problem affects many vehicles. Contactless electronic ignition is the substitution of the mechanical cam-activated 'make-and-break' with an electronic/optical sensor; once fitted, no variation in timing can result from wear and no further attention to the mechanism is necessary.

The long-established Lumenition system is highly recommended and can be retro-fitted using available kits for the 2.25 and 2.5 litre Land Rover 4-cylinder, the early V8 and quite a number of Japanese vehicles too. Lumenition is available through local auto-electrical outlets or the manufacturers Autocar Electrical Equipment, 49-51 Tiverton Street, London SE1 6NZ, tel 0171.403.4334.

Tachometers. An engine rpm gauge (tachometer) is an invaluable accessory with which to monitor your driving and engine handling. Essential during the running-in period with a new or recently overhauled

Replace mechanical ignition contact breakers with optical/ electronic type. Tachometer is invaluable for enhancing your engine awareness.

engine, it will always enable you to avoid over-revving as well as, less obviously, making certain that you do not drive in too high a gear with too few revs. It can also obviate those lapses we all have on a long hot day of finding that you have been bumbling along for miles in fourth when you could well have changed into fifth gear! The majority of new vehicles are already equipped with tachometers or one is available as a standard option but if yours is not, retro-fit kits are available for four-, six-, or eight-cylinder petrol engines tapping off the ignition circuit.

Diesel tachometers. Without spark ignition, diesels are less easy to retro-fit but the alternator is used in the same way – ie using an rpm-related electrical pulse to operate a tacho. Operating a diesel tachometer in this way is obviously dependent on the gearing (relative pulley sizes) between the engine and the alternator but many after-market instruments have a range of adjustments that can be made to accommodate this. In the case of some Land Rover products, since both vehicles in recent versions take the same diesel engine – the 200 Tdi or 300 Tdi – it is possible to fit a Discovery tacho to a Defender. Or an add-on is available from VDO or Stewart-Warner (see below); the latter have a wide range for diesels.

Instrument sources

Narrowing field. In the UK, Halfords (and quite a few others) no longer handle add-on gauges and tenacious trudging through *Yellow Pages* is necessary to find the equipment you need. Hone your discernment as you go. You must differentiate between the glitzy junk and an instrument that will do the job well and accurately under demanding conditions. Some starting points in the UK:

1. VDO Instruments Ltd, Special Products Division, Holford Drive, Holford, Birmingham B6 7UG, tel 0121.344.200 (VDO instruments of all kinds.)

2. Time Instruments Ltd, 5 Alston Drive, Bradwell Abbey, Milton Keynes, Bucks MK13 9HA, tel 01908.220020 (Tim and Motometer instruments of all kinds.)

3. Gordon Equipments Ltd, Durite Works, Valley Road, Dovercourt, Essex CO12 4RX, tel 01255.502324 (Durite instruments and wide range of auto electrical parts.)

4. Stewart-Warner Instruments Limited, Jubilee Road, Letchworth, Herts SG6 1LY, tel 01462.480400 (Full range of instruments including tuneable rev counters for diesels.)

5. Demon Tweeks, 75 Ash Road South, Wrexham Industrial Estate, Wrexham, North Wales LL13 9UG, tel 01978.664466 (Mail order motor sport accessories of all kinds including instruments.)

6. Carnoisseurs, Brittany Court, High Street South, Dunstable, Beds, LU6 3HR, tel 01582.471700. (High street accessories outlet. 13 other branches country-wide.)

Oil system improvements

Oil temperature gauge, oil cooler. Most modern 4x4s will have been tested thoroughly at the design and development stage to withstand normal operating ambients of 45-50°C – the 'normal' here meaning that operation would be accompanied by reasonable forward speed to moderate engine compartment and other temperatures. This breeze over the bottom of the oil sump is often the only means of cooling the engine lubricating oil though some vehicles (all the current Land Rover range, for instance) have an oil-cooling matrix contiguous with the engine coolant matrix in the radiator – look for the extra two pipes of about an inch in diameter going into the radiator at the side. Here, at least, the oil is cooled by air drawn in by the fan.

In expedition or sustained off-road work where boggings can be frequent, the heat load can rise dramatically – high temperatures, high revs, high torque, very high re-radiation from very hot ground surfaces all combined with not much forward speed. Stress on the oil is rising as, due to temperature, viscosity, film thickness and film strength is going down. So if you have an

Diesel tachometers are different and instruments not available in every high street. Don't be put off. Engine oil temperature important to monitor; fit a gauge.

Ambient temperature here was 44°C, oil temp (no cooler fitted) was near 140°C. Pointing into wind with bonnet open reduced oil temp surprisingly quickly. Oil temp gauges are electric (right) or mechanical with capillary tube – more accurate, larger scale, something of a pig to fit! Both gauges need sump adaptor plug.

older vehicle without a built-in oil cooler:
  • First, know the oil temperature.
  • Preferably have the means to lower it – an oil cooler.

Even with a modern vehicle that does have an oil cooler, the repeated boggings you may encounter in the desert or on soft tracks could be beyond the capabilities of the oil cooler and an oil temperature gauge should be put high on your list of priorities.

Fit oil temperature gauge. Fit a gauge with quantitative readings of actual temperatures rather than just a 'hot' zone. The temperature sensing bulb should be fitted to sense the temperature of bulk oil in the

engine, ie in the sump, not at the neck of the oil filter. There are two types of oil temperature gauge:

1. Mechanical gauges where the gauge is permanently joined to the sensor by a bendable metal capillary tube. These are usually more accurate, have a 270° needle sweep, are not dependent on electrical power but, because of the metal capillary tube, permanently fixed to the gauge, are very awkward to fit and care has to be exercised in allowing a multiple coil of capillary tubing to accommodate engine movement relative to the bulkhead to which the instrument is fitted. Nevertheless go for this kind of gauge

Know engine oil temperature, preferably fit a cooler too. But at least you can monitor temp; repeat soft sand boggings can cause oil temp to soar and risk engine damage.

in the highest quality if you possibly can. Accuracy, typically, is better than 5% of full scale deflection; the Stewart-Warner gauge (previous page, left-hand instrument) on calibration check was less than 1°C out.

2. *Electrical gauges* where a sensor with spade terminals is connected to the instrument by removable electrical leads; a lot easier to fit than a mechanical gauge and probably half or two thirds the price. Almost invariably using only a 90° needle sweep, these are also less accurate – typically 8% of full scale deflection, plus (or minus) the sensor error so could be quite a bit out.

Whichever gauge you fit, do a pre-installation test by putting the bulb in boiling water and checking how accurate it is; if you have a school lab thermometer to check a second point then you will get a clear idea of the overall picture and can make allowances and corrections later on. If you can do this, the shortcomings of the electrical type gauge can be minimised. Whilst having a quantitative readout is a great help, you are, in the end, using the gauge to trigger remedial action and some could argue that you don't need to know the difference between 128 and 130°C.

Capillary tube oil temp gauges more accurate than electric but less easy to fit. Give the engine a treat – fit the best! 120-130°C is time to get worried and let things cool.

Both kinds of gauge usually require a special tapping for the sensor. You can arrange this by removing the engine sump and brazing on an adapter to take a screw-in sensor or, in some cases, where a large sump drain plug is fitted, the drain plug itself can be drilled and tapped to take the sensor bulb.

How hot is hot? How hot 'too hot' is varies, strictly speaking, with the design of the engine. Lightweight racing engines pushing the limits with the smallest bearing surfaces they can get away with will be seeking to squeeze the last drop of performance out of the oil but most production engines will be designed to the same kind of less demanding margins. Such engines commonly run at oil temperatures of 80-100°C on normal motorway conditions and up to 130°C when pushing it hard. Oil has to pass a 150°C test during its ACEA certification so will not 'break down' at 130°; however, it

begins to degrade fairly rapidly (oxidation, thickening etc) at these temperatures – mineral oils more so than synthetics.

The danger lies in increasing engine loads and decreasing film thickness that could, in the end, lead to metal-to-metal contact. The trigger for remedial action – ie stopping to let the oil cool – is if engine oil reaches 120°C (140°C if using synthetic oil). Stop with the bonnet raised and pointing into wind. In these conditions the oil temperature will drop surprisingly quickly.

As with rpm gauges, obtaining the instruments is not as easy as it once was albeit the quality strata are more clearly defined. The suppliers listed under 'Instrument sources' on page 4.2 - 6 above will be a reliable starting point.

Fitment of an oil cooler. Fitting an oil cooler is not a ten minute job and must be carefully considered first, with specialist advice. Use a manufacturer's kit, eg military Defender unit on a Defender. Usually taking the source oil from an adapter introduced between the oil filter and the engine, be absolutely certain that the unit is suitable for your engine and will not – as it could – actually restrict the flow of oil due to incompatible pipe sizes. Appropriate lengths of the right (and adequately flexible) pressure hose must be used between the oil cooler and the engine allowing for plenty of movement by the engine on its mountings under maximum torque conditions. Mount the oil cooler ahead of the radiator so that air drawn through the radiator by the fan passes over the oil cooler first. Radiator matrices are prone to fatigue cracks through vibration so ensure the cooling matrix is rubber mounted, not 'hard' mounted direct to the chassis.

Beware over-cooling. Cold oil doesn't pump as well as hot oil (even multigrades) and some of the most important additives (anti-wear, anti-oxidants) don't start working till around 75-80°C so beware of over-cooling. An oil cooler fitted to deal with the worst aspects of repeated sand boggings in the Sahara will almost certainly need a sheet of cardboard over it in Europe. Water vapour products of fuel combustion will form 'mayonnaise' emulsions in cold oil. On a UK spring day it takes about five miles to get oil up around 70°C. Regard 75-80°C as a minimum working oil temperature and aim to keep it at 80-100°C and, see above, not above 120°C (140°C synthetic).

Transmission oils get hot too. Remember an oil cooler only cools engine oil; transmission oil gets very hot too, especially under high torque conditions encountered during boggings and recovery. Moreover the transmission is always situated aft of a potentially already overheating engine so some thought must be given to this when driving. (To quote the 1-tonne military Land Rover again, the V8 was fitted with an oil cooler and as a result the hot climate limitation was in fact the temperature of the main gearbox oil.) Use the best oil you can; do not cut costs or corners here – see Section 2.6 'Fuel, oil, fluids'. Read your engine oil temperature gauge as an indication of what may be going on elsewhere as well.

Fuel system improvements

Long range fuel tank. Fuel systems these days amount to more than just a pipe coming from a tank. Most systems incorporate a spill system with a return pipe allow-ing a constant trickle of fuel to pass through the carburettor or injection system so as to avoid vapour lock in the lines. Fuel tanks thus have twin pipes, not one, and fitting a random second tank without a spill pipe could result in fuel from it being slowly transferred to the first tank ... ! So care (and coupled dual cocks) are required – to the extent that the best advice is to use only an auxiliary plumbed-in tank designed by the vehicle manufacturer and factory fitted during assembly.

Of course fuel can be carried in other tanks for transfer manually to the vehicle system – for example, a truck fuel tank strapped down in the back of a pick-up or sport-utility vehicle – but there are potential disadvantages: such a tank cannot be unloaded if it is necessary to lighten the vehicle in a major bogging and secondly fuel has to be decanted into the vehicle specially. This latter also has its advantages (see page 2.6 - 33) as fuel is best downloaded via jerry cans which enables an accurate mpg to be worked out when you top up the main vehicle tank.

In general, however, fuel is best and most easily carried in steel jerry cans lashed down within the vehicle (not on top of – see 'Roof-racks' below). A reminder that, if fuel

Plumbed-in long range tanks require spill return pipes and ganged taps. Best to use manufacturer's own system, factory fitted. Separate bulk container? Pros and cons.

Bolted-down truck tank in back of soft-top immovable; holds 200 litres but takes less space than 10 jerry cans. Note location well ahead of rear axle for best weight distribution. Fuel siphoned out to jerry can. Bracketry on top provides stowage rack; space for water jerry cans either side. Wooden skip aft has customised lashing points for cargo boxes.

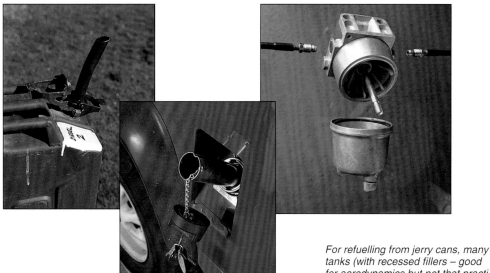

For refuelling from jerry cans, many
tanks (with recessed fillers – good
for aerodynamics but not that practical for an expedition) will require a
jerry can spout (top left); unless it
has a filler pull-out extension (left).
A sedimenter (above) sorts the
water and grit from the diesel; tap at
bottom permits periodic drain-off.

provisioning is a problem, trailers can be
one solution – see also 'Fuel, oil, fluids', at
page 2.6 - 4.

Fuel sedimenter, filter. As mentioned in
'Fuel, oil, fluids', page 2.6 - 16, a fuel sedimenter for diesel vehicles can be invaluable
when poorly stored fuel with water or other
contamination is encountered overseas. In
all honesty it is a good thing to have at any
time. Such an item on Land Rover products
is sometimes standard, sometimes can be
retro-fitted, according to the manufacturer's
specification by territory. Standard parts are
easily obtainable. An extra in-line filter for
petrol engines is useful for the same reason.
These are often available with a glass filter
bowl so that you can see when it needs
cleaning; take spare filter elements.

Fuel filler extension. Filling a fuel tank
from a jerry can is an everyday task on an
expedition but with modern recessed filler
caps is virtually impossible without either a
spout extension on the can or a filler-orifice
extension. These are also illustrated in
Section 2.6 on page 2.6 - 33. Don't be tempted to think that a funnel will be a suitable

*Jerry cans most
convenient way
to carry extra
fuel but be sure
you can pour
into your tank.
Diesels benefit
from fuel sedi-
menter (water,
dirt); fit in-line
filter for petrol.*

alternative. Firstly funnels are bulky and
awkward to stow. When they have just been
used they will drip fuel back into the area
where they are stowed, the wet fuel will
attract dust or sand which will subsequently
be flushed into the fuel tank and, especially,
if you are using diesel, the drippy funnel
(even if optimistically wrapped in a steadily
deteriorating polythene bag) will cause the
entire contents of the vehicle to reek of fuel
from the day of its first use onwards.
Having said that, Demon Tweeks (see
above) sell a funnel with caps at each end
though whether this will keep diesel out of
the cucumber sandwiches is not recorded.

Fuel system/block heaters. Extreme cold
weather operation can lead to severe waxing
problems with diesels and the danger of
cylinder block damage through freezing.
This can be dealt with selection/treating of
the fuel and by use of fuel and block heaters.
It is covered comprehensively in Section 2.6,
'Fuel, oil, fluids' on pages 2.6 - 14/15.

Electrical system

Batteries

Heavy duty battery. You are hugely vulnerable to the integrity of your electrical system on an expedition. In truth you are also vulnerable when you are not on an expedition but two facts exacerbate the situation when you are in the outback – first there is no purveyor of new batteries or charging facilities just round the corner and, as noted above, there are a number of accessories which can make known or inadvertent calls on your reserves of power.

Getting a new, heavy duty, battery fitted a few weeks before departure makes a great deal of sense – note, not the day before departure; you do need to check it out and be sure it provides power and takes a charge satisfactorily. A really good battery is expensive but there are few purchases that will be so worthwhile.

Diesel engines need bigger batteries; each glow plug takes around 11 amps – so that's 44 amps on a 4-cylinder engine to add to the cranking load that already has the high compression to cope with. (Well appointed and complex vehicles such as the new Range Rover also need large batteries just to accommodate designed-in accessories, never mind expedition add-ons – a worst case situation being a start on a cold morning followed by use of windscreen de-icer, rear screen demister, heater boost fan, fog lights and headlights all at idling or low engine rpm.) In preparing for an expedition you will need to know:

- What is a heavy duty battery?
- How are they classified?
- Do I already have one?
- Battery maintenance?

You will either have a new or very recent vehicle, a 'not very recent' vehicle or a used one that you have bought specially for your trip and whose history (and battery) you are not all that certain about. Either way, go back to basics – start with the handbook battery recommendation, then check what you have in the vehicle and then look over the battery manufacturer's catalogue – in the UK Exide and Lucas/Yuasa do comprehensive and informative ones.

What is a heavy duty battery? This is a relative term since each vehicle will have an appropriately specified battery – a 'normal' battery for a 2.5 litre diesel engine will be a 'heavy duty' battery' for a petrol engine of the same capacity. There are, however, figures (below) enabling you to make up your own mind. Use the handbook battery type number as your starting point and take it from there. The Lucas/Yuasa list recommends optional high spec batteries where these are feasible – dimensions have to be taken into account.

How are they classified? Batteries used to have designations that were not all that precise in terms of in-use performance. Number of plates per cell was one indicator and 'amp hours' (a/h) was a typical easy-to-grasp single figure that gave a good feel for how muscular a battery was – 56 a/h was fairly small beer, 72 a/h was pretty heavy duty diesel stuff and 110 a/h was quite a battery. (72 a/h means it could theoretically yield a one-amp discharge for 72 hours, 36 amps for two hours or a 72 amp discharge for one hour; needless to say there was more to it than this since starter motors on cold diesels take an inordinate number of amps and the new designations below address this kind of thing. For the die-hards, however, a/h is still usually, and usefully, indicated.)

Batteries are classified by a new system these days. The designation is now more comprehensive:

1. BBMS (British Battery Manufacturers Society) type number. Type numbers range from 001 to the 700s; a higher number is usually a bigger and 'better' battery in terms of capacity but not always. This, often stated baldly as a simple number like '072', is what you will probably find in your handbook.

Batteries are too often taken for granted. It is enormously important to have a good one in first class condition. Learn the classification system and get a heavy duty one.

Specification figures shown on top panel of battery give clear indication of performance under demanding conditions. Shown here is a Type 072 – a beefy 'diesel spec' for a 2.5 litre diesel and paired with a second of the same type (see opposite).

Know what spec figures to look for; visit the Lucas/Yuasa depot and/or study the catalogue. See how you can upgrade spec for extra power reserve.

Note there are near equivalents covered by European DIN spec numbers (nearest DIN equivalent is listed in the Lucas/Yuasa catalogue)

2. SAE. Cold Cranking Performance (SAE) – the current that can be drawn from a battery at -18°C for 30 seconds before voltage drops to 7.2 volts. This is sometimes referred to as the 'SAE 30s' and is the test usually applied to car or light 4x4 vehicles. SAE 30 numbers (in the US often referred to as CCA: cold cranking amps) range from 200 up to 900-odd amps and these figures apply – to give you an idea of size – to batteries weighing between 7.5 kg and 57 kg.

3. IEC. Cold Start Performance (IEC) –

the current that can be drawn from a battery at -18°C for 60 seconds before voltage drops to 8.4 volts. Referred to as 'IEC 60s' this is most often applied to commercial vehicle batteries usually having to cope with more extended cranking. IEC 60 numbers range from 140 amps to 680 for the same battery weight spread as at 2. above.

4. Reserve Capacity (RC) – the time in minutes over which the battery will deliver a steady current of 25 amps at 25°C before the voltage drops to 10.5 volts – a most useful figure. Figures here might range from 34 to 420 minutes for batteries of the weight spread shown above.

5. Amp hours (A/H) – see above. For the battery weight/size range indicated here, figures spread between 26 and 200 a/h.

6. Physical attributes – weight, dimensions, terminals layout etc.

Do I already have one? Comparing your handbook battery specification or a major battery manufacturer's catalogue recommended item with what you actually have will show whether you have a minimum spec or a heavy duty battery on board. The list below summarises the specification data and shows three batteries that may be found in, say, an old petrol Series 3 Land Rover, a current diesel Defender and a new Range Rover with 6-cylinder diesel (column numbers refer to paragraphs above):

TYPICAL BATTERY SPECIFICATION FIGURES AND APPLICATION

1 Type (BBMS)	2 SAE 30s	3 IEC 60s	4 RC mins	5 A/H	6 Wt kg	6 Size l.w.h – mm
Type 091	380	250	90	60	17	257x176x205 – Series 3 petrol
Type 072	590	420	130	72	20	255x175x205 – Diesel Defender
Type 664	825	590	200	115	27.5	344x172x232 – New Range Rover

Looking at the Lucas/Yuasa recommendations for the petrol Discovery, for example, an indication of normal, heavy duty and extra heavy duty can be obtained as shown below:

1 Type (BBMS)	2 SAE 30s	3 IEC 60s	4 RC mins	5 A/H	6 Wt kg	6 Size l.w.h – mm
Type 071	370	265	85	60	16.5	255x175x220 – Normal
Type 074	470	335	105	66	17.6	255x175x205 – Heavy duty
Type 089	570	405	125	73	18.7	255x175x205 – Extra HD

BATTERY CHARGING – OFF-VEHICLE

You may find yourself with a battery in need of a charge and actually have the facilities to do something about it externally – a small garage in the back of beyond, for example. Include a small multi-meter in your toolkit – one that can measure voltages; the open circuit voltage (OCV) of the battery is important to know as it affects the time of recharge. The following is based on a fuller treatment in the Lucas/Yuasa battery catalogue.

• Do not attempt a recharge if the temperature is less than +3°C.

• Disconnect both terminals from the vehicle.

• Measure the open circuit voltage (OCV) – ie the voltage of the battery with nothing else connected to it, only the voltmeter across the terminals.

• Every battery has a 'bench charge rate' – the rate at which you would charge a fully discharged battery to fully charged in 10 hours. For light 4x4 batteries this is usually 9-14 amps. The Type 072 Defender battery bench charge rate is 9 amps.

• For best results charge the battery at half the bench charge rate.

• Time of charge: The lower the OCV, the longer you should charge (at the half bench-charge rate above – 5-7 amps in the case of many 4x4 batteries), ie

OCV	Charging time (hours)
12.4	4
12.2	8
12.0	12
11.8	16
11.0-11.6	20

• Stop the charging if the battery begins to 'gas' freely – ie bubble like a fizzy drink.

• In general the slow steady charge is the best way to put your battery back on form. Boost charging is not recommended.

Battery maintenance? Most batteries these days are listed as 'maintenance free' but remember that this applies only to normal operations in temperate climates. If you are operating in unusually high ambient temperatures or incurring unusually high under-bonnet temperatures due to prolonged static running or, more likely, debogging a vehicle in desert sand, your battery may need topping up with *distilled* water. Take a 500 ml or 1 litre plastic bottle, well wrapped and secured in the battery compartment; fill to about 10 mm above the separators. There is more to 'maintenance free' than the fact that it is maintenance free. Such batteries in the Yuasa/Lucas range carry a three-year guarantee, the 'low maintenance' ones only two years. Don't use 'Leisure batteries' except for caravan-type use; they only carry a one-year guarantee and tend to have low SAE amps figures. Even if you have a second battery (see below), make it one that can take over the job of the main battery.

Second battery, split charge system. Getting a new, high specification, battery is a very good start. Having a second one as back-up and kept specifically for accessories use is what will really help you sleep well at night. Certainly on Land Rover expedition vehicles it is possible to install a second battery and a split charge system that will keep it topped up at all times – a voltage-sensitive switch and a relay. The circuitry will ensure that engine starting is carried out only on one battery and, by the suitable arrangement of accessories wiring, it can be ensured that accessories run only off the second battery – typically the evening camp lighting or a navigation device. Indeed if some accessory is inadvertently left on overnight it will not risk a no-start of the engine next morning.

The modification actually gives further peace of mind yet, in that sometimes a minor item of equipment may need its nicad battery topped up at very low current drain and this really can be left on overnight in safety.

Needless to say, it is wise to ensure that both batteries in such a split charge system are of the heavy duty type – such as a pair or Type 072 batteries in a Defender. (See box on next page regarding fitment of twin batteries to Defenders with under-seat battery positioning.)

Fit a second battery with a split-charge system and allocate one of the batteries for accessories such as lighting. This will preserve the other for engine starting only.

SECOND BATTERY – DEFENDER

A special note regarding second batteries in Defenders. The normal place to install this is side-by-side with the first battery under the passenger seat. The small amount of space between the top of the normal battery and the slide-out metal cover to the battery compartment is even smaller with the aft battery in a twin battery installation. With the seat squab removed, any weight on this panel – such as when anyone sits directly on the panel – can cause it to bend and touch the positive terminal of the aft battery

with near-catastrophic results. Be sure that the positive terminals of both batteries have purpose-designed snap-fitting thick rubber terminal caps – Lucas produce some very businesslike items. Then, to be safe and guard against the inevitable case of someone forgetting to snap the terminal covers on, stick a sheet of 3 mm rubber on the underside of the slide-out metal cover; finally stick a label on its outside saying 'NO WEIGHT ON THIS PANEL'.

Battery master switches. This is a large, very robust high-amperage switch mounted on or very close to the battery enabling it to be isolated from the vehicle electrics; it involves heavy 10 mm cabling but is a useful anti-theft and safety device in the event of electrical fires. In this latter context, potential faults in old vehicles seem to be brought to a head by dry, bush-type operations where there is often very severe vibration due to track corrugations.

Twin batteries with split charge system in Defender 90 (see box information above). Note the positive terminals are heavily protected by terminal caps of thick rubber. Slide-on lid similarly insulated.

Fit a battery master switch for each battery to preclude static drain and as a safety cut out. A flattened battery with even a tiny load will be irreversibly damaged.

Flat battery, irreversible damage. Be aware that a constant small current drain, such as the 60 mA for a clumsily installed burglar alarm will flatten a battery over a period of time – statistically, a fully charged 72 amp/hour battery will become exhausted in a storage period of only 50 days. Far more seriously, however, if the battery is left in this condition, with the load still across it, the plates will buckle and the battery will be irreversibly damaged so that you will not be able to recharge it. Hence the need to quantify actual current drain of accessories in the static condition. As indicated below, install a battery master switch for use during periods of storage or inactivity.

Battery master switch for each battery in twin installation (recessed to preclude foot damage). Switch key is removable for extra security – shown below with simple rotary switch.

Just as important, a battery switch can be used to isolate a battery during periods of inactivity or storage when permanent small current drains such as radio or alarm can, as indicated above, pull voltage down, flatten and irreversibly damage a battery.

Be sure not to operate the battery switch when the engine is running. Doing so, the alternator and charging circuit will 'see' an instant requirement for maximum charge rate and a voltage spike as high as 80 volts can result. Whilst most car accessories are designed in theory to withstand this, other ancillaries used on expeditions could be permanently damaged by the surge. Therefore make it a rule to operate the switch only when the engine is stationary.

Battery warmer. In exceptionally cold conditions cranking loads go up and battery power goes down. As already covered in Section 2.6, cylinder block heaters and diesel fuel tank heaters that plug into the mains at low wattage for overnight warming can be invaluable. A battery warmer is the third item of the troika – overnight cold soak temperatures at or below -35°C are accepted as a zone to start considering such equipment. Blanket types that surround the battery or pad types that sit beneath it are available but, as with the fuel tank and fuel line warmers, be sure you have insulated the box well so that the heat does not waft away into the night air. The US firm Kim Hotstart of Spokane, Washington make such equipment – address (with UK agents) shown on p 2.6 - 15 (Section 2.6, 'Fuel, oils, fluids'.)

Other electrical modifications

Accessory power points. Accessories need somewhere to be plugged into if they are not hard-wired in. It is very useful to have two or more auxiliary electrical power points – being sure that they are run through the accessories fuse and that that in turn comes off the second (accessories) battery. Short-wave radios, GPS or video camera battery chargers, shavers, wander lights and the like all need this kind of socket and there seem never to be enough power points – just like at home. When you install these

Accessory power points are best installed using DIN power sockets (top) rather than the rickety cigar-lighter adapters (bottom). DIN socket here has snap-shut lid; its plug (upper right) is actually a dual-purpose type that, with a collar, <u>can</u> be used with the socket below. Be sure to wire all such plugs through the accessories fuse and make sure this comes off the auxiliary battery if you have a twin battery set-up (see text).

items be sure to use the DIN plug and sockets which are far more secure and businesslike than the rickety US-origin 'cigar lighter' socket.

De-activate the courtesy lights. There are a dozen ways in which you can inadvertently flatten the battery. Classically, door-switch operated courtesy lights are the worst offenders. Vehicles on expeditions spend an awful lot of time during the day or at overnight camping areas with the doors open and with members of the team to-ing and fro-ing in and out of the vehicle. What is even more insidious is that courtesy lights do not show up in the daytime. Some vehicles have interior lights kill switches. If yours does not either fit one or, safer still, remove the courtesy light bulbs. You will still need interior lighting of course – and to a higher standard than a courtesy light offers anyway – see next paragraph.

Extra interior lighting. Additional caravan-type fluorescent tube interior lights are invaluable and, as well as running far cooler than filament bulbs, take a lower wattage

Deactivate the courtesy lights to obviate door-open current drain. Fit DIN-socket power points and switchable fluorescent interior lighting for evening chores.

Moonlight in the Sahara seems to be four times as bright as anywhere else but really good interior lighting – run off the second battery – is still a necessity when you are faced with long hours of writing up logs and planning the next day's navigation. Fluorescent tubes give more light per amp used so fully adequate lighting is possible with minimal battery drain. Built-in and 'wander lights' useful.

Fluorescent lights give more light for less current. Fit one for the cab, one for the cooking area (on slide-out pole?). Have another on a long lead for inspections.

for the light output they provide. They can be installed as fixtures – ideally one or two independently switchable in the cab and one over the rear cargo area of the vehicle. Alternatively they can be used as portable, clip-mounted units plugged into a power point for vehicle inspections or other close work. They are especially useful near the back door/hatchback of a vehicle to use as a camping and cooking light. As mentioned, however, guard battery capacity; see above under 'Second battery'. One 'why-didn't-I-think-of-that' idea recently seen in the bush is (literally) a beanpole slide-out extension

from the back of the vehicle with the light on the end of it so that it lights the area immediately over the cooking stove. A power point near the rear door is invaluable

Moveable hand spotlight. Mounted on the windscreen pillar, a hand-moveable spotlight can be of use when you have been caught out and have to choose a campsite after dark and are unable to turn the vehicle to point the headlights at it. Use sparingly as such lights use a lot of current; and get a well-engineered compact one that will not loll around when you travel over bumpy roads and corrugations.

Vehicle security

Precautions

Precautions and alarm. A regrettably and depressingly important item of expedition equipment these days is some form of security alarm and your approach needs thinking through in some detail. An alarm shrieking after the vehicle has already been broken into is better than no alarm and may frighten the thieves into making off without taking too much, nonetheless, as ever, prevention and deterrence is better than a post-violation shindig. It is appropriate here to cover one or two points on precautions as well as the modifications themselves. Alas, you may well have heard a lot of it before but skim it anyway as, hopefully, the tips on the expedition context may be helpful:

Precautions. You are trying to deter people from breaking into your vehicle to steal its contents as well as trying to prevent them from stealing the whole vehicle.

• *Apparent impregnability.* The big lock-on bar through the steering wheel and steel wire mesh on frames over the side windows together with signs in the windows to indicate an alarm system are all variations on the same theme. Wire mesh frames may be too extreme for people with luxury vehicles especially since they cannot sensibly be made to cover the windscreen and immediate front windows without making your machine look like the riot police on its afternoon off. An ex-military Defender, however, can wear the trappings in moderation without looking too over the top.

• *Reduce inward visibility.* Keeping valuables out of sight is a well-known piece of advice and that can be extended to reducing inwards visibility. Smoked glass and reflective foil coatings on the windows work to a certain extent but as well as having almost laughable Mafia overtones (like those hugely irritating reflective sunglasses), are permanent and reduce visibility outwards rather too much. If they don't strike you as too twee (or equally laughable) ordi-

nary net curtains on spring-wire hangers are highly effective, adaptable for any vehicle, somehow do not look sinister and may be drawn back at will when you are away in the bush or need all the visibility you can get. They do not obstruct outward vision significantly, even in the mirror and if they do, they can, as above, be drawn back temporarily.

• *Lockable compartments.* It is a good idea, as a matter of principle, to make all boxes and compartments lockable anyway. It is definitely worth extra thought and ingenuity to install a 'safe' of some kind in a part of the vehicle that is hard to find. Hardware shops sell small boxes of this kind – cashboxes, key cabinets and the like – and, properly fixed into a vehicle with 'blind' bolts only accessible from inside the box, can prove a safe repository for passports, cheques, the carnet etc. Against this, of course, is that if the vehicle gets stolen so too do the contents of the box so the use of such an arrangement must be graded to the current risk – roadside shopping vs leaving the vehicle overnight in a distant car park, for instance.

• *Lost key.* A spare key fixed with shiny new tape to some part of the underside of the vehicle is not the most subtle way of guarding against the horrors of losing your keys and it would be counter-productive to enumerate here ways around the problem. You will get the drift, however, and doubtless be able to think of other ways of providing cover. Usually a second set of keys with your co-driver should look after the problem but make sure, even if it costs you accusations of fussiness, that they keep the keys in a pocket with a proper zip or Velcro closure and that a routine is worked out to ensure that one set is not left in the vehicle.

• *Locking wheel nuts.* New or good condition tyres are worth a fortune in some regions overseas so be sure to fit locking or security wheel nuts to your road wheels and

Sadly, anti-theft precautions should be gone into thoroughly. Deterrence is the first aim – kit out of sight, reduce inward visibility. Then locking wheel nuts, alarms.

spare. An additional lock and chain on the spare will help get the message over. Favourite locations for saying goodbye to tyres are dock holding areas – after unloading from a ship – and hotel car parks.

• *Other external gear.* Though you will want instant access to things like sand ladders and shovels on the trail, be sure they – and any other external kit – can be locked to the vehicle when it is unattended

Vehicle security – alarm systems

Deterrence preferred. A number of considerations affect expeditions when it comes to alarm systems. Prevention and deterrence really must be prime the aim since a chased-off thief leaving a broken window behind presents you with a spares acquisition problem as well as possible loss of kit. What is also different about expeditions is the growing risk of vehicle hijacking where, to spare themselves the tedium of having to break in and mobilise your vehicle, the criminals get you to do that for them before, at gunpoint or under other threat, relieving you of the driving seat. A further possible problem is that of alarm system malfunction and what, out in the blue, you can do about it.

Peripheral and volume coverage. Modern alarm systems usually work on two superimposed systems – peripheral coverage which guards the periphery of the vehicle by sensing when entry points such as doors, boot or bonnet are opened and then internal volume coverage where sensors scan the internal volume of the vehicle for body heat or movement. Use of this latter method is why modern vehicles have a means of incapacitating this aspect of the system when you have left pets in a locked vehicle. By the same token, leaving a vehicle, windows down on a hot day, to nip into a shop, you can set the alarm as you leave and a thieving arm put through the window aperture will trigger the alarm – a useful feature when 'mischievous' children overseas can negate all your careful equipment planning by random opportunist theft.

Built-in alarms and retro-fits. Recent-

Even with alarms, deterrence is better than post-intrusion shindig. A warn-away system is best. Be sure you can cope with in-the-field malfunctions.

build vehicles will almost invariably have a built-in alarm system which usually also involves remote locking of doors. This is usually a good basis for fitment of further systems as indicated below but may not be if there are system incompatibilities. In this case you may have to scrap your existing system in order to fit a higher capability alarm. Where an older type vehicle or one not designed for either central locking or peripheral alarm systems is considered, then more work will be involved – door-open sensor switches obviously is the starting point.

Remote operation – rolling codes. Remote setting of an alarm using the key-ring 'blip' is accomplished by a tiny battery-powered UHF transmitter using a set code for your vehicle. Ne'er-do-wells around car parks can 'grab' these codes from simple systems using UHF receivers and open your car as soon as you have left the scene. To overcome this, recent systems employ a 'rolling code' that changes with successive use of the blip. When you lock your vehicle using code A, the next code (to unlock it) will be code B. Both transmitter and receiver are designed to use the same sequencing so the frequency and code grabbers are foiled. Ensure your vehicle is fitted with a such a system.

Proximity alarms. Getting now to the concept of prevention and deterrence before a window is broken, some systems are capable of being set to trigger when a would-be thief touches or gets close to the glass to look into the vehicle. With a user-set sensitivity, such devices can trigger either the alarm itself or – to the considerable shock of the potential miscreant – set off a synthesised voice warning the person very loudly that 'ALARM WILL SOUND IF YOU DON'T BACK AWAY'' (Clifford's 'Sense-n-Tell' system – see below). In some parts of Africa, demonstrating this system proves to be a riot of entertainment as well as subtly getting the message across.

Anti-hijacking systems. Basically working around the concept of setting the system when you get into the vehicle, an 'unscheduled' opening and closing of the driver's door (as when you are forced out of the vehicle and someone else takes over) will set in motion events that lead to the killing of the engine with alarm and light flashing some hundreds of yards further down the road. By this point the hijackers are some distance away from you (and thus unable to offer you immediate violence) and, saddled with an incapacitated vehicle with screaming alarms, will usually take to their heels with enthusiasm. Actuation of this procedure occurs (in the Clifford BlackJack system) when the vehicle slows down for its first bend or obstacle. BlackJack is a stand-alone system not dependent on any other fitment.

Thatcham rating, manufacturers. Within the UK the Motor Insurance Repair Research Centre at Thatcham list and evaluate equipments and give them 'OK' ratings within four system type categories and related to vehicle applications, eg saloon, off-road, light commercial, trailer protection etc. Note that the categories are generic categories, ie types of alarm, and category one is not necessarily better than category two – just different (albeit Cat 1 and 2 both incorporate anti-scan and anti-code-grabbing technology). Thatcham categories are:

- Cat 1: Combined alarm/immobiliser
- Cat 2: Electronic/electromechanical immobiliser
- Cat 3: Mechanical immobiliser

Thatcham 'evaluation' implies that it has been approved by people (insurance companies, for goodness sake!) very much concerned that it should prevent theft so it is of relevance to your scan of the market place. Thatcham recommend that your alarm is fitted by a dealership accredited by VSIB – Vehicle Security Installation Board – from whom detailed advice may also be obtained. A list of Thatcham approved equipments (including vehicle manufacturers' OE fitments) may be obtained by sending a stamped addressed envelope to Association of British Insurers, 51 Gresham Street, London EC2V 7HQ.

Makers of the BlackJack and Sense-n-Tell systems are Clifford Electronics of the US. Details of UK dealerships in your area

In some parts of the world, hijacking of vehicle and contents is catching on. There are devices that can address this hazard.

Navigation system

The need? Details of navigation systems are covered in Section 5.2 'Navigation' but it is worth considering here the need or otherwise of such a system and the main criteria that you could follow to guide your decision. 'Navigation system' these days almost invariably means some manifestation of the Global Positioning System (GPS) satellite constellation that can yield position fixes accurate to better than 30 metres in real time as you progress along a track. Without doubt there is a kind of open-mouthed magic about such a system and it is hard to imagine any circumstances when it would not be useful. However, it is only as good as the maps you can use with it and their grid or latitude and longitude overlay. It is absolutely not a substitute for knowing the principles of sound navigation nor an excuse for abandoning that general awareness of your approximate heading and position that should be part of your operations at all times.

So it will not always be necessary on an expedition. With the right maps and background knowledge, however, it will be a delight and a jewel and a source of wonder – especially if you have navigated the hard way in the past.

The framework. GPS-based navigation devices come in different formats – many readers will be familiar with the hand-held devices running off AA batteries. There are marine and airborne equipments as well and the main differences are simply in the power source and their display ergonomics and features. Hand-held devices can be run in small dashboard racks either off their built-in aerials or off aerials roof-mounted. A roof-mounted aerial will always be more efficient, albeit by less of a margin now than before. Whatever you choose, get a unit with a high-contrast display – see below.

Vehicle use. The important difference between a hand-held, on-foot use of GPS and vehicle or marine use is that in the latter two cases you are using the navigation system as an adjunct or secondary input to another primary task – that of driving the vehicle or boat. Accordingly, the ergonomics must allow you to use it in this way. The display must be a lot larger and clearer in a vehicle cockpit display than on a hand-held unit since you will not want to take your eyes off the road for long to take in the nav information. Most hand-held units, used in vehicles, require you to stop to squint at a slightly too-small, too dim display; some are better than others but be aware at the equipment choice stage of what the conflicting

needs are. A hand-held unit, vehicle-mounted, does have the advantage that it can be removed, used on the hill or mountain and then put back in the vehicle to use as a vehicle navigator running off vehicle power.

Mounting the unit. Whatever unit you choose, it will need to be wired-in from the vehicle electrical source and it will have to be very carefully positioned in the cockpit. Some points to watch for:

1. Take your electrical supply through the accessories fuse and in turn from the second (accessories) battery, not the main engine-starting battery.

2. Be sure you have chosen an electrical source that does not dip voltage and trip out the navigation equipment every time you

All GPS is gold-plated magic but vehicle systems need large-digit, high contrast displays that can unambiguously be read when driving in bright external light. Marine units?

Hand-held GPS units are usually available with a dash-mounting kit with or without external aerial but display is usually too dim and too small for safe or convenient en-route use as a secondary task to driving. With sun on display, as here, it is clear but still too small. Marine-size display (left, Silva Nexus) is optimum especially when steering a compass heading. See also Section 5.2 'Navigation' – p 5.2 - 23.

start the engine. This can be a maddening characteristic in everyday use and is not good for the equipment either. Using the second battery as above it will not happen.

3. In positioning the unit or display in the cockpit be sure that you can see it in bright sunlight and in dim light conditions. Most likely is the worst combination of both – bright sunlight outside and the cockpit in shadow; that is where the need for a high contrast display with large figures and letters comes in.

4. Angle the unit so that you do not get reflections on its display face from windows or other strong light sources when viewed from either front seat.

5. Position the unit, ideally, so that it can be seen clearly by the driver – who will need

it for heading reference when trying to steer a compass course over open desert, for example – and by the co-driver who will likely be using the fix information for monitoring the navigation position. Again, it points to a large-digit display and being situated between the two crew – probably favouring the driver who will be using it in snatch-a-glance mode while concentrating on the driving.

6. In the context of security, ensure there is a cover of some kind if the unit is fixed. If it not fixed remove the unit and put it under cover when the vehicle is left unattended. Thieves seeing GPS units for the first time think they are either mobile phones or small TV sets – and probably throw them on a tip when they discover they are neither.

EXPEDITION FUNCTION MODIFICATIONS

Tyres

Tyre for the job. A fact of life with which tyre designers have to cope continuously is that every task or set of operating conditions a vehicle encounters demands a discreet design of tyre in order to obtain the best performance. By definition, therefore, tyres can be optimised for only one set of conditions and there will be some shortfall in performance – grip, flotation, traction, longevity – when operating outside the set of conditions for which it is designed. Thus tyres designed for mud will do badly in soft sand and not too well on tarmac, tyres designed for the desert will not perform well on mud and will need watching on wet tarmac. New sets of tyres are not cheap and your decision on which type to go for – your best compromise – will be influenced by the proportion of your route that lies in muddy conditions, stony tracks, desert terrain or tarmac. There may be expeditions where you are able to go with the tyres you have, despite OE tyres invariably being road ori-

ented, but getting the best performance on a given terrain type will usually necessitate a change of tyre and skimming over the selection process below will be useful.

Do you need new tyres? When talking about depth of tread here we are not talking about the minuscule European roads legal limits of tread (one or two millimetres) but depth of tread relative to doing an off-road tyre's job really well. Mud, snow and pre-churned sand (tracks) require tread to be in a robust state of health; remember this and the fact that tread wear can be quite high under expedition conditions – not as high as you might expect because your speeds will be moderate and you will not be doing much on-the-limits cornering.

If you have the wrong *sort* of tyres then, yes, you need new ones (see below and the tyres section of *The Land Rover Experience*). If you have the right sort but they are worn, a good guide is first to compare your on-the-road tyres with your unused spare. For a trip expected to be less than 8,000 miles,

Tyres, like batteries, are often taken for granted but are very important. Select tyre type according to the most demanding expected terrain; be aware tarmac compromises.

tyres that are less than half worn (comparing tread depth with your spare) should last the trip. If much of your route is on loose sand – less demanding on tread depth for performance and less wearing on tyres anyway – you can probably push the mileage and reduce the tread depth requirements a little.

Garage equipment needed to fit tubeless tyres; fit tubes so you can do your own in the outback. This will require wheels designed for tubed tyres. Spares? One will do.

First of all – tubeless? Tubeless tyres save weight and cost, puncture less dramatically than tubed tyres and are fitted as original equipment (OE) tyres on most modern vehicles. They are perfectly suitable for expeditions in moderately civilised areas not too far from a garage but they do require large amounts of high pressure air and benefit from special equipment when they are fitted – which rules them out for the more adventurous type of expedition where you will be fixing punctures in the field. There, because no giant compressors are available in remote areas, you must learn the (surprisingly simple) art of removing a cover and tube by hand using tyre levers, repairing the tube and putting it all back again (without further damaging it). Tubeless tyres are not the tyres to have in the outback.

Wheels. Alas, tubeless tyres are only fitted to special wheels and these wheels are not suitable for tubed tyres – internal ridging, needed for tyre retention on a tubeless cover, are liable to cause chafing and punctures if such a wheel is fitted with tubes. So for remote area trips where you must fit tubed tyres you will have to ensure you have the correct wheels as well.

How many spares? A single spare wheel and tyre is perfectly adequate for expeditions in even the most distant region; quite simply, the weight and bulk of one spare wheel is quite enough of a handicap when you are pushed for payload. But you must equip yourself with the knowledge and skills to change a tyre confidently – many garages, especially if that is where you are buying your new set for the trip – will be glad to show you the technique (and watch you through your faltering wrestling stage on the garage floor!). Do take a couple of spare inner tubes, the right tyre levers – three 18-inch levers will be ideal – and a complete and balanced set of tube and cover repair patches and adhesives (see Section 5.5.1 – 'Spares and repair kit').

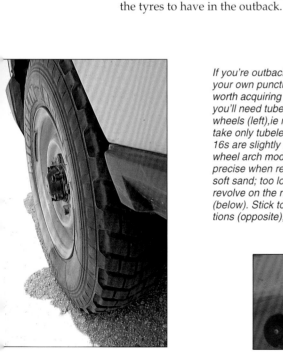

If you're outback enough to be doing your own puncture repairs – a skill worth acquiring wherever you are – you'll need tubed tyres and appropriate wheels (left),ie not alloys which usually take only tubeless. Note these 7.00 x 16s are slightly oversize, necessitating wheel arch mods – see p 4.2 - 25. Be precise when reducing pressures for soft sand; too low and the tyre will revolve on the rim, pulling the valve out (below). Stick to deflation speed limitations (opposite); re-inflate soonest.

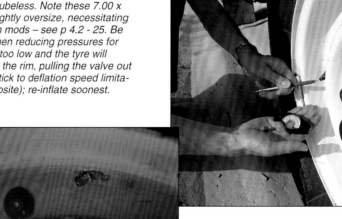

Tailored for the job. Sand (opposite page, Michelin XS type tread on the Michelin Africa S), mud (Michelin XCL near right) and mud/tracks/- general expedition conditions (Michelin XZL, far right) each demand an optimum tread design. All are radials; note (far rt) circumferential sidewall ridges to protect flexible sidewalls from rock damage. XZL will shine for general expeditions, XS best for desert. See next spread.

Radial ply tyres. Except for certain types of sustained and continuous operation at full inflation pressures on rock and stone where cross-ply tyres are preferable for reasons of cost and minimising sidewall damage (commercially this would equate to quarry operations) radial ply tyres are better than cross-plies for general expedition conditions. They confer lower rolling resistance so detectably lower fuel consumption as well as permitting (due to their inherently more flexible sidewalls) lower inflation pressures without overheating when really soft going demands this. They also have a far longer life. Fortunately, most reputable tyres are built today on the radial ply principle.

Reduced tyre pressures. See below reference to the companion book to this one, *The Land Rover Experience* for detail on the subject but increased flotation – less sinkage and better traction without wheelspin – will be derived by reducing tyre pressures in certain conditions. These are best broken down into three classifications; rule of thumb pressure reductions are shown *for radial ply tyres only*:

- On road up to maximum speed; use 'book' pressures.
- Tracks; 75% road pressure – 40 mph maximum.
- Sand, mud, emergency soft; 50% road pressure – 12 mph maximum.

Note these are rule of thumb figures and you should establish manufacturer's inflation recommendations; note too that the speed limits must be rigidly observed and you should always re-inflate to track or road pressures after soft sand or mud has been cleared. Never run far or fast on soft tyres; doing so will cause irreparable damage to a tyre with the likelihood of blow-out at speed. With these provisos, however, surprising performance can be extracted from reduced-pressure tyres on soft ground. Running on reduced pressures will adversely affect vehicle handling – body roll will be excessive and steering response slow. Drive with appropriate caution.

Tyres – the full treatment. Around a dozen pages are devoted to tyres in *The Land Rover Experience*, Edition 2 and although a lot there refers to Land Rover vehicles, the principles regarding pressures, types, axle loads etc read across generically to apply to any type of vehicle and certainly to guide your own research be you driving a Unimog, Shogun or Fiat Panda 4x4. Extracted from there, however, is the tyre type information summary overleaf:

Reduced tyre pressures – with associated speed limitations – can enhance traction and flotation in emergency situations. Re-inflate when crisis over.

TYRE TYPES AND CHARACTERISTICS		
Road oriented	Optimised for tarmac. Close tread, relatively smooth with sipes ('knife cuts')	**For:** Long life, quiet, smooth running, best braking. **Against:** Close tread susceptible to filling in mud, reducing traction.
M+S tyre	M+S = Mud and Snow. Bolder tread version of road tyre. Quite a close, small bold tread. Sometimes provision for studs also.	**For:** As above but slightly less so. Good grip in snow and on grass. **Against:** Better in snow than mud. Close tread susceptible to filling in mud, reducing traction. (Note: Tread too bold for virgin sand.)
Mud tyre	Bold, open tread pattern, sharp right-angle edges. The best are quite narrow, have 'swept-back', self-cleaning tread pattern (illustration) designed for particular direction of rotation.	**For:** Very good in all types of mud and clay. **Against:** Grip on wet tarmac slightly impaired. 'Heel and toe' wear on tread blocks shortens life. Noisy. Limited speed rating. (Note: The worst possible tyre for dry sand.)
Multi purpose	Combination of mud tyre and road tyre build – usually a zig-zag centre band with bold transverse edge lugs. Wide variation in off-road performance among brands. Non-directional.	**For:** A good compromise for frequent on/off road use, eg farming. **Against:** Grip on wet tarmac slightly impaired on some multi-purpose tyres. Wears faster than road tyre, slightly noisy. (Note: Poor on virgin sand.)
Sand tyres	Subtly shaped tread with shouldered blocks to compress sand in 'cups' (enhancing flotation and traction) rather than cut through it.Circumferentially grooved tyres look good but are ineffective in sand.	**For:** This design superb all types of sand. Robust enough for all desert terrain. **Against:** Poorer grip on wet tarmac must be allowed for. Some 'heel and toe' wear on tread blocks, some noise.Watch sidewalls on rock. (Note: Good flotation but poor performance in mud.)
Tyres for rock	There are no tyres made specially for rock – by rock is meant any rough surface of large or small angular rocks or stones. The key to traversing rock lies with the driver. Clearly a robust tyre is best, in most cases a radial with a reinforced tread – but see below. The M+S, mud and multi-purpose types listed above would do well though the mud and multi-purpose tyres would have greater tread thickness. See below for special conditions applicable to sustained off-road operations in rocky conditions without on-road use*.	

Every optimised tyre has its pros and cons; best off-road performance usually at cost of on-road grip in wet conditions. Best sand and best mud tyres are opposites.

*Cross-ply tyres. Where operations are almost exclusively off-road on rock or stone – such as fleet operations in quarries – the more damage-resistant qualities (at full inflation pressures) of cross-ply tyres could help keep operating costs down. It is essential, however, to consider and accommodate the following criteria:

a. Virtually all 7.50 x 16 cross-plies are 'L' speed rated, ie limited to 120 kph(75 mph), so should not be fitted to high powered vehicles operating on-road.

b. Cross-ply tyres have higher rolling resistance so will marginally reduce fuel economy.

c. Cross-plies have marginally less grip than radials on-road so handling affected.

TYRES – WHEEL ARCH MODIFICATIONS

Minor surgery. Not all the right tyres are available in a wide variety of sizes but a small degree of oversize fitting is acceptable - eg fitting the 7.50 x 16 onto a Range Rover Classic. In this case there is room in the actual wheel arch but the body panels at the wheel arch will have to be trimmed back to accommodate the tyre on full lock. Oversize tyres cannot be fitted to all vehicles as they will affect the torque loading on the transmission and thus its fatigue life. They also,

of course, will affect the overall gearing of the vehicle - including the accuracy of the speedometer and odometer (see below and Sec 5.2 'Navigation'). Related 7.00 x 16 tyres, eg the Michelin Africa S is a high-speed lighter weight version of the Michelin XS – see photograph on page 4.2 - 22), can be fitted to a Discovery with minimal clipping of the wheel-arch plastic mouldings; the Discovery will not accommodate the 7.50 x 16 tyre as the Defender will.

Tyres – what to look for. The table opposite gives an idea of the strengths and weaknesses of the various specialised tyres and what they look like. Decide what it is you are actually looking for:

1. Tread suitable to your main terrain type without too much sacrifice on others you will encounter.
2. Flexible sidewalls to permit lower inflation pressures where needed but without sacrificing resistance to sidewall damage.
3. Speed rating appropriate to your vehicle.
4. Low inflation capability appropriate to emergency conditions you may encounter – specially soft sand.

There are many brands of tyre and in the past there was a wide capability difference between the 'can-do' and the 'can't do' brands and designs. The gap has narrowed now and there is the additional – inevitable – tuning of national brands of tyre to national makes of vehicle. Without in any way denigrating other brands which have developed or are developing their own credentials, it is worth singling out the long-established and well-deserved reputation of Michelin for their wide range of tyres and especially their skills with on- and off-road tyres.

Tyres – what to choose. Taking the bull by the horns and naming names – if only as a starting point and to compare with other brands – the following will yield very good

results indeed on typical 16-inch wheel, light 4x4s of the Defender/Discovery kind:

• *Mixed going.* Tarmac, tracks, mud, desert, churned sand – Michelin XZL. Almost putting the lie to the saying 'there is no such thing as a good compromise', the XZL confronts typical mixed-going expedition conditions with extraordinary efficiency. Capable of an exceptionally low 0.6 bar emergency soft inflation (12 mph max) it has circumferential sidewall ribs to protect against sidewall damage at these vulnerable pressures.

• *Mainly mud.* Camel Trophy type conditions or Zaire mud-bath, on or beyond the limits of vehicle movement at all – Michelin XCL. Exclusively mud traction oriented with some sacrifice of grip on tarmac, hardroad durability and maximum road speed rating (75 mph max, full inflated). May be deflated to 0.9 bar emergency soft (12 mph max). If XCLs are not available (limited production at present), use XZL above.

• *Mainly sand.* Michelin XS: a very good desert tyre (and 'desert' means gravel, stones, rocks as well) that really shines on sand of all types – virgin sand (unbroken), very fine sand, crust sand, soft sand, churned sand (pre-travelled by other vehicles). Like the XZL, capable of deflation to 0.6 bar in emergencies. Grip on wet tarmac needs watching. Sidewalls not as well protected from glancing rock cuts as XZL. A brilliantly effective tread design shamelessly copied by other manufacturers.

Forget fancy sidewall lettering. If bewildered by multiplicity of makes (or even if you aren't) go for Michelin. If still bewildered, go for XZL (XS if mainly desert).

Speedometer calibration

Know the errors. For navigational purposes, you will need a really accurate odometer. As mentioned above, fitting different tyres may result in different speedometer and odometer accuracy unless the circumference of the new tyre is identical to that of the original item. Knowing these figures from data on both tyres (which will be listed in catalogues or will be available from the manufacturer) you can calculate a theoretical error and correction for your odometer. Probably better than this, since you do not know the original error of the instrument, is to carry out a physical check using the distance markers on motorways – small white 'sticks' every 100 metres alongside the hard shoulder on UK motorways. Do this with a colleague as it requires considerable concentration to count enough markers for the calibration to have a worthwhile accuracy.

Speed too. You can also check your speedometer for speed accuracy by comparing your reading with the figure given on your GPS navigation system – provided you have held a rock-steady speed for not less than about 10 seconds on a straight road. This will give the satellite data a chance to 'settle down' with consistent repeat values.

If oversize tyres fitted do remember this will affect accuracy of speedometer and odometer. For navigation it is vital to know errors, if any, in distance measurement.

Roof modifications

Roll-over bars, roof-rack. Note the grouping. You will have noted already the considered advice of this book is to avoid roof-racks because of the effect on fuel consumption (air drag), centre of gravity (also too high), the guarantee of poor handling, the danger of roll-over and the fact that any vehicle capable of taking a heavy roof-rack without strengthening is probably over-engineered and thus too heavy; and any vehicle *not* capable of taking a roof-rack is that way because it is not strong enough and should not therefore be burdened with one.

With soap box duly aired, however, there will be some who may need points to ponder – having first taken the oath that they will use a roof-rack only for low density, light loads like sleeping bags, a tent and possibly to hang sand ladders from (total *not*

Well made roof-rack (left) attached only to the rain gutters of an aluminium roof – a recipe for future fatigue failure. And all those lights; what ever for? Tested in Zimbabwe game parks, less beautiful but braced to the waist level structure, roof-rack (below) takes lightweight baggage of tour passengers within. Probably well within vehicle GVW but watch for body roll.

more than 100 kg). At its simplest, you can benefit, with great caution, from the fact that Camel Trophy vehicles exist – not to go and do likewise but to learn from. Do not be tempted to emulate their roof loads since the vehicles have been fundamentally re-engineered to have stiffer suspension that resists roll and is also stronger, and also the roof racks are tied in mechanically to internal roll-over bars – which in turn carry through to anchor at the chassis. This is the part to copy, if you really have to. Don't put a roof-rack on a vehicle for a demanding expedition without an internal roll cage of some kind that in turn is fixed to the vehicle chassis.

This is a generalisation but the concept is valid: do not put loads on a roof that it was not originally designed for. In most vehicles mentioned above the body is actually rubber mounted to the chassis so you are in danger of coupling a flexibly mounted item to a fixed item with predictable results in the fatigue field. In the case of Camel Trophy vehicles rubber grommets at the roof-rack-to-roll-cage points permit the body to shake where it will relative to the chassis.

Roof-racks – fatigue loads. An inadequately braced and overladen roof-rack on a Defender, clinging by its fingertips only to the rain gutters and plying African corrugated tracks every day of its life can be expected, in time, to fatigue crack along the A-posts (windscreen pillars) and most of the rest of its upper bodywork. Be particularly careful with the Defender which now has aluminium, not steel, cant rails as earlier models had. This vehicle, with its light bodywork and inherent low centre of gravity, was designed in the days before roll-over legislation demanded much heavier upper bodywork which would have given better margins for roof-rack loads.

The appearance of the built-in external roll cage on US specification Defenders reflects roll-over legislation primarily, though it also makes a light-capacity roof rack a more practical proposition. This cage, ingeniously, is rooted to the chassis but sits outside the body which is permitted to 'flex'

on its rubber mountings within the cage.

The fuse may be long or short but a roof-rack hanging on the rain gutters of any vehicle with a large load on bad tracks is – never mind the handling problems – a fatigue failure in waiting.

Roll cages or not? Roll-over cages in themselves can be life-savers and as insurance against the seriously unforeseen, they make some sense. Safety Devices of 30 Regal Drive, Soham, Cambridgeshire CB7 5BE, tel 01353.624624, as well as making the well designed and thought-out North American specification units for Land Rover Defenders, do a very wide range of such equipment for other vehicles too (as well as – see below – front and rear underbody protection equipment).

Roof tents. A roof tent is an acceptable example of a lightweight roof load and in most cases you will be able to use a roof-rack base without an accompanying roll cage. However, on vehicles like the Defender it is important that the roof-rack in such an installation is tied into the body structure rather than relying solely on the rain guttering – note detail in left-hand illustration on page 2.2 – 13. See Section 2.2 'Camping'.

Everyone does it – and everyone is wrong! Do not fit roof-rack and overload it. Low density loads only. For best fatigue life, tie-in roof-rack to chassis via roll cage.

Better than no roll cage but this would have been better to go forward to the windscreen A-pillar which is where most roll-over loads are taken – a combination of roll-over and forward speed. Not many vehicles roll while stationary. Safety Devices cages (see above) mostly external.

Underbody, peripheral protection

Steering gear, fuel tank. Proper track awareness and on-foot marshalling by your passenger in tight spots can usually reduce the risks but there are nevertheless vulnerable areas front and rear in 4x4s that can in some cases benefit from extra protection. Steering gear track rods at the front are often perilously at hazard from deep wheel ruts which make the centre of the track high enough to cause damage; when trying to straddle such ruts you can sometimes slip in inadvertently. Additionally, the hazard of unseen rocks in deep mud or when wading may take you by surprise. Both Safety Devices (see above) and Southdown Engineering manufacture suitable protection plates for the Land Rover product range. Southdown 4x4 Products are at Zeal Monachorum, Crediton, North Devon EX17 6DR, tel 01363.83819.

A rear-mounted fuel tank can be at risk when a vehicle with pronounced rear overhang begins to ascend a steep bank or is crossing a ditch. Fuel tank protection plates are worth investigating if you are likely to be traversing very poor tracks that have been subject to seasonal rainfall erosion. Be aware, however, of the weight penalty;

Some vehicles may need underside protection for steering gear, fuel tanks, in deep-rut conditions. Think carefully – weight, easy removal for maintenance ...

nothing is for nothing and it will have to come out of your payload allowance.

Bull bars, side bars. Regarded by some as both a pedestrian safety hazard and pretentious over-ornamentation in European hard-road surroundings, it is easy to forget that bull bars on the front of a vehicle did originate from a utilitarian need to protect headlights and push overgrown vegetation out of the way on the kind of 'half-width track' that is not uncommon in remote areas. Think quite hard, however, before fitting one as their weight is prodigious, they make engine access less easy and – most ironic of all – many, when actually subjected to real bush tracks, are found to be wanting in fatigue strength! Be warned that many are inadequately engineered and instead look out for ones that common sense tells you have at least been made properly. Headlight guards alone will in many cases suffice.

Side bars – protective bars close beneath the door sill panels – can be useful when cresting small sharp bumps or when small boulders cause unforeseen lateral rocking that would otherwise ground the sill panel.

'Are you sure about that toe-in figure, Hoskins?' Ruts made by larger vehicles with bigger wheels cost this track rod hundreds of miles from the nearest workshop. Protection plate helps save steering components but track rod still exposed.

All but the shorter 4x4s have quite large rear overhang that can make them prone to damage through rear grounding when crossing ditches or climbing steep slopes. Protection for aft-mounted fuel tanks afforded by this rear end 'bash plate'.

As above, prevention – ie, don't ground the bodywork – is better than merely transferring a dent from a soft panel to a hard bar but if you can afford the weight and wish to cover against minor misjudgements then sidebars are worth considering. These often double as side steps but beware steps that hang down too far since these can invite trouble that did not exist before. For Defenders, Rogers of Bedford, Castle Mill, Goldington Road, Bedford MK41 0JA, tel 01234.348469 make some well engineered items.

Underbelly protection. Some 4x4s are more off-road oriented than others – for very good reasons which were discussed in Section 4.1. The lightweight fun vehicles and some of the luxury vehicles may have independent front suspension (IFS) and a generally lower stance on the road than vehicles with beam axles. These lower vehicles are built that way because they are aimed at a market favouring on-road handling in preference to off-road athleticism but the IFS, specially, means that the sump of the engine and the belly of the vehicle is closer to the ground. Some manufacturers have accounted for this with protection plates – so called 'bash plates' – at these locations. Should you, because of the inherently lower ground clearance of the vehicle, touch a rock in these parts of the underbody you will usually get what may be termed an 'audio warning' – the noise of scraping metal – first. This will give you a slightly dented bash plate but it will save the high value hardware it is protecting.

If you have a low-slung IFS vehicle and have plans to expand its operating envelope on your expedition, take a good look and a long look underneath for vulnerable areas

Some vehicles have vulnerable underbelly exhaust systems requiring 'bash plate' protection on sharp humps. Bull bars heavy, usually superfluous; often badly designed.

If you really do need a bull bar to sweep bush from the front of the vehicle and can afford the weight, this one (left) indicates a thorough approach. But think hard first. Extra underbelly protection against grounding on bumps of this kind is necessary on some vehicles. Exhaust systems can often be vulnerable.

that could get damaged by inadvertent contact with rocks; not all manufacturers have taken appropriate steps to protect their vehicles underneath. If there is a potential problem take steps to have plates or other kinds of protection installed. Vehicles with beam axles and large wheels like Land Rover Defenders, Discoverys or Toyota Hilux pick-ups invariably have their engine sump up out of harm's way (above the axle) and the mid-belly point – the most likely point for a grounding going over a sharp-crested hillock – has usually been taken care of by proper routing of the exhaust pipe and by mounting the gearbox on top of very robust cross members.

Think ahead about recovery: large towing rings, ropes with shackles and hooks, slots and stowage for HiLift jack – heavy; rattle-free stowages for sand ladders.

Recovery add-ons

(see also Section 5.4 'Recovery')

Tow hooks and rings. Easily accessible, strong and properly sized towing hooks or rings are not always as routinely provided on 4x4s as you would have thought – especially on the more cosmetically endowed models. Make this a positive check in your preparation and do so resolving that your tow ropes – be it you being towed out or you coming to someone else's assistance – will include a U-bolt and shackle. Knotting a rope round a hook or lashing-down eye will result in an immovable knot and a lot of broken fingernails after being subject

to some energetic recovery manoeuvres.

HiLift, jack sockets. Think hard before you decide to take a HiLift jack as it is heavy and difficult to stow unless you have made a special rack for it to be carried outside the vehicle. A Hi-Lift jack, whilst being invaluable when you really need one, needs a certain type of square-section girder to get a grip on. Land Rover Defenders might have been designed specially for it but vehicles with more rounded contours and flimsier bumpers will shrug off the ministrations of a HiLift as if it were an orange pip gripped between adjacent toes. With foresight, however, it is possible to equip your vehicle with a socket that a HiLift will 'see' and get a firm non-slip grip on/in.

Likewise be sure that your under-axle jack – and your spare – has the right profile to cup the axle when lifting. With both this jack and the HiLift you will need a small baulk of timber (maybe 30 x 20 cm x 5 cm thick) to spread the load and stop the jack from merely disappearing downwards into the ground when called upon to lift the vehicle.

Sand ladder and shovel racks. Recovery gear such as sand ladders and shovels are best stowed externally if possible; some find that hanging sand ladders from a vestigial roof rack is most convenient. Stowing

Large beefy tow rings (left), versatile tow hook (below) will act like a plough or ground anchor off road. Don't fit it for expeditions. HiLift jack (right) needs ground load spreader and a square bumper or special sockets. See Section 5.4.

PSP (left), in steel or aluminium is a reasonable load spreader but awkward, heavy and has no longitudinal strength. Purpose built aluminium sand ladders are light enough to run with (you'll have to to follow a floundering vehicle in sand), have minor bridging capability and are multi-purpose – see photo page 4.2 -16. Stow them on side, back or front of vehicle; they don't keep desert rain off, though. Note shovel racks ready for action.

along the sides or across the back of the vehicle is another way of carrying them. External mounts with over-centre clips or bungees afford ready access, easy shedding of residual sand or mud when re-stowed and, with bicycle locking chains or cables, straightforward security in inhabited regions. If Barong sand channels (see Section 5.4) and small folding shovels are used, these are small enough to be stowed within the vehicle where they will be less vulnerable to thieves. In this instance, use canvas bags to keep dirt off other cargo.

Sand ladders – not PSP. Hallowed by decades of use by those who knew (and still apparently know) no better, so called 'sand channels' have, to some, come to mean those awkward, over flexible, leg-cutting, over-weighty bits of perforated metal planking originally designed to make airfields from green fields in the Second World War; that was called PSP. It will certainly spread loads over soft ground but a proper sand ladder – literally that – will do the job a lot better, be

light enough to run with, will not cut the side of your leg as you carry it and will offer a degree of bridging strength as well. Five and half feet long, maybe 13 inches wide and with rungs spaced at around five inches (so that a wheel rests on never less than two rungs at a time) the side members should be of aluminium about 65 mm depth. This depth will take the weight of a light 4x4 and has even been used with medium trucks such as the Bedford 4-tonner on reasonably supportive ground. Articulated Barong sand channels, are even lighter and can be stowed without the need for external racking.

Winch. Fuller treatment of winches is given at Section 5.4 and in the matching volume to this one, *The Land Rover Experience*, Edition 2. Winches are heavy and expensive in the context of equipping an expedition vehicle. If the proposed winch is to be elec-

Most people use them and most people are wrong! PSP is a cheap option for fleet (too flexible, awkward). Aluminium sand ladders are lighter, effective, versatile.

If you do decide on the weight and cost of a winch, consider a capstan winch – inappropriately shown here in desert – which operates without the frenzy and overheating risk of an electric unit. It can handle a rope of limitless length – which has to be stored separately.

desert and bush particularly a winch would be a poor investment. In such conditions, even apart from the fact that there will be no trees to winch onto, recovery methods are more effective when involving sand ladders or other flotation/traction aids and long tow ropes.

If you do opt for a winch, a mechanically driven capstan winch has much to commend it since it can carry out continuous heavy duty work all day with the engine just ticking over and has none of the high amperage, frantic stress of an electric winch with its attendant potential for overheating and need for extra battery or alternator upgrade. A winch installation is a major job requiring the highest standards of engineering and would best be left to specialist installers. If you have a winch, take a day's training in its use from an off-road school well in advance of your expedition.

Maximise cargo space

Seats out. As mentioned in Section 4.1 'Expedition vehicles', in a station wagon or any three- or four-door vehicle carrying only two persons, maximise cargo space by removing the rear seat(s) and save weight at the same time. This will reduce your kerb weight and increase your available payload considerably – you will be aghast at the weight of the hardware you remove espe-

Winches heavy, expensive, rarely needed except for trialling. If you do need one, consider capstan type. Remove seats: save weight, gain space for internal cargo.

tric a second battery (if you do not already have one) and possibly a high output alternator will be almost essential. The cost and especially the weight will rise even more; the extra weight may necessitate heavy duty front springs being fitted to the vehicle. Winches do an invaluable job in particular and exceptionally bad conditions where there are trees or other vehicles to use as an anchor to winch onto; this usually means deep mud on unusually bad forest tracks.

Paradoxically, such conditions do not always prevail in expeditions and the cost and weight of a winch and all it brings with it would not usually be worthwhile. In

Classic back-end modification. Removing seats and trim boosts residual payload considerably and makes a huge difference to the loadability of the rear. Rack with lashing points puts heavy load – the water and fuel cans – almost centrally between front and rear axles. Angle alloy beams at back floor locate boxes and anchor lashing cleats for tiedowns. Note extinguisher.

Controlling the cargo – first locate it so it cannot move laterally, then tie it down so it can't hop on the bumps. Wooden skip has tie-downs; note internal stowage of sand ladders (not ideal but minimises bodywork drilling). Flush cleats don't damage cargo.

cially if the vehicle is in the 'luxury' class and can revel in the additional fuel or water cans that it represents. Seat anchorages can conveniently be used as the basis for cargo lashing points.

Tie-downs to secure load

Internal tie-down cleats. (A roundup on loading and lashing information scattered through the book – it impinges on so many aspects of vehicle-dependent expeditions – is repeated and gathered together at Section 4.3 for easy one-place reference)

As mentioned already on pages 2.1 - 6 ('Equipment basics') and 2.5 - 4 ('Water'), lashing down the vehicle load – storage boxes, water and fuel cans – is essential to avoid damage to vehicle and cargo when travelling over rough tracks; corrugations will demolish your equipment as well as your vehicle, given the chance. First-loading the vehicle the day before departure will not do; a detailed loading plan must be made and checked out in practice some weeks in advance; appropriate tie-downs and strapping must be worked out and installed so that pull-tightened luggage strapping (or industrial straps with mechanical tension-

ers) can be used to secure and easily release the load. Note that this is a job you will do three or four times a day so make it easy to do and effective when it is done.

Some vehicles are fitted with tie-downs as standard and these will be the best since they will have been designed-in to anchor on the appropriately strong parts of the structure. You will probably find these vehicles do not have enough lashing points and there are some vehicles which have none at all. 'Having enough' or not enough will be clear when you plan your loading. Rows of

Install and use tie-downs to secure cargo and prevent damage to it and vehicle on rough tracks. Plan interior loading well in advance for modular boxes, lashing points.

jerry cans, modular boxes, boxes of rations will be of consistent sizes that require lashing in certain points of the vehicle floor in sync with each row of cargo.

Establish where these points should be and plan enough tie-downs for each row of cans or boxes to have its own lashings. Make your cleats big enough for the straps or hooks to fit easily and slip through easily when tightening is carried out. Lashing cleats that stand proud of the floor or wall of a load compartment are better than nothing but will often damage the cargo because they protrude. Recessed lashing points – cargo professionals use them all the time in aircraft and heavy trucks – are less easy to engineer but you will bless them a hundred times over in use. Equally you will curse protruding ones just as many times – and a lot more vehemently – as they dent boxes, fracture plastic jerry cans and prevent boxes being slid smoothly into position.

Having chosen the position for your lashing points, be sure that the surface you recess them into is strong enough to take the strain. A small readjustment in position will sometimes mean you are able to pick up on a reinforcing bar or bracket. If not, insert some local reinforcement of your own. Without it, vibration and stress will cause the lashing point to crack the surrounding metalwork and pull through.

Lashing cleats as fitted internally to military Land Rovers are available on the Land Rover parts list – RRC3588/3674 – but these are not recessed.

Special equipment mountings. If you are carrying delicate scientific equipment such as gravimeter, theodolites, radios, cine cameras etc. careful thought must precede their stowage. The mid-wheelbase point gives the gentlest ride so this region, if possible, should be chosen for mountings. Anti-vibration mounts (government-surplus instrument/radio shops will have them) can be used but beware rubber-only mountings; without the essential damping such mounts can actually give equipment a rougher ride than being bolted direct to the floor. If in doubt, a light plywood box with small poly-

Fit lashing points where they really can take the strain and not merely enhance fatigue cracking. If necessary, insert reinforcements behind sheet metal.

thene bags full of polystyrene chips or pellets will give a cushioned and reasonably well damped ride to delicate equipment.

DIBS-mirror for virgin desert

'Beige-outs' in the desert. A somewhat specialist but, in use, invaluable modification applies to travel across previously untrodden desert sand. Where prolonged off-tracks driving over completely smooth sand is undertaken, particularly in high-sun conditions, it is often difficult or impossible to focus on the actual surface of the ground. As there is nothing for the eye to focus on, it tends often to revert to a 'rest focus' distance of around a metre – and this makes the situation even worse. A consequence of this lack of ground texture – smooth ground and no shadow – combined with poor eye focus is that a driver will not see changes of terrain slope or even – and there are, alas, many recorded instances of this – the edges of dunes. Vehicles have inadvertently gone over the edges of dunes or hit sand ridges simply because of the lack of surface irregularity or texture on which to focus, combined with shadowless lighting conditions.

(It is worth mentioning that these small hard windblown sand ramps – often not more than 30-40 cm high – unseen and hit at speed can produce hazardous results. One such case of down-sun driving caused a long wheelbase Land Rover to get airborne for a horizontal distance of eight metres; the closely following medium truck attempted the same feat and bent its front axle on landing.)

A DIBS-mirror is a way of overcoming the problem by reflecting the sun as a spot of light on the surface of the sand about 30 metres ahead of the vehicle which not only gives the eye something to focus on but also gives advance indication of surface irregularities or changes in slope. The spot disappearing or moving up, left or right, will give advance indication of a dune edge or slope change so that appropriate action can be taken by the driver.

Heading marker too. The light spot can also be used as a heading marker where a

Direction of light – behind or directly over-head – can make terrain appear two-dimensional. Wheel tracks show point where Land Rover (2nd from left in photo) got airborne on unseen dune ramp, landing 24 paces further on. DIBS-mirror provides reflected sun spot ahead of vehicle (just above of sun compass, lower right photo) that will move or disappear if it encounters ridge, slope or dune edge. Device proved invaluable in vast sand expanses of Mauritania 'Empty Quarter'. Installed in top-less Range Rover (right), sequence shows mirror adjustment.

featureless horizon provides nothing to aim at when you are attempting to hold a given compass course; once the direction of travel has been established, the spot of light can be adjusted (by moving the mirror) to lie dead ahead and it is then followed, the vehicle being driven so as to keep the spot in the same relative ahead-position. By the laws of optics applying to reflected light, deviation of the vehicle from the desired course by 5° causes the light spot to move through 10° so a sensitive heading director is available to keep the driver on course. (Due to sun movement, of course, realignment of the beam must be carried out every 15 minutes cross-checking with your compass.

In practice, a DIBS-mirror is a forward facing, flat (not convex) truck or van rear-view mirror about 15 x 20 cm in size, ball-joint mounted high up on the windscreen pillar of the vehicle in such a way that the driver can alter its alignment in order to reflect the sun onto the sand wherever the

sun may be in the sky. Driving conditions in which the problem of distinguishing the surface are most severe are when driving on smooth unbroken sand with the sun either overhead (around noon) or in the sky hemisphere directly behind the vehicle – driving 'down-sun'. Mounting of the mirror arm requires thought and care if the ability to reflect the sun onto the ground ahead of the vehicle with the sun in any position is to be achieved.

(Those curious as to the name of the device will be pleased to learn that, meeting the modern appetite for involved acronyms, the name derives from the tongue in cheek SATSAHDIBS – Sun Activated Terrain Surface And Heading Director Invented By Sheppard.)

DIBS-mirror addresses a special case in bright-light untrodden desert but nothing else so effective in preventing inadvertent dune edge accidents.

CREW FUNCTION MODIFICATIONS

Philosophy overall. Crew function modifications are mostly aimed at crew comfort, the habitability of the cab under sustained hot- or cold-climate expedition conditions and to take account of long days of continuous driving over often rough tracks. It is worth taking considerable trouble to make the vehicle as comfortable as possible in advance. Part of the doctrine of thinking things through and planning in detail, concentrate on keeping cool (or warm), well ventilated, comfortable, reducing noise and rattle, reducing heat loss or heat gain from outside and ensuring adequate lighting for evening work – without hazarding battery life for starting next day (see above). Anything you can do to enhance or increase the number of small secure oddments storages will be helping resolve the daily quest 'Whatever happened to the ... ?'

Floor, roof, sides insulation

If, like many, you are using a hard-top 'van', roof, side panel insulation is well worthwhile to reduce noise and heat transfer. In the bundu you will bless it a hundred times.

Extra floor insulation. If you are planning to use a metal-floor Land Rover not equipped with floor trim, 1-2 cm of felt on top of the special under-floor material offered by car interior silencing firms is effective against noise and heat. The subjective effect is immensely beneficial and contributes to smooth confident driving and acquisition of what has been termed the 'Rolls-Royce syndrome' – particularly smooth and elegant driving resulting from finding yourself at the wheel of particularly smooth and rattle-free vehicle. Early Land Rovers (even up to 1987) were not well insulated against heat from the engine compartment and extremely high metal temperatures could be experienced in the cab on the floor, seat-box and gearbox tunnel. If the engine is being removed for overhaul before the trip do all you can to alleviate the problem from the outside by adding insulation to the engine bay bulkhead to the standard of current production vehicles. An aluminium-faced insulating trim on the engine side of the bulkhead is effective though it should

be something that is waterproof and non absorbent of the water, dampness and oil that may prevail.

Roof and body-side insulation. In any hard-top or 'van' type body there is scope for introducing a large portion of instantly successful 'Rolls-Royce' syndrome – and comfort – in the form of insulation to the roof and body side panels of the vehicle. Current hard-top Land Rover Defenders have improved roof insulation – where full interior trim is fitted but interior body panels aft of the driver are bare metal. Remember in this, or any type of metal-sided van-type body, very high heat-load (as well as noise and reverberation) can result from the sun on the sides of the vehicle; the sun is only overhead for a few minutes each day. Take the trouble therefore to insulate the body *sides* thoroughly; it will reduce heat input (and heat loss in cold climates) and make a blissful difference to interior noise. Heavy bitumen stick-on panels of the kind available in sound insulation kits should be used as initial noise deadening, followed by a layer of thin polystyrene foam sheeting for heat insulation; then panels of hardboard faced with a tough short-pile carpet material. The result is extremely effective, keeping heat gain and loss to a minimum and conferring greatly reduced interior noise levels.

If a hard-top Land Rover of early type (ie without adequate interior roof insulation) is used, a double skin 'tropical roof' is very worthwhile; these were available as a standard part.

'Van' side window

Adding road safety. The need to legislate against misuse of tax rules designed to help people who use their vehicles for work has resulted, alas, in some bizarre regulations regarding the fitment of side windows to 'vans' in the UK. The result is that all such vehicles are supplied with sheet metal sides and no means of seeing beyond the 9-

Side window (left), shown with anti theft net curtain, is invaluable safety asset at T-junctions. Roof photographic platform, load lashing rails, seats out and rear door 'kitchen unit' enhance expedition role.

o'clock position at road T-junctions where such junctions are not a true right angle. Fit at least one small side window on a van on the side remote from the driver in order to remedy this situation if you can. If, in the UK, you have bought a 'van' type vehicle and not reclaimed the VAT, this will be no problem; if the VAT *has* been reclaimed there will usually be a liability for it to repaid when the window is fitted though appeals are possible where the vehicle really is a working machine. There is a case, for security reasons, for limiting fitment to just one window and here, as mentioned previously under security (page 4.2 - 17), installing some 'see-out-but-not-in' arrangement such as a net curtain.

Places to put things

Stowages, shelves. You will find it very hard to get enough stowages and places to put things in an expedition vehicle. The more modern the vehicle and the more exotic the studio styling of the interior the larger, it seems, are the featureless sweeps of beautifully crafted but blank plastic at just the locations you would like to put down a pencil, a note pad, spectacles case, compass, lens cap, lipsalve, map or a cup of coffee. That a designer has had to incorporate an airbag into the dash is seldom a completely viable excuse and the panels can just as easily be topped with a little lipped shelf as with a slippery slope of grey plastic. Make a mental note to twist the ear of any vehicle interior

designers you may come across in the future and settle down to think what you can yourself do about it.

The Defender Meccano set. Loved for its character and simplicity but also for its practicality and Meccano set DIY potential, the Defender is the easiest of all vehicles on which to begin an expedition modifications programme. It is not the only one, however, that can be modified and in most cases the extent of what may be done is limited only by your own courage and knowledge of where those infuriating hidden nylon snap fasteners are located on the vehicle trim panels. The illustrations here show extensive modifications to a Defender interior that (even for a Defender) required courage, time and a budget for professional sheet metal-workers to ply their craft. The modifications were extremely worthwhile, however, and have proved of value even in routine home-base day to day trips. Examine some of the latest and best MPVs if you are short of ideas as to what may be done but in general you will find you need flat places to put things, flat places with a lip to stop things from rolling onto the floor and flat places with sticky rubber mats to stop things sliding on corners. Boxes with lids – under

Van side-window an important road safety modification. Spend time planning boxes, shelves, fold-down places to put things; you can never have too many.

There's often a lot of room <u>under</u> the panels too. Here a hinge-forward cubby box permits stowage of jack and etceteras (far left). Typical lunch snack break on a real-world trip shows the need – and use – for flat shelving and stowages.

Upholstery and ample cab ventilation make great contributions to comfort. Never use vinyl seats. Air conditioning heavy, costly, power-sapping, two edged weapon.

seats, in bulkheads, beneath other things – will also provide invaluable stowages. And thin, vertical slots to stuff folded maps and books into are invariably useful. Take your pencil, take your time and take your screw-driver ... !

Upholstery, ventilation

Vehicle upholstery. Regard seat upholstery as part of your clothing system – which it surely is – and choose accordingly. In a phrase; cloth upholstery, hot or cold, not leather or vinyl. See Section 2.3 'Clothing', page 2.3 - 52.

The hot climate case is worse than the cold climate case since in cold climates you will usually have enough clothing on to form your own sitting environment and immediate micro-climate. In hot climates it is often just you and a shirt before you get to the seat itself. Few older vehicle seats are sufficiently ventile to avoid sweaty discomfort in hot climates – 'Vinyl, old chap; indestructible!' is the kind of thing they used to say. Seat/back pads of mesh and sprung wire (or even basket work) can sometimes be bought and will ensure a centimetre or so of air between the seat and occupant. Alternatively some of the thick sheepskin-type seat covers are also effective; genuine

sheepskin is not only ventile and absorbent but also resilient. Better, though, is to bite the bullet and change your seats for cloth-upholstered ones before you go.

Extra ventilation. It is worth examining the possibility of improving ambient-air ventilation in a vehicle, especially if your expedition is to a hot climate area. The alternative of air conditioning is heavy, expensive and power-sapping and also subjects you to thermal shock every time you get in and out of the vehicle – tropical heat feels a lot worse if you have just got out of an air conditioned vehicle. Van roof ventilators with opening flaps are worth considering. If workshop facilities permit, a top-of-the-windscreen scoop can be devised to duct face-level air to the interior through aircraft-type eyeball vents; too many modern vehicles have so-called fresh air ducts that direct air to your hands on the steering wheel leaving your face sweltering. On early Land Rovers with sliding cab windows the complete side window panels are easily removed by undoing two nuts.

Audio

Discreet installation. While the wise will use music on an expedition as a special treat rather than bathing the entire trip in ceaseless decibels, the ability to play your favourite tapes from time to time will be a welcome luxury. However you do it, it is again worth taking the trouble to do it well. Common areas requiring attention are:
- Position and type of speakers.
- Position and type of radio.
- Short wave reception.

Speakers. While most vehicles have provision for a radio/tape player, many designers seem to have forgotten that the human

Conceptually simple modification snatches air from top of windscreen to provide plentiful, true face-level fresh air through eyeball louvres from above. Modifications far right optimise fresh air vents, put audio speakers and tweeters at ear level, provide enhanced shelf space, improved ergonomics. Not cheap or quick to do but hugely effective.
Customising your vehicle in this way very rewarding.

ear is located in the side of the head, not in the kneecaps and speaker location seems to favour the latter rather than the former configuration. Especially where there are high levels of ambient cab noise, speakers should be mounted close to the head to obtain clarity of sound; speakers mounted in the bottom of the doors and the volume cranked up does not amount to the same thing. Secondly – and surprisingly to some – fit the best speakers you can; plus tweeters for immaculate high frequency reproduction. If this sounds bizarre in a diesel-engined expedition truck, reflect on the fact that poor quality sound is easily muffled by high ambient noise; as you will have noticed on any good public address system (and there are not many!), it requires clear, accurate higher sound frequencies to pierce background noise and this is what works in an expedition vehicle.

Radio type and position. Clearly you must have a radio that can produce clear sound in the first place and which is capable of accenting the top frequencies by use of a wide-ranging tone control. One that also has an auto-seek of some kind is surprisingly useful when you are in a foreign country and have no idea of the frequencies and what language they broadcast in. If you have the option, position the radio in a centre console cubby box or other compartment where it is both out of sight when you leave the vehicle and can be protected from dust in the rougher parts of the trip; tape drives

and dust do not mix well.

Short wave reception. Someone once wrote that no expedition was a proper expedition without the BBC World Service coming in on short wave (SW) with its wheezing, crackling and narrow band-width. Certainly it is good to keep in touch (and for once hear balanced news broadcasts rather than domestic crime reports and political tittle-tattle). Few car radios are made that can tune short-wave frequencies and even those do not do so digitally which makes them a waste of time. You can get sets that will take the input from another short-wave receiver, either through a plug (designed for add-on CD players) or through adapters that fit into the tape slot. Play your SW portable (digitally synthesised frequencies, not analogue tuning) into this and it will benefit from the main car audio's tone and volume controls. In all honesty the system is seldom satisfactory since you must still allow your SW radio a view of the sky for its aerial; unless you can also rig an external SW whip aerial, you will probably have to regard World Service as a treat to be savoured when in the evening camp rather than on the move. Short wave radio specification requirements are covered in more detail at Section 2.7 'Communications', page 2.7 - 21.

Good audio is to do with clear high frequencies not booming bass. Mount speakers high in cab, close to ears to cut through ambient noise. Cover radio to deter theft.

Section 4.3

Vehicles:

Loading and lashing

COVERAGE OF THIS SECTION

Note: Carriage of equipment and liquids, loading, and securing the load is an important part of expedition vehicle preparation and is a theme cropping up throughout this book. Section 4.3 is a one-section summary and round-up of the subject as it occurs in other sections – 2.1 'Equipment basics', 2.5 'Water', 2.6 'Fuel, oils, fluids', 4.1 'Expedition vehicles'.

The overall picture

The main principles. It will have become clear in the book so far that because of the isolated and hostile operating environment in which it operates, an expedition is only as sound as its logistic infrastructure and back-up. Repeatedly the vital role of vehicles and the importance of safeguarding them is highlighted with emphasis on careful operation. Careful operation means keeping well within the vehicles' operating limits in the way they are driven and loaded. The procedures are very straightforward. Indeed the very observance of strict limits and methodical loading provides reliable guidelines that eliminate the uncertainty of tackling the problem without previous experience. The general principles are:

• *Weight.* Keep as far below GVW (the manufacturer's maximum loaded weight – Gross Vehicle Weight) as you can and never exceed it. A light vehicle has better power weight ratio and is less stressed.

• *Weight distribution.* Keep the weight evenly spread between front and rear axles. Normally that means stowing the heavy payload as far forward as possible.

• *Bulk vs weight.* Be aware of the potential problems here. With a high density cargo you will run out of payload (ie weight allowance) before you run out of space. Don't keep loading until the vehicle is 'full'. When you reach payload limit – GVW – stop.

• *Packing.* Aim for a methodical modular system so that it is easy to load and unload (for customs inspections and if you should get a very severe bogging) and so that you know where everything is.

• *Lashing.* Ensure everything is lashed down to prevent rattling and to prevent damage to your equipment and vehicle. You will usually have to install lashing cleats at the preparation stage.

Liquid containers

Fuel. Built-in fuel tanks cannot be off-loaded when a vehicle is badly bogged but do offer compact storage low-down (ie low centre of gravity) when underfloor tanks are fitted. Metal jerry cans for extra fuel can hardly be bettered for safety and ease of handling. For large quantities, 200 litre (45

Keep within, or below, GVW; heavy equipment forward; modular boxing; fluids in jerry cans. Ensure all equipment is lashed; position lashing points accordingly.

Hundreds of kilometres of this kind of shaking (above) is what the vehicle and cargo have to suffer on a trip. Tie-downs essential; can be done even on a soft-top (right).

The non-stop round the world approach! Max payload allocation to fuel and water; truck fuel tank (not plumbed) athwartships behind driver, fuel cans lashed in trailer and hard plastic water cans securely lashed. Note timber frames. Valuable theodolite (orange, bottom of shot, left) given smoothest ride midships.

Jerry cans rather than built-in tanks make fluids easier to handle and offload. Use hard polythene water cans. Make and calibrate dipsticks for all containers.

gallon) steel drums are effective and very robust but the drums themselves are very heavy and, being round, are not space-efficient within a vehicle; such drums (suitably lashed down – see Section 4.2. – 'Vehicle modifications') are more appropriate to carriage of fuel on trucks than in relatively lightweight 4x4s. For these vehicles – if you do decide on built-in fuel rather than jerry cans – a large ex-truck fuel tank is lighter and saves space because of its rectilinear shape. Be sure, however, that such a tank, if used, is fitted forward in the load area so that its considerable weight is shared as equally as possible by the front and rear axles (photo p 4.2 - 9). Do not carry cans of fuel or water on roof racks – see Section 4.2.

Dipsticks. Dipsticks to ascertain the contents of part-used containers (photo page 2.6 - 4) and accurate records of cans used are essential to give an accurate daily fuel consumption. If you have a strapped-down truck fuel tank, make a dipstick for that too. It will not be very accurate but will be better than estimating. If possible, install a dipstick access with screw-down bung (in the middle so it is not sensitive to levelling).

Decanting. Decant from large containers via a siphon tube into a 20 litre jerry can (photo page 2.6 - 33) with calibrated jerrycan dipstick; litres/gallons put in since the vehicle tank was last full gives mpg over that

span of miles covered. If you are using jerry cans check before departure that you can decant satisfactorily from a jerry can into your vehicle's filler neck. For example, a Discovery, Range Rover and many 'plush' 4x4s, need a long-necked funnel in order to get fuel from a jerry can into the tank. Use that or a jerry can spout extension. Funnels are cumbersome, smelly, difficult to stow.

Water. For large quantities, 200 litre (45 gallon) drums, formerly used for chemicals storage (so hard-polythene lined), can sometimes be obtained though again there is the penalty of weight of the drum to contend with. Otherwise hard polythene jerry cans, 5-gallon military pattern, are very robust, taste-free and unsurpassed for normal use. If thinner-gauge 'civilian' ones have to be used (usually made from white translucent polythene), lash them down with padded or felt-lined cradles to preclude scuffing and leaking through abrasion. The soft, flexible polythene of such low-quality containers will taint water even in small water bottles; warm and chlorinated, it tastes bad enough to inhibit necessary drinking. Be sure to choose water bottles and containers made only of hard polythene. Leave the jerry cans strapped down and decant water using a 'squeezy pump' – photo page 2.5 - 4.

Equipment boxes

Modular storage. Methodically organised modular storage within the vehicle(s) – see Section 4.2 'Vehicle modifications' – is essential if you are to keep track of and prevent damage to the equipment you take. Professional expedition organisations such as British Antarctic Survey have for many years used plastic-lidded boxes that locate one above the other without slipping sideways and storage boxes similar in concept are now available from most DIY superstores. Light, strong, flexible and designed so that one box fits into a slight recess in the one below it, they are perfect for stowing expedition kit in neat rows and tiers within the back of a vehicle – food, cooking gear, vehicle spares, lubricants in plastic bottles, tools. It is useful to number or label each box (on the side and the lid) so that its content may easily be located. For customs declaration purposes as well as your own convenience, have a list of the contents of each box. Such boxes, when stacked or arranged, must be properly secured to tie-downs within the vehicle load area – see below 'Lashing' and Section 4.2.

Safe packing. Packing within the storage boxes should also be methodical and careful. Specifically, be sure that items cannot rattle or chafe against each other or get damaged when the vehicle is on rough ground or a corrugated track. This will not only prevent breakage but – a repeatedly observed phenomenon – result in better driving; the driver of a quiet, rattle-free vehicle becomes subject to the 'Rolls-Royce syndrome' and drives more confidently and more smoothly than when his nerves are a-jangle with internal noise.

Overall payload

Keep within the limits. It cannot be stressed too often that the overall payload limit of the vehicle must always be kept in mind. We have here dealt with liquid containers and stores boxing first so that you

know the components of your load but these must be related to the overall capacity of the vehicle in terms both of weight and bulk – examples of the Land Rover product range, likely expedition contenders in the UK, are given here. Typical bulk-weight combinations of standard load items are shown in the diagram below.

STANDARD 205 litre (45 Imp gal) BARREL, JERRY CAN DIMENSIONS: mm, (inches)

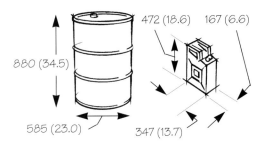

TYPICAL UNIT WEIGHTS	
205 litre (45 Imp gal) barrel, empty	20 kg
205 litre barrel full of petrol, kerosene	185 kg
" " diesel, lube oil	200 kg
" " water	225 kg
20 litre (4.5 Imp gal) steel jerry can, empty	4 kg
20 litre steel jerry can full of petrol, kerosene	20 kg
" " diesel, lube oil	22 kg
" " water	24 kg

Put equipment in modular, similar, plastic-lidded and nesting containers so box on top is located by box below. Cushion gear within boxes to avoid damage.

Load distribution

Even it out, front and rear. The vehicle's load must be as evenly distributed as possible between the two axles so that when each axle load is ascertained on a weighbridge, the difference is as small as practicable. Bonneted vehicles – as opposed to 'forward control' vehicles with the cab over the engine at the front – are designed to accept the inevitability of a higher axle load at the rear than at the front but in soft terrain the

*Know the cargo capability of your vehicle –
its maximum payload and the dimensions
of available space and of standard cargo
items like jerrycans and modular boxes.
Defender One Ten shown is easy example.
Get heavy items forward – here removing
the spare wheel (32 kg) to allow row of
water cans (120 kg) to sit farther from rear
axle makes sense. Keep rear overhang
area for featherweight cargo – if you have
such a commodity!*

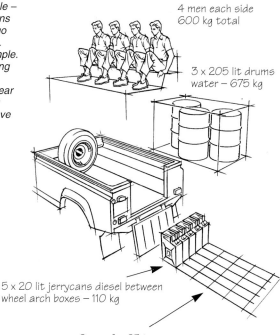

4 men each side
600 kg total

3 x 205 lit drums
water – 675 kg

5 x 20 lit jerrycans diesel between
wheel arch boxes – 110 kg

Space for 25 jerrycans

heavier axle will break through
the crust first – witness scenes
involving long wheelbase Land
Rovers stuck in the sand, tail-
down because the operator has
staggered to the rear of the vehicle and placed the heaviest load
items just inside the back door.

Maximum axle loads. There
is in fact a maximum axle load
for each axle on every vehicle
and you must be aware of this
when planning your load. Find out the actual weight on each axle independently on the
weighbridge. The sum of each axle's maximum permitted load amounts to more than
the maximum GVW of the vehicle in most
cases, in order to allow the operator some
leeway for imperfect load distribution. The
subject is dealt with in more detail in *The
Land Rover Experience* referred to in the
Introduction to this book. But the overall
lessons come out as follows:

1. Try to equalise front-rear load – or at
least minimise the difference – by always
putting high-density cargo forward in the
load bed.

2. Weigh your loaded vehicle on a
weighbridge – whole vehicle and then each
axle separately – to make sure you are within the GVW and individual axle maximum
loads.

3. Based on these axle loads you can
ascertain the minimum emergency-soft tyre
pressures you can use in extreme soft-sand
conditions (with associated speed limitations – see page 4.2 - 21 under 'Tyres'). Note
these figures for future use.

*Distribute load
between axles,
avoid the rear
overhang area.
Get dense cargo
forward. Install
lashing cleats
and tie downs to
eliminate cargo
movement and
rattle.*

Lashing

Tie-downs. Secure your load, both for
the sake of avoiding damage to the vehicle
and the load itself. Not all vehicles have the
right number of tie-downs – cleats to which
you can attach straps or ropes – so positioning and installing these will be part of your
modifications programme (See Section 4.2
'Vehicle modifications').

Straps and nets. Grip-buckle luggage
straps or quick-release tensioning straps are
the only reliable ways of securing a load
against the provocation of a vehicle ride
over a bad desert track. You will learn too
that often the use of a soft item between the
box and the strap will enable it to be cinched
tighter. Storage boxes are strapped-down in
ones and twos but when soft baggage such
as personal kit is then put on top, that too
has to be secured, especially in a soft-top
vehicle. In this case a groundsheet or other
dustproof fabric sheet should be used first

Not far off a 'how not to do it' above. Some no-option one-off box sizes ruled out modular approach but lack of box lashing in back gives bounce on bumps and rough track. Optimum modular approach and weight distribution shown above right plus elastic net on hard top wall for lightweight sleeping bags. Keeping out dust, rain and thieving hands makes soft-top packing even more demanding (right). Groundsheet, cargo nets, lashing tape, elastics and special lashing cleats keep cargo clean, undamaged and the ride rattle-free.

with a cargo net on top. Such a sheet has the additional advantage of denying to thieves a view of the vehicle contents and also keeps the cargo cool. (Cargo nets are purpose-made items using nylon webbing for the restraint net with lashing rings around the edges.) A range of suitable grip-buckle and tensioner straps is usually available in DIY stores but the larger ratchet-tensioner webbing and cargo nets may have to be obtained through commercial vehicle or air freight oriented outlets.

Groundsheet over cargo keeps out dust and prying eyes. Then cargo net and lashings to keep cargo in place.

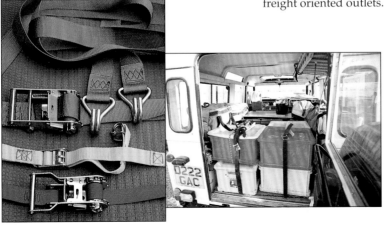

Commercial vehicle lashings with over-centre tensioners (far left) are needed for high density cargo like fuel drums, groups of jerry cans, pump sets. Lighter or low density loads can be secured using luggage straps

Section 5
Operations

Section 5.1

Operations:

Routine and operations

COVERAGE OF THIS SECTION

Pre-planning

Type of trip

Angle your planning. Although planning ahead and preparation could easily be described as being the theme of this book, don't let over-planning or preoccupation with planning spoil the *content* of your trip. Don't let its purpose become the grim determination to fulfil the original precepts of the planning phase. Don't let it all get too much ... ! Let the planning be directed at ensuring that in certain aspects of the trip you are free to play it by ear; that you will have set up an infrastructure enabling the planning at certain times to be switched off. Daily and weekly routine is worth thinking about a little. It will vary according to what sort of trip you are on and it will determine the kind of supplies you take. Is your trip:

1. A mile-athon? Solely getting from A to B; putting the greatest distance possible into each day. There will be trips of this kind where you do have to work at covering the distance but beware of getting a miles fixation; it is a recipe for getting the least out of

a trip and for 'coming-to' at the end with only the haziest idea of where you have been. It has been noted on many trips that a low-mileage day stands out as a specially enjoyable one.

2. Visiting sights? This will usually be preceded by a certain amount of item 1 above but in the 'region of operations' will probably demand a different routine.

3. Science, study? Similar to item 2 in that the middle part of the day is often cleared for static working and the other routine items are compressed into either end of it. Unlike item 2, however, you may well be close to your vehicles throughout the day so that snacks, water and access to equipment will be easy.

Even if the whole idea of your trip is to get away from it all – including routine – there will be benefits in organising things a little. The planning aspects involve deciding which chores to do when, which facilities you will need at what times – the anchor points of your daily existence.

Planning a routine will free-up time for other things; it need not turn your trip into a military exercise! And don't let covering miles become an obsession.

Some expeditions will need the 'working day' kept clear for study or project work but all trips will benefit from a well organised start and camp routine.

Anchor points

Things to be done. 'Thromboses in the life-blood of the expedition!', railed the team doctor (only half jokingly), on being informed that the chores roster had him flattening tins and burning the rubbish while the cook cooked and the vehicle person got on with the inspection. The fact is, of course, that there are certain jobs to be done on a team and each being allocated his or her task ensures that everything gets done with the professionalism and speed that repetition fosters.

Hang your routine on anchor points of jobs that have to be done. Early start, early stop makes for satisfying efficiency and time to relax in the evenings.

Typical of the list of chores that have to be done every day and other interruptions during a typical trip are:

- Cooking
- Refuelling
- Vehicle inspection
- Nav log transcription
- Nav planning for next day
- Water/rations stock
- Photography
- Project work
- Lunch stop, breaks

Start and stop time. Getting things done the night before is invariably better than 'I'll do that in the morning.' Early starts and early stops are better than late starts and late finishes. In your eagerness to get going

Each has his or her own job but cooking affects everybody – and the timing is critical if it is not to interfere with other tasks. Stop to camp 90 minutes before sunset and that gives time for vehicle fixing, refuelling, puncture mending etc. When it's all done a good meal is bliss. Light needs thinking about; see pages 2.4 -15, 4.2 - 16.

early, however, you will find it counter productive getting up more than about 30 minutes before dawn. Stumbling about in the dark and dropping things actually slows you down most times. Especially if you sleep out without a tent Nature's alarm clock seems to work very well when the glow in the east begins. If that fails the 'duty fly' never does; there is always one to buzz around and settle on your face as the sky gets light!

Circumstances will often dictate otherwise but in general stop to camp an hour and a half or more before sunset. This gives time for the vehicle inspection and refuelling to be done whilst there is still light to do any remedial work by should it be necessary. See below 'Evening chores' also.

Cooking. A brew of tea is invariably welcome as soon as possible after the evening halt and other team members can carry on working with their particular jobs with the mugs and their sides. Though lighting will have been arranged to cope with cooking at night (plus Petzl head-torches, of course), the cook usually finds it a lot easier to operate by daylight and the preparation and cooking of the main meal can be timed to deliver the steaming plates just after sundown. The cooking, of course, should not interfere with everyone else's jobs – a splendid dish produced just when you are up to your elbows mending a puncture is not good timing. An established routine in relation to the main meal ensures that everyone is aware when it is due; a '10-minute- bell' (or yell!) helps too.

Cooking always takes time and especially so in the morning. Team choices will vary and in specially cold conditions, some teams will opt for a cooked breakfast of some kind.

In most instances, however, a cereals, biscuits and jam kind of breakfast with coffee or tea will be enough to set people up for the day and this way elaborate cooking and utensil cleaning is avoided at a time when you are keen to be away. On small teams you can even avoid the need to light the stove for hot water by storing it in well-wrapped vacuum flasks the night before. It does work and the faffing about with stoves and kettles can be eliminated when there are tents and sleeping bags to be put away and tyre pressures (cold) to be checked.

Midday halt. A midday halt is welcome for a snack and brew and again with due attention to the laws of physics a flask can often be persuaded to keep water hot enough for coffee at this point from the night before. If not, better to light the stove at breakfast time, use it for the brew then and then fill a flask for the midday break. The remainder of the midday snacks can usually be put aside in a 'goodies bag' so that again, the kitchen equipment does not have to be broken out at that time.

In hot climates, the midday halt is a convenient time to refill water bottles and you will find it worth ensuring the 'duty can' and squeezy pump (see Sec 2.5 "Water", p 2.5 - 5) are handy and access does not involve elaborate unlashing or burrowing under loads.

Navigation log, If your navigation log (see Section 5.2 'Navigation', p 5.2 - 5 and - 31) has been kept on tape the midday halt is a convenient time to transcribe the morning's notes. As you record notes get into the habit of doing very short re-winds and playbacks to ensure the last message did record. Transcribing halfway through the day ensures that if the recorder is on the blink or the batteries a bit sad, only half a day's information is lost rather than a whole day's. Where navigation is more tricky you may find it useful to transcribe and indeed plot out the position more often than this.

Photography. Contrary to the views of many non-photographers, a photograph does not need only 1/125th of second to take ... ! Face this at the planning stage; cer-

'Goodies bag' for midday snack precludes need to get kitchen gear out. A brew when you stop to camp is bliss, main meal later planned not to clash with other chores.

It's useful to transcribe the navigation log from the tape during the day – lunch-snack time is handy. Here en route position fixes are downloaded the old fashioned way!

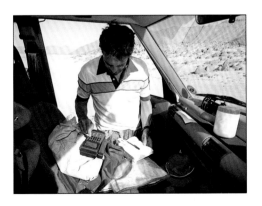

Photography is a hard and relentless taskmaster. Stills are demanding enough but film with its sequence-planning requirement, maintenance of narrative, walk-aheads to get oncoming shots, run-throughs and repeats will provoke insurrection unless you brief clearly at the beginning of the trip. If expedition funds depend on a film, it has to be done.

Good photography will demand time, sometimes a return when the light is better. Project work may be ad hoc 'en route', or demand specific visits to sites.

tainly brief the whole team if you will have serious photographers in your midst. Photography takes time. It is hard to tell which is worse, being a non-photographer kept waiting whilst a pursuer of aesthetics tramps the bush for the best viewpoint or being a photographer pressured by the knowledge that your colleagues are becoming impatient. A 'stop for photos' seldom takes less than half an hour and whilst the light itself favours photography at the evening stop or before departure in the mornings, ie, when the sun angle is below 30°, the subjects may not always be at the places you camp.

If you are making an expedition film with the object of raising funds, the demands will be even more uncompromising. Movie sequences, to the uninitiated, take forever to get right. To the person behind the camera the pressures are enormous. Run-throughs and repeats are the norm. 'Hold everything while I dash ahead with the cameras!' is a standard procedure. 'Dashing ahead ... ' with a tripod, fluid head and equipment at midday to get that telephoto 'Lawrence of Arabia' mirage shot, preferably without leaving footprints, is exhausting.

Getting the best photography will be demanding on the whole team; there must be full explanation in advance and understanding on both sides. It will take time and

is thus one of the factors to be built in to your en route routine and planning schedule.

Science, study. Scientific or study work will come under the same heading and must be allowed for in daily schedules or planned stops for a longer period if that is what it demands. Some stops can be scheduled – a stop every hour to measure temperature and humidity, every 20 km to take a gravity reading – but others will of necessity be random or opportunist. This will have its hilariously surreal moments; charged with collecting desert lizards, one expedition, to the excited cry of 'Lizard!', would come to a skidding halt and members run madly around with butterfly nets in the middle of the Mauritanian 'Empty Quarter' (photo on p 5.2 - 8) pursuing the hapless creature.

Probing elephant dung on a track in the Botswana forests for an indication of its diet will probably elicit less overt enthusiasm but ' .. a man's gotta do what a man's gotta do .. ' when it comes to project work.

When to wash. Epitomising the expedition dictum of getting the most from the least and deriving satisfaction from meeting small (or big) challenges, keeping clean is not that difficult. A large part of the skill is in, where possible, not getting dirty (see p 2.3 -37, 'Workwear') in the first place. That in no way implies shirking dirty jobs but it is less inconvenient for a boiler suit to get grubby than trying to scrub that same grime out of human skin which is peculiarly retentive of dirt, especially when mixed with sweat.

No matter who you are calling on, the scruffy explorer look went out of fashion a long time ago. It's amazing what can be achieved with a well timed cup of water and care!

The 'I haven't washed for three weeks' look, despite some proponents, never was *de rigeur* for expeditions, is not necessary and is definitely counter-productive at border posts and other visits. Expeditions are invariably limited in the water they can carry and the art of washing self and clothing is covered in Section 2.5 'Water', page 2.5 - 6. In a phrase, washing can be achieved using little more than a cup a day but timing the blissful experience is important. After the evening chores and before the evening meal is best; there is usually some light to see what you are doing at this stage and it is not cold enough for the strip off to demand too much willpower. If you want, there is at this stage also the opportunity to put on the track suit you use for sleeping (boiler suit on top) so your clothes can be shaken and hung out to air on some leafy bough (where the ants can find them ... !)

Who does what

Sharing it out. Already touched on in Section 3.1 in regard to specialist qualifications, it makes sense to split the known expedition tasks so that each member has their own responsibilities and can get

straight on with their jobs as soon as the wheels stop turning at the evening halt or other break. This way more time is free for other things. Typical task allocations:

- Vehicle inspection and mechanic
- Refuelling, fuel consumption, stock
- Water dispensing, purification, stock
- Cook, food stocks, replenishment
- Navigation, log, all aspects
- Medic
- Finances, local currency, receipts etc

Don't fear accusations of over-regimentation by organising and allocating tasks in

Effecting a dream jacuzzi with a damp face flannel is a skill only expedition people acquire. Feels wonderful; keeping clean and presentable helps with officialdom.

A funny thing happened on the way to...... Tamanrasset

Following the routine of a special clean-up before 'hitting town', the night before arriving in Tamanrasset I invested my spare water in a good wash and some laundry (p 2.5 - 7 too). Putting on my still damp shirt later, I nearly jumped out of my skin at the presence of something huge, hostile and very energetic in the sleeve. Turned out to be a giant locust, gone in to cool off. Very smart locust!

this way. Everyone knows where they stand, things get done quickly, a sense of responsibility and achievement is fostered and, subject to the general ethos of helping one's colleagues, those that have done their tasks can get on with other things they want to do with a clear conscience if their allocat-ed contribution has been made.

Driver changes. If you have two-driver crews a suitable 24 hour change point is the lunch break. That way each driver gets to drive an afternoon and a morning separated by an overnight rest and no driver drives solely afternoons or solely mornings.

Routine – mobile expeditions

Big and small

Knowing where you stand. Be it a 25-vehicle convoy, a group of six light pick-ups or a single 4x4, setting some kind of frame-work routine helps. The anchor points, the pegs to hang it on, are covered broadly above. No two expeditions will be the same; no two leaders will do things the same way; no two routines will be the same. On the basis that it is better to see what has worked in the past than not, the following is the kind of routine that has been used on African trips in desert or bush terrain:

Think through your whole day routine and tasks before the trip. Discharging it efficiently is sat-isfying and clears the decks for other things – like relaxing!

• Wake up, dawn minus 30 minutes.
• Unlock vehicle, dress.
• Kettle on, roll up sleeping bag, pack personal kit.
• Breakfast.
• Check tyre pressures, coolant level (cold).
• Put together lunch-snack, flask, coffee makings, in ready-access bag; plus en route sweets, snack biscuits, etc.
• Litter bag: either burn and bury, bury bio-degradables, flatten and burn and remove non-biodegradables or tie up litter bag for disposal at en route points such as filling station litter drums (see p 2.4 - 21).
• Put out fresh on-board litter bag for day's use.
• Check vehicle load properly lashed down.
• Check area round vehicle for any equipment left.
• Start off, usually within an hour of wake-up.
• Start day's nav log.
• As required stops for photos, project, nav checks.
• Lunch-snack break, cross check nav, about one hour.
• Change drivers at this point for 24 hours.
• Afternoon as morning en route.
• Stop for camp as near as possible to predetermined time, at least 90 minutes before sunset.
• Kettle on for brew.
• Hang litter bag.
• Crew start chores (see 'Who does what', above) at once (it is fatal to 'take a breather' at this point; it is very hard to get going again if it has been a hot tiring day).
• Continue working with mugs at your side (or maybe a five minute break).
• Put out beds or tents, unload bags etc.
• If bug-free space/climate allows, sleeping bags can be unrolled to air.
• Cook starts meal prep or timed to esti-mated end-of-chores time.
• BBC World Service News on short wave radio.
• Personal washing before meal.
• Know day's water, fuel consumption, mpg, stock levels, note in nav log.
• Prep maps etc for next day.
• Prep food etc for next day.
• Evening personal chores, logs, etc.
• Evening pre-bed brew.
• If appropriate and safe, leave water can, film boxes on roof of vehicle overnight

More obviously for big expedition groups, a thought-through routine is invaluable for any expedition of any size. Like the cavalry-man attending to his horse's welfare before his own, maintenance of the vehicles comes high on the list of priorities.

to cool. Repack immediately you get up before the sun can heat them up .

• Pre-bed, pack vehicle (valuables well out of sight) and leave locked overnight. Be sure litter bag is inside vehicle with no animal-attracting smells. Alarm set if need be.

• Sleep alongside vehicle(s), key (2 sets) with different individuals, kept inside individual's sleeping bag. Each team member knows who has a key.

• Also within reach of each sleeper: powerful torch, footwear of some kind (but out of reach of animal life seeking refuge – typically, sleeping tentless by the Land Rover wheel, moccasins would be placed upside down on top of the tyre).

• If team size allows and circumstances dictate, two-hour guard/patrol shifts.

Routine and operations – fixed-base projects

Major fixed-base expeditions

Multi-skeined routine. As far as routine is concerned virtually all of the items mentioned in the previous section will apply to large fixed-base expeditions, at least in principle – the 'static-ness' of the fixed base expedition means that the driving interludes above will be substituted by periods of study activity, possibly on an out-and-back ferry basis or possibly on the basis of leaving the fixed base for a few days at a time in order to complete field-work on site. The other main difference in routine is that a fixed-base expedition will have a higher population which in turn will imply a multiplicity of disciplines and a great inter-twining of many routines at once, coming together at points like meal times, or briefin-gs or starting and turning-in times.

Benefit of experience. The Royal Geographical Society has in recent years run many large expeditions, a lot of them involving fixed-base operations – a base camp from which roving sub-groups departed for periods of fieldwork which was then co-ordinated and processed, at least in part, at the base camp. Each of these projects represents an enormous pool of organisational and logistical experience and is documented in comprehensive reports held in the RGS library. If you are contemplating organising or being involved in any role within a fixed-base project or any large expedition you would be well advised to read a selection of these reports.

An efficient routine is just as important on a fixed base expedition as when mobile. Inter-twined routines of other people will have to be accommodated.

Oman Wahiba Sands Project

RGS arid-region project. One such major project, the Royal Geographical Society's Oman Wahiba Sands Project (OWSP), gives an overview of the implications of working within a major fixed-base context. An operation of this kind will, of course, also encompass and utilise the driving, navigation and allied skills covered in the rest of Section 5 but it is worth considering the broad picture first.

The OWSP was a major multi-disciplinary scientific expedition project operating on a multi-base format with a Capital-base

(in Muscat), Taylorbase (the purpose-built main base near the operations area), Fieldbase (a tented advance base offering support for a smaller number of scientists in the field) and Mobilebase – a mobile version of Fieldbase but a little more basic. Involvement of the Sultans' Armed Forces and local contractors (Taylor Woodrow) was a major item in the smooth operation of the base – a lesson in itself.

The following very brief notes are taken from the OWSP report, available at the Royal Geographical Society for detailed examination if required.

Case study: Report – fixed-base operations and routine

Summary

Taylorbase was a custom-built research headquarters, resulting in fewer administrative problems than experienced on previous projects. The layout of the camp area afforded adequate space and accommodation for all the project's needs and the arrangements for power, water and sanitation were virtually maintenance-free. The standard of the facilities at Taylorbase, as well as those provided by the Sultan's Armed Forces at Field and Mobile bases, eased the burden of responsibilities on the support team and left time for concentrating on more science oriented administration problems. In addition to the above-average accommodation and workspace the project was also fortunate in that it had support staff on loan from the armed forces. In Taylorbase alone the numbers were increased by a mixture of 17 Omanis and Asian expatriates who comprised the nucleus of the camp's mess and maintenance staff.

Routine

The dynamic phase of the project was broken into two week-long Field Phases with a two-day workshop in between each phase. The routine during the workshops was rather hectic with numerous inter-group discussions as well as many operations and

planning meetings. During Field Phases the routine was more predictable but nonetheless very busy because of the relatively short period of time the project was in he field.

The day would normally begin at 0700 with tea in the Ops Room. As the Ops Room was located in the men's block this served as an alarm call as well as a social gathering to discuss the day's work. Breakfast was at 0900 but always flexible for those who wished to depart early or who had been making the most of the early morning coolness. A snack lunch was served at the 'Yacht Club' at 1300 and was usually available until 1430. Afternoon tea at 1630 was followed at 1800 by the opening of the 'Yacht Club' for sundowners. The evening meal was served promptly at 2000. Most members continued to work into the cool of the evening with writing-up tasks; however there was a ban on use of computer printers after 2200 because of the disturbing noise they produced (daisy-wheel type).

A system of Duty Officers was established, the responsibility of which was spread among the admin team. The idea was that one member of the team would support the Field Director in looking after the camp and field operations for a 24 hour period and would be responsible for everything

The support staff were controlled by the Field Director in conjunction with the Mess Manager and their superior officers at Ibra army camp.

Supply

As with any expedition or project the supply and resupply of basic necessities was critical to the smooth running of the operations in the field and at the research camps. The task of supply was potentially problematic due to limitations of vehicles and administration personnel available. The problem was largely solved by the help of the armed forces and primarily the Coast Security Force under the command of Capt Chris Griffiths.

Food. Standard rations were bought from the army through the quartermaster facilities at Ibra camp. Sufficient was drawn on periodic basis to feed numbers that had been agreed in advance for each of the bases. Food distribution was by truck to each of the bases. The vehicle visiting Taylorbase also brought the mail. Army rations were supplemented by groceries that the project bought on periodic visits to the capital. The project had a discount with Matrah Cold Stores which meant that a supplement could be made to the diet in the form of European

from radio-watch to resupply. Tasks of the Duty Officer included security rounds, operations updating and reception of any visitors to the camp.

A daily log was kept to assist handover from day to day as well as a series of wall charts to outline the day's events and task for the Duty Officer. With Racal remote handsets the Duty Officer could keep radio-watch from almost anywhere in the camp which gave the flexibility of being able to deal with crises as they occurred without losing touch with other operational elements. It was always important for someone to be able to offer hospitality to any guests, both as a matter of diplomacy as well as courtesy. Appearances could be deceiving and what would appear to be a travelling Bedu would often turn out to be a visiting Sheikh.

Briefing at the RGS Fieldbase (right), one of the advance fixed bases in the field operating area. Not all fixed bases (RGS Brunei Rainforest Project above) will be at the end of a motorable track but the aims will be the same – a research and field-work centre for the team.

cereals and other delights. Vegetables were purchased locally from traders in the Mintirib area. The benefits of having refrigerator and freezer facilities were greatly appreciated as the temperatures rose in mid-February. This was enhanced by a constant supply of cold drinks brought from Muscat and Ibra. The project spent approximately 6000 Omani Riyals on food and beverages which equates to approximately two Riyals per head per day.

Water. Taylorbase was supplied by the army bowser which made an average of two visits a day during the project. The water was stored in a total of four 600 gallon water tanks at both ends of the camp and distributed by normal plumbing means through the camp. The system was successful and produced enough pressure even at low water levels. The cycle of water was sufficient to rule out the possibility of becoming infected. However there was one case of water infection but it was suspected to have originated at source rather than on the premises. The sewage system was completely underground using a central septic tank situated outside the camp.

Petrol. Whilst fuel was expensive and potentially a big drain on the project's limited funds, there was also the problem of high consumption by the V8 Land Rovers in sand conditions. Resupply problems were lessened by fitting the vehicles with extra tanks and 120 litres capacity of fuel panniers. Seventy barrels of fuel were generously donated by British Petroleum Arabian Agencies Ltd. The fuel was transported by CSF and Force Transport Regiment's four ton truck. The remainder of the project fuel was purchased locally at BP fuel stations.

Electricity. The project was ultimately supplied by mains electricity from the local grid. The camp had been originally located by proximity to existing power sources. However, because of cost and local administrative difficulties the camp was not connected to the source until the end of December. In the intermediary time the camp was supplied by two high-output diesel generators supplied by the army's

engineering division. The use of these generators, whilst gratefully accepted when no other supply existed, were not favoured as the long term supply because they were located within the compound and therefore the noise and exhaust were not conducive to a work and living environment. They required constant maintenance and refuelling and were not a sufficiently reliable source for the computers, a breakdown or power surge causing loss of data. After connection to the grid the generators remained in the camp as a standby source and were used during the infrequent local power failures.

Gas. Gas was used only for cooking. It was delivered by the army engineers in the form of commercial bottles and connected by a system that they had constructed. The gas was supplied by the country's only gas plant at Risayl.

Other supplies. Virtually all other items of daily requirements such as soft drinks, batteries, notepads, pens, electric plugs and light bulbs etc were purchased at local shops to promote the policy of trading with the local people of Badiyah. Periodically purchases were made in the capital for technical or luxury goods such as spare parts for computers or vehicles and the occasional birthday cake.

Organisation and management

Although the responsibilities of the administrative organisation and management were spread equally amongst members of the support team, the overall responsibility rested on the shoulders of the Field Director. This included the management and organisation of the various camp stores, the documentation and allocation of repairs to the camps and their facilities, the ordering and purchasing of supplies for both consumption and research and various other duties such as organisation of visits and trips to the capital.

Stores. As outlined in the equipment section, the stores were located at Taylorbase and were run on a similar basis to a military system as many of the stores

items were from the armed forces. Kit was issued and signed for as and when needed. The equipment was reviewed from time to time and replacements made when necessary.

Repairs. Any camp maintenance problems were referred back to Taylor Woodrow-Towell and were dealt with promptly. A few problems with electricity and plumbing were dealt with during the dynamic phase by a simple passage of information via Capital base to the TWT headquarters in Medinat Qaboos. Equipment repairs were often more troublesome with long delays in the case of the more sophisticated equipment. The items had first to be conveyed to the respective agent in Muscat and then collected on completion, a time-consuming occupation with the trip to Muscat taking between three and four hours.

Visits. The project generated much interest amongst both Omanis and European expatriates from other parts of Oman; as a result the project welcomed many guests at Taylorbase (over 500 day visitors and approximately 100 who spent at least one night). This provided the project ideal opportunity to communicate the aims and findings of the members' work. Taylorbase also served as a known landmark for travellers in the Sands to call in for advice and refreshment. The visits from all areas of the community were encouraged and a number of special open days were also arranged to cater for larger groups.

Fixed base and living/paperwork area for the Oxford University / Royal Geographical Society research programme at Mkomazi, Tanzania. Fixed-base expeditions of this kind will encounter a wide range of accommodations. Pre-recce is of course essential to establish if services such as water are available – from Day One.

Conclusion. When considering the strategy for quartermaster and management, forward planning is of the utmost importance. Only when requirements have been assessed can a complete system be put into effect. Although the ultimate responsibility for the quartermaster aspects and management of the project administration are in the hands of the Field Director, it is essential that he is supported at all times by the members of the admin team and if possible by the scientists in between fieldwork. Frequent admin meetings were an absolute necessity during the project and were planned as far in advance as was possible. Importance was placed upon the passage of information and was implemented by the use of numerous notice boards in the communal areas. A duty officer routine needs to be established from the outset of the field work with forecasts of duty dates posted well in advance.

Section 5.2

Operations:

Navigation

THE PROBLEM, SOLUTION INGREDIENTS

Background. There is no implied criticism in the observation that some people seem to be navigationally inclined and some do not – or perhaps just have not been brought up in the ambience of bearings, distances and where north is. You may have found yourself, phone in one hand, map in the other trying to get your friends to tell you how to get to their house. 'Yes, I think I've got it. Are you then north of the A214 or south?' and they have no idea. To be fair, this mild disorientation seems to manifest itself most around the immediate area where people live – because they take that area for granted – but it is worth being aware of and gently trying to do something about. Let 'north' into your life. Carry a tiny compass in your pocket; use it like worry beads – and subliminally to soak up where north is all the time. Think of all that magnetism going to waste.

Always take a map and compass on a country walk; you often use street maps but do you always have a small compass to check directions? The sport of orienteering is invaluable for laying down the basic language of navigation and accepting it as part of life. With on-board car navigation guidance systems entering our lives, honing the messages from the north-pointing genes is going to have an everyday payoff. End of sermon, food for thought.

Nurture your navigational genes. Make a conscious effort to be compass-aware wherever you are. Orienteering is good training.

Navigation counts. Wonderfully, there are still parts of the world to which the miasma of overpopulation and man-made barriers have not seeped. Such a spot is 22°36'N, 01°07'W. Nevertheless, some formalities have to be observed ...

Where am I? Where should I head?

Two components. Navigation breaks itself down into two components in the majority of cases:

- Where am I now and
- Where should I be heading.

Nowhere is a structured approach more appropriate than in navigation where the tendency to jump to conclusions prematurely is the most common error. It is almost invariably necessary to solve the first problem – where am I now? – before you can sensibly go on to the second – where should I go? The known limits of accuracy on that first solution will always govern the accuracy with which you can achieve the second; your heading and where you are going has to be relative to where you are now so establishing present position comes first.

Famine or feast. In remote areas you will either be awash with possible landmarks but be unable to evaluate them because you don't know which ones have been marked on the map, or there will be nothing to relate to the map in the first place. Deserts present conflicting views of

*1. Where am I?
2. Where should
I head? The two
ingredients of
navigation – fix-
ing your posi-
tion and know-
ing which way
to go from there.*

the task of navigation. In some ways it is the most daunting navigation environment since, off-tracks, it is usually bleak, devoid of either good mapping or reliable landmarks. On the other hand it is arguably also the most perfect navigation environment, particularly with the arrival of the era of GPS satellite navigation, since you can navigate, as it were *in vaccuo*, without conflicting inputs from landmarks (that require judgement or interpretation) or from tracks – of whose destination and alignment on the map you can never be certain until you actually arrive.

The attitude

The right stuff. The best expedition navigator will therefore be someone who is meticulous, unhurried, balanced and calm. We can all nod sagely as we recognise ourselves from this description but less easy to achieve is immunity from the pressure of others in the team wishing to 'get on' whilst you are making your deliberations. So often, those who modestly consider themselves 'hopeless at navigation' do so because they feel themselves under pressure to make up their mind when they are not ready to do so. The establishment of an estimated position fix, without GPS, is most often a measured decision arrived at after carefully weighing sometimes conflicting evidence.

*' ... awash with possible land-
marks ...' but are they on the
map? Some regions are still
poorly mapped. A detailed nav
log and running DR picture are
essential. DR? See p 5.2 - 30.*

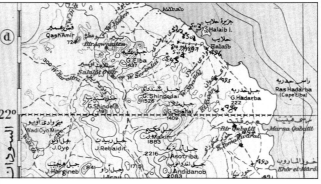

Where are we? Weigh <u>each</u> ingredient of your decision carefully; don't jump to conclusions. The plot-out of previous navigation, the look of the terrain, is it all on the map, how accurate has the map been so far. Even if you have satellite navigation, don't follow it blindly. <u>Everything</u> has to be accounted for, not just the ingredients of the solution you want.

Leaping to conclusions. The most common trap of prematurely leaping to conclusions, accepting only the evidence that suits your preconceptions, should be avoided. Read that sentence again, if you will; simply discarding evidence that does not fit is the commonest source of navigational error. If the information does not fit, establish *why* before discarding it.

For example, you have stopped to establish your present position. Your maps are old and not very reliable; you have already seen that topographical detail is a bit borderline. You are heading east and passed a track junction 4 km back, there is a big hill and two smaller ones to the north and you can just see another medium sized outcrop in the distance, also to the north of your track. The map shows two single hills north of track and no track junction..... Which hills have been marked on the map? Put your decision on hold pending further evidence. The corroborating evidence could come from earlier entries in your navigation log – a river bed seen 10 km back – or from evidence yet to be seen. Build up a case for deciding on your position; don't jump in with both feet on inadequate evidence. We shall see the vital importance of the navigation log – nothing more than a notebook, shorthand pad or tape note-taker but essen-tial for your safety.

Maintain the overview. Part of the attitude too, relates to maintaining a navigation overview. With hand-held and/or vehicle-powered satellite GPS (see below) now providing accuracy and availability that would have been undreamed-of only eight years ago – and for less than the cost of a set of tyres – an even more dangerous trap would be to abandon mental navigation altogether and rely exclusively on the electronics. Learn and nurture a navigational awareness and keep it switched on all the time. Map and compass walks in the country and, best of all, orienteering will make map reading and that vital sense of distance and direction second nature. Don't be tempted to label this warning as reactionary or Luddite; you would probably not relish the idea of flying with a pilot who, if the autopilot quit, could not fly manually!

The navigation log. Keeping a mind's-eye broad picture of the navigation is immeasurably aided by keeping a navigation log – see page 5.2 - 31 – a simple record of heading, events and landmarks against odometer reading and time; the impact of getting a blank screen when you press the button for an electronic position fix will be lessened if you have an overall idea of what is going on.

The commonest error in navigation is jumping to conclusions. You have to rationalise <u>all</u> the information at your disposal, not just the bits that fit your preconceptions.

Ingredients and applications

The recipe. So the ingredients of expedition navigation are already emerging:

1. A careful navigator who worships at the altar of truth rather than the altar of convenient results.
2. Maps, a prismatic compass and binoculars.
3. A meticulous navigation log.
4. A vehicle odometer of known or calibrated accuracy.
5. Satellite navigation equipment – GPS (dealt with later).

Item 5 comes under the heading of an independent method of position fixing – ie not dependent on the accuracy of navigation up to that point. In the past this function was met by astro fixing using a sextant or theodolite or by other radio aids such as Decca or Omega. These have now been so comprehensively eclipsed by GPS as to rule themselves out for practical expedition use. GPS is not always necessary, of course; it does, after all require an accurate overlay of latitude and longitude or a known national grid system on an equally accurate map.

Most important ingredients of expedition navigation are a calm approach and a meticulous navigation log. Calmly get the best maps (or imagery), compass and GPS!

What you need for what tasks.
Application of the ingredients listed will vary according to terrain and whether on or off tarmac roads; they may be grouped as shown below:

1. Applications – on tarmac roads.
Assuming the roads are accurately mapped, items 1-4 should suffice. Tarmac roads, unlike tracks, stay where they were originally aligned but beware of new developments and old maps. You are likely to encounter newly built roads that are either not shown on your map or are indicated by a vague 'projected road' dotted line. Do not therefore relax your vigilance in regard to your heading and the maintenance of your navigation log (see below).

2. Applications – on routes, tracks.
Ingredients 1-4 again should suffice on unsurfaced routes but with extra vigilance and somewhat dependent on whether you have an accurate in-car direction indicator; compasses in vehicles are notoriously unreliable. Tracks and routes in bush or desert vary according to who went where with how many vehicles since the map was made. Users often leave the main track to get to firmer ground and soon the diversions are more obvious than the original track alignment. In some regions where the ground is soft or unpredictable 'the track' can be a seemingly endless skein of vehicle wheel marks covering a swathe of terrain up to five kilometres wide, all going in roughly the same direction. Buried within that skein will inevitably be a further diversion to a different destination. It is easy to get mesmerised by the seemingly interminable nature of such tracks and get inadvertently drawn away onto a different route altogeth-

Alignment of roads: tarmac roads stay where they were built. Not so tracks. This (below) is how it starts – the route diverts from the main track because of soft sand, then it happens again until the track is wide and confusing skein of tracks quite different from the alignment shown on the map.

er. As before, monitor the general heading carefully and also note landmarks and distances in your log in case of future confusion. Vigilance is all.

3. Applications – off-tracks. For up to 100 km of not-too-difficult going in reasonably flat terrain, ingredients 1-4 may still be adequate provided painstaking use of the magnetic compass is applied – all readings taken well away from the vehicle, ie you stop, get out and take your compass reading after walking four or five paces. It is assumed in this case also that thorough dead-reckoning (DR) navigation (see p 5.2 - 30) is used so that your position relative to a known start point may be deduced at any given moment. In good conditions such as open desert where it is easier to set and hold a given compass heading this DR navigation can be applied over much larger distances with surprisingly small errors – but see section on heading measurement. Where the terrain – rock outcrops or small dunes – forces you to make many deviations from the desired heading the task of keeping a log of headings and heading changes will be a great deal more challenging. However, in the context of the current availability of GPS, independent fixing aids really are desirable to the point of being essential in all off-tracks conditions. Their contribution to an expedition's safety and efficiency – for example the ability to return to an exact spot should you wish to do so – makes them hard to exclude from an equipment list. On top of that they provide their own back-up in the form of an accurate in-vehicle heading indication, unaffected by compass variation (see p 5.2 - 34) so that your back-up DR nav log will be even more accurate when you wish to plot out the track you have covered.

4. Applications – fieldwork. Non-vehicular off-tracks navigation on foot or using animals predicate the same requirements as with vehicles but the problems are greater, principally the problem of accurate distance measurement, so that applying the tenets of DR navigation – 'so many kilometres on such and such a heading' – are made even more difficult. Working among rocks or small dunes out of sight of the base camp can lead to disorientation, particularly if the sky is overcast or there is dust blowing. Careful note should be kept of heading as you proceed so that at all times a bearing-and-distance to base is available. Again this becomes a classic application for GPS in the right conditions since, by defining the camp as a waypoint, bearing-and-distance to it can be summoned at any time using a hand-held unit (see below). The right conditions however, can mean not being in amongst tall rocks, canyons, trees or built-up areas since this equipment has to 'see' the satellites in order to work.

Indpendent fixing aids like GPS are worth gold bars but don't fall into the trap of relying on them as the sole navaid. Maintain nav-awareness all the time.

Randomly inaccurate map alignment, unpredictability and ad hoc re-routes can almost be guaranteed with this kind of 'main route' (Zaire). You could pass within half a mile of the biggest landmark in the world and not see it so on-board monitoring of heading and distance is vital. Satellite position fixes, if tree cover permits, will be salvational.

WHERE AM I ?

Maps and satellite imagery

Planning maps, working-area maps

Broad brush and fine detail. Start with the maps when your project is only at the 'What if ... ?' stage. As you develop the idea, list what you will want on the expedition itself. You will need:

- Planning maps for broad brush route planning and
- Detailed maps of the route as you traverse it.

In some regions the difference between planning maps and working-area maps are more obvious – Africa is a classic case. Here the traveller is well served by up-to-date planning maps and the Michelin 1:4,000,000 scale (1 cm equals 40 km) series are probably the classic – and best – examples. These maps cover Africa in just three sheets and, with new editions every three or four years,

give regularly updated information on the type of roads (tarmac right down to tracks) and the facilities available in each settlement – fuel, water, hotels and rest-houses, everything the planner would be interested in from a logistics and facilities point of view. The Michelin maps also provide a summary of weather statistics for a number of spot areas shown on a month-by-month basis. Relief, terrain detail, is only conceptual; just enough to get a feel for the country. The edition number and date is printed in the top left corner of the map; get the latest edition.

Spend a lot of time selecting maps. Many are junk, unable to combine roads and topographical detail. Get planning maps and detailed maps. They are different.

At once the most challenging and most exhilarating setting for navigation – no previous route, maps of unknown reliability. Sun compasses for en route heading, dead reckoning to establish the traverse, night astro shots for fixes.

Learn the style of your maps if you can. British Ordnance Survey maps are among world's best. Be prepared for low standards. Compare same-area maps.

Style and scale and detail. Map scales, from the top, are 1:200,000, 1:1m, and the 1:4m Michelin planning map. You expect a dramatic crater but the photo, looking south-east from the centre is something of an anti-climax after the maps. (Plus it is so huge you don't even see the circular rings till you are nearly in the middle!) Get to know your maps' style.

Even these maps do have occasional errors, mostly in relation to alignment of new roads.

Make your planning map selection slow and deliberate with as much comparison between maps as possible. Looking at world coverage there appear to be many more bad maps than good ones and topographical detail – relief, ground cover – seems hard to come by.

Detailed maps. Working-area maps are usually the largest scale you can obtain, depending on your activity in the area – typically 1:200,000 (1 cm equals 2 km) or 'quarter mill', 1:250,000. Sometimes a 1:1,000,000 or 1:500,000 (1 cm equals 10 km or 5 km) may suffice. Working-area topographical maps vary enormously in quality, accuracy, and how up-to-date they are. In some countries where possession of accurate maps is considered to have security overtones, you may find they are only obtainable (or not!) through the military. If you can get them, aeronautical maps at a scale of 1:250,000 will usually give excellent topographical detail – but the alignment of roads and their type will often be out of date. When you do get them you must know what to look for.

Maps - what to look for

Spoiled at an early age! If you are fortunate enough to have been brought up on British Ordnance Survey maps you should savour the standards of quality, clarity and accuracy of these maps while you may. Most other countries are less well catered for and, if he or she is lucky, the traveller will likely be using maps resulting from military surveys conducted in colonial times. Thus in many cases the maps will be very old and will reflect not only the then state-of-the-art survey methods (in some cases non-aerial) but will certainly show outdated centres of population and roads – both the alignment of routes and the type of road. Names of towns and villages will in some cases have changed too. Nevertheless, topographical detail will still be accurate and a lot of the maps will have been prepared with extraordinary attention to detail. But a word of caution.

Know the style of the map. A case in point is a series of maps of Algeria, many scaled at 1:200,000, originally published by the Institut Geographique National in France but now only obtainable in Algiers. You will be left humbled by the devotion of the French cartographers who prepared them but you will also find a different carto-graphic style – rather more extravagant to our eyes – in which quite mild topographic features are made to look far more dramatic and, in particular, deep water-courses seem to proliferate where there are only shallow dried up depressions. The depiction is accurate but overstated.

The opposite case may also be encountered – huge areas of the northern Sudan, covered by very old maps, shown as virtually plain white sheets with only notional indications of relief shown. The in-between case, harder to rumble, is the US ONC and TPC charts some of which contrive to look well mapped but are in fact a nicely packaged nothingness of inadequate detail, astonishing omissions and vague inaccuracies. (If you feel short-changed by this kind of American mapping, thank them – deeply – for providing the world with GPS!)

Maps – where to buy them

Choice. It is inevitable that only the biggest map shops will have the widest choice of maps and choice, with so many poor maps on the market, is important. This does tend to make the quest big-city oriented and, unless you live there or can really cope with buying maps over the phone, you are faced with special journeys. Try *Yellow*

What to look for on a map? Date of publication, a good combination of roads, topographical and ground cover detail. Often roads and topo detail on different maps.

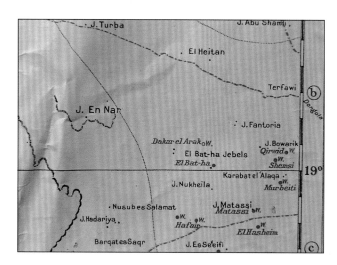

Not a lot to go on! This is a section from a 1:1m map and the distance from the edge of the map to the line of longitude represents around 60 miles on the ground! A case for summoning help from above – in both senses of the phrase! Traversed before satellite information was widely available, the other super-terrestrial assistance worked quite well.

Even a good 1:1m map is woefully short of the detail afforded by a satellite image on the same scale (each mm on the ruler is a kilometre on the ground). Note specially how the area to the north-west of Ardrar Ahnet on the map looks fairly innocuous but on the sat-pic the picture is very much clearer in terms of where you can take a vehicle. Precipitous scarps naturally match better; the view looking south from the point 50 mm above the 92 mm mark is shown in the sun compass photo on page 5.2 - 40. See also Sec 5.2.1 re selecting imagery.

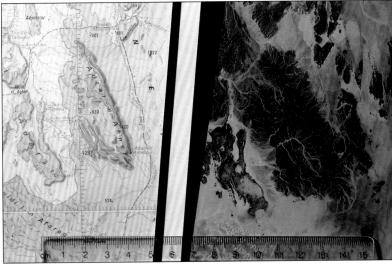

Pages first, though, as there are a multiplicity of local map shops with well informed and invariably enthusiastic proprietors who can often offer the prize of personal recommendation. Additionally, the Royal Geographical Society's *Expedition Planners' Handbook* has a long list of map suppliers, map publishers and map libraries. The well-known London Mecca for maps with an enormous stock is Stanfords, 12-14 Long Acre, London WC2E 9LP (tel 0171.836.1321).

Satellite imagery

Huge choice. Where mapping is poor, satellite imagery can come to the rescue in a large number of cases. (Note avoidance of the word 'photography' since the images usually derive from electronic sensing of radiation at different wavelengths.) There is almost no region of the world not covered by satellite imagery and this can provide a vast choice of scenes captured at different times of year, sun angles and degrees of cloud cover. Most can be made available at different scales and in different media – hard copy, transparency, digital. Also selectable when you buy this material are the radiation wavelengths to be shown; choice of particular wavelengths can determine types of vegetation and ground cover depicted – invaluable for an agricultural or some kinds of geological project.

How to buy it, cost. (See also Section 5.2.2 'Satellite image selection' for a particular case study.) Internet sites – you can take your time – are available for US Geological Survey and EOSAT (for Landsat imagery) and also the French SPOT Image. In the UK, satellite imagery (black and white, colour, and in varying sizes and resolutions) may be obtained – preceded by data giving date, time of day, cloud cover, angle of sun, type of coverage etc – from:

National Remote Sensing Centre Ltd,
Delta House, Southwood Crescent,
Southwood, Farnborough,
Hants GU14 0NL,
Tel 01252.541464.
(NRSC is also on the Internet)
or:
Nigel Press Associates Limited,
Crockham Park,
Main Road,
Crockham Hill,
Edenbridge,
Kent TN8 6SR,
Tel 01732.865023

Unsurprisingly satellite imagery is expensive but greatly dependent on source, resolution, age and post processing. A recent image rendered in full colour and

Satellite imagery is worth its weight in diamonds (and in the same price bracket!) Look at the picture above – that says it all.

The 1:500,000 map is a good start albeit confused by the over-enthusiastically rendered gray areas representing gravel. But more detail is needed to find a way into the round mountain. The 'raw' sat-pic above helps enormously but very careful comparison establishes named landmarks, longitude and where north is so that cross bearings on peaks can be used. In practice the image, hours of work and photo enlargements were a solid gold investment.

bought-in (rather than being on archive at NRSC) might cost £3000 plus as much again for the post processing and geo-location (ie locating the image with appropriate latitude and longitude or UTM grids). With scales as large as 1:25,000 this information, even at this price, can be worth its weight in gold to survey companies and, with the saving in transport and survey team costs, pay for itself many times over.

Satellite imagery need not cost the earth if you select with care and know what it is you want. Older images are cheaper. NRSC will guide on more exotic material.

Rock bottom? At the other end of the scale a small, undergraduate expedition merely wanting to improve on poor local mapping in order to carry out a brief project at a particular location can obtain 'raw' single-band black and white prints at 1:1m (ie about 10 inches square) sometimes with geo-location data for under £100. As shown above, where there is a fair correlation or set of anchor points on the available mapping

and the image, it is fairly easy to produce a crude do-it-yourself lat/long overlay and still finish up with an invaluable image.

If on private-expedition budgets, it is important to know what you are getting in advance to be sure it is going to be of value to you in the field. Usually 'quick-look' photocopies of reduced scale shots may be obtained to see if you are on to the right kind of product – see Section 5.2.2.

Deserts and jungle. In desert regions, black and white prints can be chosen showing the ground very much as it would appear if an aerial photograph had been taken. This is very useful since, in the main, flat terrain is light coloured and rocks and mountains are darker and there is thus a sensible correlation between appearance and what is good going for an expedition convoy of vehicles. Moreover, if shots taken at appropriately low sun-angles are selected when buying the pictures, even more indication of relief may be obtained by hill shadows and even the location of large sand dunes.

The situation is not so clear-cut in jungle regions where, in a simple print, there is little by which relief and the underlying ter-

The business – gift wrapped: lat/long and UTM grid, selected colour, full data! One of NRSC's top drawer products covers 150 km square at 1:250,000 (about 70 km square shown here). Not cheap at up to £6000 but to anyone doing a land usage survey or planning a pipeline route a snip that would save its cost many times over. False-colour images can be generated; in general red equals vegetation, blue water penetration, soil, some rock types. NRSC offer detailed interpretation.

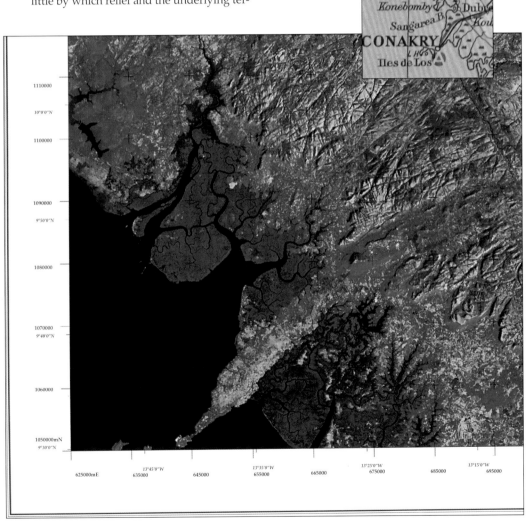

The best imagery for professional use such as land-use or pipeline surveys will cost up to £6000 but pay for itself many times over.

rain may be judged and only waterways and, with low sun angles, steep mountains may be seen. As the accompanying illustration shows, however, false-colour rendering can make very distinct differentiation between forest and ground and add uniquely and irreplaceably to the value of the image.

Which source? Now that high quality Russian satellite images are commercially available, imagery can be obtained to suit particular applications in a variety of resolutions down to as fine as 2.5m. Available from a number of base sources, or via archive or on-line databases in the UK at NRSC or Nigel Press Associates:

Study your sat-pic requirements well in advance and think hard exactly what you want from it. As a simple substitute for poor mapping it can be relatively cheap.

SOME CURRENT (1997) SATELLITE IMAGERY SOURCES IN UK

Source	Spectral bands (IR = infra red)	Scene size; resolution	Typical applications	Approx cost
1. Landsat TM (Thematic mapper)	7 (3 visible, 3 IR, 1 thermal IR)	185x185 km (or 50x50 km); 30m	Surveys for geological, oil, resource exploration, general mapping. Land cover, vegetation type and health. Scale down to 1:50,000.	£500-2900
2. Landsat MSS (Multi spectral scanner)	4 (3 visible, 1 near-IR, 1 IR)	185x185 km (or 50x50 km); 80m	Broader, less detailed version of row 1 uses.	£150-500
3. ERS-1, ERS-2 (European Remote Satellite)	Misc plus microwave	100x100 km; 25m	Unique sensors for sea-state, sea-surface winds, current data. In land image mode, microwave permits images irrespective of cloud cover. Land use, geology, glaciology	Up to £980
4. Radarsat	Single sensor; 7 resolution modes	500x500 km down to 50x50 km; resl'n 10-100m	General mapping, agriculture, forestry, sea ice mapping. Re-visit can be as low as 0.5 days for changing situations.	£2000-2850
5. Resours F (Five Russian satellites)	Bridges gap between photography and sat data; 1 or 3 bands	Varies. 220x220 km down to 21x21 km at 15m to 2.5 m resl'n	Applications as row 1 but down to high 2.5m resolution where required.	£1100-3000. Approx 20% higher for recent material.
6. SPOT Panchromatic	1 (visible wavelength)	60x60 km; 10m	High resolution for infrastructure and detailed geological structure. Imaging instruments can be set for off-nadir viewing to yield stereo pairs.	See next row
7. SPOT Multi-spectral	3 (2 visible, 1 near IR)	60x60km; 20m	As row 6 but additional capability in relation to vegetation.	£900-3400 spans pre-1989 scenes to multi-spectral stereo pairs.
8. Aerial photography	Visible only	As required	Finest detail urban surveys and elsewhere much dependent on availability. NRSC accumulating colour aerial coverage of UK .	Dependent on size of coverage and region

Position fixing 1: manual/terrestrial

Where am I? Position fixing

Methods. Fixing your position can be done in various ways and they will be split into two categories:

1. A fix dependent on earlier navigation; strictly speaking not a fix, more an estimated relative position.
2. Independent fixing that will confirm or correct earlier navigation.

Thus a position derived from the knowledge of your heading and distance from a known earlier position (see Dead reckoning on page 5.2 -30) will usually be an estimated position – termed a 'DR position'. This contrasts with the second type which is derived from known landmarks or astro shots or radio bearings and the like and is independent of the accuracy of earlier navigation. Satellite position fixes come (comfortingly)

Position fixing is important at any time – bearing and distance to next waypoint, kilometres to next fuel – but especially so if a scientific programme, like the gravity measurements shown here, is under way.

into this category and are dealt with under 'Position fixing 2 ... ' p 5.2 -18.

However ... map accuracy. The 'Yes, but .. ' proviso on fixing must always be in the back of your mind. Independent fixing is only as good as the maps it is used on. Take a few seconds to think about that. UK Ordnance Survey maps are of superb quality and accuracy so an extra-terrestrial position fix – astro or satellite based – can be meaningfully plotted using the maximum accuracy available. Some remote area published mapping, however, is still large scale, crude and sometimes not very accurate so you may get a metres-accurate fix on a latitude/longitude or other grid not bearing much relation to the terrain depicted beneath that grid.

Map datum. It will only affect precision satellite fixing on the best and latest maps but at this stage be aware that map datum affects the tie-up between information on a map and fixes obtained from independent sources. See below under GPS (p 5.2 - 22, 'Map datum, GPS fixes').

Position fixing can be done with reference to observed landmarks and the map – or using independent fixing like astro or GPS. In both cases map accuracy is critical.

Guides and their limitations

Human fallibility. Somewhere in a chapter on expedition navigation the subject of guides must be covered. As so often in life, all is not as it may seem despite the well-known image of a guide being the key to all navigational problems. Though often seen as having a role of getting you from A to B, a guide – 'one of the locals' – has two separate roles; one is knowing the best route and the other knowing where the party is at any given time so that times, distances and bearings to other points may be considered.

The two capabilities seldom go together and are almost invariably linked to particular modes of travel. It has often been recorded that desert guides familiar with camel travel are completely thrown by the different rate and capability of vehicles. Worst of all the problems of navigation by guide is that very human failing of pride. A guide will seldom if ever admit that he is uncertain of the way or that he has got it wrong or that he is currently engaged in a bail-out operation to cover up an earlier error.

Tactful cross checking. A surreptitious but all too revealing compass and distance plot was once carried out covering the fumblings of such a guide employed to navigate a British-officered overseas levy unit whose usual navigation method was to say 'Driver, take me to ...'. It is also rare to find a guide completely or even marginally at home with a map and the quantifying parameters commonly used by Western-world navigators.

That said, there is no substitute for a dis-

Beware of the fallibility (and pride) of guides. Often they are unused to maps and compasses and the different speeds of 4x4s, trucks, animals. Keep a discreet check.

tinctly separate attribute of a guide's knowledge – that of knowing how good the terrain is; the 'best route' local knowledge of a competent guide who would know that a particular ravine is passable to mules whilst another one is not; or that the sand in a particular area is soft enough to bog your convoy whilst a detour round the area will be less troublesome. For this knowledge – that you would otherwise have to discover the hard way – you may well have to sacrifice the quantitative absolutes of bearing and distance to a special waypoint. The important thing for an expedition leader is to maintain a sensible perspective and, as with all his or her specialists, recognise what they have to offer but also their limitations.

Cross-bearings on landmarks

Fixes from mapped pinpoints. It is surprising how often school-geometry type cross-bearings may be utilised to establish a fix position – provided the mapping is good enough. In the example quoted at the beginning of this section to illustrate the dangers of jumping to conclusions, when the dilemma is resolved the intersection of two bear-

Cross-bearings help. Here, looking south from a known position ('SBH', upper, left of centre, sat-pic on p 5.2 - 12) and bearing on Tadraq Ti-n-Ademi (peak, extreme left, below) confirmed massif, right, as the round mountain goal. Climb helped recce the route. Never let one factor rule. Balance info against map accuracy and possible ambiguity of other peaks.

Things that come at a price are valued more ...! When you get a good astro fix you feel you have earned it. Theodolite (right, on tripod), has to be set up, meticulously levelled and then left to acquire ambient temperature for an hour or so. Then the star ident, the three, four or five star fix and all the calculations. Timing accurate to better than two seconds required.

ing lines (the two hills) with that of a known line feature (the track) can yield a nice three-line fix. Similarly, bearings from identified peaks – always use more than two if possible as a safeguard against misidentification - – will improve significantly on the 'We're about here' kind of approximation which at the time you may think is sufficient.

This method of fixing is especially useful when you are in an area which you are getting to know and can with certainty identify particular peaks from which to take bearings. Misidentification of landmarks from which to take bearings – the old problem of jumping to conclusions again – is a potential problem.

At the risk of stating the obvious and offending one or two readers, do not forget to apply magnetic variation to your bearings! (See below use of magnetic compasses, p 5.2 - 32 et seq.)

Astro fixing

Classical navigation – the hard way. Astro fixing using night star shots will yield the same kind of three (or more) position-line fix as you would get from taking bearings on mountain tops. For all practical purposes astro fixing is now outdated by satellite fixing aids though, for what it may occasionally be worth, it is non electronics-dependent (albeit still needing batteries to provide cross-hairs illumination when targeting a star). For land navigation where the motion of a boat would not upset the accurate tripod-mounted levelling that is possible, a T2 theodolite can be used for measuring the elevations of the selected stars. With such an instrument, position accuracies of around 500 metres should be possible; a sextant needs a horizon, is a lot less accurate (about 2000 m) but is lighter and more easily portable.

The three main disadvantages of astro as a means of position fixing are that it can only be done at night with at least three suitable stars visible or (if fitted with a purpose-made sun prism) around midday if a sun-shot fix (as opposed to a single position-line) is to be obtained; the processing of results, like the learning of the basic skills, is time consuming. Lastly a theodolite and tripod is a very heavy package. Weighing around 25 kg and needing careful handling and setting up, it can take an operator two to three hours to complete the process of levelling and obtaining an accurate position.

Thanking your lucky stars. For those that have navigated this way in the past, astro – more than any other method of navigation fixing – will make you realise the magic and wonder of GPS!

Be aware of on-land use of astro fixing as a hard-graft, no electrics, fall-back method of position fixing – if only to make you savour GPS (see p 5.2 - 19).

Radio/electronic terrestrial navaids

Electronic position lines. There are a number of terrestrial (as opposed to satellite-based) radio navigation aids, mainly used by mariners, that could, in some circumstances be used by expeditions. Be aware, however, that in general there is a tendency for low-frequency ground-wave transmissions to be error prone when used for taking bearings on land. Coastal and mountainous terrain errors can take place when, for example, using radio direction bearings on land.

Decca is a short-range intra-continental positioning aid that gives very accurate results, for example, in European waters but networks are not set up worldwide. VLF/Omega, however, is a world-wide network originally established for the navigation of long-range submarines and which can in certain circumstances be successfully used at ground level to give fixes accurate to better than a mile. Unlike many other fixing aids, satellite systems included, it has the ability to yield consistent results even when the operator is in deep-valley mountain areas.

Use of equipment under this heading is a specialised subject and advice should be sought, probably via marine experts such as yacht chandlers, from the equipment manufacturers themselves.

Position fixing 2: satellites, GPS

Sat-fixes – Transit, GPS, Glonass

Satellite navigation is the most mind-blowing development in the history of navigation. Use it, value it, thank the scientists but don't abandon navigation awareness.

Navigation revolution. The advent of satellite-based navigation fixing systems has transformed expedition navigation in the space of about eight years. First three or four kilogram's-worth of equipment running off vehicle battery power gave fixes within 15 minutes and now, with GPS, an ever widening choice of hand-held, dry-battery powered devices give virtually instantaneous fixes – in three dimensions, height as well as latitude and longitude. Commercial competition is bringing units' cost and dimensions down; and satellite navigation systems are just that – systems, not merely a means of fixing a position. In other words they encompass both halves of the problem highlighted at the beginning of this section – they will answer the 'Where am I?' question and then go on to tell you your heading, (true, *or* magnetic), your speed and how to get to your destination, via any number of alternative waypoints. The tiny black boxes will usually also tell you the bearing and distance between any two of the waypoints, they will show you a plot of your route, they will superimpose it all on a map – where will it end ... !

Transit. Three systems presently exist – of which Transit is one. What may possibly be termed 'recent generation' equipment, the five-satellite Transit system was, like VLF/Omega, originally established for the US navy. It is eclipsed by GPS now but is covered here briefly in case units are available at low cost for expedition use. Equipment about the size of a small portable typewriter (remember typewriters?) and, with antenna, weighing about three kilos, consumes about 15 watts of 12 volt vehicle battery power when switched on. Manufacturers include Magnavox, Walker and Navstar. Fixes may be obtained approximately every hour or so – or whenever satellites come into view at a suitable elevation. When this occurs, the equipment will usually emit a bleep and then, over the next 15 minutes or so, take a fix derived from the passing satellite. If the equipment has been switched off for any length of time and moved, eg as it would be if dormant in a moving vehicle, it has to be 'told' its posi-

The sheer magic of GPS never loses its power to amaze – and produce the goods: position fixes to accuracies of better than 100 metres usually. This does not consign the art of navigation to an ancient ritual for a fix is only as good as the map it is used on. Care is still essential.

less skies. It is far lighter than astro equipment and can produce a fix accurate to 150 metres in the time it takes to boil a kettle for an en route brew. In many expeditions this performance will be adequate – a few well spaced en route fixes and a sound fix for the overnight camp.

Some versions of this equipment have been found to require care regarding high temperatures in use.

Glonass. Glonass is the Russian equivalent of GPS – dealt with next – and comprises 24 satellites. It is slightly more accurate than GPS and does not suffer from 'Selective availability (SA)' – see below. Some equipments are available that will receive both systems' signals.

GPS

The ultimate navigator? GPS (Global Positioning System) is the current generation of satellite fixing equipment – like Transit, courtesy of the US Department of Defence. Based on a mind-bogglingly audacious concept in terms of data transmission and micro-accuracies and taking the form of a constellation of twenty-four, 850 kg, 5.2-metre spread satellites orbiting 23000 kilometres above the earth, it yields even more accurate fixes than the Transit system. Simple GPS has the potential to be accurate to something like 30 metres with no other references!

Typically, however, it yields accuracy of the order of 100 metres from true position due to 'Selective availability' – a deliberate form of scrambling, see next page. Also dealt with here, differential GPS (DGPS) and

GPS typical position fix accuracy 100 metres. It offers speed and heading information too. Most equipments also offer navigation functions as standard.

tion to within about 40 km before it can get an accurate fix.

Such equipment is an enormous advance over astro fixing since it can be used at any time of day and is not dependent on cloud-

carrier phase GPS, with the help of accurate reference points within around 100 km of the user's position and another transmitter, can produce accuracies respectively of 2-5 metres and less than one metre.

You may hear enthusiastic talk of centimetric accuracies being the norm with all GPS. Good as GPS is, this is not so. But 15 or 50 metres is good enough for most expedition purposes!

Typical time-to-first-fix – TFF – from switching on is 30 seconds to two minutes depending on the particular manufacturer, surrounding obstacles to clear sky vision and time since last switch-on. TFF is getting shorter, routinely around 15 seconds for some 12 channel equipments.

Speed times time equals distance .... even when dealing with overall transit times as quick as 6/100ths of a second (to cover the 23000 km) and speeds around (and, just to make it difficult, variably below) the speed of light. Of the 24 orbiting satellites your receiver must 'see' at least four at once in order to get a position fix – the unambiguous intersection of the four timed range radii. To achieve this you would expect the need for large dishes, 'out-and-back' transmissions that would take huge power,

Savour this special time in navigation history. Ten years ago a clear sky, three hours and a 50 lb theodolite were required for an independent fix; now, 300 gm, 30 secs.

equipment complexity and cost. But the scientists and designers have, with an elegant ingenuity that almost makes you laugh in delight, made it practicable to measure just the time it takes for a signal to leave the satellite and arrive at the receiver (how do you know when to start the 'stop-watch'?) using an antenna smaller than a matchbox and the power of some AA cells. This little bit of brilliance puts the expensive stuff – like four $100,000 caesium atomic clocks per satellite just for a start – all out in space and the cheap lightweight stuff in your rucsac or bouncing about on the dash of your 4x4. (If this all sounds like a tiny one-para eulogy to the people behind GPS, it is. Join in; they did a good job. A very good job.)

Small and light. Unlike their space-travelling counterparts, minimalist GPS ground equipments, usually less than 500 gm, can, at their simplest, sequentially pick off four satellites and give you a fix with a single channel set. A set that has channels to spare to track four or more satellites at one time will cope more easily with the dynamic situations that prevail in moving vehicles – quicker lock-on, quicker updates, more accurate fixes, speeds and 'compass' headings. Most GPS equipments will give you a graphic display of satellite acquisition status at any time (photo opposite). More channels take more power so, in hand-held units keep an eye on battery condition. Many equipments, though, also have continuous operation kits running off a vehicle's 12v power supply, a mounting rack for a vehicle dashboard and probably also an external antenna that may be mounted on a vehicle roof and thus get a clearer view of the sky.

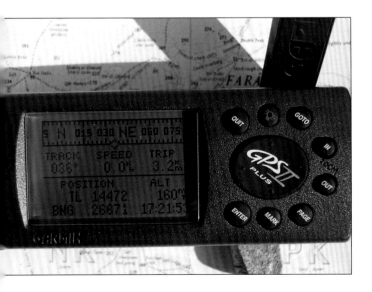

Typical 'current situation' kind of display with GPS – position (in Ordnance Survey grid), track and speed. Attempting to please both the 'N, NE, E .. ' proponents and those accustomed to degrees, the 15° increments on the heading display results in slight confusion. Garmin is astonishingly compact; a 12-channel good performer.

What GPS does. Once on and juggling the satellite appearance schedules, position fixes are usually taken at the rate of up to two per second and the receiver will be able also to determine accurate speed and heading once it is moving over about 20 mph. Below that speed these parameters will be less accurate but the latest 12 channel units (see below 'Number of channels') will yield heading accurate to better than 10° given a steady brisk walk of 100 metres or so. Slow walking over a lesser distance and headings will be only good to the nearest 20-30°. See also below 'Heading - true or magnetic?'

GPS screen read-out options would typically be some combination of the following:

• Position in lat/long or grid reference – updated every half second or so, and/or

• A readout on screen of usually at least four parameters:

    1. Track – usually abbreviated to TRK or 'COG' (Course Over the Ground) – the compass heading you are achieving as you move forward.

    2. Ground speed – may be abbreviated to G/S or 'SOG' (Speed Over Ground) If a target destination waypoint has been dialled-in, both these items may be shown together with ...

    3. ... your bearing (BRG) and ...

    4. ... distance (DIST) to the destination waypoint.

• Lateral displacement from optimum heading for destination – 'cross track error' or 'XTE'.

• A number of interim screen displays enable you to define waypoints with position co-ordinates, names and waypoint numbers. These can be stored for call-up later singly as an individual destination or can sometimes be strung together to form a route which itself has a number.

The readout of bearing and distance to a selected destination will be a continuous one, varying and updating as you drive nearer to it or divert from your best-course for reasons of your own or because you have to divert around obstacles such as hills. There is often also an intuitive display

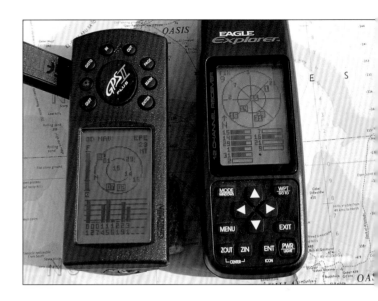

Bar-chart display is locked-on satellites and signal strength. Circles show azimuth (relative to north) plus an indication of elevation. Anything below 15° elevation may give 'noisy' signal. Numbers on bar and circle are satellite numbers. Fix needs minimum of four satellites. Check position formats available when buying GPS – lat/long, UTM grid, national and military grids (see Section 5.2.1.). Eagle very comprehensive.

option – sometimes a miniature plan view of everything – showing whether or not you are pointing at your destination waypoint or whether it is off to the left or right.

'Selective availability'. Selective availability (SA) is the means that the US Department of Defense has of reducing the accuracy of GPS for strategic reasons. The artificially introduced corruption is quoted as resulting in a position error less than 100 metres for 95% of the time and less than 300 metres 99.9% of the time. Practically, this usually means accuracies of up to 120 metres which would otherwise be in the region of 15-30 without SA switched on. Watching the co-ordinates of a fix – especially in a national grid – you can often see the values swing steadily up and then down again even while you are stationary.

Most GPS equipments give you position fix, bearing and distance to selected waypoint plus – if your speed is over 20 mph – an accurate heading and speed.

Map datum: GPS fixes. As mentioned above, map datum affects the relative accuracy between information on a map and fixes obtained from independent sources. The earth is not truly spherical and a number of different mapping datums – well over 100 – accommodate the irregularity in 'local' regions. Every map will have been made to a given datum and it is important that your GPS receiver has been set up to the same regional geodetic system. Most GPS units are set to a default of WGS84 datum (World Geodetic System) but have the facility for selecting the regional datum – for example Oman, Philippines, UAE, Ordnance Survey Great Britain (OSGB).

'Selective availability' will degrade accuracy of GPS fix to 100 metres or so. Remember to select the correct geodetic datum and set true or magnetic headings for display.

Where maps are of top quality and large scale the difference in position is significant in relation to the accuracy of which GPS is capable and can exceed the error due to selective availability. In the UK, for example, the difference between a sample fix taken using WGS84 and OSGB36 datums was around 200 metres. Values will change in different parts of the world.

All maps should state their datum – or if they were not made to a regional datum. Some remote region maps will still say 'No datum', 'International Spheroid' or maybe 'European datum' – see Section 5.2.1.

Height. Familiarise yourself with the heighting errors of GPS before using it in 'real' situations. Although it claims to yield a 3-D position, accurate height appears to be one of its weaker capabilities under the influence of selective availability. Many equipment manufacturers relegate the altitude readout to an obscure screen some way down the menu.

Heading – true or magnetic? Normally a GPS will show a heading of true north. But because many units are used on boats which are routinely steered by reference to a magnetic compass subject to magnetic variation (see below, page 5.2 - 34) many GPS sets are equipped with their own database for world magnetic variation related to latitude and longitude and can also be programmed to show magnetic north instead. Do be aware of this – especially because not all units alert you to what they are showing. Selection of true of magnetic is usually done in the GPS's 'system set-up' mode and the best sets will, as in proper navigation logs, indicate a heading as, for example, '090° M' or '090°T'. Beware of the sets that just give

Silva Nexus marine unit (left) offers large, clear display – well suited to prime task of on- or off-road driving. Hand-held units very versatile but displays usually too small for driving (see also photos p 4.2 - 20). Eagle Explorer clearer than most; same software drives the Eagle View with larger display for fixed fitting. Note (above) depiction of 'GS 50 mph' – about double the size on the View. This unit close to the ideal, combining Explorer's versatility and intuitive interface with excellent what-you-want display.

you '090°' on its own.

Hand-held vs marine units. It may be a brave or foolish thing to say but in use, it is hard by present standards to see how GPS, as a general utility and for its bottom line end product of telling you where you are to a matter of metres, could be improved for expedition use. Things could still improve, however, in terms of user interface and ergonomics in vehicles – more intuitive operation plus bigger display figures and higher contrast so that you can snatch a glance at it whilst driving (See para below 'Display quality' and also Section 4.2 'Vehicle modifications', pp 4.2 - 19 and 20).

Marine units normally have larger clearer displays; the hand-held units are usually not ideal for cab use on the move. Adapted, cab-mounted hand-held units do have the advantage, however, of being removable from the vehicle for use on walking treks and recces. If they can be removed this can be done when the vehicle is left unattended to preclude theft. Ideally, and with prices continuously falling, have a large-display vehicle-mounted set and a small hand-held set for back-up and on-foot use.

Other applications, DGPS *et al*

Improving on the amazing. The other roles and refinements of GPS – distinct from the dynamic mobile navigation role – are mentioned here to keep a perspective on where vehicle-mounted navigation equipments sit in the GPS spectrum of capability. The GIS role (item 3 below) could well be of interest in short or long period expeditions.

1. Differential GPS (DGPS) is a method of use involving locally determined position error corrections being transmitted to passing traffic or field users – eg ships passing a lighthouse or field users doing survey work. This can improve accuracies from tens of metres down to 2-5 metres. DGPS accuracy enhancement is available now as an add-on to some equipments and is built-in with others. It relates only to localities (50-100 kilometres) around the particular specially surveyed 'base' receiver/transmitters, usually located on coasts so in most cases is unlikely

to be of use to a vehicle-based expedition – albeit there is, in fact, total inland coverage in the UK and some other countries.

DGPS, in practical terms always requires a 'first order reference point' – ie the known super-accurate fix position at which the 'base' receiver/transmitter is sited. Accuracy degrades as the distance between base station and field receiver increases. Trimble quote 2 ppm or 2mm for every kilometre. This requirement for an accurately surveyed base reference point thus rules out DGPS for many remote-area kinds of operation in the context of expeditions. In use, DGPS fix results can be obtained by:

• Real-time data correction in which the data correction is transmitted to your hand-held receiver by some means – it can be medium wave radio, VHF, telephone – in a set format or protocol (RTCM SC104). Position fix data is then corrected on-board your own receiver and you get a real-time readout.

• Post-process correction is a procedure where your receiver stores enough data-per-fix to be downloaded later to a computer or lap-top in which appropriate software and correction parameters are stored. The 2-5 metre accuracy fixes are thus retrospectively obtained using data collected in the field.

2. 'Carrier phase' GPS may be regarded as a kind of 'super-DGPS' and brings 'sub-metre' accuracies – ie fixes accurate to centimetres. Like DGPS it depends on the existence, within the closest range possible, of a first order reference point. Results are obtained on a post-process basis only and require fix data to be taken over a ten minute period or thereabouts at the fix position. All of this data is subsequently processed after downloading. Applications include precision surveying, movements of structures such as bridges etc. These are very specialist applications.

3. GIS – geographical information systems. A GIS is something of a buzz-phrase but indicates a system of position fixing allied to detailed information pertaining to those positions – it may be pure mapping, positions related to land use, urban facilities

Marine unit displays more suited to vehicle use; larger, clearer. With nearby base station DGPS can yield accuracies of 2-5 metres; 'carrier phase' GPS under one metre.

locations, utilities such as oil pipelines or power lines, or environmental and scientific research. A position fixing system capable of undertaking DGPS or carrier phase GPS fixes as above may be allied to a data recording system of some kind. Whilst big boxes and clip-boards used to be the minimum requirements for this kind of job, almost unbelievably, it can now be done by hand-held equipments like the Trimble GeoExplorer II. With the aid of a back-pocket camcorder battery, a day's worth of GIS data can be secured before trudging wearily home for a recharge – of both battery and operator.

4. Inmarsat-C/GPS. Originally developed for high-value, long-haul truck transport, equipments such as the Trimble Galaxy combines GPS with Inmarsat-C two-way store-and-forward low-cost satellite messaging. Typically it can be used for automatic position reporting to dispatch centres with messages relayed to users by fax, e-mail etc. Facility could be invaluable for large expeditions in very remote areas

Which GPS?

Basic magic plus add-ons. With a display, buttons and a fancy designer shape, most GPSs look pretty much the same. Some are more expensive than others. What to look for and what are you paying for? As already indicated, the basic magic of GPS is its ability to give a position, heading and a doppler-derived speed. All models will do that. A 'good' receiver will do so in more difficult conditions (tree cover, for instance) and will do so more quickly but many of the add-on features like navigation displays and route storage are vendor additions to the basic capability. Some of the features are nautically oriented and will be of no interest to you in a vehicle. There are similarities between choosing a sleeping bag and choosing a GPS – you don't always want the warmest sleeping bag – but there is usually peripheral or safety-related benefit to having 'the best' GPS equipment. And there are certainly variations in user interface to dis-

Buying a GPS, more channels is better for quicker fixes and performance among trees, mountains and in 'dynamic' situations. Cheap sets OK where you want more operators on foot.

tinguish the good from the less good equipments.

To confuse things a little – and for once it is to the buyer's benefit – price is not the guide it used to be. Some of the best equipments are now startlingly undercutting their peers – the Eagle Explorer, at the time of writing among the best and most user-relaxed units, is about half the price of one of its erstwhile competitors.

The end product is what counts. As this section will note, it is the end product that counts when buying a GPS:

- How well does it perform?
- How simple is it to use?
- How good is the user manual?

The latter two points really are important. You have only to try grappling with some ill-documented little box and find yourself slipping into the trial-and-error mode of operation to know that all is not well. The temptation to put it down to your own lack of understanding is not always a valid self-accusation – and certainly not a resolution of the problem. A good unit will be easy and intuitive to use; if it is not you will find yourself always postponing that promised detailed repeat session with the book, using the equipment in the simplest switch-on default modes and in short not getting out of it what you could. (If computers and software take up any part of your life you will recognise the condition!)

Well-known manufacturers do not always provide the best either in performance or ease of use – see 'User interface' below. Some manufacturers are relatively small and use a bought-in chip set such as the excellent Rockwell Zodiac, others make their own; others may be long established and huge like Trimble, once described as 'the Honda of GPS – they could make whatever they want'. In the end, however, it is down to the individual software engineer to make the equipment friendly to use and those attributes will be present (or not) irrespective of the size of company involved.

Number of channels. Number of channels is one of the main criteria to note in an equipment specification. This is not neces-

Even where roads are well established and maintained, distances can be huge and information about distance to go valuable. In less well ordered environments, you may have landmarks but uncertain identification. In both cases GPS can be a valuable back-up to your navigation – note, back-up!

sarily the number of satellites used to get a fix but bears a close relationship to it. On a five-channel set four will be used to take data from the necessary four satellites and the other one will be darting between other satellites looking for the best back-up when one of the four breaks lock or when the geometry of intersecting position lines is wrong. A single-channel or three-channel unit will be working sequentially – taking data from one satellite, noting it, dashing to another one, noting that and so on until it has data from four and from this it can obtain a 3-dimensional fix. Such a single or three channel unit, of course, will depend on your being stationary whilst it is doing all this and, in general it will require to be on clear open ground so that it has a good view of the various satellites as they rise and set on the horizon.

A three-channel set is cheaper, has a low current drain since it is not keeping so many balls in the air at the one time but will have relatively poor 'dynamics', ie it will be less able to cope with subject movement, 'g', and will need open ground so it can dart between satellites more easily.

Conversely a six- or (1997/8) 12-channel

set is a lot more capable. The performance jump between a three-channel set and a a six-channel set is considerable; the jump from six to 12 less marked. A five-channel Rockwell Navcore chip as in the Silva XL1000, already outperforming rivals in difficult conditions, will probably have nine satellites on the books at any given time and it will be doing a bit of shrewd selection as to which ones are best to use and which to keep in reserve. The 12-channel Rockwell Zodiac chip in Eagle equipments will have even more performance up its sleeve and is claimed to provide greater accuracy by 'over-resolving' a position fix solution.

Dynamic use. A multi-channel set can get a better and more accurate fix at any given time since it has more satellites to choose from. It can cope with faster subject movement – as in a moving vehicle – and, with so much data in reserve, can cope better with 'blockage' from trees, streets, canyons and the like. Such units, because they are handling so much data, usually also

Six-channel set will cope better with tree cover than three-channel. 12-channel better still but the jump is smaller. 12-channel best for vehicle use.

have faster processors – watch for the term 'gallium arsenide' which will out-perform a silicon processor in terms of speed and in aerial sensitivity. The latter also contributes to capability in conditions of 'blockage' from trees.

A many-channel set will also have a quicker TFF – Time to First Fix from the moment you switch it on. This has obvious advantages at any time but is particularly relevant if you are using the unit hand-held in short bursts to conserve internal batteries.

Given the choice, a many-channel set would be preferable for a vehicle installation but if you have a tight budget and want to equip as many on-foot teams as possible then the more modest specification will get you more teams in the field. And their slightly reduced statistical accuracy will be unlikely to affect safety at all.

Overall sensitivity. There is more to GPS performance than just number of channels. There is the question of sensitivity and the way the antenna and the rest of the equipment interfaces with the chip. There is, alas, nothing you as buyer can do about this except read quantitative comparative tests (if you can find any) on rival equipments. Look for real-life, bottom-line tests like actual TFFs, side-by-side tests in wooded areas, and, though this will often be more affected by selective availability, position accuracy tests against known Ordnance Survey bench marks or positions on large scale maps.

Battery life. A plug-in, continuous-use power source is virtually essential for any vehicle-mounted GPS equipment and you should be keenly aware of battery life limitations when using a unit in hand-held mode. In theory, the better multi-channel sets use more current than the simple ones and these are the types more suited to the dynamics of vehicle use but design is improving and current use is reducing. An early Magellan took eight AA batteries, yielding about seven hours in continuous use. Units such as the Silva XL1000 use six AA batteries giving 12 hours continuous use or 20 hours in its subsidiary standby or programming mode – this latter is a very useful

If going for hand-held GPS think about battery life. What used to be 8 hrs from 8 AA cells is now up to 20 hrs on 4 AAs. Trend is not uniform though. Rechargables?

facility. And the latest sets use four AA batteries yielding around 7-8 hours use; some claim as much as 20-24 hours. Even eight hours may seem quite a long time but a lot of GPS switched-on time is taken up with waiting for fix acquisition and in what might be termed operator fumbling and thinking time; it will be rare to switch on, take a position fix and switch off again. Use of the display illumination will seriously reduce battery life.

As well as the latest equipment using less electrical energy, battery technology is itself advancing and doing so to user advantage. Many nickel-cadmium (ni-cad) batteries have well known but curious characteristics that demand they should not be recharged until they are practically exhausted – and they do run out of power very suddenly compared to an alkaline battery. Now nickel metal hydride batteries are available (with Eagle equipment for example) and these may be recharged at any time. Although expensive to buy, they are claimed to be rechargeable up to 500 times and will have paid for themselves many times over in this period.

Not all small hand-held units are the same. Some that are designed for very large data input such as the Trimble GeoExplorer II is soaking up a steady 2 watts (doubling as a hand warmer?) and, as mentioned above, is available with a camcorder battery auxiliary power source.

Intermittent use – navigation. In the interests of battery life with a hand-held set or perhaps because of numerous starts and stops with a vehicle-mounted set, an equipment used on a long navigation leg may be switched on and off a number of times before the destination is reached. In some equipments this will wipe the navigation data which will have to be reprogrammed (destination waypoint, for example) every time it is restarted. Other equipments will remember the navigation task and will resume the route when you switch on after a break. This is an important point to recognise when selecting your equipment – the difference between having to keep it powered-up all the time to achieve continuity or being able to switch off and use it intermittently to save battery power. The Eagle Explorer is of the latter type and will resume navigation to a pre-selected waypoint when it is switched on after a break. Similarly, where a graphic 'map' plot is being kept, some units retain this facility as a default setting – ie you will get a track record unless you specifically erase it. Very useful.

In this context, as noted on page 4.2 - 20, be sure that any vehicle installation uses a second-battery power source that does not dip when you start the engine. This voltage dip can sometimes be enough to throw the GPS unit off-line.

Getting back – be aware. A few GPS equipments provide a facility for retracing your steps – either simply reversing a route or, more usefully, taking a series of automatic fixes outbound that can be made the basis of a retracing of your steps on a very complex journey. As with all GPS operation, *never* rely on this alone, but build it in to a safety-first navigation method-with-backup way of operating. In fact, for this latter system to work at all you will have had to clear the map plot memory at the start of the trip – thus making positive recognition of the start of the route – and, vitally, have had the unit switched on throughout the outbound journey; if it was switched on intermittently the 'record' will assume straight line transits between fixes which may not be the case.

Garmin's GPS II Plus has what they term a 'TracBack' feature that breaks a recorded outbound plot down into 30 legs which can be activated, with directions, for a return to base. Clearly for this to function accurately you will have to be alert to the beginning of what could be a complex route – for example, trying to cross the grain of transverse wadis, thread a skein of sand dunes or find your way through a collection of small hills along same-level valley bottoms. Magellan too have a facility of this kind in their equipments.

Getting back – be safe. It would be essential to train with this feature so that you can familiarise yourself with it before

departure and – most important of all – monitor its accuracy and the compromises it has to make in breaking down your return into a set number of separate legs.

On balance such a system, for the reasons stated above, is as much a trap as a benefit. In real life, safety awareness would demand not having the unit switched on all the time on a difficult on-foot exploration. Real life would demand too that you recognise in advance an impending difficult section and take a number of present-position fixes at key points as you progress. The action of selecting the key points would help fix them in your mind; the sequence of fixes – by default stored against date and clock time – would then give you your own return route.

Display quality. Already mentioned and very important to emphasise is display clarity. Do pay attention to this in a vehicle mounted unit. Large display digits are important and, probably even more so, the degree of contrast. Remember you will be driving your vehicle as a prime task and flicking a glance at the GPS display will be a secondary, albeit important, input. When you glance at the display you want to see the information clearly and unambiguously first time; you will have just taken your eyes off the brighter-lit road so you don't want to have to squint at a dim green low-contrast display. You will probably already have

Backtrack facility built into some GPS but it can be a trap; better set your own en-route return waypoints. Display quality important for vehicle use.

A GIS (geographical information system) in the palm of your hand (see p 5.2 - 23) and a day's worth of battery power at your waist-belt. Trimble Geo-Explorer 2 looks just like their humbler Scout but packs a far bigger punch – including PC software for post processing (.. at about seven times the price!)

experienced this kind of shortfall on your car radio ('I've got to wait till sundown to find out what station I'm on!'); on a frequent-reference nav display it is just not acceptable.

Hand-held units have displays ade-

Mode and menu. The Eagle Explorer, as well as performing very briskly as a 12-channel receiver, has an excellent user interface. A typical options menu here invites you to press 'up' or 'down' arrows to move selecting cursor and then to press the right-facing arrow to say 'Yes, this is the one I want'. As an aside this straightforwardly selected 'distance between waypoints' is invaluable when planning a route.

Probably most important quality of all when buying GPS is user interface and quality of user manual. Look for intuitive operation – rare and very important.

quate for hill walking and other activities where you can stop to consult the equipment but many will find the readout too small and lacking in brightness or contrast for use in a vehicle. Marine GPS units, made for small boats, have a larger display – usually a display window 100 mm square. Equally, some hand-held units with a standard plug-in interface (called NMEA 0183 – rather like a SCSI on a computer) can output their data to a large-screen display that is easier to read in a tossing boat or a vehicle on a rough track.

Screen types and options. As mentioned on page 5.2 - 21, screen displays come in a wide range of contents ranging from the simple four-parameter display mentioned above – shown in the biggest possible digits – to the frankly rather fiddly 'plotter' display which attempts to show a map on an unsuitably small display screen. Pre-empting customer fussiness or indecision on this score, manufacturers like Eagle offer a customisable display offering a wide choice of parameter combinations. Beware of an excess of screen information – too many parameters on a display gives clutter and confusion in the context of carrying out a

prime task of driving a vehicle.

User interface. It is difficult to do in the teeth of some fast talking and usually non-user salesman but try to establish how intuitive the user interface of your proposed equipment is before buying it. It seems to be the rule rather than the exception that some equipments are shot squarely in the foot by their own user interface – brilliant performance but illogical to operate – and this is often compounded by user manuals specialising in refined obfuscation. Whilst this does keep alive the great traditions of computer software manual writers, it is no great help when you may want the equipment to be actually helping you rather than being a techno-centric end in itself.

Satisfy yourself about all this before buying. Unfortunately a quick switch-on in the shop accompanied by the usual excuses about it not picking up satellites inside a building will make it hard for you really to get a feel for how an equipment works anyway. Remember a good shop demonstration should leave you saying, 'Hey, I could do that!' not 'Great Scott isn't that incredible!' The inevitable 'find a friend who has one' is the ideal, of course, since it will take you some time to learn the equipment – and then to find out whether it is easy or not very easy to use all its facilities.

To quote specifics, many will like the large clear readout and excellent performance of the Silva units but find the user manuals (of current 1996/97 models at least) so incomprehensible that you have, by trial and error, to write your own – and still keep referring back to it. In contrast, Eagle's Explorer not only has a well-written manual but the screen display, with its computer-like visible menu selection process, arrow screen prompts and 'Enter' and 'Exit' keys, is logical to use for what you want almost without reference to the manual.

Mode and menu. Virtually all the equipments are operated on a mode and menu principle – in effect headings along the top (modes) and menus (selectable functions) dropping down from each mode. This amounts to a small spreadsheet and unless you are using the device every day you will simply not remember where everything is on it and the display screens are not big enough to do show menu heads the way it is done on a computer. Quoting the above examples again, Silva, despite their dreadful book, produce a little crib card of screens in each mode and sequence of menu alternatives which is brilliant as an aide memoire. Eagle manage to incorporate arrow prompts and a highlighted menu on each tiny screen.

Do look out for this kind of thing when choosing equipment. An intuitive, friendly user-interface with prompts and listed alternatives means the difference between using your equipment to the full and constantly putting off a re-read of the manual

UK GPS suppliers. Some current (Autumn 1997) suppliers and distributors of GPS equipment suitable for expedition use are:

Eagle UK
Salt Quay House
Sutton Harbour
Plymouth
Devon PL4 0RA
Tel 01752.662.129

A funny thing happened on the way to...... Ijafene

In pre sat-nav days, the recce was to go 250 miles out into the dunes. Arriving, expensively, in Mauritania, we found the theodolite malfunctioning, unable to yield position fixes. Turn back or press on using dead reckoning nav – distance on heading recorded up to 120 times a day? It worked. Returning after five circuitous days we hit on our set-out point; 500 mile round trip!

Garmin (Europe) Ltd
Unit 5 The Quadrangle
Abbey Park Industrial Estate
Romsey
Hants
Tel 01794.519.944

Next Destination Ltd
(Magellan)
25 Clarendon Centre
Salisbury Business Park
Salisbury
Hants SP1 2TJ
Tel 01722.410.800

Silva (UK) Ltd
Unit 10 Sky Business Park
Eversley Way
Egham
Surrey TW20 8RF
Tel 01784.471.721

Trimble Navigation Europe Limited
Trimble House
Meridian Office Park
Osborn Way
Hook
Hants RG27 9HX
Tel 01256.760.150

GPS operating modes, menus are arranged like a miniature spreadsheet. Look for on-screen prompts in the equipment you buy or you will continually lose your way.

Acknowledgments and thanks:

Grateful thanks to the above companies for assistance during preparation of this Section. Thanks also to the British Geological Survey (address on page 35).

Heading? I know this compass. Distance? Should be there in the morning. Done it before? You could say that. Bandar Abbas to Dubai is done on DR, as practiced over the centuries. Heading and distance-on-heading are the hallowed ingredients of DR navigation.

DEAD RECKONING (DR) – WHERE TO HEAD?

Dead reckoning navigation is school geometry on a grand scale: just direction and distance-on-heading. Simple.

Two components

Heading and distance-on-heading. All navigation, be it in Concorde, a nuclear submarine or in mist on the Yorkshire moors, is based on dead reckoning (DR) principles. DR embraces simple vector geometry and thus comprises two components:

1. A direction and

2. A distance along it.

You start at position A; position B is a certain distance along a certain heading from the start point at position A. That one leg – bearing and distance from start point – is dead reckoning navigation at its simplest. You then go on to positions C, D, E and so on, so that your navigation traverse is put together with a number of separate legs all defined as a bearing and distance from the end of the previous leg. The resultant 'DR position' is where you calculate you are at the end of the succession of legs.

Principle of dead reckoning

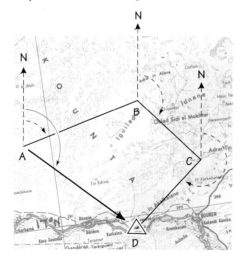

1.   Route is A - B - C - D.
2.   A - B is 070°/34 km
3.   B - C is 133°/23 km
4.   C - D is 223°/25 km
5.   DR position (triangle at D)
       124°/39 km from start at A.
6.   Keep log of headings and
       distance-on-heading with notes.

The navigation log

When to keep a nav log. The short answer is 'always' but the detail required will differ according to whether DR is your sole method of navigation or is a monitor of navigation based on a reasonably detailed map. Clearly with dead reckoning, where you expect to derive a DR position based on the accuracy of previous navigation, you will need an accurate and very detailed record of headings and distances. When this is all you have, *every* change of heading on your route must be recorded – on legs as short as 0.1 km. When you are on tarred roads with a reasonable map, however, still keep a record of events against odometer reading and time but the heading information can obviously be more general. Set targets rather than letting the navigation occur passively. Say: 'I should expect to meet the track for XXX at a speedo reading of ZZZ '; that way you are on the lookout and can quickly spot when things have gone wrong.

When you know you are facing a navigational challenge you will usually get it right. It is when you are just cruising along and think there is no problem that you suddenly find you made a mistake 'somewhere back there'. You're expecting a road junction; could it have been that small track 3 or 4 km back? *Was* it 4 km back or was it 10? On a long day's driving details blur and compress if they are not written down.

Make it second nature. Like dipping the clutch and engaging first gear, make it a habit to note time, odometer and heading even on the shortest trips. Having GPS does not preclude the need for keeping a note-down broad picture of the navigation situation. That way, if the GPS goes down, your route-so-far and distance since last fix will be known parameters – written in your log or recorded on your tape. Smart as it is, GPS does not make a note when you pass a track junction or know if it was accurately mapped; you will frequently find yourself having to do some reasoned decision making at the roadside based around your log, a dubious map and any fix information you may have.

Importance of the nav log. So keep a written – or taped and transcribed – navigation log that records the odometer reading, time, headings, distances and events *all* the time. Thus, as the previous diagram shows, knowing your start point and doing the subsequent DR plot you will be able to determine from measurements on the map the bearing and distance from the start and to your goal. Notice, in the sample log above, the 'leg' or distance on the given heading, is the result of subtracting that line's trip reading from the trip reading on the next line. All of this, of course, is dependent on being able to measure the two components of DR – heading and distance – with accuracy. And this is what is dealt with next – first heading measurement, then distance.

SIMPLE NAVIGATION LOG – TYPICAL ENTRIES

Time	Speedo (Trip) km	Event	New heading	Leg
0730	0	Left camp	125°	5
0740	5	Junction, go left	090°	4
0755	9	Resume SE Average hdg SE Open savannah	130°	10
0815	19	Track crosses L to R Straight on	145°	7
0830	26	Village, 3 o'clock about 4 km	165°	5
0845	31	Bridge over river Stop for photos.	-	-

Basic navigation log – events related to a time and odometer reading so that you can, firstly, determine your position and second, determine where you may have gone wrong. Use a tape recorder and transcribe frequently.

Keeping a navigation log is probably the most important task in navigation. It disciplines you to quantify your progress and will help hugely if you get lost.

DR – heading measurement

Heading – the references. Though we always tend to think about magnetic compasses when talking about heading information, heading measurement can be derived from:

1. Magnetic sources:
   Earth's field
2. Non-magnetic sources:
   Sun and stars
   Sun compass
   Satellites
   Gyros and inertial equipment.

Gyros and inertial navigation will be omitted from this section. Though very elegant in concept and well suited to their allotted slot and job in the avionics bay of airliners, several major expeditions could be mounted for the cost of one system...! Non-magnetic sources, of course, can give references relative to true north, ie the geographical north pole, whereas a magnetic source gives an angular reference in relation to the position of the north magnetic pole positioned at about 78°N, 104°W or a whisker over 1300 km from the geographical pole.

Terminology: heading, bearing, etc

Mild confusion reigns. So long as *you* know what you mean, arguably it does not matter much that there is a degree of confusion (or should that be confusion of degrees) and misuse of the above terms – even among manufacturers of navigation equipment. Just for the record, though:

• *Heading* is the direction in which you are pointing; if you like, the angle between north and the centre-line of your vehicle (or yourself!) Abbreviation: HDG.

• *Course.* (Just to confuse things course and heading used to be used for the same thing and is more of an aeronautical and nautical term.) Course represents the heading you would be on in no-wind/no-tide conditions to reach your destination, ie the on-the-map compass heading from where you are to where you want to be. If there

was a strong wind from the right your *course* would still be the same but your *heading* would more to the right to counteract the wind. So *course* doesn't really come into land navigation ... unless someone drops it in by mistake! Abbreviation: CSE.

• *Track.* Track is sometimes referred to as 'track made good' which makes the term self-explanatory – this is the heading of your path, or track, over the ground. If you are wondering why the term is used at all (since 'track' sounds pretty much the same as 'heading'), it is to distinguish between the direction you are pointing in and your actual track if you are in an aircraft or a boat. Thus flying north with a strong wind from the east, your heading might be 015° in order to achieve a track (made good) of north or 000°.

• *Bearing* is always relative to something else – usually another position. So you take a bearing on a mountain top or radio mast that is due east of you and it then bears (or your *bearing* on it is) 090° from where you are in your present position; if it was south of you and you took a bearing, that bearing would be 180°. This is also usually the reciprocal to a steer; so that a radio direction finding service might say, if you were to the west of their station 'You bear 270° (or 'your bearing is 270'), steer 090° to reach this position.' If, in GPS parlance, 'bearing and distance to waypoint' is 135°/50 km, then it means the waypoint, if you could see it, would be on a bearing of 135° from where you are. If you turned around and drove straight for it, then your *heading* would be 135°. Abbreviation: BRG.

Hand-held magnetic compasses

Unbeatable simplicity. For accuracy, simplicity and independence from ephemera such as batteries and electronics, the magnetic compass takes some beating. The value, accuracy and potential pitfalls of the magnetic compass are sometimes under-

Half the DR nav task is knowing your heading (the other half is knowing distance travelled). Know difference between track, heading, course and bearing.

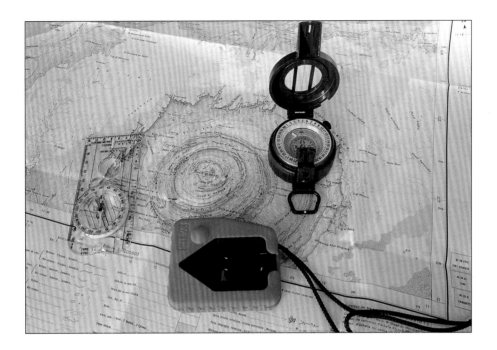

Three Silva compasses (clockwise from top right) – the Mk4 Prismatic (£172), the Model 80, non-illuminated (£67), Model 4 (£23). The last two, together as a pair, would be the choice. Reasons:
1. Lightness – very light; lighter as a pair than the Mk 4 on its own.
2. One-handed operation.
3. Magnifier on the Model 4.
4. Use Mod 80 for accurate bearings on objects for fixes and the Mod 4 for 'marching' and short range map work.
5. Mod 80 has a 'rear sight' to position the object in. Though not quite as precise as the Mk 4 which has a spot-on rear lubber line as well as a front one, you can still sight to ±0.5°.
6. Mk 4 very accurate and can be used for 'marching' (albeit less clearly than the little Mod 4) but is heavier and bulky and would be an irritant round the neck all the time – sufficient for hand-carrying to be preferable. Has focus adjustment in the prism slide.
7. People will find themselves taking more bearings with an 80 than with a Mk 4; no lid or prism to hinge up. Mk 4 too expensive and the prism is vulnerable to knocks and damage which would render it useless.
8. Mod 80 would be able to take knocks – no protrusions, silicon rubber covered etc. If you really only want one compass, take the Model 80.

estimated, though. There are two roles for a magnetic compass:

- For 'marching' on and ...
- For taking precise bearings on distant objects.

To get the best interface for these different roles you will find yourself using two different kinds of magnetic compass.

• *Marching compass.* A marching compass is one that you can hold at waist level and look down on the compass needle with your chosen heading set against it. It is good for quick reference without stopping but, even with the reflective cover with which it is sometimes equipped, will not be as accurate for distance bearings as the prismatic type.

• *Prismatic compass.* For taking distant bearings, as required when you are trying to establish a position from known distant landmarks, always use a prismatic or lens-sighted, fluid-damped compass with a sharp aiming line and the capability of giving readings to half a degree. This type is held up to the eye for accurate sighting and your

Take a lot of trouble selecting your compass(es). A simple marching compass and one that gives you spot-on bearings to ±0.5° is best combination. See caption, left.

Object, 'rear sight', and the vertical lubber line all lined up. Now swing the compass a little right, then left to check that the compass card is free to rotate – no sticky bearings and the card is not catching on the 'roof' of the enclosure (see next spread.) A day's DR plot (right) yields bearing and distance from start. Traverse can be scaled and transferred to map. Note tape for log.

Magnetic variation (difference between true and mag north) is important to know for your operating area. Find out <u>before</u> leaving; values can be 10-20° in common haunts.

vision of the compass card is effected by use of an internal prism of some kind. If you only carry one magnetic compass this is the type to have; to use it for marching, select a distant landmark on the heading you require and then walk towards that. When aiming it at your objective move the compass and your line of sight slightly left and then right by about 3° to check the needle responds and is free to move. This guards against a 'sticky' pivot and also the possibility that you are not holding the compass level; this latter – or (see below) high angles of dip – can cause the card or needle to touch the inside of the compass and hinder movement.

Ferrous metal influences. Ferrous metals, either magnetic or not obviously so, will affect the accuracy of a compass if close to it – steel-rimmed spectacles as you squint

through a prismatic, a machete hanging from your belt when using a marching compass at waist level. See below under 'Magnetic deviation'.

Magnetic errors – variation, deviation

Poles – apart. Especially after the note above, few readers will need reminding about the location of the magnetic poles relative to the earth's geographic poles but the terminology of magnetic variation, declination, deviation (often casually and incorrectly interchanged) and dip angle should be clarified and grasped.

Magnetic variation. It is worth treating under a separate heading the subjects of magnetic variation and deviation - often confused. 'Variation' is the angular difference between true north and magnetic north and is solely the result of the displacement of the magnetic poles from the geographic poles. (To further confuse things, some people call this angular difference 'declination'! Don't let them confuse you. They are wrong since declination has a quite separate meaning when used in astro navigation.)

Variation is different in different regions of the world. In the UK at the time of writing it is around 3°W – enough to throw you significantly out in cross-bearing fixes or at the end of a day's DR – but in some of the commonest 'expedition' regions it is as high as 20°. Variation is also steadily changing. It is a miracle of the geophysicists' skills that this change can be predicted. As high as 1° per year near the poles, typical rates of change in the UK, western Europe and Africa are up to 8' per year.

The value of variation for the expedition operating area should be checked by the expedition navigator before leaving UK as it is often difficult to establish the value in the field. Information on worldwide values – and dip angles, see below – is available from maps published by the Hydrographic Office, Taunton, Somerset TA1 2DN. Sheet 5374 covers world magnetic variation; other sheets larger scale coverage of reduced areas, and world values of dip and magnetic intensity. These maps are valid for (and updated every) five years.

For detailed spot variation values make direct contact with:

Magnetic variation

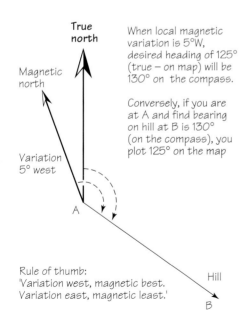

True north

Magnetic north

Variation 5° west

A

Hill

B

When local magnetic variation is 5°W, desired heading of 125° (true – on map) will be 130° on the compass.

Conversely, if you are at A and find bearing on hill at B is 130° (on the compass), you plot 125° on the map

Rule of thumb: 'Variation west, magnetic best. Variation east, magnetic least.'

British Geological Survey
Murchison House, West Mains Road
Edinburgh EH9 3LA,
Tel 0131.667.1000

If there is an airfield in your area of operations control tower staff should know the local magnetic variation (but experience indicates they often just leave this to the pilots!). Another way of obtaining a value for variation is to consult your sat-nav or GPS equipment; sometimes they are programmed to come up with a figure if they are given the latitude and longitude of the location concerned.

There are all manner of rhymes (see diagram) and rules of thumb to 'help' you remember whether to add or subtract a variation figure when taking a magnetic bearing if you are wanting its value relative to true north – or if you are taking a true bearing off a map and wanting to know what you should read on your compass – but many of the rhymes are themselves liable to confusion! If in *any* doubt, draw it on the back of an envelope, just like the diagram here – slowly and quite unambiguously – a little arrow showing true north with magnetic north to its left if variation is west and to its right if variation is east!

Magnetic deviation. 'Deviation' is the effect on a compass of local magnetic influences such as DC electromagnetic fields in a vehicle, the ferrous sheet metal of its body or chassis, the ferrous content of its cargo or, in a human-held compass, the nearness of quartz watches, steel spectacle frames or other magnetic influences. As indicated above, the basic and golden rule with hand held magnetic compasses is to take the instrument away from such influences before using it.

Ferrous metal influences should be carefully guarded against (see also below 'Compasses in vehicles'). Always dismount from a vehicle and walk four to five metres away from it before taking a reading. Less obvious and easily forgotten as a source of error are metallic objects in the immediate vicinity of the compass when it is read - steel items on your waist belt if used at

Magnetic deviation is error caused by local magnetic influences – ferrous metals, electrical gear, even steel-rim spectacles. Take bearings well away from vehicle.

waist level and, with the prismatic type, steel-rimmed spectacles and, surprisingly, analogue quartz watches. These watches have step-down motors which can generate quite powerful magnetic fields. Ironically (or perhaps one should say ferrously) the best and most durable watches have the strongest effect; a Rolex quartz movement, being more powerful than any other make, was found on one expedition to have introduced a consistent 7° error in the DR plot! Lateral thinkers will at once think of dental fillings and the like being close to the compass when readings are taken but it can be confirmed – after experimentation carried out in private – that chrome-cobalt denture bridgework does not affect a compass. Nor, according to specialist advice, do any other dental materials.

See below auto-deviation correction in electronic compasses and also opposite 'Compasses in vehicles'.

Never ignore it. And finally never be tempted to ignore the figure for variation and deviation as being too small to matter.

Dip is the angle at which the lines of magnetic force point down towards a point beneath the surface of the earth; your compass needle should be balanced accordingly.

Magnetic dip – needle 'weighting'

Magnetic poles not on the surface. Dip is the angle at which the earth's magnetic

Magnetic dip angle

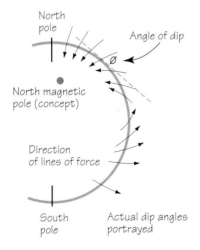

North pole

Angle of dip

North magnetic pole (concept)

Direction of lines of force

South pole

Actual dip angles portrayed

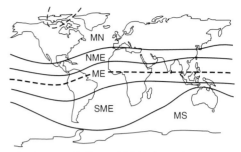

MN

NME

ME

SME

MS

In dip zone NME, use NME balanced compass

field strikes the surface of the earth. Only in small areas of the world – mostly around the geographic equator – do the magnetic lines of force lie parallel to the earth's surface so that the compass needle will rotate in a horizontal plane. The earth's magnetic poles – the actual locations, defined in three dimensions, to which the compass needle points – are not actually on the surface of the earth but are a long way beneath it. Thus when you use a compass anywhere other than quite close to the equator, a magnetised needle will, unless otherwise constrained, point in the correct horizontal direction (azimuth) but also point in the correct vertical direction too, ie downwards toward where the magnetic pole is, under the earth's surface.

Weighting the compass needle. To overcome this, compass manufacturers making compasses for, say, walkers in Europe, will offset the needle pivot so that one side of the needle is longer than the other (in effect weighting the needle at one end) so that it lies flat and swings in a horizontal plane. Take that same compass to South Africa and you will find the needle hitting the underside of the compass transparency and the whole unit must be used tilted over to one side in order to obtain needle freedom of movement as outlined in the test above (page 5.2 - 34).

So if you know you are going to use your compass in a particular part of the world – especially if it is the opposite hemisphere to that in which your compass shop

Compass needle balance

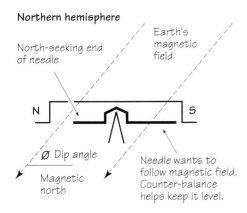

Northern hemisphere

North-seeking end of needle

Earth's magnetic field

Ø Dip angle

Magnetic north

Needle wants to follow magnetic field. Counter-balance helps keep it level.

Southern hemisphere

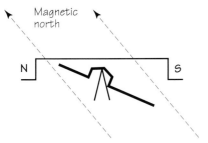

Magnetic north

Northern hemisphere needle counter-balance causes excessive tilt in southern hemisphere. Choose compass balanced for region.

is situated – contact the *manufacturer* (the shop you bought it from will probably deny knowledge of the problem or the solution) and obtain the correct compass for the area to which you are travelling. The well-known compass makers Silva, make compasses balanced for five separate zones of the world:
- MN – magnetic north, areas north of about 30°N
- NME – north of magnetic equator, approx 0°-30°N
- ME – zone of the magnetic equator, approx 15°N to 20°S
- SME – south of magnetic equator, approx 20°-25/60°S
- MS – magnetic south, south of 25°S in Australasia (diagram opposite)

A non-prismatic 'European' compass will still work in southern Africa but will be much less easy to use accurately; a prismatic compass, built for northern latitudes, however, can incur enough needle or disc tilt to throw the image of the figures out of focus when viewed through the prism – an unacceptable problem.

Magnetic compasses in vehicles

Big problems. Magnetic compass units in vehicles represent a clash of almost incompatible technical requirements. To be read by the driver or navigator the compass must be forward and mounted in the region of the rear view mirror or above the fascia so the driver can actually see it. In most vehicles this is an area of magnetic turmoil often coming at the intersection of the fields due to the engine and that of the chassis and body. Thus small changes in either one – eg a change in electrical load on the engine – can cause varying changes in the magnetic field in the vicinity of the compass. So attempts to correct the compass by use of correction magnets mounted underneath it are not always successful or consistent. By comparing readings taken within and outside the vehicle a deviation correction card can be prepared but be aware that compass deviation will differ on different headings – don't just establish one error and apply it throughout the 360° azimuth circle. A constant cross-checking process should be adhered to since bumping and banging of the vehicle can further cause discrepancies. In general, magnetic compasses mounted within a vehicle in this way should be treated with extreme caution. If not avoided altogether (arguably the best idea) they should be used only as a guide to which quadrant you are in or for the period of time it takes to get up to around 20 mph when the GPS heading can be relied on.

Care of magnetic compasses

North for south. It is enormously important not to stow a magnetic compass next to strong magnetic sources – or demagnetising fields. If the devil himself had heard this

Unless they have a remotely mounted sensor (usually aft) and electronic relay, magnetic compasses are unacceptably unreliable (and uncorrectable) in vehicles. See p 38.

and decided to do his worst he could not have come up with a worse scenario than door pockets and powerful door-mounted loudspeakers. This could, if it was not your day, reverse the polarity of your compass. You are unlikely to store a compass strapped to an alternator pumping out a high amperage under the bonnet but that could demagnetise it altogether. If you were really bent on storing your compass under the bonnet you could stow it next to the starter motor cable and that, again if the needle was stuck because of the angle it was resting, could also reverse the polarity of the unit.

Absurdities are quoted to make the point. Do not store your compass next to strong magnetic or demagnetising sources. The door speaker set-up is the most likely to cause problems but just remember to play safe and keep your compass somewhere – reliably, all the time when it is not is use – away from magnetic fields.

Cetrek 555 marine electronic compass display is fed from sensor mounted aft. Magnetic signature of vehicle (after investigation) was found to be asymmetric so off-centre mounting location was tricky. Sensor gimbals were clamped for vehicle (as opposed to marine) use. Auto-calibration compensations were inadequate for a vehicle so residual deviation correction values were listed and stuck to fascia.

Electronic compasses in vehicles

Electronic compasses can work in vehicles with proper mounting and give static readings as opposed to 20 mph minimum needed for GPS heading to be accurate.

Sensing the field electrically. Electronic compasses sense the earth's magnetic field electrically in coils with the aid of a power supply and then relay the value to a remotely mounted dial readout thus enabling – in a boat or a vehicle – the sensor to be mounted away from the worst influence of ferrous materials, engines and generators whilst the actual readout is close to the driver. The local value of magnetic variation can usually be set on the readout so that – subject to deviation correction – a true heading may be obtained.

Electronic compasses are almost invariably adapted from marine units and thus have damped-gimbal-mounted sensors that allow the sensor to stay level when a boat is heeled over. Such gimbals and their fluid damping are tuned to nautical kinds of motion. They are monitored in many cases these days by solid state gyros which make allowance for centrifugal force arising from turns but cannot cope with longitudinal acceleration errors resulting from braking or acceleration.

Such a unit in a vehicle can thus be expected to give erratic and incorrect readouts when a vehicle is getting up to speed or decelerating. Slightly older units (see photo) that had gimballing sensors can have these sensors strapped (anchored) so there is no excessive swinging around. In practice that works well since you tend not to look at the compass during passage over very rough ground ... !

Auto-deviation correction. Electronic compasses usually have a form of auto-deviation correction. When compass controls are appropriately set for calibration, the vehicle or boat has only to execute a single 360° turn for the unit to pick up and correct for the vehicle's deviation. It must be remembered that this correction is valid only for the magnetic signature of the vehicle prevailing at that time. So a vehicle or canoe being prepared for an expedition should only have a deviation correction swing carried out with a representative expedition load on board -

spares, jacks, jerrycans and any heavy ferrous-metal objects – all in their correct and permanently allocated positions. Periodic en-route checks should be done since varying dip angle – compared with that prevailing at the home base, for instance – can affect the deviation correction parameters.

Early marine compasses of this kind had software within them that is capable of correcting for deviation values found most usually in boats. In vehicles compensation values are generally a lot higher, even with the sensor mounted as far aft as possible. A marine compass therefore cannot always make full corrections and at best you will be left with a correction table to apply when steering particular headings. At worst, as experienced by one expedition, readings may be wild and accompanied by irrational reactions - such as a 100° change in compass readout after a 10° change of vehicle heading. (Careful relocation of the sensor, off vehicle axis, partially cured this – see photo left.) Later units, capable of correcting for external magnetic influences a lot stronger than that of the earth's field have now overcome this problem.

Magneto-resistive compasses. A new generation of electronic compasses presently being pioneered by Terrafix of Stoke on Trent (tel 01782.577015) may be termed magneto-resistive compasses rather than the conventional fluxgate type described above. Working on a different principle, their software has been designed to cope with vehicle values of deviation correction and that correction is automatic without the need even for a 360° turn. Operating on its own (ie without a GPS interface) accuracies are of the order of 2°.

Electronic compass application? With GPS so good and so versatile, who needs a separate and fairly expensive electronic compass? The gap filled by such equipment is the slow-moving or static application such as would apply to large heavy expedition vehicles (five tonnes or more) travelling cross country on difficult terrain. GPS heading readings are not comfortably reliable until something of the order of 20 mph or

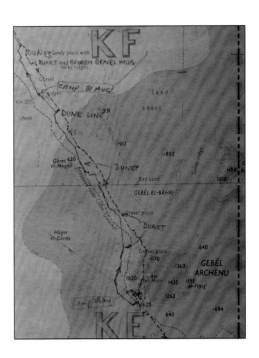

150-odd miles worth of DR plot carried out using Coles sun compass and vehicle odometers, transferred to 1:1m map to give indication of track alignment and suitability of terrain for light and medium vehicles. The 'beaconed track' annotation was, as is often the case, somewhat optimistic – ie not there! Note military grid lettering (KE, KF): see Section 5.2.1.

more has been achieved and this could well be just outside the operating limits of vehicles engaged in geological or other exploration off-tracks.

Non-magnetic direction devices

Sun compass. Since time immemorial navigators have deduced direction from stars and sun. Clever but simple sun compasses were invented during the Second World War and yielded results accurate to one degree – far better than an on-board magnetic compass – when appropriately levelled and used with strict attention to local sun time. The Coles sun compass was used in the desert and is very versatile; it is, however, virtually unobtainable now. The

Electronic compass could be valuable for large slow vehicles off-tracks and unable to make the 20 mph required for GPS headings. Nimble vehicles use GPS.

Properly used, a sun compass like the Coles is superb in its simplicity and dead accurate. All instructions are on the dial. Designed in WW2, alas not now available.

Translucent base sun compass, based on WW2 Coles, is viewable from beneath. Sensitive to levelling and dependent on15-minute manual movement of the cursor (pink), result is accurate to 1 °. See also map/satellite image comparison on page 5.2 - 11 re depiction of mesa formation in the distance.

required. Versions of this could also be produced for use in polar regions where magnetic compasses require very high corrections.

Being very sensitive to correct levelling, a sun compass is well suited to desert use and, since it requires frequent manual manipulation of the dial, application in long straight legs on a single heading. That said, extraordinary accuracy is possible on a DR plot-out; one was used for a traverse of sand dunes in which there were 120 separate legs in a single day. The manual plot-out of the DR took some time (!) but the results were astonishingly accurate (see panel on p 5.2 -29).

GPS heading information. As already mentioned, another invaluable attribute of GPS is that the unit can, so long as the vehicle is moving over about 20 mph, display quite accurate headings – see also above 'What GPS does', and 'Heading – true or magnetic?' (Bearings from present position to desired waypoint are uncompromisingly accurate as they are calculated trigonometrically.) This, together with an immunity from weather limitations (to which the sun compass is naturally vulnerable) makes GPS, in this as in other roles, the answer to just about everything an expedition navigator could want.

At least one hand-held GPS – the Silva XL1000 – has an electronic compass built in so that it will work when the unit is stationary, sensing the earth's field electronically. This device only claims an accuracy of 5° and in practice is so sensitive to levelling that it is quicker and more accurate to use a magnetic compass.

pressure of the 1991 Gulf War, however, caused the School of Military Survey to re-invent versions of the very basic Howard compass with dial data computer-generated according to the latitude and time of year

DR – distance measurement

Crucially important accuracy. The other half of the dead reckoning equation, after measurement of heading, is measurement of distance. As with the output of heading, the old computer adage of 'Garbage in; garbage out' applies and DR navigation is only as good as the care with which its ingredients are input. There are two aspects to distance measurement in DR navigation:

1. Historical – recording the distance you have already travelled so that an accurate DR leg may be plotted.

2. Estimating the distance you have yet to travel on a route you are planning.

'But it *can't* be the main road, we just came off a wide tarmac ...' Familiar words in the bush and reasonable cause for concern. A clear three-dimensional reason for keeping a navigation log, monitoring headings and distances all the time, and, if you have one, confirming with a GPS fix. 'What do you mean, lat and long aren't marked on the map?' That's familiar too!

The first relates to the accuracy of your odometer – the distance-measuring part of your speedometer – and the second relates to how accurately you can relate a measured distance on the map to actual distance-to-go. This is covered in 'Terrain factor' below.

Vehicle odometers, calibration

Vehicle and tyre maker info. As mentioned already at Section 4.2 'Vehicle modifications' on page 4.2 - 26, new or different tyres can affect wheel revolutions per kilometre or mile and this will affect the accuracy of your odometer. Consultation with vehicle and tyre manufacturer will establish the theoretical accuracy of the vehicle/tyre combination you are using. The tyre manufacturer will give you revolutions per mile or kilometre and the vehicle maker will know the figure for which the odometer was designed. From these a known error may be calculated – or corrections made. Some

Knowing accurate distance travelled is the other half of DR navigation. Be sure your odometer is accurate with tyres you have. Consult, calibrate, correct.

models of Land Rover, for example, have different speedometer gearing sets that take account of (in the Defender, for instance) the 6.50x16 tyre or the 7.50x16 tyre. As indicated at Section 4.2, you can check a vehicle's trip meter against the kilometre distance markers on UK motorways. There is nothing like seeing it all work and this – whatever else you may have been able to find out – is a final test worth doing.

Wheel spin? An oft-voiced concern in relation to odometer accuracy when used for DR navigation is about wheel spin but this should not give cause for concern. Experienced drivers will know just how little wheel spin it takes to bog a vehicle into soft mud or sand and they will hopefully have learned to avoid it at all costs for this reason alone. 'One rev of wheel spin is one rev too much', has been uttered at many a training session. If an expedition has a distance measurement problem due to wheel spin it will also have much more serious problems on its hands!

Tyre pressures? Note, incidentally that revs per mile for a tyre is constant irrespective of tyre pressures. Though the wheel radius at the tyre contact point seems to decrease due to tyre deflection at low pressures, each revolution of the wheel will, especially with braced-tread radials, move you forward by the (unvarying) circumference of the tyre.

In DR nav, take account of the 'terrain factor' – the difference between actual distance travelled and the on-map equivalent. As you drive a route, refine the value you use.

'Terrain factor' and the map

Line on a map vs distance covered. When determining expected distance to destination from a map, the actual distance travelled will be longer than the distance indicated on the map in all but a handful of cases. Obvious, of course, but relevant to DR in that you may *plan* a route as a series of headings and distances-on-heading but 340°/50 km on the map may turn out to be 10, 20 or even 50% more on your odometer due to terrain roughness and minor diversions. In deserts, the classic domain (with sea and air navigation) of DR, this ratio of distance travelled to distance on the map can be quantified:

'Terrain factor' – map vs actual distance

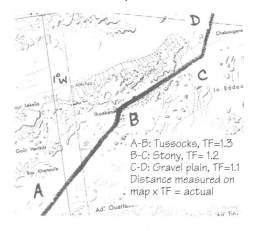

A-B: Tussocks, TF=1.3
B-C: Stony, TF= 1.2
C-D: Gravel plain, TF=1.1
Distance measured on
map x TF = actual

Yes, you saw this in Section 2.6 too! Accurate distances vital for fuel planning.

- Flat gravel plain is about 1.1,
- Gravel or sand with sparse vegetation 1.15 to 1.2,
- Dunes 1.5 to 2.0 ... and so on.

Though in most cases you will know when you have reached your destination (albeit you may only be heading for a lat/long position), these estimations are essential for the purposes of estimating fuel requirements – see also Section 2.6 'Fuel, oil, fluids'. It would be an interesting exercise, if you have GPS, to compare fix-to-fix distance measured on the map and measured on the odometer so that you can deduce your own 'terrain factor' for use at a later date on similar ground.

Trust the map? The terrain factor approach applies in classic off-tracks navigation such as open desert. In the majority of cases, though, you will probably have a map that gives point to point distances but it is wise to treat these with circumspection and cross check by doing a quick on-map measurement too. Too often when point to point routes change the map distances are not amended too. Mostly such changes are from 'the new, direct route' – but you can't always be sure!

THE REST

Electronic equipment - care in the field

Clean, dry, cool. A final note is worthwhile about the care of electronic equipment on expeditions. The obvious things apply, naturally – like (as a default) keeping electronic equipment clean, dry and not jarring it. Less immediately obvious is its susceptibility to the effects of heat; not just ambient shade temperatures but the extraordinarily high acquired temperatures that can result from equipment being left in the sun for

Plotting out the DR. Do it two or three times a day if you are dependent on your position to intercept junctions or landmarks. If the nav log is on a tape this also permits transcribing and checking on the recorder's functionality.

even a very short time – either outside or in a vehicle under a sloping windscreen or behind a window.

Behind-the-dashboard temperatures in 4x4s in hot climates can be frighteningly high from the viewpoint of electronic gear. Likewise, equipment stowed between the front seats or under the front seats gets very hot in simple vehicles like early Land Rovers or pick-ups. The cause is air entering the engine bay at high ambients, gaining heat from the radiator and more heat from the engine and exhaust pipe and then passing under the floor and centre seat position.

Operating limits of electronic equipment built for civilian markets are not very wide – the upper temperature limit is sometimes only 60°C though modern gear is often specified to 70°C. Military equipment built to 'Mil Specs' often have higher upper limits but use very much more expensive components.

The solutions are straightforward and commonsense once you are alerted to the problem. Dashboard-mounted dials such as remote compass readouts should be shaded from the sun – a cardboard and sleeping-mat foam shade covering, but not in contact with, the item thus providing a further insulating air space. Never leave your portable GPS (camera, radio or other electronic gear) in open sun or it will quickly acquire temperatures in excess of its operating specification.

As with all expedition navigation – or indeed any expedition task – infallible care and attention to detail is what makes things work and keep on working. The safety and survival of your expedition could depend on it.

Electronic equipment dislikes high temperatures, vibration, and wet. Dust not helpful either despite solid-state build: sand, dust bring static electricity – very bad news.

Equipment list

Navigation equipment. List of typical navigation kit taken on an expedition appears at Section 2.1.1 'Office/nav kit' on page 2.1 – 19.

Section 5.2.1

Operations:

Map grids

COVERAGE OF THIS SECTION

Lat/long and grids

Why do we need to know about grids?
Some maps you use will show UTM or Military Grid. Because this is overprinted on the whole map you will find it more accurate and easier to use than latitude and longitude which is generally indicated only at the edge of the sheet. Your GPS unit can often give readings in grid co-ordinates and you may as well benefit from this. Just as important, in the field, you should have the means of correlating and cross checking lat/long and grids with each other in fairly straightforward, back-of-an-envelope calculations. You may find yourself directed to locations only available as grid references and it is well to be able to double check where they are and your ability to navigate to them.

What is wrong with latitude and longitude? A geo-location system is a means of locating a position on the earth's surface. The classic and most widely used is latitude and longitude. You probably know most of this already but it is worth highlighting just a few points about lat/long:

• Parallels of latitude are *evenly* spaced all the way from the equator (0°) up, and down, to the poles (90°N and 90°S)

• Each degree of latitude is nearly 60 nautical miles wide on the surface of the earth; so 1 minute of latitude equals about 1 nautical mile (6080 feet as against 5280 feet for a statute mile) on the ground.

• Lines of longitude run from pole to pole and, because the earth is (roughly) a sphere rather than a cylinder, they converge as they go north or south from the equator. So a 'square' of lat and long has parallel top and bottom but sides that converge towards the top or bottom. Measuring distance according to longitude is thus not practical.

• 'Reference' latitude is the equator (0°) and every latitude is annotated as N or S of that. 'Reference' longitude is the Greenwich meridian and every longitude is measured E or W of Greenwich.

• The other important line of longitude is 180°W (the same as 180°E, of course). This is where most world grids (eg UTM, military grid) start – see below 'Where it starts'.

• Notation of lat/long is by:

•Degrees, minutes, seconds and decimal seconds (DMS.S) eg 22° 49' 25.00"N *or*

•Degrees, minutes and decimals of minutes (DM.M) eg. 22° 49.416'N

The latter is the recommended notation.

• Measurement of distance on a lat/long map is not intuitive and usually has to be done by reference to the scale at the bottom of the map.

What is a grid? A grid is a constant-scale (usually metric) piece of rectilinear 'graph paper' overlaid on a section of the earth. World grids are tied in to the lat/long system in a fairly simple way (see next spread); national grids may not be so simple!

Why do we need them? Grids have operational advantages:

• Horizontal and vertical scales are the same, usually based on tens, hundreds or thousands of metres so spaces between grid lines are always the same and 'square'. The British Ordnance Survey 1:25,000 and 1:50,000 maps show 1 km squares so the grid, can also be used as a scale. (Beware: there *are* grids based on feet, eg Malaysia.)

• Grid references can be defined right down to single metres.

Basis of grid systems

Tie-in with lat/long. There are national grids and world grids and in the latter case a simple tie-in with lat/long is virtually essential. In the case of national grids it is desirable, not always so simply done and often (UK) abandoned altogether for practical purposes. Superimposing a rectilinear, constant-scale, essentially two-dimensional grid on a converging longitude system, itself on a sphere, is a potentially oil-and-water situation but it has been done. You will come across:

• UTM grid
• Military grid (MGRS)
• National grids such as the British National Grid.

Latitude and longitude is not easy to work with on a map unless overprinted in small increments. A grid offers constant scale, rectilinear format, 1-10 km overprint.

Many maps of military origin – the serious topographical maps that you will find yourself buying for a wilderness expedition rather than the often trashy 'national route maps' – are overprinted with the military grid. It pays to understand the system.

Why three grid systems? In fact there are many but the UTM (Universal Transverse Mercator) and the closely related Military Grid Reference System (MGRS) are two world grids you will encounter as map overprints. UTM usually consists of a zone figure (sometimes plus one letter N or S) followed by seven figures (may be only six) plus 'E,' indicating 'eastings', and then seven figures plus 'N' (indicating 'northings). So a UTM position might be:

'35N
0279496E
2413898N'

(**Note:** If this were a *southern* latitude – 21° 49.000' S – the northings would be expressed as 10 million minus the figure shown, ie 7586102N, to avoid negative numbers or confusion between north and south. Note still having a terminal 'N' to show it is a northing as opposed to an easting but the initial figures would be '35S'.)

The military grid attempts to simplify the two lines of figures above by introducing an alphanumeric notation to guard against corrupt communications in the heat of battle; certainly there are fewer figures but working out the correlation with UTM – as you may have to do in field – may best be described as involved. Simple when you know the rules but ... ! UTM and the MGRS have a lot in common. The above position in MGRS, depending on accuracy, might be:

'35Q.KE.794139' or
'35Q.KE.79401390'

Shorter, with some similarities to UTM figures but how does it work?

Where it starts. On the 'zero' and on the left is where the UTM grid starts:

• 180°W and
• 0° N, ie the equator.

(Beware. The Russian grid uses the Greenwich meridian, 0° longitude, as the start of its longitude reference.)

UTM and military grid (MGRS) are closely related – the main difference is the MGRS notation which takes the form of an alpha-numeric single line.

Tips. It is worth noting at this point the 'along the corridor and up the stairs' tip for remembering the order of grid co-ordinates; ie unlike latitude and longitude, grid eastings are always quoted first, then northings. It is important to know because in MGRS you just get a single line of figures – six, eight or ten after the (above) 35Q.KE. Split them in the middle and the first half of the figures (3, 4 or 5 figures) are the eastings, the second 3, 4 or 5 figures are the northings. So in the MGRS reference above you have 794 as eastings and 139 as northings.

Eastings. From the 180°W and 0°N point the UTM system goes to the right and up (for northern hemisphere) or right and down (for southern hemisphere). The 360 degrees of longitude that encircle the earth are divided into sixty 6° zones – the first 30 cross the Pacific, the US, Atlantic and up to the 0° Greenwich meridian; from zone 31 on (the first one to the east of Greenwich), the numbered zones cover the Middle East, Asia and the Far East till zone 60 abuts zone 1 at the International Date line, 180°E. So each 6° zone of longitude has a number. For instance, zone 35 is between 24°E and 30°E; the centre line of that zone is therefore 27°E. Important, that; we'll be coming back to it because it is the way a 'square', rectilinear grid copes with a 'tapering' band of longitude. Both UTM and MGRS share this designation for longitude zones or 'columns', if you like, so zone 35 is the same longitude band in both systems. Eastings *within* the zone is covered on the next spread.

Northings. If eastings are 'columns' of longitude, then northing are the 'rows'; horizontal bands of latitudes that define how far north or south of the equator the position is. Here UTM and MGRS notation differ. UTM defines northings quite simply as the number of metres north of the equator whereas MGRS divides latitude into 8° bands and allocates letters to each one. In the examples above UTM is saying the position is 2.4 million-odd metres north of the equator; MGRS is saying it is in band Q. (South of the equator, northings are measured from a false origin – see Note ,

Military grid zones based on UTM

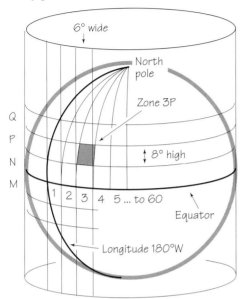

UTM uses 6° longitude zones 1, 2, 3 ... 60, metric eastings within zone, then northings from equator

MGRS uses same longitude zones, lettered 8° latitude bands, two further letters within zone, then metric eastings and northings.

Mercator projection used above for clarity. Actual projection is **transverse mercator** (right) giving slight latitude curvature (next page).

The 'KE' part actually represents a 100 km square within 35Q. It is a means of turning the '02' (or '2') of the UTM eastings and the '24' of the UTM northings into letters. The means of doing this has its own jaw-dropping logic that smacks of WW2 code-breaking rituals but in truth you do not need to learn the method since even a map overprinted with MGRS will have the '02' and '24' of the references above printed (in a smaller type size) at the edges of the map as well as the 100 km square letters pair – see box, p 5.2 - 53.

You can check these small figures (see why next page) assuming you have the map yourself to look at. But if someone gives you a military grid reference to go to and you do not have access to the actual map they are using then you must ask them for one (preferably both) of the following:

1. The above small prefix number(s) that precede the grid eastings and northings, and

2. As a double check ask them to give you an approximate lat/long reference for the position too; this latter you can enter into your GPS as a waypoint, then change the units and ask for a readout in UTM. The similarity between the UTM and MGRS figures will tell if you have valid figures and

Always do a rough cross check of latitude and longitude when given a military grid reference – there are traps! MGRS though is excellent for 'local' use.

left.)

That 'Q' and 'KE' in the MGRS? The diagram above shows how the 8° latitude bands on the MGRS are allocated letters. MGRS runs only from latitude 80° south to 84°N. Thus 'A' and 'B' are omitted so the lettering starts at 'C' for the band between 80° and 72°S, carrying on through the alphabet (omitting 'I' and 'O') till 'X' labels the jumbo-size band of 72-84°N. As you can see, bands 'M' and 'N' are respectively the first 8° south and north of the equator. So the band 'Q' in the reference above is the 16-24° latitude band north of the equator. '35Q', therefore is the oblong contained by 24-30°E (zone 35) and 16-24°N (band Q).

Four corners. The letter groups NL, PL, PK and NK each represent the corner of a 100 km square of that designation in the military grid (MGRS). This is the <u>origin</u> for square PL; eastings go right from here, northings up. Coincidence with longitude happens at the 27°E zone median. Latitude-wise,100 km squares pile up from 24°N – Zone R start.

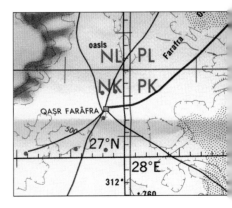

what your GPS (which sings in UTM but rarely in MGRS) will be reading.

MGRS – sting in the tail. Just in case you thought you were getting the hang of it, the relevance of this rough cross check with lat/long becomes doubly important when you discover that for some regions there is an *alternative* MGRS based on a different ellipsoid or concept of the earth's shape! Comparing a given position on both ellipsoids, you would find the second letter of the 'KE' above displaced by 10 letters in the alphabet to read 'KQ' – enough to alert you to a problem should a mistake be made. With this cheering information in mind can you not imagine a given area that has been mapped by different agencies each using a different ellipsoid?! You can't? Then see opposite; rare, but it can happen.

MGRS: a lot of spheroids? Exactly that. A spheroid or ellipsoid is a mathematical concept of how round or flattened the earth is and affects mapping datums (see next spread). The 'International' spheroid is the standard; others are Clarke 1866, Clarke 1880 and Bessel. As expeditioners you will be subject to widely differing mapping standards. Using GPS, so long as your mapping

UTM and MGRS grids align correctly north-south only at the median longitude of each zone eg 15°W in Zone 28 (12°- 18°W) – see the diagram below.

datum has been correctly set, the equipment will accommodate the correct spheroid. However, if you are reading out to a generic datum like WGS84, you may have to alert the equipment to the spheroid. The grid designations will be 'Standard MGRS' for International spheroid and 'Alternative MGRS' for Bessel and both the Clarkes.

How does all this help? Classically you may find you are given a military grid reference of a well, say, or a camp, by an organisation you are working with when your navigation gear – usually GPS – may only talk to you in lat/long or UTM. It is vital to cross check the UTM equivalent of the MGRS position. Since an error of only one figure is enough to lose you in the desert or bush, do the lat/long approximate check too to be sure. Don't be afraid to use MGRS as it will be hugely convenient but do make sure that there is no confusion – see 'Grids and datums' next spread.

Those eastings; what about the centre line? Where UTM northings start from the equator and simply measure north or south from it, the converging shapes on the ground of lines of longitude meeting at the poles like the segments of an orange need a different treatment where eastings are concerned. We have already seen that eastings are first of all designated according to which 6° longitude band (or 'column') the position is in. So continuing the above example, look at band 35 – the area contained between, to the west, longitude 24°E and, to the east, longitude 30°E. Starting an eastings grid on one or other of these lines would result in the grid being tilted due to the convergence of the lines toward the poles.

For this reason, the centre line of the zone is used – in this case longitude 27°E – for alignment. Furthermore, because it is the centre, it is given an arbitrary designation figure of 500 – on the assumption that the sector is 1000 km wide and that 500 would thus be the middle line. In fact, even at the equator no 6° sector will be wider than about 700 km so the designation is safe.

Thus any eastings figure in this zone of less than 500 will be to the west of 27° and

Grid alignment – concept

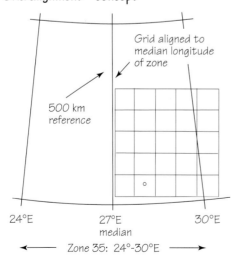

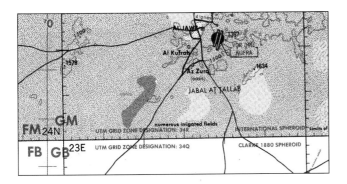

Change of spheroid from Clarke 1880 (lower, white area) to International (upper) is the reason for 100 km square designation taking a second-letter leap from GB to GM. Adjacent FB also changes to FM but the squares themselves are unbroken as they go north. The UTM grid zone change from 34Q to 34R results from new 8° band at 24°N and is unrelated to mappers' decision to change spheroids at that line. Using GPS, select 'Alt MGRS' format in Clarke area. Even if you're not confused, use lat long as a cross check!

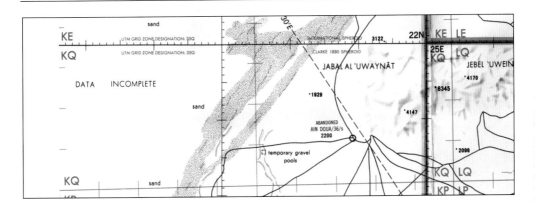

Take endless trouble when selecting maps. Even 'serious' maps such as on this page are sometimes let down down by low standard cartography.

Are you paying attention ... ? Same area, different mapping. Change of spheroid (above) at 22°N causes the 100 km 'KE' square to become 'KQ' in mid square as it changes from International to Clarke 1880. Change straddles 22°N so overall UTM grid zone designation remains 35Q ('Q' covering 16-24°N). Position ref for abandoned Ain Doua airfield above would be approximately 35Q.KQ740110 but on map below 35Q.KE740110. Choose maps with care. The dreadful TPC chart above depicts camel trails as main roads and topographical data is a non-event; no datum or sources are shown at foot of map. Amazingly, it was issued 20 years after the map below.

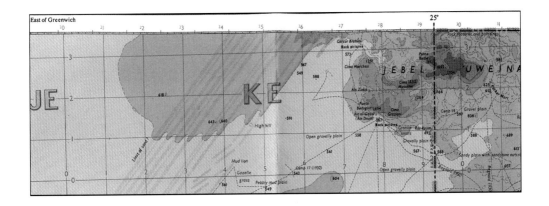

National grids and others

Different origins, different units? National grids are often organised to encompass just the country concerned and thus may or may not be tied in as neatly as UTM is with the world lat/long lattice. We have already seen Russian maps use a world grid starting at 0° longitude. The British Isles mapping grid was originally based around two north-south axes but gave way to a National Grid tied to the 2°W line of longitude – the line that most nearly ran down the middle of the country. Designed to cover a west-east spread of 700-odd kilometres, to avoid negative figures, the false origin of the OSGB 36 grid (Ordnance Survey of Great Britain) was moved 350 km to the west and found itself at a very odd lat/long. The 'median' at which the grid is perfectly aligned with the north-south line of longitude is still 2°W – not, you will note, 3°W as UTM (had it been around then) might have required!

Imperial unit grids. As already mentioned some Far East national grids are based on Imperial units, not metres. Beware; as ever, use lat/long as a fall-back.

Grids and datums

Remember the difference. Don't get confused between grids and datums, spheroids and ellipsoids – and do set the correct datum on your GPS for the map you are using; that will usually take care of the spheroid or ellipsoid. To sum up:
- *A position format* may be lat/long or a grid.
- *A grid* is a means of giving position references – UTM, MGRS, British National Grid or other national systems (Swedish, Swiss, New Zealand, S Africa etc).
- *A datum* refers to the way the map was surveyed and takes into account imperfections in the true spherical nature of the earth at the region mapped. It may also be referred to as a geodetic system such as WGS 84. This – WGS 84 – is usually the default datum for all navigation systems such as GPS and stands for World Geodetic

National grids often have apparently bizarre origins not neatly tied to lat/long as are the world grids like UTM and MGRS. They still use 100 km and km squares .

System 84, ie, it is a generalised datum, devised in 1984 and gives 'near enough' results worldwide. There are, however, nearly 200 other local datums and to ensure your position on the map best matches the results given by GPS it is essential to set the correct datum on your own unit.

Perspective. To get this in perspective, the differences in position seldom exceed 200 metres. In the 35Q MGRS example above eastings error is 45 metres, northings, 160 metres when calculated on the International spheroid as against the WGS 84 spheroid. In some cases, however – as with the Malaysian Kertaf datum – discrepancies can reach one kilometre.

GPS – choose carefully. Know the maps you will use before buying your GPS. All GPS equipments will give lat/long and it will be rare to find one that does not give UTM (eg some of the marine versions). Many will give a sprinkling of national grids too. If you have chosen well, just a few GPS equipments – currently the Eagle range, one or two of the Garmins – also give positions in MGRS. The Eagle units give both the 'Standard MGRS' and the 'Alternative MGRS' – see previous page 'MGRS, sting in the tail'; they also alert you to not having the right datum or MGRS version should this arise. In the rough and tumble of a challenging expedition using military grid maps you will find this very very welcome!

Grid north

Don't forget grid north. A quick look at the diagram opposite will remind you of the difference between grid north and map or true north. Clearly the dead-square 100 km grid squares can only be aligned exactly N-S at one longitude on the map. These differences will be greater the further E or W of the central meridian you go. Corrections or correction values should be indicated in the corner of your map; if it is not, you can easily connect the longitude ticks at the map edges and work out values yourself.

Magnetic variation/deviation too. You would never forget that, would you! For a recap see page 5.2 - 34.

DOING A GRID – LAT/LONG CROSS CHECK

World mapping series. It is easy to cross check on a map if a lat/long scale is provided. Where a series of maps at 1:1,000,000 or 1:500,000 covers the world, you will find sheets are invariably made to cover, in width, respectively 6° or 3° of longitude – either a whole or a half of one of the longitude grid 'columns'. So your map will either have the median longitude of the grid zone running down the middle of it (the 1:1,000,000 map) or along one edge (the 1:500,000).

Example: Let's say you have a 1:500,000 scale map covering the left half of Zone 35 (24-30°E), ie it will therefore cover 24°E to the median longitude of 27°E. Such a map will show lat/long and may have a military grid (MGRS) overprint. You have the position of a landmark in lat/long and your GPS has converted it to UTM grid but you want to be sure that the MGRS lettered squares have not confused you; once you have checked this, you can benefit from the higher accuracy and easy use of UTM or MGRS.

Taking the position below, the UTM eastings are 0279496. Eastings would normally only be six figures but the GPS has added a 0 to show zero millions. So we have an eastings reading of 279 thousands of metres (ie km) from the left hand edge of the 1000 km grid. Because the grid covers the tapering segment of a longitude 'column', the nailed-to-the-ground reference for eastings is the 500 km median line of the 24-30° band at 27°E. So 500 rep-

resents 27°E. OK so far because 27°E is the right hand edge of the map and your landmark is on the map, ie to the left of 27°E and 279 is less than 500 so that checks too.

What you can measure on the map, however, is the east-west distance of the landmark from (ie to the west of) the 500 line. You don't have the start (left-hand edge) of the grid on the map so you use the 500 line as reference. The distance of the 279 line from 500 will be 500-279 = 221 km. Measure 221 km west from the eastern edge of the map – either on the scale or on the grid squares – and that should be your landmark easting line.

Had your UTM eastings figure been over 500, say 650, then you would be on the next map sheet to the east ie running from 27°-30°E (the right hand half of Zone 35). Longitude 27°E would now be the left hand edge of the map and the landmarks would be a simple 150 km to the east of the 27th meridian – see diagram previous spread.

Again cross checking on the UTM figures, northings this time, the 2.4 million-odd metres is 2414 km. Divide by 1.609 = 1500.3 statute miles; multiply by 5280 over 6080 gives 1302.89 nautical miles. But 60 nm = 1° of latitude so divide by 60 [actually the figure is 59.876] and you get 21.75° latitude, or 21° 45'. The UTM position is actually the grid equivalent of 21° 49' N so we are in the right ballpark. For various reasons, such as the earth not being a true sphere, the figures don't match exactly on this scale.

Remember difference between grids (position formats) and datums. With GPS, set correct datum and you'll get the right spheroid too. Always do posn cross check.

Positions on gridded map: summary – MGRS / UTM comparison

Lat/long: 21°49.00'N, 24°52.00'E
UTM co-ordinates:
35(N)
279496E (279 km into nominal 1000 km zone)
2413898N (2.4 million metres N of equator!)
MGRS posn here:
35Q.KE.794.139

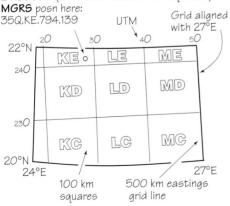

Notes:

1. 1:500,000 map partly covers left half of Zone 35Q so median 27°E at right edge aligns grid.

2. MGRS posn gives 79.4 km from left edge of the 100 km square KE, and 13.9 km from bottom.

3. The MGRS 'K' equates to the small 2 of UTM, the 'E' is the small 24 of UTM. UTM eastings are therefore 279 km from the left edge of the zone for which we can see the 500 km central grid line (RH edge of map) Position should be 500-279=221 km west of 27°N: two and a bit 100 km squares. Check!

4. Six figure MGRS ref above gives fix to 100 m. 35Q.KE.7940.1390 would fix to 10 metres 35Q.KE.79400.13900 fixes to single metres.

5. Decimal points? Is it 79.4 or 7.94 km? Remember first two figures are **percentage** of square, no matter how many follow. So 79.4 or 79.40 or 79.400 ... . (7.94 would be 079, 0794 or 07940)

Section 5.2.2

Operations:

Satellite image selection

COVERAGE OF THIS SECTION

Not like the shops. Buying satellite imagery is far easier than it used to be but is still not like going into a shop to select what you want; most cases are dealt with on an individual basis and decisions made after detailed discussion of the expedition's requirements. Two case histories (late 1997, same-area images) are given below:

Case 1. Purchase of a middle-market image, Landsat TM, 30 metre pixels, selected colour and geo-location work (around £700).

Case 2. A low cost Landsat MSS, 80 metre pixel black and white image of the same area, options for which began at £60.

Atypical customers. Not all agencies are routinely used to dealing with small expedition requirements; that the first of the following case histories (NRSC in the UK – see page 5.2-11) was directed to the Oil, Gas and Minerals Group is an indication of who their normal clients are! NPA (also page 5.2-11) seemed more geared up for those on a lower budget and as the second case history shows, the cheaper product in this case goes a long way to meeting the need simply for better maps.

Geo-location inconsistency. A preliminary note about geo-location data. Spell out, and have spelled out, exactly what you want and will get in terms of geo-location. The colour image in Case 1 came at first with geo-location on a large reference print (see below) but not on the CD-ROM digital image; bad news when the whole point of getting the CD-ROM is to print out your own working maps. On the MSS black and white image (Case 2) edge markings on the prints were inconsistent – lat/long ticks in one case, and in another, a single reference lat/long (you need at least one other to interpolate) and an odd 100 km grid NPA could not explain. Nor, amazingly, could Customer Services at the US Geological Survey in South Dakota (from UK 00.1.605.594.6151); see p 5.2-61. Don't be put off by the 'outer office syndrome'. It is their product offering a mine of information. Be sure you (and they!) understand it all.

Buy rationale. The rationale and decision stream, in a brief sequence, for a possible expedition to locate artifacts in a remote area, is indicated opposite.

Buying sat-pics, scan sources, definitions and dates – p 5.2-14. Discussion of precise need will determine colour, false colour, black and white, geo-location system.

Buying sat-pics and what you get. Centre foreground, 'Quick-look' form shows a small low-resolution indication of image plus, on a second page, data on lat/long of centre, corner points, time of day, sun azimuth and elevation – enough information to commit to the actual buy. Big colour print in background is 1:100,000 image, rectified to transverse mercator projection, with geo-location (lat/long and UTM grid) at edges. This image is also stored on the CD-ROM from which the colour A3 print at left for field use was made. The 200 mm square black and white image is a low budget 1:1,000,000 contact print, in this case coming with a single latitude and longitude line. Image can be put on desk-top scanner and enlarged and printed out for field-use copies of map. As warned on p 5.2-12, the exceptional clarity of desert shots here (rock outcrop vs sand and gravel) will not be so obvious on forest/jungle images.

Case study 1: Sat-pic buy – middle market

Map problems

Need for something better. Available mapping in the required region is to no larger scale than 1:500,000 and of varying quality. In view of the age of the maps, a cross check on geo-location would be an advantage on the satellite image. At the same time, because of the MGRS (grid) overlay on the map (see Sec 5.2.1. 'Map grids') it would be useful to have a satellite image with a similar geo-location overlay.

Satellite image selection

Contact NRSC; limited budget? In this case, the following sequence was followed:

• Clarify precise requirement – in this case improved terrain differentiation – where vehicles can go (sand/gravel vs rock) as opposed to mineral/vegetation identification.

• Older images are less expensive. In this case urban development was not sought so 10 yr old image acceptable.

• Skim sources table (page 5.2-14) – Landsat TM seems best mix of definition and value, 30 metre pixels, 10 yr old image.

• Contact with NRSC brings list of possible images – Landsat TM coverage.

• Select two from the 30-odd options – clear skies, lowish sun angle.

• Request 'Quick-look' summary – small low resolution image and other details.

• 'Quick-look' form arrives showing (see illustration opposite):

    100 mm sq image of shot (185 km sq)
    Data on time, date of shot, sun azimuth, elevation
    Comments on overall quality
    Corner point and centre lat/longs

• Decide OK: ballpark cost £330 for image, plus about the same for geo-location.

Bought image options. The image you buy can be hard copy print or transparency in which case you must specify a lot of variables in advance. If it is digital, on a CD-ROM, for example, you have more flexibility and options and reproducibility. The decision process was:

a. Medium

    Hard copy print – size, scale, colour, number of spectral bands?
    Hard copy transparency – ditto.
    Digital – software, RAM, hard-disc requirements?
    Image configurations (digital):
        File formats: TIFF, GIF, JPEG, PICT.
        Software: Any that can handle raster file formats.

b. Geo-location (overprint of lat/long, grid etc. This work is carried out after obtaining the image from archive by NRSC to the customer's requirements.)

    Cost depends on accuracy required.
    'Raw' Landsat accurate to 300 metres.
    Anything better than this needs correlation with existing maps.
    Rectification to desired map projection carried out by NRSC.

c. Final cost depends on degree of 'afterwork' by NRSC.

Digital image versatility and advantages:

• Original always safe and unsullied.

• Any number of local areas within the 185 km sq can be selected/printed.

• Working copies and spares can be printed for expedition.

• Give-away spares can be taken for locals to help dispel 'spy pictures' connotations of satellite shots.

Actual options selected

CD-ROM. In this case a digital CD-ROM image was selected and appropriate maps available at the time were sent to NRSC to aid with 'post-production' and geo-location work on the image.

• Digital image file size. A CD-ROM is capable of taking a digital file up to 650 Mb in size. From the seven spectral wavelength bands available from the Landsat data three were expected to be best for the purposes required of simple topographical map

Digital image on CD-ROM has much to commend it as secure source, easy to reproduce and print out. Be absolutely clear on the geo-location you will be getting.

enhancement – probably bands 7, 4 and 2. This was expected to occupy around 200 Mb on the disc with various options being on-disc as available.

• *Physical image size.* The image would be sized at about 6500 by 6500 pixels which would yield an actual look-at image sized according to the resolution selected. Thus at 300 ppi (pixels per inch) resolution, the print would be 6500 divided by 300 equals 21 inches square.

Other information acquired at this stage:

• *Digital shot on CD-ROM* – basic image around £330.

Digital image has been downloaded from CD-ROM to computer hard disc and may be enlarged, enhanced for sharpness, brightness and contrast and then printed out for field-use images. This is part of a 33 Mb TIFF image of Landsat TM 30 metre pixel satellite original (3 bands shown).

• *NRSC work*: geo-location to 300 metres etc – around £200 .

• *Geo-location selected* was lat/long ticks in the margin and UTM grid crosses, on-image every ten kilometres.

Computer requirements. A double check on computer requirements to handle this material was made and readout was:

• *Standard CD drive.*

• *Hard disc space*: around 400 Mb though you do not have to copy to hard disc. This figure was treated with extreme caution since earlier experience (in Photoshop) has shown that to accommodate possible 'undos' and other temporary storage requirements, most images, where any manipulation is envisaged, require about 4-5 times the basic image size to give the computer 'room to breathe'. A Macintosh with a 4Gb hard disc was being used so optimism was allowed to intrude slightly.

• *RAM requirement:* 8-16 Mb was stated as adequate but as ever, the more you

If you go for CD-ROM digital image double check computer and software compatibility – preferably with a sample disc. Be prepared for the usual 'Oh, that!' explanations.

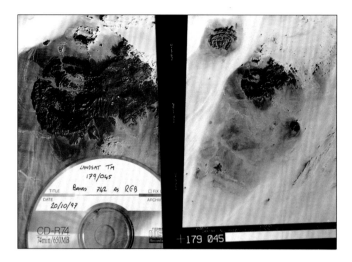

Ignoring scale for the moment, the difference between a map – this massif being depicted as a not-too-clear jumble of contours – and a satellite image is huge (see also page 5.2-11). Despite the excellent value and practicality of a low budget (c. £60) black and white image, the colour image immediately shows the mountain to be made of two separate but contiguous geological structures – the dark concentric rings and adjacent lighter rock of a different type.

have the better.

• **Software:** the usual requirement is just for image handling and thus Photoshop or similar is entirely adequate. Specialist software packages such as ER Mapper or Imagine are used by NRSC for projection rectification and the like but would not normally be required by a purchaser.

• **Printer:** the better the printer the better the print. An A3 high resolution colour printer such as (early 1998) the Epson 1520 is astonishing value for money and performance is outstanding. Equally, a good 600 dpi black and white laser printer and soft-

ware enabling you to 'tile' an image using A4 paper will produce very usable results and cheaper copies – especially valuable for write-on in-the-field use.

Consultations

Once the image had been selected and sent from US Geological Service archive, NRSC made spectral band decisions on the basis of 'natural look' requirements – bands 7, 4 and 2. Special request was made for a Photoshop compatible image. Results – superb – can be seen above and on the previous page.

Black and white image with a magnifier and photocopies for annotations is an exceptionally good deal. Better still if you can scan, enlarge, and laser-print copies.

Case study 2: Sat-pic buy – low-budget

Basic requirement

Map supplement. The basic need was the same as in Case 1 (same region) – to supplement old maps only available at 1:500,000 and obtain more detail on the ground as to where it might be feasible or unfeasible to take vehicles in a remote, uninhabited area. Detail of small valleys was again required.

Satellite image selection

Contact NPA: rock-bottom budget. It became apparent that NPA could supply archive or bought-in images of the area from older Landsat MSS coverage at very good prices (Multi-Spectral Scanner, see p 5.2-14 – 80 metres per pixel, around £60 per print). This was if a very basic spec was accepted – single-band black and white, just corner and centre-of-image lat/long data, 1:1,000,000 scale contact print.

If you are dealing with a one-off hard copy print like this (as opposed to a CD-ROM from which as many prints as needed can be run off) there are certain advantages to having a small scale image. A large image is less easy to handle and keep undamaged in the field; a small image and photographic Lupe magnifier (x8 is best) is a very practical combination.

Good photocopy enlargements are entirely practical for in-the-field use and write-on notes, keeping the original in a plastic sleeve or where the lupe is required.

Scan your own. More flexibility yet is obtained if you have a desk-top scanner. The 1:1m image – usually a 200 mm square contact print from the originator so carrying good definition – can be scanned enabling you to manipulate size, tone, contrast and selected area print-outs. On these you can then transpose your own geo-location system derived from the satellite image and your own maps. The difference between the 30 m pixels of the Landsat TM colour image and the 80 m pixels here was hard to detect.

Conclusion

The simplicity and low cost of this approach has much to commend it but see also caption opposite. 'Raw' images like this have geo-location systems that vary according to date of data acquisition so be careful at the buying stage. This image (opposite, right-hand part of shot) as mentioned on p 5.2-57 had an oddball geo-location system with a single line of latitude and single line of longitude. The 100 km grid ticks, amazingly, could not be explained by NPA or the USGS. The image, however, was invaluable even with its single lat/long lines. A photocopy on acetate laid over a 1:1,000,000 map provided a simple way of marking up the rest of the lat/long lattice.

Be prepared for differing geo-location systems on some of the older Landsat shots. Even a 'single lat/long line, plus some ingenuity, can nail your image to the maps.

Stop and reflect; don't take technology for granted. The yellowed photographs were taken only 70 years ago. Hassenein Bey (lower left), by horse and camel, was the first to take a theodolite to the massif now shown in micro-detail from space. (The valley is at the 8 o'clock position on the satellite shot.) Thirties panache later brought a Mess Dinner in by Vickers Valencia a 100 km further south to the car-pioneering explorer Ralph Bagnold and colleagues in an eventual rendezvous. Hassenein's journey was 2500 km on foot; Bagnold's cars – 4x2s – covered 6000 miles on this trip, an amazing feat of logistics and tenacity. ('Libyan Sands' and 'The Lost Oases' courtesy of the Royal Geographical Society library.)

Section 5.3

Operations:

Driving

COVERAGE OF THIS SECTION

Know your transmission
Although this is a practical Section on driving, knowing your transmission first is essential. Be crystal clear on what your system will, and will not, do.

Overall philosophy

Attitude – cool it. Restrained, sympathetic and alert driving is probably the most important characteristic to inculcate into any expedition team going on a long and arduous vehicle-based expedition, especially if it is likely to cover many miles on tracks or across open country. In this context we are unhelpfully surrounded by four-wheel drive magazines that feature brutish driving, airborne vehicles, flying dust and mud and bolt-on baubles as though these were the ingredients of professionalism. In a sense, since it is normal for the media to dramatise trivia and lionise the loud, we have at least a guide on what to avoid. The vehicle is the very core of the expedition; certainly considerable cost, if not life itself, will be at stake if it is not looked after well and driven considerately. Whilst the best 4x4s do convey a feeling of being unstoppable, anything will break given enough abuse, so the urge to prove one's manhood (or liberated status) by driving with excessive panache must be resisted.

Training. But points of technique are important as well as just care since there will be times, especially in soft conditions, where all the vehicle's power output will have to be used. There is widespread ignorance, even among the dealers that sell them, concerning the 4x4 systems, capabilities and driving methods applicable to four-wheel drive utility vehicles in limiting conditions such as you may encounter on an expedition. It is essential to undertake driver training before your expedition (see schedule at Section 5.3.1) to learn how your vehicle's and your own limitations can be accommodated to achieve a totally safe and reliable operating method.

Apart from manufacturers' own schools – Land Rover (the original), Mitsubishi, Vauxhall in UK – there are also many off-road driving schools, listed or advertised monthly in the UK in magazines such as *Off Road and 4 Wheel Drive* or *Land Rover Owner International*. Get tuition and, just as important, get practice on your own so you are making your own decisions in your own time. Many of the off-road schools provide a day-pass so that you can use their terrain to practise your techniques and become completely comfortable with them.

Forget the yahoo magazine photographs and rally antics. On expeditions, your vehicle is your life. Train, know what it can do but then treat it considerately.

Driver training must be an integral part of expedition planning (see page 3.1 - 8); every mile you drive will be affected. Where placing of wheels is critical (above) use a marshaller (p 5.3 - 18); slowly, with a small bow-wave through water (p 5.3 - 34).

Train on a marked-out course first to get a feel for it. Here the depth is getting very close to the maximum and its nice to know the bottom is firm with no unseen potholes. On a trip you would be preceded by a crew member with a long pole and an anxious expression!

Training: end product? What, specifically, should you expect from driver training? See below: 1, 2, 3. Training should cover two segments, overlaid by a third:

1. Transmission and suspension. Familiarisation with the transmission and the inter-dependent suspension arrangements of your vehicle so that you know what is at your disposal. Read and be comfortable with Section 4.1, pages 15-29. Match your vehicle to the appropriate descriptions. This is fundamental to getting the best out of your vehicle – and not breaking it.

2. Techniques. Application of your vehicle – with its newly learned capabilities – to various set-piece types of obstacle:

- Diagonal ditches and ridges
- Slopes – up, down, lateral
- Weak ground – sand, mud, salt
- Rocks and corrugations
- Water, dust

3. The overlay – attitude. Noting all the above, developing the right attitude – ie keeping within the vehicle's limitations and not damaging it. (See 'Mechanical sympathy', page 5.3 – 17.)

Why am I stuck? You will get stuck many times; everyone does. But if at any time you don't know why you are stuck or did not have a fair idea of what manner of sticking you could expect, then you will likely not have taken on board how your transmission and suspension work and what their limitations are. As above, make a

Knowing your 4x4 transmission system and suspension is half the battle. Know their weak points (diagonal wheel spin usually), be kind. The rest is easy.

cup of coffee, sit down and re-read Section 4.1, pages 15-29; slowly!

The book. Driving is a difficult subject to cover comprehensively in one section such as this and *The Land Rover Experience*, published by Land Rover, is recommended as a prime reference book on the subject of driving 4x4s. Though titled and copiously illustrated with that marque, the techniques covered apply to any 4x4.

Convoy driving. On a multi-vehicle expedition observe the simple but essential rules of convoy driving – responsibility for the vehicle behind. See Section 5.3.1 'Driver training' on page 5.3 – 41.

Driving schedule. Driving is tiring; on an expedition with a two-man crew, have Driver A hand over to Driver B at midday and vice versa next day thus ensuring a mid-session night's sleep in any 24 hour duty cycle. Off-tarmac, never drive at night; it is too easy to hit unseen potholes or ill-lit changes in slope and to get lost. Off-road during the day you rely on light and shadow from the sun and sky to establish the relief of the ground in front of you; at night, with the only light coming from your own headlights, that modelling is absent and it is too easy to make mistakes. On hard roads night-drive only if absolutely necessary; in inhabited regions of Africa, India and the Middle East unlit vehicles, bicycles and bullock-carts abound and compete with sleeping livestock for your road space.

Transmission, gearboxes

What 4x4 is for

Nomenclature. First something on nomenclature; four-wheel drive vehicles are known as '4x4s', spoken as 'four by four', ie four (wheels driven) by four and a normal two-wheel drive car is a 4x2 or four (wheels driven) by two. Apart from the size, weight, load carrying capacity and distance from the ground, the main differences the tyro expedition aspirant will notice about 4x4 vehicles when compared with ordinary 4x2 on-road cars concern the transmission arrangements – gearboxes, transfer gearbox, gear levers and associated controls, centre differentials, traction control, locking/freewheeling hubs … etc. It all sounds baffling at first but there is a pleasing logic to it and all the 'complications' are there specifically for your benefit

Calmly under control. 1st gear low box, foot off the brake and clutch. With an auto transmission you must select '1'-hold to prevent it changing up (see p 5.3 - 25).

and to ensure that you do not get stuck when you are on difficult tracks or in the wilderness. Again refer to Section 4.1, pages 15-29 if in any doubt about your vehicle's transmission system. Compare it with the table on page 5.3 - 14 for confirmation.

Why 4x4? The aim of it all is to spread the engine power *evenly* – note that, it will come up repeatedly – between all four wheels and thus ask less of the ground in terms of traction than if all the power was going through just two wheels. The system aims also to preserve this situation by eliminating wheel spin (lost traction). This is where traction control, locking differentials and the like come in. All such devices are aimed at curbing wheel spin before, or as soon as, it starts.

Manual or automatic. You may be surprised to see a heading such as this since most people associate 4x4s with somewhat intimidating manual gearbox arrangements – what in the UK a few years ago might have been termed 'the Yorkie bar syndrome', all checked-shirts and hairy arms. Virtually all the world-class 4x4 manufacturers, however, fit automatics and such transmissions offer significant benefits in terms of vehicle durability and protection from transmission shock loads and driver misuse – all on top of the principal advantage of making life simpler for the driver so that he or she may concentrate more on placing the vehicle when conditions are demanding.

Quick, imperceptible gear-changes when traction is at a premium – soft sand or slippery mud – is what is required. That is what automatics do best and is what the operator of a manual gearbox will seldom do as well. Do not let it hurt your pride; benefit from it, enjoy it! About the only disadvantage of automatics is the extra initial cost and the implications, should anything go wrong (very rare), of trying to get them repaired in remote regions. See Section 4.1 'Expedition vehicles', p 4.1 - 23 for more on automatics.

Don't dismiss automatic transmission – or regard it as an invitation to switch the brain off. Know what it is up to, use low box and benefit from its gentleness.

Main gearbox

Synchromesh? As with the overall transmission and suspension systems, know your gearbox and, if it is manual and on an older vehicle such as a Series 2 Land Rover, especially know which gears have synchromesh. If you have an automatic transmission or all-synchro manual gearbox you may want to skip to the next side heading 'Transfer gearbox ..'.Some large old trucks – the kind that seem to gravitate towards service on expeditions – do not have synchro gearboxes and you should know about it; if you do it will make driving a lot easier, smoother and be a great deal better for the durability of your gearbox and transmission.

Just as there was a time when all aeroplanes were pulled through the air with propellers and TV sets were black and white, rumbling into the twenty-first century you can be forgiven for taking synchromesh for granted. Don't feel therefore that you would lose credibility by reading this next bit that tells you what synchro actually does and why it hasn't always been there.

Obviously a gearbox contains wheels and shafts going at different speeds. 'Changing gear' entails, in effect, sliding one gear into mesh with another and, unless they are going at compatible speeds there will be a 'grinding of the gears' or a huge and solid 'clonk' when the move is made. Synchromesh is a means, through the fric-

Synchromesh is now so widespread you may have to check what it means! Classic expedition vehicles – Series 2 Land Rovers, Bedfords have some non-synchro gears.

tional drag created by cones mounted on the cogs – a 'male' cone on one gear engaging with a 'female' cone on the other – of slowing or speeding up one gear wheel relative to the one it is about to engage with before it actually engages.

Although the idea is decades old, synchro was once only fitted to passenger car gearboxes and then usually only the upper two or three gears. So first gear and maybe second too was non-synchro and virtually all trucks or working vehicles had no synchro on any gear. Cost was the reason for keeping synchro out of a lot of gearboxes but with the recognition that truck drivers are people and all people respond (in quantifiable, bean-counter terms) to good ergonomics, all cars now have all synchro and most trucks do too.

What you may encounter, therefore, as assemblers of expedition vehicle convoys, is older vehicles that were not built with all-synchromesh gearboxes. What should you do?

No synchro; what to do. If there is no synchro on a gear (or all gears) in a gearbox you should change gear into that gear in a different way. To most people who took their driving test on a modern car, changing gear consists of dipping the clutch and moving the gear lever from one position to another. What actually happens (in the gearbox) is that as you move the lever the syn-

Shoulder to the wheel – a term that could be used for the synchromesh cones on gear wheels. Early Land Rovers like these Series 1s (and Series 2s) had synchro only on 3rd and 4th gear. But no synchro on 1st and 2nd was better than a baulky obstructive synchromesh and, with the right double de-clutching, very quick down-changes could result.

chro cones touch, synchronise the speed of the approaching gear wheels, and then, with the last part of the gear lever movement, the gears are engaged. As you may have already found, even on a synchro box, you can often get a smoother take-up of power by adjusting the throttle a little bit as you engage the next gear to 'cushion the change' – that is, for example, if you are going down from third to second, blip the throttle slightly to raise the revs while the gear lever is passing neutral; going up, make sure the engine revs do die off a bit going from second to third. That way, when you let the clutch in again you will avoid the lurch and transmission snatch that sometimes occurs due to engine revs not matching the road speed in that gear.

Double de-clutching. In a non-synchro box, without the speed synchronisation of the gear wheels going on at the behest of the synchromesh, there is more we can do with the throttle and clutch to ensure a smooth gear change. It is called 'double de-clutching' and, as its name indicates, it involves de-clutching twice with some rev adjusting in between. It will sound complicated to describe but, like riding a bicycle, after a little initial concentration it becomes far more difficult to describe than to do!

In general it can be described as spending a fraction of a second in neutral with the clutch up, before dipping the clutch again and moving the gear lever on to the gear you are about to select. A bit like this:

Clutch	Throttle	Gear lever
Dip	–	Move to neutral
Up	Adjust revs	–
Dip	–	Move to next gear
Up	Resume drive	–

What this does is get the gear wheels and layshafts within the gearbox going at the right speed for a clonk- or grind-free engagement. You may hear people say there is no need to double de-clutch on up-changes; they are wrong! Obviously going down you need to adjust revs by increasing them, and going up you need to take your foot off the throttle. So, specifically:

• *Double de-clutch – down-change.* This is the procedure for a down-change on a gearbox with no synchro, say third to second:

Clutch	Throttle	Gear lever
Dip	–	Move to neutral
Up	BOOST REVS	–
Dip	–	Move to next gear
Up	Resume drive	–

You will get to know the amount by which the throttle needs to be boosted but, if you think about it, you must select the kind of engine revs that would apply at that road speed in the gear you are about to select. Going from second to first at any but the slowest road speed you will find you have to boost the throttle a surprising amount; only do this at about walking speed.

• *Double de-clutch – up-change.* This is the procedure for an up-change on a gearbox with no synchro, say second to third:

Clutch	Throttle	Gear lever
Dip	–	Move to neutral
Up	FOOT OFF	–
Dip	–	Move to next gear
Up	Resume drive	–

If you don't double de-clutch on a down-change you will get the most awful grinding of gears and the gear may not go in at all. If you don't on an up-change you will 'just' get a heavy clonk when the gear goes in. This equates to a small sledge-hammer being applied to the transmission; don't let it happen!

Practise – off-road too. Practise the procedure first with the vehicle stationary in your driveway without the engine even running, just to get the sequence into your head. Then practise on quiet roads so that you get to know the best speeds and engine rpm boosts suited to change-downs. Change ups will be easier. Practise until a smooth silent change can be made into all gears - including first. Because the whole thing is tied up with road and engine speeds and vehicle speed decay during the time spent in neutral, it will be different on-road compared to when on rough terrain or even grass. The technique will be slightly differ-

Double de-clutching is hard to describe, far easier to do. Remember revs adjustments take place with gear lever in neutral and clutch pedal up. Practise static first.

ent off-road.

The sort of on-road to off-road adjustments to technique to expect would be:
- Down-changes – a little less rev boost.
- Up changes – a little less rev drop.

Touching third ... . A trick worth knowing, especially in old Series 2 Land Rovers, is how to avoid that dreadful grinding of gears when engaging a gear to move off from stationary. Get into the habit of 'touching third' – before engaging first or reverse, ie, dip the clutch in the normal way, touch the gear lever into third gear (the synchro cones on that gear will stop the gears revolving in the gearbox) and then, when you engage first or reverse the gear will go in quietly without any noise.

Gearboxes without synchro on 1st or reverse can make dreadful grinding noises engaging either gear from stationary. Touching third first will still the layshafts.

This is a particularly valuable tip when doing any backing and filling – three or four-point turns getting out of tight spaces where the noise of tortured metal can grind your nerves as well as your gearbox.

The procedure will apply to any vehicle where you have synchro on an upper gear ratio like third or top and no synchromesh on first or reverse. (Indeed it is only on the recent R380 gearbox that Land Rover have completely nailed the problem on their vehicles: that gearbox has synchro on reverse too.)

Avoid slipping the clutch. A final word on gear changing. Keep your foot off the clutch pedal unless starting, stopping or changing gear. By all means 'cover the clutch' ready for an instant gear change or stop you can see coming up but resting your foot on it or slipping it will do it harm and shorten its life. Keeping your foot off it may require will-power at first but it will save the life of your clutch.

Transfer gearbox – what it does

Transferring and reducing. A 'transfer box' usually bolts onto the side of the main gearbox and literally 'transfers' drive from the gearbox to the propeller shafts. Because the prop shafts go fore and aft and have to do so alongside the engine, the transfer gearbox is usually laterally displaced alongside the main gearbox – see diagram on page 4.1 - 17. A transfer box usually has two functions:
- Transferring drive to the front prop shaft
- Providing a 'low ratio' (or low range) gearing.

Strictly speaking the above should be called a two-speed transfer box. The two functions can be separately controlled – ie a

In good time – top of the hill – driver will have selected 4x4 (drive to the front wheels) and low ratio. Probably 2nd gear low OK for this. Marshaller can see what is happening to all the wheels and avoid rears dropping into hole avoided by front ones. To get into 1st, double de-clutch necessary but here vehicle would gain too much speed on de-clutching so a stop would be best.

Classic simple transfer lever selection sequence on a 'part-time 4x4' vehicle – see below. Here, with no centre differential (see caption on p 5.3 - 10), 4H and 4L should not be used on hard grippy surfaces. So long as you don't have free-wheeling hubs, changing 2H to 4H on the move is OK – but dip clutch first. Stop to engage 4L.

at p 4.1 - 17 'Types of four-wheel drive' together with the owner's manual for your vehicle. You will probably find your vehicle fits into one of the categories below (see diagram at page 4.1 - 19):

• Simple selectable or part-time 4x4 (eg Jeep Wrangler)

• Pseudo or 'automatic' 4x4 (self-engagement, eg Honda CR-V)

• Permanent, full-time 4x4 ('gears, shafts, levers', eg Defender)

means of selecting drive to the front axle (going from two-wheel drive to four-wheel drive) and also a means of selecting the low ratio set of gears. This latter applies a low gear overlay to *all* the gears in the main gearbox so when you select it all the gears are geared down by a set amount – usually about 2:1 – see both diagrams on page 4.1 - 24. Invariably, transfer boxes are arranged so that selecting low ratio also selects four-wheel drive.

A common combination of selections at the transfer box would be:
• High range 4x2
• High range 4x4
• Low range 4x4

There are, of course, variations. For example the whole Land Rover product range since 1983 features permanent or 'full time' four-wheel drive so you cannot select 4x2. A new breed of vehicles in the sport-utility sector of the market – Toyota RAV4, Honda CR-V and Land Rover Freelander – has no low ratio facility fitted (and indeed, arguably no 'transfer gearbox' since the drive to the front wheels comes straight out of the main gearbox).

Types of 4x4. A proliferation of 4x4 types is available on the market nowadays and before attempting to hone your driving skills as outlined above at 'Training: end product?', clear your mind on exactly what your vehicle is fitted with. Read Section 4.1.

Transfer box 1: selecting 4x4

Selectable and permanent 4x4. It is essential to be aware, from the driving point of view, of the differences between a vehicle with part-time 4x4 – i.e. a two-wheel drive vehicle in which you can select four-wheel drive when required – and a vehicle with permanent or full-time 4x4 in which it is in four-wheel-drive all the time. A fuller description appears on pages 4.1 -18 and 19 but you should recall now that:

• The 4x4 with *permanent* 4x4 will usually have a differential or viscous coupling between the front and rear prop shafts which accommodates the small speed differences between front and rear shafts that occur when driving and manoeuvring on all surfaces.

• The 4x2 with *selected* 4x4 will usually have the front prop shaft locked to the rear prop shaft. This rules out any speed variation between front and rear shafts.

• (There is also, as we have seen, 'pseudo 4x4' where the transition from 4x2 to 4x4 is automatic. Though not up to the *performance* of permanent or selected 4x4, from the point of view of driving you need not even know it is fitted!)

Part-time, selectable, 4x4. Let us take as part-time 4x4s the case of an early (Series 2 or 3) Land Rover or a current Japanese off-roader most of which still favour this arrangement. For normal on-road high-ratio

Refresh your memory (p 4.1 - 19) on <u>selectable</u> 4x4, '<u>pseudo</u> 4x4 and <u>permanent</u> 4x4 and know what your vehicle has (chart pp 5.3. - 14 and 15). It affects your life!

Different paths taken – and thus distance covered – by front and rear wheels in a simple turn to the right is shown here. This is the reason a 4x4 has to have a centre differential if it is to operate on hard grippy surfaces. Without a centre diff (as in a part-time 4x4 vehicle) different distances have to be accommodated by one or more wheels scuffing or spinning. Bad for the tyres, bad for the transmission.

Selectable or part time 4x4 should not be used in 4x4 mode on firm grippy surfaces. Prop shaft wind-up and very stiff steering will result if you do.

driving the vehicle is driven in two-wheel drive (4x2) and use of the transfer box lever (or in the case of the Land Rovers mentioned here, the 'yellow knob' plunger) enables you to engage 4x4 for high range (4H in current parlance) on-road conditions such as snow or icy roads.

When this 4x4 selection is made (page 4.1 - 19, top diagram), as mentioned above, the front and rear propeller shafts are locked, non-variably, together. As well as improving traction, ie getting the front wheels to drive as well as the rear wheels, this also means that the small differences of rpm between the front and rear wheels (due to steering etc) cannot be accommodated. If, in a part-time 4x4 vehicle, 4x4 is selected on hard grippy roads the transmission system is placed under higher than normal strain (transmission 'wind-up') and rotational tyre scrub will take place. If you drive any 'part-time' 4x4 vehicle in 4x4 on hard grippy surfaces and try a full-lock turn you will feel the stiffness in the steering sometimes accompanied by a strange 'jerky' feedback from the front wheels. On loose surfaces the wheels can slip rotationally and so accommodate this difference in axle speeds.

Note that this basic problem is caused by the front and rear prop shafts being geared, non-variably, together. The small differ-

ences in axle rotation speeds can be accommodated if a 'centre differential' is fitted, essentially allowing a bit of give and take between the front and rear shaft speeds. 'Centre diffs' are, for cost reasons, rarely fitted to part-time 4x4 vehicles. *Thus part-time 4x4s should only be driven in full four-wheel drive on loose surfaces such as sand, gravel or snow since to do so on grippy surfaces is to risk damage to transmission and tyres.*

Another implication of this is that if you have, in a part-time 4x4, to select 4x4 only in appropriate conditions, you must know when you are just about to encounter those conditions. You must then de-select it when it is no longer needed. It is a complication you would be better off without as well as not covering the 'unseen need' case. As mentioned in Section 4.1, 'Expedition vehicles', there is much to be said, from the point of view of choosing an expedition vehicle, for having full-time 4x4. From the driving point of view, however, note the differences and act accordingly.

When to use selectable 4x4. Having said all this - and it will be clear that the main use of selectable or part-time 4x4 is in poor traction, soft sand or mud conditions - there are additional times when 4x4 should be selected. These are when travelling corrugated (see 'Corrugations' below) or exceptionally rough tracks. In these conditions the shock load reversals on half-shafts are extreme as the wheel jumps from one bump to another; use of four-wheel drive spreads these loads over four half-shafts rather than two thus halving the fatigue loads.

Full-Time 4x4. In a permanent 4x4 vehicle where drive is always to all four wheels, such as the post-1983 Land Rover product range, the transmission wind-up and tyre scrub inherent on a part-time 4x4 operating with 4x4 selected is eliminated by putting a differential gear between front and rear prop shafts (page 4.1 - 19, bottom diagram). Normally this effects and allows a variable gearing between the front and rear axles that can accommodate the slight difference in rotational speeds. Thus a full-time 4x4 with this centre differential can be driven on firm surfaces without increased tyre scrub or stress on the transmission and without odd steering characteristics. There are, however, a couple of things to know about full-time 4x4 centre differentials (also covered in the panel on page 4.1 - 20):

1. Lockable centre diff. To those new to the concept it may seem odd, having gone to the trouble of having full-time 4x4 and a centre differential to then make provision to lock this centre diff – in effect reverting to the situation applying to the part-time 4x4 with 4x4 selected as noted above.

But by definition a differential allows a split of output between the shafts that can vary from 50/50 to 0/100 – in other words one shaft stopped and the other spinning at twice the speed. So there are occasions when to cope with extreme off-road low-traction conditions that are different front and rear, the 'free' centre diff must be locked; as shown in the photo, loose sand on a hill where weight transference will off-load the front wheels and encourage them to spin whilst the rear wheels are stationary. With the centre diff locked the front and rear prop shafts are then geared directly and invariably together (like the selectable 4x4) so the output is 50/50 front/rear. Thus a driver who engages this diff-lock in soft going and forgets to disengage it on tarmac will, as in the part-time 4x4 case above, be causing excessive tyre wear and stress on the transmission shafts.

Because you may, unknowingly, be experiencing a difference between front and rear axle speeds (see photo below) *always dip the clutch when engaging centre diff-lock* (or in the case of a Cherokee fitted with Selec-Trac, going from '4x4 full-time' to '4x4 part-time' – see caption p 5.3 - 12).

In summary, full-time 4x4 with centre diff is good, so is a lockable centre diff; but, de-clutch when engage it and you must remember when to unlock it.

2. Lockable centre diff – VC. To preclude the human error of forgetting to unlock the centre differential vehicles such as the post 1986 Range Rover early Jeep Grand

Distance travelled by front and rear wheels is different so permanent 4x4 requires a differential between front/rear shafts, and way to lock it. Unlock it on firm surfaces.

Why centre diff lock? Here it has been deliberately (and incorrectly) left unlocked. Weight transference offloads front wheels allowing them to spin while rear axle is stationary. On Discovery and Defender diff lock is manually selected by transfer lever; on Range Rover and early Grand Cherokee (Note 5, Table, p 5.3 - 15) a viscous coupling sits across centre diff effecting gradual lock-up when speed difference sensed.

Big bruiser, big load – lovely 4x4 system. Full time 4x4 with centre diff that is lockable pneumatically with the pull of a tiny plunger. To ensure no front rear prop-shaft speed dis-crepancy, though, dip the clutch before engaging to remove drive from any axle. Big wheels equals big under-axle clear-ance. Just as well; on the limit here.

Cherokees replace the manual locking mechanism with an automatic one that, through a viscous coupling, senses the conditions that demand a locked diff and also the conditions when it can be unlocked. (See Section 4.1, page 4.1 - 18, 'What is a Viscous Coupling?'.)

If you are thinking the Ford Explorer and Honda CR-V have a similar set-up you are only half right! Both have, instead of a VC, a multi-plate clutch between front and rear prop shafts that (Ford electrically and Honda hydraulically) 'clamps up' when prop shaft speed differences are sensed. But neither of these vehicles has a centre differential or 'hard drive' 4x4 at all (Chart p 5.3 - 14). Both are 'pseudo 4x4s' as shown in the diagram at page 4.1 - 19. With the Explorer you can select this clutch clamp-up so it equates to a centre diff lock – without the centre diff!

Using a full-time 4x4 vehicle in the case of corrugations mentioned above, it would not be necessary or desirable to lock the centre differential; however, during use of such a vehicle in very soft sand, it will obviously be beneficial to lock the centre differential to prevent – photo previous page – one axle spinning at the expense of the other.

'Pseudo' 4x4 may be termed 'soft drive' – no shafts-and-gears connection between front and rear prop-shafts; viscous coupling (VC) or clutch instead.

Transfer box 2: selecting low ratio gears

Options. As mentioned above, the transfer lever that selects 4x4 on a part-time 4x4 vehicle is usually also used to select 'low ratio' or 'low range' which gears the vehicle down in all gears selected on the main gearbox (see both diagrams page 4.1 - 24). The function will be clearly marked on the transfer lever '2H, 4H, N, 4L' etc, respectively indicating two-wheel drive in high ratio, four-wheel drive in high ratio and four-wheel drive in low ratio (as the photo on p 5.3 - 9 shows – Daihatsu). In the case of the series 1,2 or 3 Land Rover there are three '-gear levers; the 'yellow knob' plunger selects 4x4 in high range when pressed down (dip the clutch when you do it), the 'red knob' lever selects 4x4 and low ratio at the same time when it is moved aft (STOP before you do it).

Follow the manufacturer's recommendations regarding when range changes can be made; in many older vehicles this – certainly the engagement of low ratio – must be done while stationary. Whatever the technique recommended, the overriding consideration is to make these changes without clunking, crashing gears or shock loading the trans-

You want everything? Here it is! To suit supporters of selectable 4x4 ('Saves fuel') *and* permanent 4x4 ('Always there, safer'), Mitsubishi's 'Super-select' on Shogun, Pajero (left) and Jeep's 'Selec-trac' on Cherokee 4.0 litre offer both. (You can imagine the 'debate' between engineering and marketing!) Mitsubishi's sequence is logical – 2WD high, 4WD high (free centre diff), 4WD high Lc (locked centre diff), 4WD low Lc (locked diff). Jeep's is less so with the two 4WD high positions transposed. Terminology is strange too '4WD part-time' here meaning 'centre diff locked, you can only use this mode *part* of the time', ie not on hard surfaces. Likewise '4WD full-time' means you can use it *full* time – even on hard surfaces – so the centre diff is not locked. Got it? System is OK, nomenclature and ergonomics unusual.

mission; so if you are in any doubt as to your skills or ability to execute the change cleanly and quietly, make your range changes while the machine is stationary. However, as indicated below, an on-the-move change from low to high is a useful technique to perfect (see panel, p 5.3 - 31). Do not try to execute high range to low range changes with the vehicle moving.

Use of low ratio gears. Low ratio gears have the obvious function of providing 'more power' but in fact are used in two distinct scenarios:

1. 'Power'. One where gearing the vehicle down to climb very steep slopes or ploughing through deep sand is required, and ...

2. 'Control'. The other is what may be termed the 'control' situation. Typically this latter might be when you have to traverse some extremely rough rocks and a 'crawler' gear is needed to do so without jolting the vehicle or when you descend a very steep slope..

These situations are dealt with in 'Driving techniques' on page 5.3 - 17.

Low range of a two-speed transfer box should be used where 'power' or 'control' required – towing buses or tip-toeing over boulders. Some 4x4s don't have low range at all.

'Power' (left) and 'control' (above) – the two classic uses of the low range gears in a transfer gearbox

SOME 4x4 TRANSMISSION SYSTEMS

Items down the left side of the table will affect the driving of your vehicle on expeditions. If your vehicle is not listed, those are the features to find out about.

	Series 2 Land Rover	Series 3 Land Rover	Defender	Discovery	Range Rover >'86	Current Range Rover	Wrangler TJ	Cherokee 2.5 TD	Cherokee 4.0	Grand Cherokee pre-'95	Grand Cherokee post-'95	Fourtrack
1. Four-wheel drive system	•	•	•	•	•	•	•	•	•	•	•	•
Selectable 4x4 ('part-time')	✔	✔					✔	✔	✔+			✔
'Full-time' 4x4 (Permanent except where combined with with 4x2.) Centre diff lockable/locked.			✔	✔	✔				✔		✔ low	
Permanent 4x4 (full time). Centre diff controlled by VC or other.						✔					✔	
2nd axle driven only after front/rear speed difference sensed by VC. Drive <u>through</u> VC; quits when done.											✔ high	
As above but drive through clutch (hydraulic or electric) not VC.												
As above but VC 'pre-loaded' so some rear drive all the time.												
2. Manual gearbox – synchromesh												
Synchromesh all forward gears		✔	✔	✔	✔	✔	✔	✔				✔
Synchromesh only on	3,4											
3. Automatic transmission												
Optionally available or standard (S)				✔	✔	✔	✔		S	S	S	
Special facilities (Note 3 below)						✔						
4. Two-speed transfer box												
Fitted	✔	✔	✔	✔	✔	✔	✔	✔	✔	✔	✔	✔
Lever actuated (L), button/other (B)	L	L	L	L	L	B	L	L	L	L	L	LB
5. Cross-axle wheel spin control												
Axle diff-locks rear (R), and/or front (F)												
Limited slip axle diff lock, rear							✔	✔		✔	✔	
Traction control						✔						

Left margin note: Do you need to, know all this? Yes – to drive properly, to know your vehicle's potential or limitations and, if you're at that stage, to enable you to choose the right vehicle.

Side labels: 'Hard drive' – shafts and gears; 'Soft drive' – viscous couplings (VC) etc

Notes   **1.** Read table in conjunction with Section 4.1 pp 15-29. Optional items (such as limited slip diff) given a tick.
2. VC = viscous coupling – see page 4.1 - 18.
3. Automatic transmission special facilities. Range Rover: Automatic 1st gear is held if lift-off takes place at 2000 rpm or above. Honda CR-V 'intelligent auto' senses throttle position etc and imposes one of six control criteria sets on its auto transmission. Freelander, when fitted with optional ABS and automatic gearbox, has HDC (hill descent control) that enhances downhill engine retardation in 1st or reverse by selective use of braking system.

The following grid shows the 4x4 systems for various vehicles. Each row represents a different system attribute; marks are ✔ (applies), • (applies), with inner labels S, B, L, R, R,F and numbers 2,3,4.

Mercedes ML320	VW Syncro Caravelle	Mitsubishi Shogun	Mitsubishi L200 pickup	Toyota HiLux pickup	Toyota Landcruiser VX	Toyota Colorado	Toyota RAV-4 (manual)	Land Rover Freelander	Honda CR-V	Ford Maverick	Ford Explorer	Nissan Patrol GR ('98)	Frontera	Pinzgauer 4x4	Bedford RL 4-tonner	Bedford MK 4-tonner	Leyland 4x4 4-tonner
•	•	•	•	•	•	•	•	•	•	•	•	•	•	•	•	•	•
		✔+	✔	✔					✔			✔	✔	✔	✔	✔	
	✔		✔	✔	✔												✔
✔																	
		✔															
								✔		✔							
							✔										
	✔	✔	✔	✔	✔	✔	✔	✔		✔		✔	✔	✔			✔
														2,3,4	2,3,4		
S		✔		✔	✔	✔						S					
							✔	✔									
✔		✔	✔	✔	✔					✔	✔	✔	✔	✔	✔	✔	✔
B		L	L	L	L					L	B	L	L	L	L	L	B
	R	R	R		R,F	R						R		R,F			
											✔		✔				
✔	✔																

Don't let it confuse. The 4x4 systems are stilll as on p 4.1 - 19. What you have here are the different versions. 'Hard drive' systems better for demanding expeditions.

Notes 4. 'Hard drive' 4x4. Cherokee 4.0 ('Selec-Trac') and Shogun ('Super-Select') are unusual in offering 2WD in addition to 4WD (centre diff free) and 4WD (centre diff locked). Mercedes' axles, centre diff monitored by traction control.

5. 'Soft drive' 4x4. Grand Cherokee, after mid-'95, has 'soft drive' for the front axle driven through a VC in high ratio; in low ratio front and rear shafts locked together. Pre-'95 it had permanent 4x4, VC across centre diff; unsuited to Hookes-joint front halfshafts. Explorer in 'Auto': 'soft drive' through electrically operated clutch bringing in front prop shaft when slip sensed; in '4x4 high' or '4x4 low' this electric clutch engagement is selected. Freelander: see p 4.1 - 18 panel.

Transmission – the rest

Axle diff-locks. As you have seen above and in Section 4.1 page 20 (panel), a lot of engineering is directed at ensuring that the benefits of the differential gears fitted at the join of the front and rear propeller shafts are not negated by allowing one shaft to spin while the other stands still. The same potential problems attend the normal axle differential – a situation most of us have seen more times than enough in the winter when one wheel spins on ice and the other one stays stock still and the result is a car that ceases to move forwards.

So some 4x4s have axle diff-locks fitted which have to be positively selected, electrically or mechanically, the status usually being prominently displayed by a warning light. *WARNING*: Select axle diff-locks only when the shafts are stationary and, for good measure, the clutch is depressed. (Some vehicles have a *limited slip* diff which requires no controls but, as its name implies,

Manually engaged diff-locks best but have handling problems; limited slips have durability problems; traction control elegant but prolonged use causes wear.

Godzilla in ballet shoes? Not quite. The formidable Pinzgauer 6x6 takes a lot of stopping – mainly because of its front/rear diff lock and cross-axle diff-locks on each axle (portal axles to boot – p 4.1 - 27!). But driver must be one his toes disengaging diff-locks – especially the front one – immediately they are not needed. Steering feel with diff lock engaged on any vehicle is appalling.

will allow only so much speed difference between left and right wheels before locking up to a greater of lesser extent.)

As with a centre diff-lock – only more so – the policy here is to use axle diff-locks only when you are in imminent trouble with traction. Then disengage. Sometimes a diff-lock may be fitted to rear and front axles and in the case of the front axle it is essential to disengage it as soon as possible as it confers a feel to the steering akin to its being set in concrete; this, of course, is accompanied by considerable torsional trauma at the axle half shafts. See also Section 4.1, pp 22, 23.

Traction control. Another way of achieving what a cross-axle diff-lock achieves is to design-in a system called traction control. This is usually associated with very powerful super-cars which are so overburdened with power at the back axle that the wheels are prone to spin at the merest hint of a heavy right foot. The traction control checks the situation by sensing the difference in wheel speed between left and right wheel and applying a touch of brake to the over-revving wheel. Some systems compare the speeds of the driven rear wheels with the non-driven front wheels and, where one axle (ie both rear wheels) are spinning relative to the front wheels, will back off the throttle. Whether it administers a slap on the wrist is not documented but the principle will be clear.

Such a system has obvious applications in 4x4 vehicles and one of the first to utilise its potential was the current Range Rover. Hardware necessary for the ABS brakes included wheel speed sensors and as the vehicle is designed with a live-line hydraulic system the two components were used to check an errant wheel that had lost traction. Much the same principle is also used on the Mercedes M-type and the Land Rover Freelander where the option is fitted.

Whatever the vehicle, the system is an

Transmission brake concept

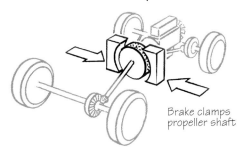

Brake clamps propeller shaft

auto-boon to a driver faced with severe traction problems. You do not have to remember to engage and later disengage it as you do with lockable differentials and it has none of the handling implications a fully locked diff has.

Transmission brake. A final point on transmission. If a transmission brake is fitted, ie where the 'hand brake' consists of a brake drum on the propeller shaft behind the gearbox as on most Land Rover products or 4x4 trucks such as the Bedford MK and RL, it should <u>*never* be used except when the vehicle has been brought to rest</u> with the wheel brakes and is *stationary*. If used on the move it can cause severe stress in the transmission and even half-shaft failure. Think of it as a parking brake only.

Transmission brake ferociously effective but ... Use only when weight squarely on all four wheels and never use when vehicle is in motion – even a little bit.

Driving techniques

Reference. As mentioned above, a comprehensive coverage of driving techniques is given in the companion volume to this, *The Land Rover Experience*. Despite the title, the techniques described are applicable to all 4x4 vehicles.

Mechanical sympathy

'TLC' for your vehicle. As hinted in the opening paragraph, right at the beginning of Section 5.3, one of the most important characteristics a driver must have on an expedition is mechanical sympathy; some 'tender

loving care' for the vehicle that he or she is driving. Gritting your teeth, white knuckling the steering wheel and blasting through will break something quite early in the trip. Certainly there will be times when you must use all of the vehicle's capabilities but develop a feel for what the engineering is going through; know what it is you are asking of your machine.

The importance of training. This is where the driver training will be quite simply irreplaceable. Developing your skills, getting to know the interplay between your skills and the vehicle's capabilities is the very essence of preparation for a demanding expedition.

On-foot recce and marshalling

Have a look first. The image of the all-conquering 4x4 careening over impossible terrain with clods of flying mud or big water splashes has a certain cachet derived from TV ads. But it is not real-world operation on an expedition. If you find an obstacle or terrain that looks close to your vehicle's limits, stop and take a look – on foot.

The best way of avoiding accidental underbody or other damage to your vehicle in difficult conditions is to stop, get out and look before driving on. As with servicing, so with driving; prevention is vital, cure an admission that you got it wrong. So it is better to avoid hitting under-body obstacles than it is to fit heavy sheet steel guards. Keep alert at all times to the geometric limitations of your vehicle. If in doubt, recce on foot – hills, gullies, bumps in the track, anywhere you have any doubts that the vehicle can clearly and cleanly traverse the obstacle ahead. On the umpteenth hot, sticky day of a rough expedition in the tropics the temptation to press on and hope for the best will be high, but the cost of getting it wrong – just once – will be higher. If the clearances look tight use another team member as a guiding marshaller – especially over rocks (see photo page 5.3 - 32).

Don't use your vehicle as a landscaping tool. Use a marshaller to see you over tight-clearance obstacles and guide you where wheel placement is critical.

Marshaller – just one. If it is a serious obstacle and everyone is out of the vehicles there is a tendency for all to shout at once (even in simple backing-up it happens) but the driver should take his directions from just one marshaller – about 10 metres ahead and facing the driver with a good view of all four wheels and the underbelly clearance. These directions should be visual rather than by trying to shout over engine noise. An agreed system of marshalling signals should be practised during pre-expedition driver training; go-right, go-left, advance, stop and reverse are all that is necessary. The driver must obey and trust the marshaller completely and watch him, not the track, when being guided. Never disobey the marshaller; if you are really not happy stop and query by all means.

Tell the team. Brief everyone about marshalling before the trip, about the pitfalls of everyone shouting at once, about the importance of the calm approach and one marshaller being in charge. Practise it, marshalling the vehicle over or between cardboard boxes without touching them: one marshaller in control, no shouting, no noise, signs only. Calm. Don't like it? Stop, back off, try again on a slightly different route. Don't open your mouth, except to smile. See photos pages 5.3 - 3 and 8.

Landscaping. In difficult going of the kind where marshalling is needed, shovels should be regarded as an emergency low

Standard marshalling signals

   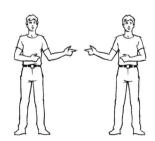

Come forward   Go back   Stop   Steer in this direction

All the lessons so far. Full time 4x4 with diff-lock locked? Low ratio for 'power'? On foot recce first? Tail-pipe OK on the left side? Scraping body-work on left side? Water looks silt-and-soft rather than running-and-firm; how deep on left side? You get to know the 'look' of terrain after days of the same kind of thing but you keep alert too.

gear and – environmental and land-owner-ship aspects permitting – should regularly be used to safeguard the vehicle; if the obstacle is likely to hazard the vehicle then 'landscaping' can remove the offending rock or bump or provide a feasible path for a wheel. Do not skimp the digging; invest another five minutes in shovelling and be sure of getting through first try. Your tyres are the only part of the vehicle that should touch the ground.

Use of transfer box

Choice of gear. Choice of the right gear is something that will grow on you and from your driver training if you have the right degree of mechanical sympathy. Too low a gear is as bad as too high a gear. The extremes have the following disadvantages:

1. Too low a gear
- Excessive engine rpm
- Excessive torque at the wheels leading to wheel spin

2. Too high a gear
- Excessive strain on the engine and bearings
- Not enough power to get through the obstacle.

Get to know the sound of a happy engine, even when you are asking a lot of it. If you were asked to explain this to an alien

from another planet you would probably say that the best range is somewhere between the 75% max torque rpm and the max power rpm. That makes it around 1500-4000 rpm on a diesel and maybe 2500-5000 on a petrol engine.

Know your peak-torque rpm and, on a diesel, where the turbo gets going. That is the sort of range to be in when you asking the most of the engine. Equally, when you are trickling along and feathering the throt-tle gently you can use a surprisingly low rpm for economy. Under such conditions you would almost invariably change down to do any meaningful acceleration.

Low box. If in doubt, use low box in tricky off-road conditions. This may mean you are using a high gear like 4th or 5th but it does mean that if the situations gets more demanding and you need power or extra control, you have the remainder of the low range of gears to go down into. Were you doing the same speed in the high range, you would find yourself with not enough lower gears to go into and probably have to stop to get into low ratio.

Low box and auto. Don't forget to use low range properly in auto. Check the tacho the whole time. The tendency sometimes is to let the auto 'get on with it' on its own but in heavy going you can finish up with the

The lowest gear in low range is not always the best gear to start in unless for steep downslope retardation. Don't over-torque ground or overload the engine.

Use low range gears to keep auto transmission happy. Tendency to 'leave it to get on with it' can lead to excessive slip and overheating of transmission fluid if severe 'power' or 'control' situations are encountered.

Use transfer box's bounty of 4x4 and low range gears to reduce stress on ground and engine if in any doubt. Reversing a bit helps disengage part-time 4x4.

engine operating in an inappropriately low band of rpm and a great deal of slippage going on in the automatic transmission – bad for the engine and a certain overheating of the gearbox fluid.

Use of 4x4. If you have part-time 4x4 a similar philosophy applies to use of 4x4. If in doubt, use it; don't judder to a rear-wheel spinning halt in 4x2 before selecting 4x4. The only proviso, as we have seen is that, with no centre differential you must not use 4x4 on hard grippy surfaces.

Getting out of 4x4. Vehicles with part-time 4x4 will, even on loose surfaces off-road, suffer from a degree of transmission 'wind-up' due to the lack of centre differential. This will manifest itself as stress in the

propeller shafts and considerable pressure on the components associated with the 4x4 selection mechanism.

When you try to de-select 4x4 you may find the transfer lever virtually immovable. If this happens it is a sign of wind-up in the system. Select reverse and go backwards for 10-20 metres, at the end of which, dip the clutch and administer a sharp fist-thump on the lever while the vehicle is still moving. This will usually do the trick. If it does not, reverse some more. In very extreme cases, a jacked-up wheel will release the problem. Anything with long propeller shafts like the Bedford RL and MK is likely to need, what may be termed persistence – a clenched fist and a sharp backward thump – when disengaging 4x4.

Suspension affects traction

Golden rule No 1. Keeping all the wheels on the ground, with weight on them as evenly distributed as possible, is important where best available traction is needed; this is done by having compliant suspension with lots of wheel movement. If your vehicle isn't like this and has limited movement with arthritic leaf springs, know its limita-

Classic use of auto and low range transfer gears to minimise torque converter slip. Coil sprung Grand Cherokee offers respectable axle movement to keep wheels on the ground and maintain traction without resorting to limited slip rear differential.

tions and make the appropriate allowances. Often the full potential of coil springs is inhibited by anti-roll bars which are fitted to reduce on-road cornering roll. Either way, the suspension movement you have – the articulation – affects a vehicle's traction in extreme off-road conditions such as you might encounter off-tracks or on damaged tracks on an expedition.

Diagonal ditches – the classic. A common problem probably responsible for more than half of all 'failed traction' situations – bogging in soft-going included – is the 'diagonal suspension' case. Imagine a driver's eye view approaching a shallow V-shaped ditch going diagonally, 30° left of dead ahead direction, from distant left to foreground right. In crossing it the vehicle will reach a condition where the front right wheel is on the far side of the ditch, the rear left is on the near side of the ditch (the diagonal suspension situation) and the other two remaining wheels are hanging down into the bottom of the V. When the ditch is deeper than the extent of the wheel movement allowed by the vehicle's springs, these wheels (left front and right rear) will, owing to the axle differential, spin in thin air while the 'hung-up' wheels stay stationary. Traction, and therefore forward motion, will be lost.

Different variations of this classic basic situation will manifest themselves in a hundred ways - scrambling up bumpy slopes,

crossing ruts or ridges, on rough ground or in soft going. Almost invariably it will be 'diagonal' wheel spin that stops a 4x4 in severe going.

As we have seen above, the presence of the usual axle differential that all vehicles are equipped with to enable the outer wheel on a corner to travel further than the inner wheel is what allows this wheel spin to take place. Again we have seen a lockable or limited slip differential in the axle(s) is one solution but since this is rarely available; it helps to be on the look-out for, and quickly recognise, the condition so that you can stop or lift off the throttle before wheel spin makes things worse; wheel spin will result in scooping sand or earth from beneath the afflicted wheels.

Articulation. The extremes of wheel suspension travel – left wheel up, right wheel down and vice versa – is what governs the ability of the axle to follow the ground in 'twisty terrain' situations such as the ditch mentioned above. Refer again to the pictures on page 4.1 - 21 which show the problem and the two approaches to its solution.

'Diagonal wheel spin' is the microcosm of just about every failed traction situation. Be on your guard always for when it may happen; quick recognition helps.

Even class-leading articulation such as Defender has (left), can be beaten by extreme conditions and a wheel will spin despite centre diff-lock being engaged. Pinzgauer (below) with short half-axles, makes little attempt at articulation, relying on cross-axle diff-locks. After-market axle diff-locks (ARB is popular) can be fitted to Defender et al.

Diagonal ridges too. It applies equally when it is a small ridge that you are taking diagonally rather than a ditch. A vehicle's ability to allow its axles to move freely relative to the chassis and to each other in this way is termed its 'articulation'; vehicles with long-travel coil springs will therefore do better off-road than one with the more limited axle movement inherent with leaf springs.

Driving? The relevance of all this to driving is, of course, knowing what is going on and what to expect (see 'Why am I stuck?' above). Know your vehicle's articulation limits. If you see a diagonal hang-up situation looming:

- Use momentum to carry you through, if terrain permits.
- Choose another route.
- 'Landscape' with shovels.

Go easy with that right foot. Wheel spin in sand results in bogging deeper. Better here to let the slight gradient help you reverse out gently; never mind the manly pride!

Avoid wheel spin, reverse out

Golden rule No 2. Just as Golden Rule No 1 says keep all the wheels on the ground so they can't spin (and inhibit this tendency with locking differentials or whatever), so Golden Rule No 2 says control of the throttle foot should also be directed – in general – at eliminating wheel spin. The reason is that wheel spin almost invariably results in merely using the spinning wheel like a milling machine and scooping ground from under the afflicted wheel – which makes the problem of obtaining grip worse and worse. Also, as you will recall from school physics, a sliding object suffers from a lower coefficient of friction than a static one so it is important to retain that 'rack-and-pinion' relationship between your wheel and the ground – the wheel covering the ground like a gearwheel progressing down a rack.

Wheel spin in sand, should always be avoided. Sand is invariably firmer near the surface and with spinning wheels you will

Be alert to kill, wheel spin the moment it starts. In general it will cut ground under the wheel and worsen bogging. Sometimes a little spin can help in shallow mud.

Aim: zero wheel spin

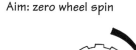

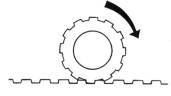

Concept of rack and pinion

be cutting your way down to a bottomless layer of soft sand that will quickly result in the vehicle sitting with its chassis rather than its wheels resting on the ground. So the moment you sense wheel spin and any degree of sinkage, quit and reverse out. (See page 5.3 - 28, 'Soft sand, poor traction'.)

You will also notice, should you get a wheel spin situation in soft sand, that the torque of the propeller shaft power tends to tilt front and rear axles in opposite directions relative to the chassis. By quitting early, excessive under-wheel scooping is avoided and reversing out conveniently tends to tilt the axles in the opposite direction thus enhancing your traction for getting out backwards. As in line one, it comes down to restrained, sympathetic and alert driving.

Mud: rule 2a. The reason for the 'in general' caveat above is that sometimes, in mud, a finite amount of wheel spin will cause a wheel with a generously treaded tyre to 'dig through' to drier, grippier ground. When it does, back off the throttle and resume normal driving. It is a difficult process to cover in a book and in real life is a matter of judgement for each individual situation; another way of saying 'trial and error'! (See page 5.3 - 30 'Mud' and photo on the same page.)

The advice on quitting early before things get too bad and reversing out to try a different route or method still holds.

Steep slopes – up

The 'right' angle. Not on expeditions, going up a steep hill on a road is a common sense combination of momentum, the right gear, the right throttle opening and usually backing off on all three as you reach the top. Expedition driving is the same but, unsurprisingly, there are one or two extra factors to consider:

- On track or off-track? See below.
- Bumpiness of the slope limits speed.
- Weight transference off-loads front axle.
- Same thing promotes wheel spin.
- If off-tracks, tackle slope at right angles.
- Consider failed-climb back-down.

Any red-blooded tough to whom that last item sounds altogether too wimpish is probably reading the wrong book. It covers, of course, the philosophy of not getting into a situation that you can't get out of or which will have dangerous consequences. Calm consideration of the back-down route – see below– obviates an all-or-nothing white knuckle approach that may be (literally!) way over the top and to the detriment of your vehicle.

It is rare to get an on-the-limits slope on a track. If you get one with a less than favourable combination of steepness and grip it will almost invariably have a section, near the top, where previous vehicles (possibly overloaded or under-powered) have tried – and failed – to get up but before backing down have scooped out dips in the surface with their spinning wheels.

This bumpiness is often combined with the effects of rain erosion and both will conspire to limit the speed with which you can tackle the slope yourself. It will occasionally be beneficial to do a little spade-work to sort out the best on-foot recce-ed route you select. Remember, though, that loose earth shovelled into scooped-out dips may scoop right out again – there's a lot of energy in a hill-climbing 4x4 – and it will pay you to add rocks and/or tamp it down well.

The angle of the slope causes weight transference to the back axle which invites the front wheels to spin as they are off-loaded so (see photo page 5.3 - 11) be sure to lock the centre differential before the climb – and axle diffs too if they are lockable.

If you are off tracks completely or, as occasionally happens, the cut-up track is so bad you are forced to pioneer your own route up the slope, be sure to tackle the slope at right angles – in effect up the slope of maximum gradient. If that sounds odd, the diagram shows the consequences of taking a diagonal path – the possibility of a roll down the slope with catastrophic results.

Up-slopes so steep you may fail to get up will be rare on expeditions but train for it so the real thing will be easy and stress-free. Always climb at right angles to slope.

Steep slopes – best path

Go straight up slope

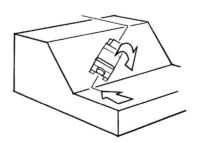

Diagonal path risks roll-over

Well hello there! View from the cab is even more impressive. Hugely capable Bedford RL uses twisty chassis to achieve 'articulation', plus excellent transmission system and well chosen gearing. Failure or loss of grip at or before this point should cause no alarm. Standard backing-down procedure (see photo opposite) is absolutely safe. But be sure to grip the steering wheel well ...!

time' with the risk that that entails. In summary:

• Don't floor the throttle and create wheel spin.

• Wheel spin can result in the vehicle slithering sideways on to the slope and rolling over.

• When you aren't going to make it, hit the brake and clutch, keep both hands on the wheel. You now have all the time you want – sitting there, pointing at the sky!

• Select low ratio reverse.

The diagonal traverse is what you might do on foot but humans on foot can remain vertical as they do so; a vehicle cannot. So in every respect, take the 'right angle'.

The right gear. Don't select too low a gear for a steep ascent since this will overtorque the wheels and promote wheel spin.

• Usually low ratio 2nd or third will do for the steepest hills.

• Get your speed before you get the hill.

• Don't try to change gear on the slope.

• Unless the hill is a 1-in-1 textured concrete engineered slope, first gear will provide more torque than the surface can cope with.

• On the limit, you may find you have to ease OFF the throttle as you reach the top to preclude wheel spin.

Backing down. Covered comprehensively in *THE LAND ROVER EXPERIENCE*, the failed climb recovery should be a comfortable part of your driving repertoire – firstly for safety and secondly so that you are not under extreme pressure to 'make it first

Don't use too low a gear – 2nd, low range is usually right. Be prepared to lift off as you reach the top to preclude wheel spin. Train for and practise back-downs.

Hill back-down – stalled engine

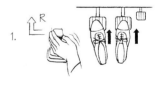

1.

2.

3.

Hill back-down if engine has stalled.
1. Clutch, footbrake, into reverse.
2. Feet off all pedals, but throttle ready.
3. Touch starter briefly. Both hands back on wheel. Reverse straight back on mirrors.

Proper procedure. Timely backing down for another go with a touch more speed. Lights indicate reverse engaged (low box), <u>straight</u> back down the slope, both hands on the wheel to preclude steering 'runaway'. More throttle at this point would have made things worse – note right rear wheel is already close to full articulation and more throttle would just give more wheel spin.

• Hands back on the wheel let in the clutch and trickle straight back down the slope on a closed throttle, steering on the mirrors.

• *WARNING.* The hands on the wheel is very important. In reverse, the steering geometry castor angle works the wrong way and, particularly in soft going, will whisk the wheel out of your hands and over to full lock if you let it – another way of achieving a vehicle roll-over on a slope! Steer straight back down the slope.

Engine stalled too? Sometimes in the confusion and feeling that you have got it wrong you will finish up with a stalled engine too. If anything the situation is even simpler, as the diagram on the left shows. Sketch 1 and 2 is what you would do anyway but with a dead engine, having engaged reverse low box and let the clutch up already, just touch the starter. The engine will burst into life and all you have to do is keep the wheel firmly in your grip as you trickle back down the slope. Reverse on your mirrors for preference as that precludes the necessity of craning your neck round; when you do that you sometimes inadvertently pull the steering wheel to one side, preventing a straight-back descent.

Steep slopes – down

Get out and look. Nowhere is the on-foot recce so important as on a steep down-slope. Coming up to it in the vehicle you will not be able to see over or down it until you are committed and that is decidedly too late. Stop a couple of metres short of the edge (so when you do go down you are in gear with the revs right) and check on foot for the evenness of the slope.

Controlled retardation. Engine braking is the best tool for the descent. In general terms, 1st gear, low ratio, trickling revs and foot well away from the clutch and brake. The reason for the latter, in general is that it is all too easy to apply excessive brake and lock the wheels, especially the rear wheels. That will lead to loss of directional control. If you are in an automatic transmission vehicle, select 1st gear hold. You will find retardation is nothing like as good as it is in a manual gearbox vehicle so ...

Brakes? Keeping off the brakes is a general rule and a safe one in most cases. Remember that if engine braking is not working well enough, the last thing you want is locked-up wheels that will provoke a slide. However, especially with an automatic, you may not be getting the retarda-

Practise engine-stalled up-slope back-downs. For steep down-slopes, on-foot recce as always. 1st gear low range best for down-slope retardation. Be brake-jab ready.

All-important on-foot recce precedes the descent. Close for the photo, park vehicle about 2 metres short of edge. Jeep begins descent, low range, auto '1' selected. Brake lights indicate readiness to use 'manual ABS' cadence braking – short repeated dabs. Bedford close to excessive retardation and nose dig-in on dune slope. Second, low, and throttle required here.

Aim for engine-only braking. Don't hold brakes on steep down-slopes. If you have off-road ABS, fine; otherwise use quick small jabs to preclude wheels locking.

tion you need and use of the brakes with care is advisable. 'With care' means avoiding lock up: pump the brakes in small dabs – a kind of do-it-yourself ABS anti-lock brake system, sometimes called cadence braking. It is a method taught in advanced driving schools for wet or icy roads and will work here. If you are lucky you may be driving a vehicle (such as the Range Rover) with an off-road ABS system that will already guard against wheel lockup. Lacking a low-ratio transfer box the Land Rover Freelander addresses this problem with an ingenious auto-application of ABS.

Long loose down-slopes. Occasionally there will be loose slopes where 1st gear low ratio will impose such retardation on the wheels that the available grip cannot cope with the load and the wheels will slide, partly-locked, down the hill. In these circum-

stances be ready to use throttle to 'catch up' – to match the laying down of the tyre tread to the ground – the rack and pinion effect shown on page 5.3 - 22. There will be down-slopes – classically sand dunes or long shale or gravel slopes, where it is wise to use low ratio 2nd gear rather than 1st to keep the wheels in firm rolling contact with the ground and to avoid, on a dune, the nose digging in to the soft sand.

Lateral slopes – traverses

Great care. Nature seems to have imbued the human brain with built-in alarm-signals in relation to traversing lateral slopes in vehicles. In short, terror sets in significantly before there is real danger of vehicle roll-over. Treat it as one of life's bonuses. Obey it; chicken-out early, live longer! If you do have to traverse a slope, again the on-foot recce is essential, looking especially for those small indentations that will suddenly lend extra lean to the vehicle. Secure the load, have people cling to the uphill side of the vehicle lending weight to the uphill wheels. If you can, and the terrain permits, prepare yourself for an escape manoeuvre – turning down the slope with a touch of accelerator.

Weak ground

Soft and/or slippery. When a vehicle moves forward it is asking both horizontal and vertical strength from the ground it is on. Horizontal strength is what we would often call grip. Dry tarmac takes plenty of horizontal push from vehicles accelerating or braking sharply – ice doesn't. In-betweeners like fresh snow or damp mud will take so much and then shear, causing wheel spin. We try to get round all this with four-wheel drive, to spread the required push between four wheels instead of two, or by going easy on the throttle and brakes.

Vertical strength determines whether the vehicle sinks into the ground or rides over the surface. Deep snow, really wet deep mud, soft sand are examples where flotation is not enough to support a vehicle properly and it will sink till it finds firmer support – or rests on its chassis. This latter spreads the load over a much bigger area and the sinkage usually stops at this point (but see

Snow benefits from bold, sharp-edged tread – Michelin XZL seen in ideal conditions below. Snow usually has firm ground beneath so deflation rarely appropriate.

'Salt flat' below!). The same tactics are used, in general terms, for dealing with poor flotation conditions: use six wheels instead of four, lower the tyre pressures, use load spreaders such as sand ladders or steel planking over soft patches.

Summing up:

Horizontal weakness
- Use all-wheel drive
- Gently on throttle and brakes
- Use a high gear
- Use tyres with aggressive treads
- Avoid wheel spin or wheel slide
- Reduce weight

Vertical weakness
- Six wheels better than four
- Reduce tyre pressures
- Use load spreaders in soft patches
- Avoid wheel spin or wheel slide
- Reduce weight

It is worth restating this fairly obvious information because what comes out is the general theme of being gentle with weak ground. To be more specific, overweight vehicles and flying clods from spinning wheels is not the solution. But these are generalities and there are one or two special-to-type packages of information and technique that are worth being aware of.

Weak ground can be mud, snow, sand, slime. Strategy is to treat it gently so you don't break traction or sink. Spread the load – engage 4x4, tyre treads and pressures?

Momentum. Gentleness in the appropriate conditions, ie when you are in danger of over-stressing the ground and losing traction, does not rule out the common-sense (and again, appropriate) use of momentum. Be clear what you are launching into – usually by on-foot recce first – and then get the right speed in the right gear to carry you through the soft patch. Under no circumstances should you ballistic blindly into difficult going and risk damage to the vehicle or really serious sticking; typically these circumstances lead to vehicles becoming 'high centred', ie bellied, on a ridge or rock from which the speed-related damage can sometimes be very serious. The spade-work required to re-mobilise a vehicle bellied on an obstacle is back breaking and prolonged.

Don't change down in mid-obstacle. 'In the right gear' there implies a gear in which you have enough torque at the wheels to get you through a demanding bit of terrain. Avoid trying to change down in mid-obstacle if you can; the time taken and any imperfection in the change will often slow the

In patches of weak ground use momentum but in a cool and calculated way, not out of white-knuckle desperation. Don't risk getting bellied on a hard ridge.

vehicle and break your momentum and progress resulting in getting stuck (remember the comments in favour of automatic transmission at Section 4.1). If you do get stuck, reverse out and try again; don't try a standing start where even with momentum you have already failed to get through

Soft sand, poor traction

Types of sand, types of driving. There is churned sand on tracks and there is virgin, unbroken sand on dunes and sand sheets. Surface strengths and driving techniques are different. Let's deal with dunes and unbroken sand sheet first.

Jumping off a piecrust is the best analogy to the marginal traction conditions in virgin sand of the kind found on untrodden dunes or sand sheet. There is a surface crust with weaker, looser sand beneath. Fitting big, high flotation tyres and lowering tyre pressures (see below) reduces vertical load per square inch and going from 4x2 to 4x4 spreads the traction from two to four wheels, halving the shear strength required of a given piece of ground. Both these remedies must be allied to smooth driving, use of

Unbroken sand and tracks demand different driving techniques. Close to the limits (right), 9.00 x 16 Michelin XS tyres, 15 psi pressures and feather-footed braking prevents breaking the crust but note how human bootprint has done so. Churned tracks (below) soft on top, harder underneath, tolerant of 'hard'-treaded XZL tyres. Even elephants (footprints between ruts) keep out of the wheel tracks!

the highest reasonable gear and very gentle use of the accelerator. As mentioned above, this implies getting the required gear and speed before the obstacle. Be very easy on the brakes too. on some surfaces you will need to coast to a halt since even a little brake will break the surface crust.

Unbroken sand. On unbroken sand the subtlest and cleverest tyre treads are needed (see page 4.2 - 25) to get best performance – Michelin XS is the all-time classic for desert use but shines especially well on unbroken sand. As the note below shows, it is also tolerant of unusually low pressures – provided the limiting speed is not exceeded.

The difficulties of unbroken sand are not limited to traction alone. Visibility – determining the lie of the actual surface 50 metres ahead of your vehicle – can be very difficult when the sun is high or directly behind you. In such conditions it is possible, unknowingly, to go over the edge of a dune or hit its base with near catastrophic consequences – see 'DIBS-mirror' *et seq* in Section 4.2, pages 4.2 - 34 to 35.

Soft sand on tracks. On tracks it is different since the sand crust is already broken by previous traffic and you are already into the soft sand beneath. Awkwardly, the tyre requirements and delicate driving techniques that are needed to get the best flotation and traction on virgin sand both need to be roughened up a bit on tracks where the crust is already broken. When this crust has been broken by the passage of one vehicle on a sand sheet, following vehicles should not follow in the same wheel marks; on a track you seldom have the option, albeit, if you are on a bad track with many patches of soft sand you will soon learn that

Driving on unbroken sand needs a very delicate touch if you are to retain strength of the crust. XS tyres, reduced pressures, gentle use of accelerator; roll to a stop.

Death throes! Rallies (big picture) aren't expeditions but there is lots to learn here. Small dunes are the worst – close together, no room to sweep the vehicle onto the right path, sand usually very fine – look at it round the front wheel! – and little if any crust. Optimistic driver, despite gradient and little run-up, is spinning the wheels to ensure a lot of digging. The spectators are enjoying the show! Colorado in bottom shot is sensibly being taken off cut-up track onto firmer, unbroken sand. 'Fesh-fesh' is one of Nature's surprises (below); powder-fine gypsum beneath innocuous light gravel. Flotation virtually nil.

diverting off the track onto the firmer unbroken sand sheet adjacent to it will get you through with less trouble. 'Knobbly' tyres are not suited to virgin sand since they will break the surface too easily; they *are* however, within limits and excluding excessive wheel spin, good performers on sandy tracks.

Temperature, gears. All sand offers better flotation and traction when cool, dewy or damp; a demanding stretch of sand will be easier to traverse in the early morning than in the heat of the afternoon. No cast-iron advice can be given about what gear to use except to warn against the lowest gears. In really 'sticky' soft sand, just short of an immobilising bogging, start off in 2nd gear low ratio, and progress in 4th or 5th low ratio, getting speed to get 'on top' of the sand. It is at this point that the on-the-move change from low range to high range, if it is possible, is an invaluable technique (see opposite), since stopping to engage and trying to restart in high can all too often result in a spinning clutch and stalled engine.

Tyres and pressures. Fuller details on tyres are given in Section 4.2, 'Vehicle modifications', pages 4.2 - 21 to 25. Reducing tyre

High gears in the low range often ideal for weak ground – enough power to go but not so much torque that you induce inadvertent wheel spin. Low range 4th good.

pressures enhances flotation on soft sand. It is worth repeating here that reducing tyre pressures implies a reduction of maximum speed for that pressure and load; this must never be exceeded. Rule of thumb guidance figures on tyre pressure reductions (radial ply tyres only):

• *Tracks and poor roads* – 75% of road pressures. At this pressure do not exceed 65 kph (40 mph).

• *Emergency flotation pressures* – about 50% or road pressures. At this pressure do not exceed 20 kph (12 mph).

Mud

Read-across. The lessons learned for sand will be invaluable, but need slight modification, for mud. Where sand is usually strongest on the top layers and is soft or bottomless beneath, mud is often (but not always) the other way round – a soft slippery layer on top of firmer drier ground. In these circumstances, knobbly tyres (see pages 4.2 - 21 to 25) and judicious use of wheel spin will frequently scoop out the soft surface mud and get your wheel down to firmer grippy ground beneath. Such mud is often associated with recent rainfall on a dip in a track but where there may be an underground water source or drainage feeding the soft patch, mud can be very deep indeed to the extent of appearing to be bottomless. The lie of the land will often tell you the difference but by no means invariably.

Slippery surface mud – say, mud over wet grass – where the most delicate touch is required to preclude wheel spin, will often permit effective use of a start in 3rd gear low range. Sand is usually too 'draggy' to permit this.

'Judicious wheel spin'! Classic thin mud overlaid on drier, potentially grippier earth will often respond to a certain amount of controlled wheel spin from a bold treaded tyre (Michelin XCL here) and eventually yield traction. Momentum needed too.

LOW TO HIGH RANGE TRANSFER GEARS – CHANGE ON THE MOVE

Low to high range on the move. As mentioned above ('Soft sand ... Temperature, gears') there is a strong case for developing the ability to change from low ratio gears to the high range whilst the vehicle is in motion. Where conditions may make a start in high range impossible because of soft, heavy going, once you are moving at around 25 mph in, say, low range 3rd or 4th, it is frequently desirable to change into the high range at that point without stopping and risk a no-start in the high range of gears.

The requisites. Such a technique is not possible on all 4x4s and you would in any case have to carry it out on your own responsibility with no comeback on the manufacturer, this book or your original L-test driving instructor! You are the one who must make it work – and 'work' here simply means no heavy clonk in the transmission when you do it. All you need is a transmission where the transfer box range control is by lever (not electrical button), with an 'N' (neutral) position between low and high. The bit you have to concentrate on is being able to stop the transfer box lever at the N position and not shoot through to H before you want to. The following works on the Land Rover Defender and Discovery (as the diagram on page 4.1 - 24 shows, 3rd low range equates roughly to 2nd high range):

1. Start off in 1st or second low range. Accelerate through the gears to 20-25 mph in 3rd gear low range.

2. With the main gear lever still in 3rd, double de-clutch the transfer lever from low, through neutral to high; ie, clutch down, transfer lever low-to-neutral, clutch up, clutch down again, transfer lever N to high. (NB you will need to move the transfer lever sharply low to N and be sure to stop it in N. If you go through to H there will be an unacceptable clonk in the transmission.)

3. With the clutch still depressed, move the main gear lever from 3rd into 2nd. The engine will have been losing revs while you moved the transfer lever and may now be going too slowly for a clean engagement so give a small blip to the throttle between 3rd low and 2nd high.

Like many operations of this kind, or like riding a bicycle, it is far more complicated to explain than it is to actually do. As with double de-clutching (page 5.3 - 7), practise first with the vehicle stationary and the engine off to get the sequence right.

Common first errors:
• Not stopping transfer lever properly in neutral.
• Weak rpm blip between 3rd low and 2nd high.

You could, optionally, use 4th low to 2nd high, or even 5th low to 3rd high as your change points. The diagram on p 4.1 - 24 shows the speed for the Defender/Discovery Tdi.

Low to high transfer – on the move

1.
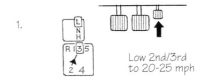

Low 2nd/3rd to 20-25 mph

2.
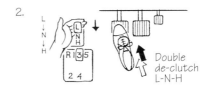

Double de-clutch L-N-H

3.
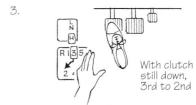

With clutch still down, 3rd to 2nd

It is routinely useful to be able to change – smoothly – from low to high transfer on the move. If you have an 'N' between L and H you may be able to.

Classic situation for low-to-high transfer gears change on the move – too heavy to start comfortably in high range but once started in low, a change up to high box would keep your speed up and 'on top' of the soft sand.

Wet (left) and dry salt marsh. Note clear firm tyre tread behind the vehicle yet only a few feet to its right, the ground is treacherously soft. Dry (near left) attests the kind of boggings that can result from the 'in between' stages of sebkha.

Salt flat

Tracks over salt flats strengthen from beneath. Keep exactly on the track; leaving it by only a metre or so can often result in severe bogging – or worse.

Keep off. Salt flat - sometimes shown on maps as sebkha or chott - consists of a crust of unpredictable strength frequently disguising soft salty bottomless mud beneath. A bogging in this can often be forever; the vehicle will break through the crust and sit with its belly on the sebkha. In some cases it will then go on sinking. Never drive at random over this kind of surface. If there is a well-used track across it should be safe, but even a metre or so away from this can be disastrously soft.

Rocks, corrugations

Rocks. Rocks are for crawling over very slowly, with the greatest care and with your marshaller five to ten metres ahead of you making sure you do not touch any rocks with the underside of the vehicle. It is a very common sense procedure but the tendency sometimes is for people to get too tensed-

Sharp rocks, too close to drive between (emulating broken bottles, far left), call for the midwife's touch when you have to drive over them. Others (above) just need very careful marshalling to keep the clearances safe.

Probably the most widespread, pervasive and damaging hazard any expedition faces is corrugations or 'washboard' tracks. They go on for tens of kilometres and can shake a vehicle and its contents to pieces. Taken at the 'harmonic' speed, the body but not the suspension gets some respite. Braking and steering effectiveness greatly reduced.

up. As mentioned already (page 5.3 - 18 'On-foot recce, marshalling'), use one marshaller, not half a dozen; no shouting, signs only; as much stopping to make sure as the marshaller wants. Back off, try again if in any doubt. Hitting rocks is very bad for the vehicle. Use low range, first gear. This is a classic 'control' situation – see page 5.3 - 13.

Corrugations. In desert, savannah or bush areas, unsurfaced tracks which carry heavy traffic and are not regularly machine-graded or scraped will often develop a surface of continuous transverse corrugations that go on for tens of kilometres at a time. These parallel ridges, at right angles to the vehicle's path, can be as high as 10-15 cm

and spaced 30-60 cm apart. Taken at the wrong speed they can nearly shake a vehicle to pieces.

However, taken at a 'harmonic' speed, dictated by your vehicle's suspension rate, dampers and tyres, the result will be that at least the vehicle body and occupants will have a relatively smooth ride. Do not let this blind you to the fact that the springs and shock absorbers will still be under enormous stress – as a glance out of the driver's window at the front axle will vividly confirm. This 'harmonic' speed is generally 50-70 kph (30-40 mph). Do not go any faster than is necessary to reach the harmonic speed; remember you are virtually skipping from crest to crest on the corrugations and ADHESION FOR BRAKING OR RAPID STEERING RESPONSE WILL BE ALARMINGLY REDUCED. Increase your look-ahead anticipation as much as you possibly can and be extremely gentle with brakes and steering.

Crawl, carefully, over rocks – with fully inflated tyres and guidance. So long as speed not over 40 mph, 25% deflation on corrugations helps. Beware brakes, steering.

Flash floods over washed-out roads can be too dangerous to even wade but small rivers on sand a safer bet. Wade with a prodding pole first, looking for swirl holes on river bed.

Water

First the recce. After flash floods or en route there may be times when you have to drive through water. People are easier to un-bog than vehicles so follow the recce-on-foot rule and wade through a flooded wadi or any other potential hazard first with a stick or shovel to test the condition of the bottom (rocky? level? soft?) and also the depth. If the depth exceeds the height above ground of the bottom of the fan, the ensuing under-bonnet spraybath could cause ignition failure on a petrol engined vehicle.

Shield and wading plugs. If the water is of this depth, drop a sheet of plastic down behind the radiator grille to hold back the inrush of water to the fan area. On Land Rover products where one is provided, insert the wading plug into the clutch bell-housing and, on the latest 2.5 litre diesel Land Rovers a wading plug must be fitted to the drain hole in the bottom of the cam shaft belt drive housing. It is essential to remember this one as damage to the toothed belt, its breakage and major engine damage can be the final outcome. Inserting these wading plugs will mean getting down on

Don't regard Camel Trophy desperadoes in 6 feet of water as heroes. They are stuck; with wrecked engines. Stop, wade, prod with a long pole for hidden holes or rocks.

your back under the vehicle so be prepared for it and do it before you get to the soft mud.

On any vehicle, satisfy yourself that the axle breathers cannot ingest water during wading. If you do not, the sudden cooling and contracting of the axle casings can cause water to be sucked in through the breathers and contaminate the axle oil. Land Rover products are fitted with extended axle breather pipes that vent high up on the body or under the bonnet and these will keep water out of the axles.

Slow; small bow wave. Always drive slowly in water to minimise spray. Driving at about walking pace will produce a low bow-wave that will dip down behind the bumper area and keep water away from the fan see photo on page 5.3 - 3. The magazine photographers would have you believe that going through water should be done fast with the maximum commotion and spray but, again, the media are wrong.

Fan belt, air intake ... no! Do not remove the fan belt to prevent spray as doing so will mean the water pump (and sometimes other accessories) will cease to revolve and serious damage could be done to the engine. On petrol engines use WD40 spray on the ignition harness. If your engine air intake is dunked and the engine ingests water the damage will be immediate and catastrophic; water in cylinders is incompressible.

Driving in dust

Avoid it. The small subliminal pressures of perceived convention lead people to accept what, left to themselves, they would not accept. Driving in dust is one such situation. 'I'm on an expedition and expeditions are dusty, therefore ...' etc. There is a surprising amount you can about driving in dust. Hanging back to let it clear the road before proceeding is the most obvious one. When the wind direction or the direction of the road changes, it is sometimes worthwhile stopping and switching off for a minute or two to let the dust clear. Don't let the feeling that you must press on subject your engine and its air filter to needless amounts of dust.

Throttle-off. On little-frequented bush roads a truck coming towards you will subject you to a dust bath of generous dimensions as you pass whether you like it or not, but even here you can reduce the intake of dust by dipping the clutch and taking your foot off the throttle. The rpm will drop from its previous figure of maybe 2000 to about 500 and, while you are in the dust cloud you will ingest a quarter the dust you otherwise would. When clear, gently up with the revs, feed in the clutch and glow with contentment!

High intakes. Raised air intakes are usually installed to enhance wading depth – provided other modifications are applied as well – but many are fashioned with aft-facing air scoops. While not doing much for the volumetric ('sucking-in') efficiency of the engine, they will help a little with keeping larger sand particles out of the intake tract and the height helps too.

Turbo diesels - stopping

Lubricant matters. Due to the extremely high rpm at which the impellers turn on turbo-charged diesels, most vehicle manufacturers using turbos lay down a procedure for switching off the engine. To ensure the turbo has slowed to minimum speed, switch off the engine only after 10 seconds or so of idling; to switch off with the turbo running at high speed means it would run-down from high rpm without positive oil pressure to the bearings. This could cause bearing failure in the turbo charger.

Dust is a killer in engines. Ensure intake hose clamps are perfect with no cracks to ingest dust. Filters can take only so much. Keep out of dust, throttle-off appropriately.

Open-top driving is a very good reason to keep out of dust but clogged air filters and the danger of dust making it through to the engine is far more serious.. In a sandstorm (left) stop, switch off the engine and wait till it is finished. With passing trucks, and thick dust (bottom) dip the clutch at this point – below – letting revs die; when clear bring revs back to where they were and feed in the clutch.

Section 5.3.1

Operations:

Driver training

Use the engines of both vehicles when towing out a stuck vehicle. And use a marshaller that both drivers can see to give the signal to let in the clutches at exactly the same time.

Training

Where to learn. For any expedition involving track or off-road driving, special sessions of pre-expedition driver training on rough country should be regarded as essential - as well as enormous fun. As indicated in Section 5.3 'Driving', off-road driving schools are now widely available in different parts of the country. Most of these schools will allow 'freelance' use of their ground for a day-pass fee. Special permission for bona fide expeditions can often be obtained for the use of military training areas which often have the advantage of being more of a sand/gravel terrain and thus nearer to some overseas conditions. It is far better to make your mistakes there first than with a heavily laden machine in the bush, desert or forest. Your aim should be to become completely comfortable with the full range of your vehicle's capabilities before you set off. The expedition itself is not the place to learn how to drive a 4x4.

Know your transmission. As already indicated, the main differences most people will find between an ordinary car and an expedition 4x4 is in the transmission. The following lesson list is based on training programmes used for a number of major overseas expeditions and starts with familiarisation with the transmission and gearbox. It then goes on to applications of the various facilities offered. It is essential to know exactly what type of 4x4 system and transfer box your vehicle has before you start; if in any doubt see:

Section 4.1 'Expedition vehicles', page 4.1 - 17 – types of 4x4.

Section 5.3 'Driving' – page 5.3 - 14 – 4x4 vehicle systems.

THE LAND ROVER EXPERIENCE companion volume has space to deal with the subject more fully and, despite the title, applies to most generic off-road situations. The book embodies the experience and teaching of Land Rover's own driving school which, in addition to one-day courses and instructors courses, can tailor a short course especially for an expedition.

Abbreviations: 4WD = four wheel drive, H = high ratio, L = low ratio, 4L = 4th gear low ratio, 2H = 2nd gear, high ratio, etc. R = reverse.

Lesson 1: Gearbox and transmission

Brief

Gear levers, diff locks. Recap on uses of both (or with early Land Rovers, all three) 'gear levers'. How, when (and when not) to engage 4WD in a part-time 4x4 vehicle; in a full-time 4x4 how, when (and when not) to lock the centre differential. When to use, and not use, axle diff locks, if fitted.

High and low ratio. Engage low ratio only when stopped – low to high on the move will be tried later (see also page 5.3 - 31). Use hand brake only when stopped if transmission brake fitted (Land Rover and Bedford.)

Synchromesh. Know which gears are fitted with synchromesh and which not – most modern 4x4s have synchro on all gears though this does sometimes make the gear change slow and obstructive.

Early Land Rovers, trucks – moving off. Early Land Rovers (Series 1 and 2) and some trucks where synchro is only on 3rd are cases worthy of special attention. Engaging 1st or R prior to moving off sometimes results in a grating noise before the gears engage due to motion of layshafts in the gearbox; make it a habit to touch 3rd (ie with clutch down go into and out of 3rd so that its synchro cones stop the layshaft spinning) before engaging 1 or R and the engagement will be quiet.

Early Land Rovers, trucks – double de-clutching. There is a need to double de-clutch into any non-synchro gear – going down or up. If you are not familiar with it, double de-clutching is a means, where no synchromesh exists, of changing gear in a way that matches the engine rpm to that appropriate to the gear you are going into and at the same time gives the layshafts in the gearbox a chance to assume the right speed too (see page 5.3 - 7). Done properly it is very quick indeed (quicker than an obstructive synchromesh) – and very satisfying!

Practice

On level tarmac practise changes up and down, first in H and then in L boxes using all gears – right down to 1st on the move. Double de-clutch if you have a vehicle that needs it. Get used to the very much lower road speeds that prevail when you are using low ratio. When quiet and making clean quick changes on tarmac (including 1st), repeat on bumpy ground which will be more demanding and more like expedition conditions. Even when you have synchromesh, boost the revs while passing through neutral on a downward change.

Axle: Remember implications of differential on soft going allowing single-wheel spin.

Lesson 2: Low ratio to high ratio on the move

Brief

The ability to do an on-the-move change from low ratio to high ratio is very useful where a stop and restart in high would not be possible or convenient, eg in softish sand where you need low ratio to start, can accelerate in low box to get some speed and would then be ready to carry on in high now that you have the vehicle properly moving. You will have noticed in Lesson 1 that there is some overlap in road speed between low ratio and high ratio – the high gears in low ratio give a faster road speed than the lowest gears in high ratio (see diagram page 4.1 - 24). You will make use of this, changing from 3rd low box to 2nd high box on the move. (This is a change-over point that suits current Land Rover prod-

ucts; it may be different on other makes. Consult your driver's handbook.) The basis of the change, having got to your speed, is to double de-clutch from low to high using the transfer gear lever followed by moving the main gear lever as well: see page 5.3 - 31 and *The Land Rover Experience* book which also covers the case of automatic transmission.

Practice

Practise this on and off-road. There will be a difference since the rate of vehicle deceleration while all the lever-moving is going on will be greater in the off-road case.

Lesson 3: Slippery conditions, poor traction

Brief

Traction is float and push. If the ground has low weight-bearing strength plus low longitudinal shear strength – and they generally go together – then you have poor traction. The vehicle will both sink and find it easy to spin its wheels rather than move forward against the resistance of the terrain. Lowering tyre pressures helps the weight bearing problem since it spreads the weight over a greater area and going from 4x2 into 4x4 helps the other by, again, spreading the horizontal stress over four wheels instead of just two. So lower the tyre pressures (see page 5.3 -30), engage 4x4 and be gentle with the throttle. A gentle right foot, smooth driving and

avoiding too low a gear reduce horizontal stress. It is analogous to jumping off a pie crust. Avoiding wheel spin will also ensure you do not dig yourself in. Get out of 4WD and blow up tyres as soon as possible; do not exceed reduced-pressure speed maxima.

Practice

Applicable throughout all driving cross country. During training this is demonstrable on mud or grass steep slopes; you will also see that use of 2nd gear gives better traction and less wheel spin than 1st which tends to over-torque the wheels and spin them too easily.

Lesson 4: Hills up and down

Brief

Basic rules for climbing and descending steep slopes:

1. On-foot recce if in ANY doubt.
2. Gear to use. Going down, for best retardation, usually 1st, L. In some cases, use the same gear down a slope as you would use going up – which is usually 2L or 3L; note this down-slope technique applies in loose, dry bush or desert conditions but not in muddy UK practise situations. Automatics tend to be poor on engine braking too so though you have gone up a steep slop in 3L, you would switch to 1L for the descent.
3. Always go straight at a slope, not diagonally or you risk roll-over.
4. Avoid wheel spin, emergencies. You get best traction when there is no wheel spin so do not select too low a gear. Emergencies: see page 5.3 - 24 concerning a

failed climb. It is essential to be aware of the correct procedures. Downhill, if the vehicle is getting away from you, add throttle or de-clutch and use gentle cadence braking (see p 5.3 - 26). If you look like failing going up: quit early before wheel spin slews you, then dead-engine reverse re-start. Be sure to come back down the hill with both hands on the wheel to stop the steering running away, and come back down the same way you went up – at right angles to the slope.

Practice

Demonstrate effects of too low a gear (which will result in wheel spin and not getting up the hill), demo reverse re-start. Familiarise yourself on steep ups and downs. If you can find one, use a long loose/dry test hill with a rapid gear down-change near to the top to consolidate lesson 1.

Lesson 5: Obstacle clearance, traversing very rough ground

Brief

Be aware of the difference between underbelly clearance and under-axle clearance. The latter is invariably the lower and the lowest points are under the axle differential drain plugs. Spend time looking at the underneath to see what would happen if you bellied-out on a hump. Bellying is not recommended but only if you are sure the belly-point is on soft ground such as the edge of a dune

then it is acceptable to do a minor plough-through. Be aware of the implications of approach and retreat angle when crossing ditches; beware tow hooks, silencers etc. Main principles, as ever, are on-foot recce first then use of a competent marshaller using signs (see page 5.3 - 18) not voice. Driver should watch marshaller not road. Minor dips to be taken diagonally to avoid both-wheels-at-once thump; but beware the frequent problems of diagonal suspension wheel spinning. Dig or remove obstacles in path. Make vehicle 'flow' over rough ground rather than jolt; use 1L for enhanced control over large rocks, steps, etc. Use of 4x4 in a part-time 4x4 vehicle spreads transmission shocks; always use on rough ground, corrugations, etc, but not (if applicable) with diff-lock engaged.

Practice
Cautious gully driving after on-foot recce. Practise marshalling procedures and threading between boulders; use sticks or cardboard boxes placed in the ground for practise marshalling first. Try low speed crawl over rocks in 1L. Provoke diagonal suspension; practise distant width-judging using two assistants with vertical poles.

Lesson 6: Recovery (see Section 5.4)

Brief
Be aware of procedures with and without a tow-out vehicle to help. With no tow, 'landscaping' and use of sand channels is usually inevitable but try reversing out before situation gets too bad. Admit defeat early rather than dig in with wheel spin. Self-recovery: reduce tyre pressures, off load, clear obstacles manually, brush-wood, sand ladders etc. under wheels for grip. Third degree by jacking vehicle up and placing driveway under the wheels. Tow recover principles: long tow rope so tow-ing vehicle is on firm ground; co-ordinated use of power from both vehicles (assistant/marshaller signals and both clutches engaged at the same moment). Tow points: do

not attach tow ropes to axles (brake pipe damage?) or centre of bumper. Consider multi-vehicle tandem tow: same principles but two vehicles pulling one. Again use a marshaller/co-ordinator to ensure all the clutches are let in at the same moment. Always have people stand clear of ropes in tension.

Practice
Practice will probably be self-generating during the course of practise driving but a demonstration of a recov-ery tow and a tandem tow will be worth it to show use of the co-ordinator and the need to use signs and not turn the exercise into a shouting competition.

Lesson 7: Rules for sand driving

Summary
There are special applications of all the foregoing when operating on sand and a summary is worthwhile. On dunes or sand sheet don't brake, coast to a halt in case sand crust breaks; for similar reasons carry out a very careful pull-away. Remember the pie crust analogy; sand is worse when previously traversed and cut up hence the need to avoid preceding vehicle tracks. Low tyre pressures, sand tyres, gentle right foot, use highest 4x4 gear possible so as not to over-torque the wheels and provoke wheel spin. Sand provides firmer going

when damp; cool dewy morning better than hot noon. Beware following winds, overheating engines and high oil temperatures – the latter often going unnoticed. Topography: the vital necessity of on-foot recce – avoid soft small hollows in dune formations which you may never get out of, beware dune crests, slip faces. It is worth repeating: on foot recce necessary as always, post helper on dune lip to marshal you towards it at right angles if you have to descend it. DIBS mirror (see Sec 4.2 'Vehicle modifications', p 4.2 - 34) is invaluable on all untrodden sand.

Lesson 8: Convoy driving

The one behind
The underlying rationale for convoy driving is the security of the group – sticking together with each vehicle in sight of the one ahead and the one following. The basic responsibility of any vehicle driver is to keep an eye on the vehicle behind at all times. Thus anything happen-ing to that following vehicle to delay or stop it will cause the vehicle ahead to stop – and so on up the convoy line so that no vehicle can break down and be left on its own. The principle naturally applies even if there are only two vehicles in a group and should be thoroughly inculcated

into all members of an expedition. The recriminations after a vehicle has got 'left behind' are probably the most common cause of altercation on any average expedition; don't let it happen on yours. Dusty conditions where vehi-cles do not wish to follow too closely and where aft visi-bility is restricted have to be accommodated by using a go-stop principle; the gap between the vehicles is increased to keep out of the dust cloud but contact is maintained by stopping every now and then until the fol-lowing vehicle catches up. See also Sec 5.6, 'Emergencies'.

Exercises

The following exercises consolidate lessons, espe-cially the egg and spoon:

Through the gears. Start in 4L, use all the gears and cross the finishing line at 25 mph. Technique: start in 4L, down to 3L, 2L, 1L using minimum distance, up to 2L, then into 1H, accelerate hard in 1H and 2H, use 3H and 4H as late as possible. 'In gear' means foot off clutch. Marks deducted for noisy changes.

Slalom. Drive start to finish through alternate poles;

then reverse through same course.

Reverse into parking slot. Reverse into 'kerb side' slot 1.5 times vehicle length, 6ft wide. Poles to be used as markers, wheels to be within 12in of kerb.

Egg and spoon auto cross. Passenger holds egg and spoon out of window during marked out cross coun-try route. Driver must drive smoothly enough not to allow the egg to leave the spoon. Very good value as an exer-cise and embodies the whole ethos of smooth operation.

Section 5.4

Operations:

Recovery

COVERAGE OF THIS SECTION

The big picture

Lift and pull

... when all about you ... . Don't let being stuck upset you, especially if you are new to off-road driving; you will learn to take it in your stride. So sudden can be the change from breezy, got-it-licked progress to a stuck-for-eternity bogging; so sudden the flick of timescales from distances in minutes to hours or days; so sudden the change of prospect from stop-for-camp-and-a-brew-soon to a doomed-forever digathon, that it may be hard, in the light of such subjective feelings, to regard a serious bogging as subject to a simple and inviolable analysis that applies to all 'recovery situations'.

It is almost worth printing out the contents list opposite onto a little plastic card to buoy your spirits when the blow strikes, but in reality all 'stuck' events do break themselves down into a lift and pull analysis. If you are wondering if it helps to know this, then the answer really does have to be yes. Any stuck vehicle is afflicted by a lack of one or the other component and many are stricken by a combination of both. At worst you may have to dig beneath a grounded chassis to put the weight back on the wheels, then jack up each wheel, one at a time to insert some flotation or traction medium beneath it – and then be prepared to do it again five metres further on. It amounts to nothing more complicated than dogged persistence and an instant adjustment of attitude, all sculpted by a little ingenuity and cunning.

Recognition, acceptance is all. A stoic 'Ah, what have we here?', or a borrowed

Handling a recovery situation is a lot to do with attitude – confidence that you can get out. It may be mucky and take time but the methodical approach always pays.

Just as well it is not raining (left). Power, conditions, and load spreaders at the bottom of huge bog-hole came out in favour of the trucks – just. Not so the innocuous looking patch below which struck at dusk. The trailer precluded a reverse-out but off-loading, disconnecting and a couple of hours work next morning succeeded. Note 'sand' ladder!

'Er, Houston, we have a problem', or a gentle Dickensian or Shakespearian oath like 'Fiddlesticks!' or 'A pox upon it!' are worth nurturing in your armoury of protective mechanisms when you feel you have a bad one on your hands. Recognise when you have a problem; recognise it may take a little time; and recognise that, with patience you will overcome it. Take your time; finish your metaphoric game of bowls or your Murraymint; put on your overalls and gumboots, empty your pockets so you don't lose your keys in the mud or sand, smile at your colleagues and get out the shovels.

When you're stuck don't dig in further with wheel spin. Always try reversing out first. Almost anything is possible but you will need basic recovery tools.

Don't make it worse

Avoid wheel spin. Above all, your acceptance of fate's challenge must prevent you from making things worse by applying bootfuls of throttle and wheel spin that will cause you to sink till the chassis is grounded and your digging debt is suddenly doubled. As you step out to size up the situation remember it only amounts, conceptually, to lift and pull. Lifting the vehicle to get something grippy under the wheels – just pushing sand ladders against the tyres may do it – and then applying some pull, either traction from the engine once it has something

to grip on, or push from passengers, or pull from another vehicle or a winch. It is always those two components and you will usually get there in the end. The use of 'usually' rather than 'always' takes account of salt-flats. Keep out of salt marsh!

Initiative conquers all. Recognising the simple two-component approach, recognising that the vehicle, with erstwhile momentum behind it has come to a halt and is unlikely to respond to trying to start from stationary with a screaming engine will direct your attention to the cerebral approach. What you have to do is improve the situation on both counts – various means of jacking/floating, various means of improving traction/grip; offloading and the like.

Reversing out. Start by trying to reverse out. If it stuck going forward with momentum, the laws of physics are trying to tell you something.

Take the right tools

Shovels and load spreaders. Take bad terrain boggings in your stride – when you stop, get out, grab the shovels and start digging without even a break in the conversation, you're getting the right attitude. But

Quite why this vehicle chose this route is not clear; even the texture of the mud at the front wheels indicates much previous churning to little avail. It does indicate the need to reverse out, however – possibly with the aid of the PSP under the rear wheels, after ensuring the centre differential is locked!

Tools of the trade. Load spreaders – PSP left, Barong articulated panels right. Note shackles and <u>long</u> tow ropes to keep tug away from soft ground that stopped the first vehicle. Optional long handled shovels or short ones that can be 'bent'; bottle jack and load spreader block. Other problems may present even when track temporarily good – chain-saw useful in forests. When rescuing others (below left) who have no recovery gear, stop clear of bad patch. Etiquette seems to demand visitors do the digging.

you must have the basic tools which amount to:
- Shovels
- Load spreader cum traction provider
- Jack(s) with load spreader
- Long tow rope – 30-50 metres
- Winch – possibly.

All sorts of hardware fulfil the functions above and each has its own pluses and minuses.

Shovels – uses. A little thought is worthwhile on shovels. Though they will be used on the trip for digging refuse holes and other routine tasks, in the recovery context their main purpose will probably be digging out in front or behind the wheels in order to insert the sand ladders. For this, quite small shovels can be made to work well, especially if they are the kind that can have the blade end set at right angles to the shaft. Such shovels are light and easy to stow but do not have the reach that a larger 'garden' or military type has when it comes to digging beneath the grounded chassis of a vehicle that has bellied on a hump. This job is back-breaking enough anyway and keeping one shovel for the purpose, should it arise, could be worth it.

Flotation and pull are invariably involved. Get the wheels back on firm ground, spread their load, give them grip and then add pull or push. Use <u>long</u> tow ropes.

Floating, lifting

Floating

Flotation. The aim is to spread the load transmitted by the footprint of the tyre to a larger piece of ground. Usually a pair of items is enough – one for each front or rear wheel – but there may be times, on a two-vehicle trip, where the load spreaders from both vehicles are beneficially used to get one vehicle mobile. The requirements are:

Load-spreader cum grip-giver is what you put under the wheel or push at the wheel edge in the hope the wheel will 'bite' on it. Digging a bit at the insertion point helps.

- Short enough to lay on the ground between front and rear wheels
- Easy for one person to carry a pair – at the run
- Load spread area 8-10 times a tyre footprint – minimum
- Enough stiffness to perform a degree of 'bridging'
- Grippy surface
- Easy to stow

A wide range of hardware has been pressed into service for this job. The oft-quoted use of 'brushwood' to give grip to a spinning wheel in practice relies more on optimism than practicality; it is never there when you want it, the small stuff is ineffective and the larger branches get flicked up into the underpinnings of the vehicle. More usual flotation recovery aids are:

Clockwise from upper left: long bridging channels are large, heavy but versatile. Classic aluminium sand ladders, here used as a foursome (look how fine the sand is) are very effective and light as a pair. Dig sand away before inserting; stow on side hooks. Note close rung spacing, pointed ends – and danger of ladder kicking up under vehicle. Articulated Barong panels preclude this; light, very grippy, easy to stow inside. PSP (bottom left) is cheap, crude, awkward to stow and handle, too flexible for bridging role. Not much top surface grip. Advantage is wide availability.

• *Bridging channels.* Long, strong, bulky, heavy, good for bridging small ditches, clumsy to use and difficult to stow but may be appropriate for wet jungle conditions.

• *PSP. (Pierced steel planking)* Bendy sheets of steel or alloy with rows of holes and hooks down the edges. Widely used, available, cheap. Little longitudinal strength, little top surface grip, awkward to carry, heavy.

• *Sand ladders.* Aluminium ladders, 5.5 ft long, specially made, rungs close-spaced (about 5.5 inches); light, versatile, effective, expensive to make as specials, can kick up under vehicle if not positioned properly. Small bridging capability. Recommended.

• *Barong channels.* Hard to obtain now, a pair of articulated triple-sets of alloy grip treads. Very light, easy to stow, no under-vehicle kick-up. Excellent.

Use. It is almost invariably necessary to dig in front of the bogged wheels to clear space to put the sand channels in position. Don't skimp this digging; a minute or two extra to ensure the wheel grips first time is well worth it. Rarely, in serious conditions, it will necessary to jack a wheel up to insert the sand channel beneath it – see below.

Other flotation improvers. Two other measures can be taken:

• Reduce tyre pressures
• Offload the vehicle.

You will probably have reduced tyre pressures to track or emergency soft levels (*WARNING:* Do not exceed the speed maxima for these pressures – see p 5.3 - 30) to improve flotation but the obvious aid in a serious and prolonged bogging is to lighten the vehicle. This is a chore but take it as part of the normal sequence of recovery measures. Removing 6-800 kg of payload can make a big difference.

Lift

Jacking. Jacking a vehicle in a recovery situation is sometimes required:

• To lift it enough to insert flotation aids such as sand ladders or
• To lift it off a rock or hump upon which the vehicle is bellying.

Again, a range of jacking devices are available, each having the usual trade-off of bulk, weight, ease of use, height of jacking, need to crawl beneath etc. Two main jacking concepts prevail:

• *Those that jack the axle*
    Hydraulic jack
    Screw jack
    Rim jacking (see below)
• *Those that jack up the body*
    Side/bumper jacks
    'Hi-lift' jack
    Air bag.

'Sand channels' is the generic term for things to stick under the wheels for grip and flotation. PSP is cheap but spend a little extra on aluminium sand ladders.

Heigh, ho! First note the unpredictability of the surface – firm wheel tracks just 30 metres away. Too much throttle beyond the 'not going to make it' point has scooped out sand; note characteristic angle of rear axle, right wheel low through prop-shaft torque. Having to jack on chassis means high lift to account for suspension drop before the sand channels can be slid under the wheels.

Jacking the wheel itself, directly or with an adaptor, is easier than lying down in the mud to jack under the axle. Spade acts as spreader, blocks as spacers. Small piece of wood at rim avoids slippage. Hi-lift jack (below) is world-famous body lifter, classically unstable. Here used to 'pole vault' out of ruts.

can sometimes be done, either straight onto the upper part of the wheel rim or using some kind of adapter. It is worth spending time to make up such an item for your particular wheels before the expedition; it will save considerable inconvenience and speed up the recovery process. Using this method, you will still need load spreaders but these can be placed adjacent to the wheel and positioned more accurately; against it is the fact that with the jack there you will not have total freedom to position the sand ladder under the wheel.

Jacking the body. Ease of access is the usual advantage of jacking the vehicle body rather than the axles. The time spent muckily grubbing under the vehicle to find the axle and position a jack safely is avoided. The disadvantage is that raising the body means that the axles have to fall to the full extent of the springs before the wheels themselves will leave the ground. This usually means a lot more jacking and considerable jacking height when it is done. Nevertheless, the well established Hi-lift is speedy and versatile, albeit heavy, difficult to stow and, like any jack of this kind, potentially dangerous for its lateral instability. Regard any vehicle on a jack of this kind as a potential 'pole vaulter' anchored to the top of a toppling pole. This kind of jack also requires special bumper or body-side adapters with which to engage; these in many cases will have to be installed in advance as a special modification – see Section 4.2 'Vehicle modifications', p 4.2 - 30.

Air bag jacks that plug into the vehicle exhaust are quick and simple and with a very soft 'footprint'. A potential disadvantage is that they bear upon what may well include sharp edges ready to puncture the bag or items that were not designed to be part of the jacking process. Establish in advance exactly where it can be used on the vehicle without damage. It is comparatively light and not too bulky.

To put things under the wheels: jack the axle – awkward but a short lift; or the body – easy access but you jack till the suspension travel is taken up.

Jacking the axle. Jacking an axle gets straight to the root of the problem – ie it lifts the needy wheel directly – but usually means lying down in the mud, digging a space beneath the axle, inserting a wooden baulk to act as a load spreader and then operating the jack. Jacking the wheel itself, directly and from the 'outside' of the vehicle

Air bag inflated by vehicle's own exhaust is a simple, low-stress, low effort jacking device, light and not too bulky. Be careful not to jack on components that cannot take the strain or may puncture the bag. A stout sack 'load spreader' on top and another beneath to preclude slip on muddy ground are useful adjuncts.

Pulling, pushing

The gamut

The next move. Having lifted the vehicle (not always necessary) or re-established traction by other means you have got it to the 'pull' stage of the 'lift and pull' big picture sketched at the beginning of the section. The gamut of options that present themselves are:

- Low transfer box – more 'power'
- People pushing
- Tow by other vehicle(s)
- Winch of some kind.

High gears – 4th or 5th – in the low ratio box useful for sprinting down tracks; also give rapid access to very low gearing.

Low transfer box

Not too low. Use of low transfer is covered in Section 5.3 'Driving'. It is unlikely you will need telling about use of low transfer gears and the only circumstances in which you will find yourself changing to low range is if the bogging took you by surprise. There is a lesson here, though and that concerns use of the high gears within the low range gearbox which can, in 5th gear low, take you up to a comfortable 30 mph. Using this rather than, say, 2nd gear high range, means you have a set of closely stepped other gears ready to go down into without stopping – a range that will take you down to a max torque road speed of about 5 mph should it be required.

So use the low range gearbox in the higher gears if there is any doubt about the terrain. The only thing to be careful of is using too low a gear and over-torqueing the ground so as to induce wheel spin.

People pushing

Power to the people. It is a constant source of surprise to find how effective is the power of people pushing when trying to unstick a vehicle. There is little more to be said except that a 'people carrier' conversion

Once you have the wheels bearing weight (with grip) the engine may get you out. Don't use too low a gear. People pushing are very effective for their small horsepower.

Pushing it ... . Back wheel sinkage indicates sand ladders should be out but a determined push saves it. This time ... !

of a 4x4 or truck can summon extraordinary unsticking powers when the cargo gets out to push; don't let the just sit there thinking their effort will be too puny. It really works; even with one or two shoulders to the wheel.

Tow by other vehicle(s)

Not too close. A tow by a second vehicle (or, in tandem tow, any number of other vehicles together) is hugely effective and one of two very good reasons for taking two vehicles on an expedition rather than just one. Make sure you do have a long tow rope – 30-50 metres – as this will ensure that the patch of soft ground that stopped the bogged vehicle will not also affect the one attempting to tow it out. See also that you have towing shackles and rings (page 4.2 - 30) and do not have to try to undo knots

Use long tow ropes so towing vehicle is not affected by the soft patch that caused the bogging. Use a marshaller to signal taking up slack and engaging clutches together.

that have been subjected to a ton or two of tightening in recovery.

Get it together – calmly. As mentioned before (see also photo page 5.3 - 38) use the engines of both (or all) the vehicles involved to aid the extraction. The only way to do this properly is to have an external marshaller co-ordinate the engagement of the clutches. A simple way, again using signs alone, is to:

- Ensure marshaller is about 15-30 metres ahead of the first vehicle
- Have the marshaller signal the first vehicle forward till the tow rope is tight
- Marshaller moves hand in a circle indicating to rev engines
- Marshaller drops hand to indicate clutches engage
- Marshaller ready to indicate 'Stop' (p 5.3 - 18) when lead vehicle is clear
- Reverse tow vehicle back a metre or so to take the tension off the rope.

The same applies to a tandem tow where two or more vehicles are involved. This technique (see photo) is a means of extracting a truck with two or more smaller vehicles. Again, the technique should be done with signals, calmly, deliberately and without a decibel competition with roaring engines. If you are helping a fellow traveller with whom you have not worked before, walk over and brief them on the signals and method you will use.

Safety. <u>Keep people away from tensioned tow ropes.</u> They can be lethal when they break. As for the rope itself, the pull required to move a stuck vehicle can, in bog or clinging clay, be as much as 50% of the

Where a vehicle is towed out backwards – a common case – a second marshaller is needed to relay the coordinating marshaller's signals to the driver with his back to the towing vehicle.

Tandem tow

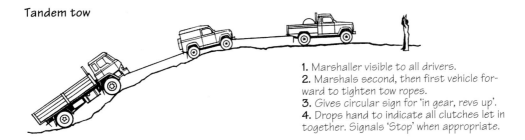

1. Marshaller visible to all drivers.
2. Marshals second, then first vehicle forward to tighten tow ropes.
3. Gives circular sign for 'in gear, revs up'.
4. Drops hand to indicate all clutches let in together. Signals 'Stop' when appropriate.

weight of the vehicle being moved. To account for possible damage and sensible safety margins factor this by three or four. Thus for a laden Defender 110 (GVW 3050 kg) you would be advised to use a rope of breaking strain 4.5-6.0 tonnes. This would equate to an 18 or 20 mm 3-strand polypropylene rope. This is the preferred material since nylon has excessive extension and is also adversely affected by ultraviolet light. Use the largest diameter towing pintles you can; never less than the diameter of the rope. Wash the grit out of it periodically.

Winches

Think hard first. Give careful thought to the implications of a winch before buying. It is more than an add-on accessory – heavy, expensive, often requiring uprated front springs or heavy duty alternator and an extra battery. Fuller coverage is given to the subject in *The Land Rover Experience* but a quick overview can be set out here. Despite knee-jerk reaction in favour of a winch, it is not always applicable to expeditions. Think where you are going and what you will be doing. There is nothing to winch onto in desert except another vehicle and if you have another vehicle you are better advised to use the long tow rope and do a co-ordinated tow recovery as indicated above. In jungle, however, through the forest or on tracks where the trees come down close to the road, a winch can earn its keep, as well as clearing fallen trees.

Think on possible usage and the time of usage – casual or heavy duty; the differences

being intermittent light use or continuous heavy day-long winching. For the latter, electric winches would seldom be suitable due to the frenetic environment in which they operate. Overheating would be a problem and the vehicle engine would have to run fast to keep the batteries charged. Hydraulic or mechanical drum winches or a capstan winch would be better suited to heavy duty work and these could do the work all day with the engine never rising above idle rpm.

A winch would have its uses in emergencies such as righting a vehicle that has rolled over or fallen among rocks. A Tirfor hand winch, however, could be used for this; it is light, cheap, versatile, very slow

Use a marshaller to control a tow-out; signals, no shouting. Calm and controlled. Think hard before investing in a winch; a second vehicle to tow takes some beating.

Classic tandem-tow situation: two smaller vehicles help a low power-weight ratio truck up a difficult slope. Visibility problems mean marshaller has to stand beside rather than in front on the lead vehicle.

but controllable.

Training. If you do install a winch it is essential that you get professional training in its use; to use the well-worn parallel about riding bicycles, actually doing winching under instruction is better than reading about it. Again, the off-road driving schools will be able to provide this. As with driving and knowledge of your transmission system, for a winch to be of any real use you must be totally comfortable with all aspects of its operation including (especially) its limits and where it would be inadvisable to use it. You are using a system not just an add-on and you will need, in addition:

• D-shackles
• Tree strap
• Split pulley block
• Ground anchors
• Back anchor-strap
• Gloves

You will see how the cost and weight rise all the time – especially if you are to carry a comprehensive set of ground anchors. Winching operations of this kind fit better into a multi-vehicle party where one vehicle can be kept light of routine payloads to be earmarked as the recovery vehicle.

Winches are unequalled where enormous power at very slow speed is required. Heavy and costly, they need accessories such as ground anchors or drive-in stakes.

From top: Capstan winch. electric drum winch, split pulley block permits cable insertion without threading; ground anchors to prevent tug moving forward. Very heavy. Large picture shows tree strap in use (to prevent ring-barking and killing tree) plus pulley used for angled pull of stricken vehicle. Note operator stands clear of cable.

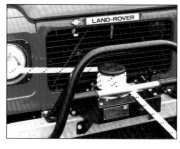

WINCH TYPES AND GENERAL CHARACTERISTICS

Type	Applications	For	Against
Electric drum	Intermittent light, medium or heavy duty use according to specification.	Low cost, simple installation, relatively low weight 54-87 kg. Wide range from light to medium/heavy duty. Easy to use. Minimal maintenance. Wire stored on drum.	Electric motor will overheat if used for long periods. Very high amperage draw from battery necessitates high engine rpm and alternator output to recharge. Installation may need second battery.
Hydraulic drum	Continuous heavy duty industrial use.	Can operate for long continuous periods of industrial use with engine at low output or tick-over. Automatic rpm control. Vehicle has capability for other hydraulic tools/applications.	High initial cost for winch and PTO hydraulic pump installation. Needs specialised maintenance for precision components. Engine must be running. Heavy – up to around 115 kg.
Mechanical drum	Continuous heavy duty industrial use.	Can operate for long continuous periods of industrial use with engine at low output or tick-over.	High initial cost for PTO gear and drive shafts to winch position. Two-man operation – one controls engine, one controls winch. Engine must be running. Heavy – up to around 112 kg.
Mechanical or hydraulic capstan	Continuous heavy duty industrial use.	Can operate for long continuous periods of industrial use with engine at low output or tick-over. Constant pulling power due to rope being constant distance from drum axis all the time. Easy to operate. No limit to length of rope used. Around 63 kg.	High cost plus specialist maintenance if hydraulic drive. No room for mechanical drive on current Tdi Defender. Rope not contained on winch. Engine must be running.

Electric winches are frenetic on continual use – lots of amps, extra batteries, engine to charge etc. Capstan winches operate at idling rpm; the best for heavy duty use.

DATA ON SOME WINCH TYPES (Superwinch)

Type	Name	Max line pull	Gearbox type	Brake type	Free spool	Elec/hydraulic power requirements
Electric drum	1. X6	6000 lb	Planetary	Dynamic	Lever	12v, 390 amps
	2. X9	9000 lb	Planetary	In drum	Lever	12v, 435 amps
	3. Husky	8500 lb	Worm/wheel	Irreversible	Lever	12v, 360 amps
	4. E10	10000 lb	Planetary	Disc, wet	Plunger	12v, 360 amps
Hydraulic drum	1. H8	8000 lb	Planetary	Disc, wet	Plunger	32 litre pump, 2500 psi
	2. H14W	8000 lb	Worm/wheel	Irreversible	Plunger	32 litre pump, 2500 psi
Mechanical drum	1. H14W	8000 lb	Worm/wheel	Irreversible	Plunger	Power take-off shafts
Mechanical or hydraulic capstan		4000 lb	Worm/wheel	Irreversible	N/A	Power take-off shafts or PTO hydraulic pump

Terminology
1. Gearbox type. This is an indication of the kind of reduction gear used in the winch. Worm and wheel can be arranged (and is here) to be irreversible hence there is no need for a brake.
2. Free-spool. Free spooling is the process of disengaging the winch in order to reel out the cable to the item being winched. 'Lever' or 'plunger' indicates the method of activating winch cable release.
3. Brake. Braking is provided for the mid-pull power failure case. Knowledge of brake principle is needed. 'Dynamic' brake is only the running of the winch motor in high-geared reverse as a generator so it is a retarder rather than a stop brake. (X6CD has centre drum brake.) Drum and disc brakes activate automatically via one-way clutch in the event of power being lost in mid pull. Worm and wheel gearing is itself irreversible so runaway after power failure is just not possible.

Section 5.5

Operations:

Vehicle maintenance

COVERAGE OF THIS SECTION

Philosophy – preventive maintenance

Prevention better than cure. The whole philosophy behind keeping the expedition vehicle fit can be summed up in two words – preventive maintenance. A really thorough, no-compromises service and overhaul before the expedition will pay off far better than trying to cope with problems as they arise in the field. Vitally allied to reasonable and sensitive driving (see Section 5.3 'Driving'), maintenance on the expedition will probably then be limited to the 20 minute nightly inspection and rectification of minor defects en route (see end of this section, page 5.5 - 8 'Nightly inspection').

The expedition mechanic

Saints only. A very great deal depends upon the team member taking on the task of mechanic. His task becomes a manifestation of personality, sense of duty and tenacity. An eagle eye for detail, a mature ability to face facts, a total devotion to his task, an ability to influence his fellow team members and as much mechanical knowledge as possible are some of the qualities he must possess. This will apply during the pre-departure overhaul, for here no detail of the vehicle's condition must escape his notice, nothing can be glossed over, no hope-for-the-best attitudes adopted. The hard facts must always be faced and acted upon when oil leaks, mechanical wear and the implications of remedial work necessary are being considered. Faults will not go away or cure themselves just because it will be expensive or difficult, in the field, to fix them.

Know your limitations. One of the first facts to face is the expedition mechanic's own experience and knowledge. He should know his own limitations, know and admit what he does not know and work with more experienced people in preparing the vehicle.

But even here there is cause for considerable caution since many 'experts' in vehicle maintenance are jaundiced, ever open to expedient compromise and will rarely have the keen expeditioner's enthusiasm for thorough preparation; most notably, such 'experts', with depressing uniformity, rarely have the honesty to admit their limitations. Do not accept glib assurances about something being 'all right' until you are personally convinced. There is no special mystique about engineering that puts it above common-sense explanations – indeed, that is its very strength. Be gently insistent until you are happy in your own mind.

Pre-expedition inspection

The inspection. A new, run-in vehicle is the best way to start an expedition but budgets do not always stretch to this and a critical and thorough examination of the expedition vehicle must start as soon as it is acquired. A workshop manual is essential. Start at the ground and work up.

Are the tyres right for the job (see page 4.2 -21) and in top condition? It is best to start with new ones. Wheel bearings – jack up, are they free, smooth running, with correct end float? Brake drums off to check linings and operating cylinders, also hub oil seals. Are the axle cases bent? A ripple on the top surface will normally tell. Axle breathers must be serviceable (page 5.3 - 34, right-hand column, top), also differential housing oil seals and gaskets. Check leaf-spring-eye and shock absorber rubbers and mountings, spring-to-axle U-bolt fixings; check no spring leaves broken or unduly eroded by dust or rust. Prop shaft sliding and universal joints should not have excessive rotational or vertical play. Check underside of engine and gearbox for oil leaks – especially from around the clutch bell-housing drain hole since a slight leak there might indicate an oil seal failure in the rear main bearing and the possibility of oil getting to the clutch plate – disastrous if it happens in the field. Engine- and gearbox-to-chassis rubber mountings should be checked, also the condition of all brake pipes and hoses (the clutch hoses and mechanism come into this too) and the security and condition of the whole system. If in any doubt about the exhaust system change it. Trying to remove it in the field when it is very old, fragile and badly corroded can also lead to the discov-

Prevention is better than cure: comprehensive pre-expedition service is better than a huge spares kit. The expedition mechanic must have saintly integrity.

ery of immovable or broken studs in the exhaust manifold when you will have neither the extractors nor spare studs to fix the problem.

Chassis corrosion. Be especially vigilant about chassis rust and any signs of inexpert patch-up repairs having been undertaken; if there are any welded-on plates from earlier repairs this is not the vehicle for your expedition. A rust-weakened chassis is liable to fail catastrophically, usually at spring attachment points, on corrugated tracks endemic to desert and bush areas. Rust can also dangerously weaken towing-point attachments. Accept no compromises on chassis condition; if there is excessive rust or structural weakness you are looking at a reject vehicle.

Engine, systems. Similar thorough visual inspection in the engine compartment should be carried out, again being on the look-out for oil leaks, condition of hoses, clips, wiring, fuel pipes and unions, accessory drive belts, exhaust manifolds, radiator. Unless virtually new, renew water and heater hoses before departure. Check spark plug and carburettor condition; a compression test on each cylinder and a check of engine tune on an electronic tuner will be essential. If you have a diesel, passing the MOT emissions test will be a good indication of fuel system and injector condition. Go on to a full functional check of all aspects of the vehicle – steering, brakes, clutch performance and adjustment, engine power, gear boxes and transfer box controls. If in any doubt on shock-absorbers, renew them. Fitting contactless electronic ignition if this is not already standard is highly recommended; the contact breaker type is susceptible to dust erosion and needs frequent re-tuning to maintain best power and economy in the field. The Lumenition optical/electronic type has been used in the Sahara at under-bonnet temperature over 82°C – a very severe test. (See Section 4.2 'Vehicle modifications', page 4.2 - 5).

Guided tour. If you are not an experienced mechanic yourself – and even if you are there is a lot of sense in getting a corrob-

Give your vehicle an exceptionally rigorous pre-expedition inspection with assistance of full time professional followed by a major service and fresh oils – see Sec 2.6.

orative second opinion – do your inspection with, or under the guidance of, a reliable specialist on the vehicle type. It will not be easy to find such as person, for the reasons already stated, but they do exist; in many cases you will have to get past a glossy and professionally indifferent 'front office'. Be aware of your own limitations; if you have 'known Land Rovers for years', for instance, and are taking a model you have not used before, take guidance on what special foibles it may have in terms of maintenance and inspection. The whole examination is little more than a methodical and common-sense check of the complete vehicle.

Pre-expedition service. It almost goes without saying that you should have a major service – a 12000 or 24000 mile check – carried out before departure. If you have this done professionally, as you may have to with regard to the demands of modern vehicles and test equipment, try, if you possibly can, to be there while it is carried out. Your dealer may well – and understandably – demur at this but explaining where you are going and why and allowing him to choose a time to suit his workload will probably win him over. Acknowledge, even, that carrying out the work with an accompanying explanation is likely to take longer and incur higher costs, but meeting them will be well worth your while.

Lubricants

Only the best. This subject is covered fully in Section 2.6 'Fuel, oil, fluids' so a very brief summary will be given here. Use the best oil. There are many areas in expedition planning where a no-compromises approach is called for and this is one of them. Since implementing it here involves merely pouring in a can of good oil instead of a can of poor oil, it is also a very straightforward solution to put into effect. Do/remember three things:

1. There will be special grades of oil recommended by your vehicle manufacturer for high operating temperatures. Take advice if in any doubt. Phone the customer

technical departments of the major oil companies with details of your vehicle, the temperatures or conditions under which you will be operating and the fuels you will use. Then go through the sequence of oil selection on page 2.6 – 26.

2. Hackneyed as the phrase may be, you get what you pay for. The best oils are usually the most expensive; use a major name brand. Synthetic or part-synthetic oil will offer the best protection in limiting conditions but is expensive.

3. If you possibly can, take spare engine oil for top-up and an en-route oil change if miles covered indicate that will be necessary. However, different oils (except the highly unlikely vegetable-based castor oil) do mix – mineral/mineral and mineral/synthetic. So if you set out with top-grade UK oils and are unable to carry enough spare, top-ups with locally available oil will be acceptable. Stick to the recommended oil change intervals even if you are using a synthetic oil.

Nightly inspection

Regular and methodical. A thorough nightly inspection of the expedition vehicles is essential in order to nip trouble in the bud and prevent actual failures. An end-of-day inspection schedule for a Land Rover Defender 90 Tdi is at the end of this Section; it is comprehensive for this vehicle but it can easily be modified with additions or deletions for any vehicle. It highlights the kind of detail to look at, and the methodical sequence of starting underneath the vehicle, working round it inspecting the chassis and underpinnings, then inspecting the engine compartment in a similarly methodical way. The expedition should aim to stop to camp with sufficient daylight left to enable the vehicle inspection and routine maintenance to be done in daylight (about 1-1.5 hours before sunset).

Workwear. A groundsheet, pair of overalls, old beret and pair of working gloves are invaluable to save you and your clothing getting dirty working on the vehicle; washing water and laundry are always a problem

on expeditions and the Ragged Look for expedition folk went out of fashion years ago. Check tyre pressures and coolant level first thing in the morning when cold; don't fill the radiator to the brim as the coolant will only expand out through the overflow.

Tools

Two groups. Section 5.5.1 lists a typical set of spares and tools for a single-vehicle trip involving a Defender 90. Substantially the same weight, bulk and cost of equipment could support a multi-vehicle group equally well provided they were the same vehicle type. The list is given, as it were, verbatim, to indicate the detail that must be addressed and it can be easily adapted to any other make of expedition vehicle. The tools and spares are divided into two broad categories:

• Tools and spares special to purpose and vehicle type

• Tools and spares of a general 'fix-it' nature for when ingenuity, initiative and basic blacksmithery has to take over where the workshop manual runs out.

Take what you actually need. The expedition tool kit must be assembled with an eye to the particular vehicle and the pre-departure work on it will have brought to light most of the 'specials' required such as extra long socket extensions, wry-neck spanners, special-sized sockets, thin rimmed ring spanners (Land Rover prop shaft bolts) and whether the vehicle nuts and bolts are metric, AF or a mixture of thread types. This is where a sober and painstaking physical inspection of the vehicle and a scan through the workshop manual will pay off as it will indicate where special tools are required. It will also focus attention on what jobs can and cannot be undertaken in the field.

Tools for oil fillers. Particularly, check what tools you need for access to all the various oil filling and level apertures around the vehicle. Write this down at the top of your tool kit list – see page 5.5 - 13. Don't rely on there being 'something in the toolbox to fit'; the point is well illustrated in the current Land Rover R380 gearbox, which,

Work out nightly inspection schedule. Take tools specially selected for your vehicle – plus a set of 'blacksmithing' tools for the situations demanding initiative!

alone among all the other oil filling/level apertures (and indeed any other regularly visible fixings on the vehicle) requires a Torx 55 special adapter to remove the oil filling plug. You will find, if you have not done so already, that a Torx is a fitment that fairly well defies being moved by anything apart from the correct tool.

Fix-it tools. Vibration and bad tracks can often cause fatigue failure of vehicle parts and modifications in the field and black-smithing or sheet metal repairs may be called for. Hacksaws, files, metal shears, a large assortment of nuts and bolts and pop rivets, a rivet gun, large hand brace and set of drills should be taken with this in mind. A portable electric drill that can recharge from a 12v DC system would be useful – if you can find one. A small clamp-on vice that can be mounted on a bumper or tailgate is well worth the weight. Two jacks are better than one, and if one is a high lift bumper jack it can often be used in recovery situations enabling sand ladders to be placed under the wheels. Hi-lift jacks are heavy and difficult to stow without a special clamp; they are more use in muddy conditions than in the desert or bush. Tyre inflator – electric motor type – will be needed frequently, as well as a wide-ranging repair kit for tyre tubes and the sometimes vulnerable side walls of radial covers. Use bags for the tools rather than steel chests; bags do not rattle.

Spares too should be taken special to need and also (Sec 5.5.1) a selection of 'botching' materials for the unforeseen. Keep level plugs, tyre inner tubes sand and grit-free.

Spares

Two categories again. As with tools, spares fall into two groups:
- Special to vehicle-type spares
- General fix-it spares such as radiator sealant, WD40, Plus-Gas, Plastic Padding, fibreglass repair kits and the like.

Main kit. The main spares kit needs dis-ciplined and realistic thought. A thorough pre-expedition overhaul is better than a large spares pack; careful and infallible dri-ving can lessen the en route requirement even more – springs and half-shafts, for example, are broken by drivers and do not fail of their own volition. (See Section 5.3 'Driving' page 5.3 - 17 re transmission

brakes and half-shafts). However, hoses, fan belts, clutch and brake cylinder rubbers, electrics such as fuel pumps, coils, con-densers, HT leads and alternators are less predictable and are worth taking. Carburettor diaphragms, oil and fuel filters, air filter elements, electrical repair materials such as wire, terminals, 12v soldering iron, tape, fuses, bulbs should be taken, as well as a length of plastic tubing to use as a gravity fuel pipe with a can if the pump system fails.

A spares kit taken on a recent single-vehicle expedition is shown at Section 5.5.1 and can be modified according to vehicle type and its particular strengths or weak-nesses.

Fuel consumption and records

Keep a close eye. As already mentioned in the fuel planning section (Section 2.6 'Fuel, oil, fluids', page 2.6 - 4), monitoring fuel stock, rate of consumption and reserves related to distance-to-go is a survival funda-mental on many expeditions. Keep a log-book with a daily entry for each vehicle in which you record mpg so that any trends may be noted and apparent anomalies dou-ble-checked. It is useful also to record mileage, price of petrol bought and any parts failure or defects and remedial action taken. Note especially those items that will need attention at the next full servicing.

Cleanliness

Keep sand, mud, dust at bay. Finally cleanliness. Beating sand, mud and dust on an expedition may sound impossible but with care it need not be. Remember that every level-plug and filler cap removed carelessly can shake dust into the clean oil it is designed to retain. A small paint brush and a jam-tin half full of petrol should be used rigorously to clean down these or any sealing surfaces or parts before removing or working on them – or even to clean a sus-pected oil leak so that its condition can be monitored at the next evening inspection. It is an extension of the philosophy of facing facts – a few grains of sand can destroy a bearing.

Tyre tubes too. Cleanliness is especially important when mending punctures in tyres. Including a grain or two of sand between the inner tube and case of a hard-working radial tyre will ensure, as night follows day, another puncture later on. Cleanliness is perfectly feasible when fitting tyres; a large ground sheet on which to carry out the operation is essential.

Tips

Main battery disconnect. On vehicles with certain types of security alarm (such as post-1995/6 Range Rover, Discovery and Defender which have a back-up battery for this purpose) main battery disconnect will trigger the alarm unless a set procedure – as shown in the driver's handbook – is followed. The majority of car radios will lose their frequency presets when disconnected from vehicle battery power but the latest radios have non-volatile memories and are not affected.

Where ECUs (electronic control units) are concerned in the controlling of sub-systems such as air suspension, engine management etc, these Land Rover products' ECUs also have non-volatile memories so settings and operating criteria will not be lost when battery power is taken off.

Vehicles have not always been designed this way so be absolutely certain, before the expedition that you are aware of the implications of battery power disconnect on your vehicle if it has any system ECUs. These items may need reprogramming (usually accomplished with specific test equipment, smart cards and plug-in modules) if they experience total power failure so beware any battery-removal or disconnects for shipping or air freighting.

Battery disconnect spanner. Keeping a ready-access spanner specially for disconnecting the battery in a hurry should be part of your expedition preparation. This emergency procedure in the case of an electrical fire or harness-roasting short circuit can help arrest a developing disaster. Well worth the trouble is ensuring that the span-

ner has an insulated handle so that when working in a dark shipping container doing a routine disconnect, accidentally touching adjacent metalwork does not provoke a shower of sparks. Wrapping the handle copiously with insulation tape does the trick.

Dry fuel tank. Beware running the fuel tank dry if you have a fuel-injected engine – petrol or diesel; the implications here being that on refuelling and attempting to start up the fuel lines will be full of air locks and the system may need bleeding. If the fuel system is a modern one with a spill return line (like the Land Rover Tdi diesels and fuel-injected petrol engines) then it will be self-bleeding and self-priming; a few strokes on the manual fuel lift pump handle followed by a few turns of the engine on the starter motor will be enough to get the engine going again once you have put fuel in the tank.

However, older diesels with a single fuel line will require the fuel system to be bled one component at a time – lift pump, fuel filter, injector pump and one or more injectors. Be sure you know what applies to your fuel system before departure, not only in the context of shipping but in case you should run out of fuel during your trip. If your vehicle has a normal carburettor and a spill return (as does the carburetted Land Rover V8) it will be self-bleeding after running dry. If your carburetted engine has a single fuel line it will eventually start up after a dry-tank episode; you will probably have an electric fuel pump that will be heard clacking away to fill the empty fuel line but in the absence of an electric fuel pump you will save your battery a lot of hard cranking if you use the manual-assist on the engine-driven lift pump to prime the lines and fill the float chambers.

If your vehicle has a catalytic converter do not run the fuel lines dry as the possibly resulting misfire may destroy the catalytic converter. Remember the fuel injector pump is fuel lubricated so running dry, albeit for the small time involved, is not recommended.

Check implications of battery disconnecting on your vehicle's systems. Know how to do rapid disconnect in case of electrical fire. Also beware of running fuel tanks dry.

Nightly inspection schedule

(Example based on 1995 Land Rover Defender 90 300 Tdi)

The following schedule is based on the precept that prevention is better than cure; that nipping a potential problem in the bud will limit the overall work involved and/or damage to the vehicle. Many of the items in this inspection comprise the inspection element of the 12000 miles service but are no less valid on a nightly inspection if conditions are demanding enough. In less severe conditions there is however, room for flexibility and simplification in this schedule – after careful thought – but, that said, the whole operation takes not much more than 15 minutes and that is a small price for peace of mind.

Note also – and this will be all too clear in the field – that this schedule, especially in the context of detecting oil leaks, will be a great deal easier to make effective in dry conditions where a leak will show as a dark stain in dust and be invisible in mud or wet conditions. Things will be more difficult in wet conditions but the need to detect problems early will be no less valid.

The basic scenario of vehicle preventive maintenance and nightly inspection is to stop early while there is light to undertake a proper inspection and any necessary rectification. It consists of an engine bay inspection followed by an underneath and wheel-arch inspection.

Know what spanners you need for oil level plug removal when this is required; it can save a lot of time. See initial list at Section 5.5.1.

The example below can be used if you have a Defender but most of all it gives an indication of the approach required and from this you can produce a schedule for the vehicle you have. It is worth spending pre-expedition time going over the vehicle with a professional (see photo below) and then putting your schedule together, in writing.

Evolve, before departure, a thorough nightly inspection schedule for your vehicle. Put it on laminated card for use till you know it by heart.

Even if you 'know Land Rovers' get a professional (selected!) to give you an inspection run-round for the latest tips. This applies to whatever make of vehicle you have. Value of your nightly inspection will be greatly enhanced.

NIGHTLY INSPECTION SCHEDULE

EXAMPLE BASED ON 1995 DEFENDER 90
(NS = near side, OS = off side, F = front, R = rear))

Sequence. Overalls, strong industrial cotton gloves, a torch and a small groundsheet to lie on are recommended. Stop, raise bonnet, allow engine to cool and oil to settle for 5 minutes then inspect engine bay. After that, spread groundsheet and inspect under front of vehicle (ahead of front axle), under off side (between front and rear axles), under rear (aft of rear axle), under near side (between rear and front axles). Then (or as you go) inspect each wheel arch.

Engine bay
Inspecting for oil, coolant or hydraulic leaks, condition and security of parts.
Dip engine oil then start at NS aft end of engine bay
Heater hose (heater and block)
Turbo intake/exit ducts secure
Steering fluid reservoir – contents, leaks, cap tight
Coolant pipes/hoses – water pump, thermostat housing, header tank, radiator
Radiator front/rear face – stone damage
Oil cooler pipes – leaks, security
Serpentine belt – tension/stretch indicator, condition
Coolant level
Brake and clutch fluid reservoirs
Diesel fuel system pipes for leaks:
    Injectors on top of engine
    Injector pipes at pump
    Fuel filter element housing
    Fuel filter: drain. inspect effluent if fuel suspect
Oil cooler exit pipes at engine
Oil filter element housing
Clutch master and slave cylinders
Brake servo hydraulic pipes exits
Power steering relay for leaks at pipes and seals

Front underside of vehicle
Inspecting for oil, coolant or hydraulic leaks, condition and security of parts.
NS and OS wheels:
    Tyre inner faces for cuts/damage
    Swivel pin level/drain plugs for leaks
    Brake hoses – cuts/damage/leaks
    Shock dampers – leaks, rubber bushes
Diff-housing – damage to underside, leaks at level/drain plugs
Axle case – damage
Axle-end flanges – leaks
Steering damper/power unit – leaks
Power steering hydraulic pipes
Steering linkage ball joints, play, gaiters
Engine wading plug aperture – signs of oil
Look aft to clutch housing wading plug – signs of oil
Engine sump bolts – leakage
Under oil filter – oil drips
Universal joints (both) – grease escape
Prop shaft – check for excessive rotational/spline play
Sump drain plug – drips
Rubber bump stops – secure, undamaged

Off side underside of vehicle
Inspecting for oil, coolant or hydraulic leaks, condition and security of parts.
Re-lay groundsheet and inspect:
OS front brake-pipe unions and pipes
Underside of fuel tank, drain plug
Level and drain plugs on main and transfer gearboxes
Random leaks from gearboxes
Handbrake drum – check bottom for oil drips (rear gear box seal)
Prop-shaft – check for excessive rotational/spline play
Universal joints (both) – grease escape
Bottom of clutch slave cylinder, hose – fluid leaks
Brake pipe condition where it follows chassis
Inner sidewalls of both rear tyres
OSR shock damper – leaks, rubber bushes
Brake pipe junction/union atop rear diff
Rear diff face and nose – leaks
Suspension radius arms – rubber bushes

Rear underside of vehicle
Inspecting for oil, coolant or hydraulic leaks, condition and security of parts.
Repeat inner tyre face inspection
Brake pipe unions, both wheels
Brake pipe condition at rear axle
Rear diff housing– damage to underside, leaks at level/drain plugs
Security of silencer and tailpipe

Near side underside of vehicle
Inspecting for oil, coolant or hydraulic leaks, condition and security of parts.
Double check brake pipes at front wheel
NSR shock damper – leaks, rubber bushes
Suspension radius arms – rubber bushes

Wheel arches, tyres
NSF wheel arch:
    Brake pipe/unions
    Tyre tread, sidewall
OSF wheel arch:
    Brake pipe/unions
    Tyre tread, sidewall
OSR wheel arch:
    Fuel filler hoses/clips
    Shock damper upper rubber bush
    Tyre tread/sidewall
NSR wheel arch:
    Shock damper upper rubber bush
    Tyre tread/sidewall
    Visible electrical connectors

Cockpit/cab
Slack in steering
Side, head and rear lights
Flashers
Security of battery mounting (under seat)

Next morning when cold
Tyre pressures
Coolant level

Main aims of evening inspection are checking fluid levels, checking for oil leaks, anything that looks as though it is coming loose and any physical damage.

Section 5.5.1

Operations:

Spares and tools

Hand drilling – for a long time – to repair a broken track rod in the bush (see also photo page 4.2 - 28) proved the utility of the 'black-smithing' tools to cannibalise iron from trailer. Bolts pack vital – as with trailer hitch attachment that had shaken asunder (right),

Electric fuel pump connections soldered in place with 12 volt soldering iron. Used in moderation, battery copes.

Spares and tools

Sample spares and tools lists for a single-vehicle expedition using a Land Rover Defender 90 Tdi. The same equipment would have supported a three-vehicle group.

Tools special note – print out and stick near tool box

Oil level/drain plugs, servicing: tool requirements Defender 90, '95 MY

Engine sump drain plug	19 mm ring
Transfer box drain plug	17 mm ring
Transfer box level plug	1/2" square bar
Main gearbox level plug	Torx 55 + 10 mm socket
Main gearbox drain plug	30 mm AF
Front axle:	
Diff drain plug	1/2" square bar/ratchet
Diff level/fill plug	1/2" square bar/ratchet
Swivel pins drain plug	11 mm ring
Swivel pins level plug	11 mm open ended (clearance)
Swivel pins filling	1/2" square socket. (Use with 10 mm allen key into wrong end of a 1/2" drive/10 mm socket)
Rear axle:	
Drain plug	1/2" bar/ratchet
Diff level/fill	1/2" bar/ratchet
Steering wheel centre nut	22 mm socket
Road wheel nuts	11/16 " socket (plus wheel security nut Code xx)

Spares

DEFENDER 90 SPARES KIT, BAS GREY BOXES

BOX 1 – Spares, fixit, electrics　　Weight: 9 kg

Air filter element ESR 2623
Electronic speedo sensor (Discovery) AMR1253
Flasher unit YWT10003
Small WD40
Plus Gas A dismantling fluid
Plastic Padding (elastic)
Rubberweld self-amalgamating tape
Sellotape pipe and hose repair (2 types of tape)
SuperGlue Gel XTRA
Hylomar
Araldite Fast
Loctite tough Bond
Bostic All-purpose Clear glue
2 x Sellotape insulation tape
Sellotape outdoor sticky fixers
2-inch wide black fabric-backed tape
1.5 inch wide plastic tape
2 x automatic brake bleeding hoses
2 x radiator leak stoppers
Holts Radweld liquid – 125 ml
Bag: misc bolts, nuts, washers – 4 mm
Bag: misc bolts, nuts, washers – 5 mm
Bag: misc bolts, nuts, washers – 6 mm
Bag: misc hose clips, 5 wheel nuts
Bag: misc door trim nylon snap fixings
Spares pack for MSR XGKII multi-fuel cooking stove

Electrics
Fuses:　　Misc selection for interior fuse box
　　　　　　Under-bonnet fuses: 3 x 30 amp, 2 x 60 amp

Small Multi-meter (fresh battery)
12v probe/light
12v soldering iron (DIN plug)
Cored solder
Wire-joining soldering jig
Spare DIN plug
Crimping/stripping pliers
Bag of misc lengths wire, crimp connectors, screw-connector blocks
Set optical/precision screwdrivers
12v/cassette adaptor for short wave radio input

Spare AA and other batteries for exped equipment, cameras, radios etc: 16 x AA, 4 x AAA, 2 x MN1203 (Petzl)

DEFENDER 90 SPARES KIT, BAS GREY BOXES

BOX 2 – Land Rover spares　　Weight: 7 kg

2 x door window winder handles DBP6287PMA
2 x packets retaining clips for above BNP4556L
2 x Land Rover spare bulb kits STC8247AA
2 x diesel fuel filter elements AEU2147L
2 x oil filter elements ERR3340
Oil/fuel filter element grip/removal tool
300 Tdi injectors:　　　1 x ERR3337
　　　　　　　　　　　　　　3 x ERR3348
3 x pkts copper washers ERR4621
Pkt of 25 joint washers 232042
2 x pkts 10 copper washers ERR894
Clutch master cylinder complete 550732
Clutch slave cyl repair kit 514244
Clutch slave cyl rubbers 8G8837L

Fuel lift pump ERR5057
(Diesel engine stopping) solenoid RTC6702
Speedo driven gear FRC9339
Oil pressure switch PRC6387
3x hub oil seals FTC2783
Hub rubber cap FTC943
4 x hub bearing lock washers FTC3279
4 x hub gaskets FRC3988
2 x serpentine accessory drive belts ERR3287
'DIBS' desert driving mirror and arm

DEFENDER 90 SPARES KIT, BAS GREY BOXES

BOX 3 – Tyre repair equipment   Weight: 11 kg

2 x Michelin tubes 16J9.15 – 7.50x16
Film container with 3 valve caps, 5 valve cores (2 spare
valve caps in cab)
Tub tyre-fitting cream lubricant – about 350 ml
1" paint brush for above
Tyre patches:
        Rema Tip-Top 10 x no 5
        Rema Tip-Top cover repair patches for rad-
          ials 10 x no 504
        Tech 2-way – 30 medium round
Fermatech vulcanising cement 250 cc
Pang Super Solution self vulcanising fluid (unopened)
Apaseal buffing solution (150 ml in small glass bottle)
Sandpaper, emery paper
Rema butyl-buff rasp
Heavy rasp for outer covers
Roller, 35 mm diam, for tyre patches
Grease-pencil tyre marker stick
2 x spare vulc soln brushes
Tech tyre talc – 5 oz
Spare 12v electric tyre inflation pump
(Stored elsewhere – 3 x 18" tyre levers and electric infla-
tor pump)

DEFENDER 90 SPARES KIT, BAS GREY BOXES

BOX 4 – Oils, jack, misc   Weight: 14 kg

1 x axle stand
2-ton hydraulic jack and handle (main Discovery jack
under centre seat)
2.5" clamp-on vice to attach to bumper as requd
750 ml can Lockheed 329S hydraulic fluid
Top-up oils:
        Axles, swivel-pins, transfer box:
                2 x 500 ml Duckhams Hypoid 90
                3 x 500 ml Castrol Syntrax
                   Universal 75w/90
        Main gearbox (R380) and power steering:
                3 x 500 ml Shell Dexron II ATF
Tin David's P40 fibreglass mix
8 ft 6mm i/d plastic piping
Fairy-liquid squeezy bottle

**DEFENDER 90 EQUIPMENT STORED AROUND THE
VEHICLE**

2 x Barong 3-piece articulated sand-channels – between
boxes
2 x shovel/trenching tools – on top of load
3 x 20 litre diesel jerry cans (metal)
2 x 20 litre water jerry cans (MoD plastic)
PUR 'Explorer' water filter and carbon filter

2 kg fire extinguisher – mounted near back door
Tent – Wild Country Ultra Quasar free standing plus sand
pegs
2 x sleeping bags and Thermarest mats
2 x garden lounger fold-up bed/chair
In centre cubby-box (padlocked)
        3 x wading plugs and spanner
        2 x tyre valve caps
        Petzl head-torch
        Mini-flares
        Windscreen squeegee
        Michelin Vigil tyre pressure gauge
        Box for removable front unit of Alpine radio
        Fuel log book and pen
        GPS instruction book
        Xenon flashing beacon
        Transparent plastic map-case
        Binoculars (small)
        Sunglasses
        Spare tyre pressure gauge
Behind driver/passenger seats:
        Map case and maps
        Steering wheel lock-bar thief deterrent
        1-litre stainless steel thermos
Under centre cubby box in special compartment:
        Discovery hydraulic jack and handle
        Jack load-spreader boards for soft ground
        Socket-key for locking wheel nuts (spare in
        tool box)
        Wheel nut wrench (11/16" socket also in
        tools)
Under driver's seat in special compartment:
        Halford's electric tyre inflator
Attached to bulkhead behind driver's seat:
        Removable lock-in safe-box (contains GPS
        when not in use)
In 'bread bin' compartment behind passenger seat;
        Small zip toolbag, Curver toolbox,
        ('Containers 1 ands 2' see Tools below)
        Tube Swarfega, rags.
        Heavy zip toolbag ('Container 3' – see Tools
        below)
'Mega-beam' long range torch
Safety triangle
Fluorescent plug-in wander light
Drill overalls
"Spaceman's blanket" groundsheet/cover
2 x bicycle cable locks for securing baggage handles to
cans etc,
3 x elastic retaining nets with hooks for lightweight items
to be secured to hardtop sides (sleeping bags, kitchen
towels)
Stuff-bags for peeled-off clothing
Manfrotto tripod
Car-cleaning/sweeping brush and wash leather
Double-walled stainless mug, stainless steel plate
Books:
        Land Rover owners manual (workshop manu-
        al stored elsewhere)
        Trimble GPS manual
        Alpine radio manual
        Clifford 'Sense and Tell' alarm instructions

Tools

TOOLS (* = for oil drain/level plugs, see list above)

In vehicle tool box: Containers 1 and 2 (below)
Overalls and tube Swarfega
Hand-wiping rags

**Container 1 – Zipped toilet bag – small tools (26 x 9
x 15 cm)   Wt 2.4 kg**

19 mm ring/open end spanner (*Engine sump drain)
17 mm"   "   " (*Transfer box oil drain)
13, 12, 11, 10, 8 mm ring/open end spanners
14/15 mm ring spanner
0-13 mm calibrated angled adjustable spanner
0-15 mm King Dick adjustable spanner
Small Mole grip
Long-nose pliers
Wire snips
Right angled 1/2" square bar (*Axle drain/fill plugs)
Right angled 10 mm Allen key (*Swivel pin filler plug –
        use with 1/2" drive 10 mm socket)
Snap-On trim button removal tool
1/4" drive socket set with:
        13, 12, 10, 9. 8, 7, 6, 5 mm sockets (*6 mm
        fits coolant hoses)
        1/2" AF
        Extension 100 mm
        Universal joint
Screwdrivers: Pozidrive 2 pt, 1 pt, 0 pt; stubby 2 pt, stub-
        by 1 pt
Screwdrivers flat blade: 3 mm (electrical), 5 mm, 6 mm
        wide blades
Philips screwdriver – 0 pt
Roll insulation tape
Swiss Army knife
3/4" paintbrush (cleaning round filler plugs)
14 swg wire (coathanger) screw/hole alignment tool

**Container 2 – Small plastic Curver toolbox (32 x 17 x
13 cm)   Wt 5.2 kg**

Spare 'key' socket for secure wheel nuts
1/2" square ratchet socket drive with extension bar and:
        Special – 11/16" for road wheel nuts
        Special – 22 mm steering wheel hub nut
        21, 20, 19, 17, 14, 13, 12, 11, 10 mm sockets
Bahco angle adjustable spanner 0-30 mm (*Main gear-
box drain 30 mm)
Large Vise Grip
Small Vise Grip, crocodile jaws
Multiple setting pipe/nut grip
Extra long-nose pliers
Medium pliers
Large screwdrivers:
Flat blade – 7 mm wide
Pozidrive – 3 pt
Angle Z-screwdrivers, large and small
Set optical screwdrivers
Set metric Allen keys
Sets feeler gauges – metric/imperial
9/16" ring/open end spanner
9/16" ring, ground down (prop shaft universal joint bolts)
Stanley knife and spare blades

**Container 3 – Lightweight canvas tool bag, (60 long x
15 x 15 cm)   Wt 8 kg**

3 x 18" tyre levers
12" hacksaw and spare blades
Junior hacksaw and blades
Norbar torque wrench
Files: Half-round 2nd cut
              Square
              Round, 6 mm dia
              Round, 10 mm dia
Stanley handbrace drill
Drill bits HSS steel 1-7 mm
Centre punch
HD pop-rivet puller, 3, 4, and 5 mm pop rivets
G-clamps – large, 2 small
1/2" cold chisel
3/16" taper punch
Small tin snips
Wire brush in protective tin

*Tool containers 1, 2 and 3.
Containers 1 and 2 were kept
handy; the heavier 'civil engineering' tools in 3 were stored deep
down. Total weight 15.6 kg.*

Section 5.6

Operations:

Emergencies

COVERAGE OF THIS SECTION

Contingency planning

The ingredients

Emergency situations. When planning any expedition sober consideration must be given to action to be taken in the event of mishap, accident or emergency. In many ways, accommodating the unexpected or the unfortunate epitomises the whole philosophy of expedition planning but when problems become serious or life-threatening they become contingencies we all class as emergency situations. These will involve attracting attention – be it that of the rest of the team, the nearest police post or a rescue organisations thousands of miles away – and/or then taking action to ameliorate the particular occurrence. Think of that sentence when planning and later when briefing your team; emergencies can concern (and procedures cater for):

- Second or other vehicle in a convoy getting held up
- Convoy being late at planned rendezvous or destination
- Persons overdue from on-foot excursion
- Breakdown of vehicle without spare part or means of fixing it
- Accident involving personal injury or illness

Attracting attention. It helps to broadly classify the sorts of action that can be taken in all the above circumstances depending on the facilities available. All are directed at attracting attention or remedying non-arrival:

- Visual:
  - Waving pre-determined signals
  - Headlights
  - Signal panel or flag
  - Heliograph
  - Flare/smoke
  - Rockets
  - Flashing light
- Audio:
  - Whistle
  - Horn

- Radio:
  - Terrestrial
  - Satellite
- Action following non-arrival:
  - Lookout in certain compass direction
  - Ditto, watch for flares/signals at specified times
  - Mount search after certain margin of time

Calling someone else. Consider who the call for help will be aimed at - aircraft, other travellers, a distant village, a radio link, a regular convoy on a given route, the other members of your team if you have become separated from them or a distant rescue co-ordination centre via a satellite. Consider also the requirements of day or night recognition. Consider inter-vehicle communication in a multi-vehicle group – see Section 2.7 'Communications'. Consider leaving details of your route, supply lists and actions-in-the-event-of-emergency with local authorities.

Rescue plan. This latter will certainly feature in your rescue plan if you have one. Whoever is coming out to find you must know your margins, what fuel and water you have, how long you can hang on till help arrives – see page 5.6 - 13.

The details

Convoy procedure. Start with the here and now. The normal procedure for any convoy (also covered in Section 5.3.1. 'Driver training' on page 5.3-41) is that each vehicle is responsible for the welfare of the vehicle behind it. Constant vigilance and keeping a keen eye on the rear view mirror is every driver's responsibility. Thus if Vehicle 5 gets a flat tyre or other reason to stop, the fact will be spotted by Vehicle 4; Vehicle 4 will stop and this will be noted by Vehicle 3 and so on up the line. The situation is further helped if Vehicle 5 uses a heliograph (sun mirror) to attract Vehicle 4's

Emergency situations can be anything from a flat tyre on a following vehicle to the need for a medevac. Attracting attention is half the problem. Plan for it.

attention. In dusty conditions on a bush or desert track the procedure will be difficult. Space between vehicles will have to be increased to keep following vehicles clear of dust and a stop-and-wait procedure every five to ten minutes will have to be adopted. Either way, the strict adoption of a reliable convoy procedure is the fundamental first building block of an effective expedition safety routine.

Rescue aids and suppliers. As well as radio rescue beacons for the expedition as a whole (see below) issue heliographs, whistles, mini-strobe and if possible miniflares to each member of the team for personal rescue/emergency situations. Certainly each vehicle should be equipped with miniflares – stowed in a position accessible to a strapped-in and possibly injured driver. Common sense and a browse round a good ship's chandlers and outdoor shop will yield the kind of practical equipment to be taken on expeditions. It may be that a full range is not on view and it would be worth contacting manufacturers and distributors for brochures and the location of stockists. Pains Wessex are long-established specialists in pyrotechnics:

- Pains Wessex Ltd
      High Post
      Salisbury, Wilts SP4 6AS
      Tel 01722.411.611
   or
- McMurdo Ltd
      Rodney Road
      Portsmouth
      Hants PO4 8SG
      Tel 01705.775.044
   or ...
- Simpson Lawrence (tel 01329.823.300) are major distributors to chandlers with main depots in four parts of the UK. They could steer you to your nearest chandler.

Simple rescue aids. Some simple rescue aids:

- *Heliographs.* A heliograph is a mirror configured to provide a way of aiming a mirror-reflection of the sun at a distant object or viewer. They are extremely effective vehicle-to-vehicle, ground-to-air or

Hone your safety-awareness. Without being paranoid, suss the potential dangers in routine situations. Issue simple rescue aids to vehicle crews and individuals.

Heliograph in use

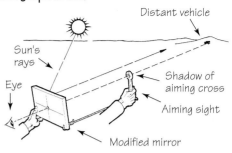

point to point from, say, the top of a hill to a base station or vehicle. Heliographs have been used effectively at distances of 8 km and more.

- *Miniflares.* Miniflares are packaged as a pen-type discharger with a number of screw-in or bayonet-fit cartridges in a waterproof pack about 150 x 55 x 15 mm. See 'Standard procedures' below.

- *Smoke flares/rockets.* A number of lightweight smoke flares/rockets are available from ship's chandlers. Select a smoke colour to show up well against the background of the terrain you're in – green for the desert, red for the jungle. Take a few really high-flying distress rockets or parachute flares. See 'Standard procedures' below.

- *Whistles.* Loud 'referee' pea-whistles are light and more efficient than the voice for attracting attention. Evolve your own code for numbers of whistle blasts.

- *Mini-strobe.* This is a lightweight miniature Xenon flashing strobe operating off a single D-cell providing continuous flashes for up to 72 hours and still visible at around 3 km at night. Available with a Velcro armband.

- *Fluorescent panels.* Bright green fluorescent fabric panels can sometimes be obtained and aid air to ground recognition.

- *Ground-air rescue codes.* The ground-air rescue code is an internationally acknowledged code of signals produced by laying out blankets or signal panels on the ground at the scene of an emergency. In all

Even when weight is very, very tight (see p 2.4 - 10), make allowance for rescue aids. Clumsy looking 121.5 MHz marine emergency radio beacon was cheap and, in fact very light. Pack of eight Miniflares sends red emergency flares to 200 ft altitude, burning for 6 seconds. Whistle gives audio attention. Square, metal-mirror heliograph with white aiming sight (see diagram opposite) is very compact and light; and remarkably effective.

honesty the chances of using it or finding a modern aircrew that will know the codes are slim but having it amounts only to a single piece of paper in your equipment and a returning pilot will be able to look up any signals he recognises.

Standard procedures – timing

Co-ordinated look-outs. Firing off a flare when you feel like it is far less effective than firing it when people have been briefed to be watching in your direction. Evolve a standard procedure for timings of rescue calls, discharge of flares, smoke or rockets – exactly on the hour and half hour is recommended – so as to ensure the appropriate agency or party will actually be looking and listening at that time. For example if you have a party going out on foot to climb a local rock out-

crop, have someone, or better still a small group, stop what they are doing at the base camp and train their eyes on the area of possible discharge of flares for three minutes before and three minutes after the set standard times you have decided. This eliminates the possibility of people not seeing the

Think through what you do with your rescue aids. Work out routines and, especially, simple timing conventions as to when aids are used, ensuring they are seen.

RV at Salwah – just a lat/long. 'Oh, that Salwah!', they said later. Hand-held day/night flare used as here-we-are signal at pre-arranged rendezvous. If using rockets, use green or white for 'safety' situations; keep red for emergencies.

distress flare just because they were not looking when it was fired.

Radio communications – see Section 2.7 regarding radio communications. Radio can sometimes be a glib supposed solution to any rescue problem but first bear in mind that a radio call is not itself a doctor or a barrel of fuel; in other words it is only the start of a procedure that may, you hope, yield these items at a later time if such an infrastructure has been thoroughly and reliably organised in advance – see 'A funny thing happened on the way to ... ' on page 2.7 - 15. It is better, in other words, to organise your rescue procedures with more immediate resources if you can.

Medevac

The great imponderable. Whether or not you have a formal rescue plan (see end of this section) you will need to give detailed planning time and considered advance research to the implications of medical evacuation at any given part of your route or project work area. This should include consideration of:

• Your own medical capabilities and first aid.

• Local medical facilities and hospitals.

• The nearest airport from which a casualty may be flown out.

• The coverage and extent of your medical insurance.

In some ways it is best to work back-

Determine the limitations of your medical insurance in advance and plan for how you meet the shortfall. Check medical facilities en route as a low key routine.

wards from the last item. Worldwide fly-back medical insurance can be obtained for most countries. Examine this and establish the gaps in cover between the moment or place where medical assistance may be first required and the nearest point where you can expect insurance-borne outside aid.

Even if you are not in need of medical attention, during the expedition it is useful, as a routine, checking on medical facilities in the towns you pass through in case you should need them later. A running check on this and communications and airfields and schedules is worth keeping in your nav log.

The giant medical kit. Previous expeditions have found that huge multi-capability medical kits are seldom of much use since field conditions of dust, dirt, wind, poor light, shortage of water or lack of proper anaesthesia almost invariably favour the patch-up and move to local facilities approach.

Vehicle insurance

Another imponderable. Unsurprisingly, vehicle insurance on expeditions outside Europe or other 'western' countries is less than straightforward but it should be faced and accepted as such in advance. It is another example of the need to avoid trouble rather than remedying it when it occurs. Just be sure, as if your life depended on it (which is often does) that you do not damage your vehicle or other people's property in any way at all through accidents. Don't even begin to think, 'Well, there's always the other idiot ..'; expect the worst, predict the unpredictable and keep out of trouble. Here's why:

• Third party insurance is usually a compulsory purchase on the border of every country you enter as a legal requirement.

• You will find it virtually impossible to obtain home-based comprehensive (ie vehicle loss or damage) insurance for your expedition.

• Buying vehicle damage insurance overseas will be horrifically expensive and complex too, usually requiring a stay in a major city to effect the transaction.

A funny thing happened on the way to...... Maiduguri

A sort of canine madness is often triggered by the noise of motorcycles. Shielded by bush, the dog's curve of pursuit was misjudged; it hit the front wheel. My broken collarbone was not painful but the doc gave me a jab. The jab caused vomiting for the next 12 hours; hot climate, no water intake. With mild shock, dehydration was the main problem till next day. Keep the medical kit small; use it only when required.

Radio / satellite beacons

Principles

20th/21st century ultimate. If point-to-point terrestrial radio communication is beset by considerations of power, frequency special to range or day/night conditions, SARSAT (Search And Rescue SATellite) and the Russian COSPAS (Cosmicheskaya Sistyema Poiska Avariynich Sudov) is rescue radio at its most effective and user-friendly. A number of special satellites now orbit the earth capable of picking up radio distress transmissions from battery-powered beacons (most are the small hand-held type) tuned to particular rescue and emergency frequencies. Such beacons are normally sealed and dormant with battery lives of four to seven years and are usually tuned to both the VHF (121.5 MHz) and UHF military (243 MHz) international distress frequencies.

When activated, the radio transmissions are picked up by one or more of the orbiting SARSAT (and/or Russian COSPAS) satellites which relays at once and in real time an approximate (see table) position fix to one of a number of worldwide rescue centres. The satellites orbit roughly every 80 minutes and continuous signals from your beacon will result in the rescue centre alerting appropriate national authorities and rescue facilities. Such facilities will differ from nation to nation but will include anything from helicopters to a police pick-up or 4x4.

Aircraft-borne homers too. The particular frequencies used also enable airborne homers to function so that rescue aircraft, if available and appropriately equipped, can home-in on the activated beacon.

Limited coverage – 121.5 MHz. Some knowledge of the infrastructure is important in the context of expeditions. An LUT (Local User Terminal) is the aerial dish ground station that intercepts the satellite message. There are presently 38 LUTs dotted round the world (see map next page) each capable of 'seeing' a circle of about 2500 km radius; each LUT connects with a Mission Control Centre (MCC) and then a Rescue Co-ordination Centre (RCC) which in turn scrambles the helicopter or other rescue medium.

Because of the 870-1000 km 'low earth-orbit' of the present Cospas-Sarsat satellites, any transmissions outside the LUT circle of visibility will not be picked up by a given LUT. The majority of the earth's surface is, in fact, covered by contiguous, overlapping LUT circles but the whole of southern and east Africa and a part of Saudi Arabia and north east Siberia have no direct LUT coverage.

Complete coverage – 406 Mhz. The implication of that word direct is as follows. There are a number of different beacon types, in general divided into:

- 121.5 MHz beacons. (sometimes allied to 243 MHz, a military distress UHF frequency)
- 406 MHz beacons.

Low-power, hand-held radio beacons' transmissions are picked up by satellites and relayed to ground stations (LUTs). 121.5 MHz cover is not worldwide.

Typical beacon/satellite/LUT process

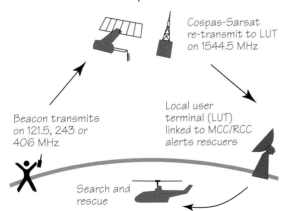

Cospas-Sarsat re-transmit to LUT on 1544.5 MHz

Beacon transmits on 121.5, 243 or 406 MHz

Local user terminal (LUT) linked to MCC/RCC alerts rescuers

Search and rescue

Cospas-Sarsat LUT world coverage

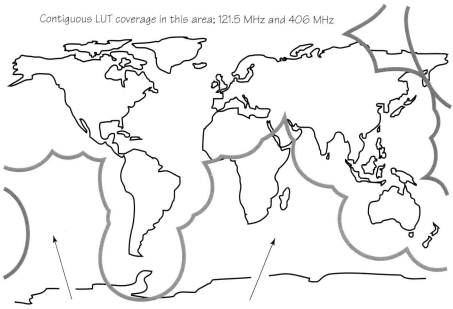

Contiguous LUT coverage in this area; 121.5 MHz and 406 MHz

Gap in 121.5 MHz coverage; only 406 MHz coverage in these areas

406 MHz beacons yield a more accurate fix and give worldwide coverage; far more expensive. Check map above; if within LUT coverage, 121.5 MHz is fine.

The 121.5 MHz transmissions enable a position fix to better than 20 km to be obtained and this data is re-transmitted immediately by the satellite on 1544 MHz. The 406 MHz beacon transmissions are handled differently. Firstly the position fix is to better than 5 km in accuracy; secondly the data is transmitted at once but also stored and retransmitted by the satellite as it moves on. Thus as the satellite progresses round its polar orbit, all LUTs will hear the message at some time.

The 406Mhz system has the further advantage of a shorter digital message at a higher power (5 watt RF burst for 0.5 sec every 50 secs) so the system can cope with more calls and (see below) identification data too.

Choice of beacon type

Suit beacon to region. From the above indication of limited coverage for certain beacons you must clearly choose your beacon with care and in relation to the area in which you will be travelling. The most commonly available and thus least expensive beacons, developed typically for small-boat operators in coastal water around European and American shores, operate on 121.5 MHz. These will be perfectly adequate for most expeditions but if your territory is going to be outside contiguous LUT coverage regions indicated on the map or there are special reasons for requiring closer position fix definition or ident data, then you should use the 406 MHz type of beacon.

Abbreviations. You may find yourself confused by, as ever, a proliferation of abbreviations and acronyms for what we might all loosely term 'beacons':

• *ELT* – Emergency Locator Transmitter. This is the term given to beacons carried by aircraft.

• *EPIRB*. Emergency Position Indicating Radio Beacon. Beacons used and installed on ships, usually fixed so that they trigger and detach when entering the water; some, however, may be hand-held. Programmed

From left, Sarbe 7 121.5 / 243 MHz beacon; note test flap; satellite cover limited to LUT areas (map opposite). Kannad 406m beacon and the hand-held manual EPIRB Jotron 45S both work on 406MHz giving global coverage.

with the ship's identity and operating on 406 MHz.

• *PLB.* Personal Locator Beacon. The small hand-held unit often also attached to personal life jackets for use by sailors. Can also be used by mountaineers, woodsmen, and expeditioners. This is the kind of unit you will probably be after; most operate on 121.5 MHz, some military units have an additional transmitting frequency of 243 MHz, some (also military) have a two-way voice facility for talking to the approaching helicopter. This latter facility adds considerable cost and is not necessary for most expeditions. Just entering the market at the time of writing are 406 MHz PLBs having an

Check what the beacons do. The 406 MHz beacons store data and retransmit later in orbit to all LUTs. 121.5 MHz beacons transmit real-time to visible LUTs only.

SUMMARY OF COSPAS-SARSAT FACILITIES

	Space element	Ground element	Beacon frequency	Coverage	Comments
1a	Cospas-Sarsat 'LEOSAR' Low earth orbits, polar. Altitude to 1000 km.	38 LUT (see note) ground stations. Not world coverage on 121.5/243. Southern Africa, part of Saudi Arabia not covered.	121.5 MHz (may be with 243 MHz – military)	Limited to LUT 'local' area only, ie about 2500 km radius from LUT. Position fix to better than 20 km.	Real-time transmission. Satellite re-transmits beacon transmission when received. Picked up by nearest LUT.
1b	Cospas-Sarsat 'LEOSAR' Low earth orbits, polar. Altitude to 1000 km.	38 LUTs accept store-and-relay messages from 406 MHz beacons.	406 MHz	Using the same LUTs; in effect, world coverage – see next column. Position fix to better than 5 km.	Store-and-relay transmission. Message transmitted at once and also repeated to all LUTs as satellite progresses round orbit.
2	Cospas-Sarsat 'GEOSAR' Geostationary satellites, altitude 36000 km.	All current LUTs plus six GEOLUT stations. System likely operational from 1999. Requires special beacons (next column).	406 MHz plus position data from GPS or GNSS (future)	Whole earth coverage. With GPS data, position fix to 100 metres. Poss high latitude deep-valley 'shadow'.	1. Real time but needs position data/ident from beacon. 2. Can work with existing beacons but gives no position data.

Notes
1. LEOSAR = Low Earth Orbit Search And Rescue satellite. Cospas-Sarsat comprises 4 active satellites
2. GEOSAR = GEOstationary Search And Rescue satellite. Comprises 4 active satellites.
3. LUT = Local User Terminal. Receives relayed transmission from satellite if satellite 'visible', ie within about 2500 km radius of LUT.

Sarbe 6 is similar to Sarbe 7 on previous page but additionally has two-way voice facility for communication with search helicopter or aircraft – capability aimed at military rescue operations. This combined with waterproofing pushes price up dramatically and facility would be unnecessary on most expeditions.

New generation GEOSAR geostationary satellites will give 'all-at-once' world cover – but not poles. System will supplement, not replace, Cospas-Sarsat.

additional 121.5 MHz transmission for use by homing aircraft – very good news , especially for remote areas.

The next generation – GEOSAR

Almost upon us. Planned to back the present system of low earth-orbit satellites (LEOSAR), four geostationary satellites positioned 36000 km above the earth's surface and over the equator are equipped to handle extended 406 Mhz data transmissions. The so-called GEOSAR system (GEOstationary Search And Rescue) is

LEOSAR and GEOSAR satellite systems

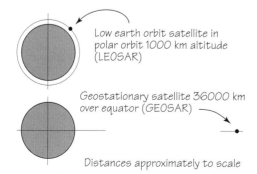

Low earth orbit satellite in polar orbit 1000 km altitude (LEOSAR)

Geostationary satellite 36000 km over equator (GEOSAR)

Distances approximately to scale

designed to operate in conjunction with earth-originated position data derived from GPS or its successor GNSS. This is encoded, together with a user ident, in the beacon's transmission. All this information is in turn retransmitted and received by all current LUTs as well as six specialist 'GEOLUTs'. This system will not replace the current LEOSAR system – for example it runs out of coverage towards the poles – but its extra data-handling capability (ident data etc) will suit it to special applications.

At the time of writing the system had recently completed its D&E (development and evaluation) phase and is expected to get the green light in October 1998. Prototype beacons are bigger and more expensive than current designs (since they must incorporate a GPS receiver) but if there was ever an axiomatically safe forecast that can be made it is that the size and cost of the electronics will come down dramatically with time. Development units have been used on transcontinental expeditions so the orientation of research for expeditioners is encouraging.

Buying your beacon

Cospas-Sarsat information. Rather as Inmarsat publishes lists of the latest satellite

GEOSAR coverage – new generation 406 MHz beacons

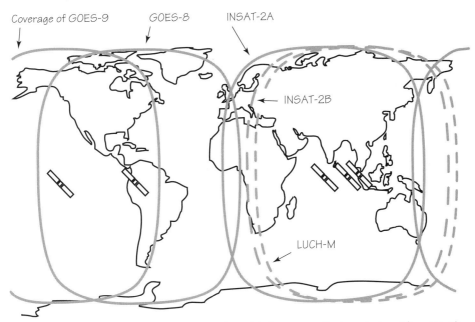

Geostationary satellites give complete global coverage. System designed for use with 406 MHz beacons that also transmit GPS-derived position information. There will be six special 'GEOLUTs' for this sytem.

communications equipment (see Section 2.7 'Communications', page 2.7-19) so Cospas-Sarsat publish a periodical System Data booklet that shows a list of equipment manufacturers and type-approved beacons currently available. Contact them at:

Cospas-Sarsat Secretariat
Inmarsat
99 City Road
London EC1Y 1AX
Tel 0171.728.1391
Fax 0171.728.1170

It will pay to keep in touch because, like GPS equipments, the rate of progress is, rapid and impressive.

Buying your beacon, As with flares and other pyrotechnics, ships' chandlers will be the best place to start looking for a beacon. Do your homework before starting out for the people there will be completely small-boat oriented and few of their regular cus-tomers will be sailing in Botswana, Saudi Arabia or Siberia! Consult the Cospas-Sarsat lists on what is currently available, obtain the brochures and look out for PLBs (personal locator beacons). Features you may wish to check:

- Test facility – for battery and transmission
- Battery life
- Removable antenna
- Operating time once switched on
- Operating temperature range
- Size, weight, ruggedness.

A limited choice of rescue beacons are made by such manufacturers as Locata, Jotron (Tron), McMurdo and Signature (SARBE). Prices currently (1998) ranging from £100 for a basic 121.5 MHz unit to around £600 for a 406 MHz unit with ident facilities. The 406 units are not yet plentiful

Cospas-Sarsat give regular updates on equipment and manufacturers achieving certification. Check latest info and brochures before going shopping.

in PLB format and the French Kannad 406m by Serpe-IESM and Tron 45S are worth noting in that context (the latter is actually a small hand-held EPIRB)

As mentioned already, for expedition use it is best to avoid speak-receive beacons of the SARBE aircrew type since these may require special operating permission (or invoke confiscation as a 'spy radio') in foreign countries. A simple safety beacon can be seen as such.

Some sources of rescue equipment:
• Simpson Lawrence, Pains Wessex, see above page 5.6 - 4
• Jotron UK Ltd, Norwegian beacon manufacturers, tel 01670.712.000
• Sullivan Marine UK (Kannad 406m beacon), tel 01622.858.458

The rescue

Know the LUT situation. What happens after a rescue beacon has been triggered and how long it takes can never be guaranteed and will depend upon national infrastructure. Check from the latest Cospas-Sarsat information whether there is an LUT in the country concerned since this will ensure that there is an MCC/RCC infrastructure in place to support it. If, as may be the case, there is not, subsequent action will probably take longer. Some countries, however, are signatories to the operating agreement and have no LUT of their own – eg Madagascar has recently joined the fold without an LUT – so response time and infrastructure will be better than for a non-party country.

Rescue plan

Think in depth about emergency and rescue situations. Do a written rescue plan containing all relevant information and send it to those you've asked to look out for you.

Known risks, known action. Taking the utilisation of radio/satellite beacons a logical stage further – or even without them in some cases – some expeditions will benefit from the establishment of a contingency rescue plan which can be left with a home-base or nominated external authority. This comes under the heading of an extension to the precaution of leaving a proposed route and timings with an external organisation who will be alert to your non-arrival at destination by a given time.

Who is the reader? Be sure to write for the people who will read the plan when the chips are down and you have not arrived at your destination. If you have your own 'base person' at home monitoring progress you will be well looked after. It may be however, that the arrangements are done by post with an agency in the country you are visiting. The plan should state that you expect to arrive in a certain area by a given date and you would like someone to be on

the lookout for you. In such cases you would send that agency a copy of the plan which, with the best will in the world, they will flick through, put on one side and hope they do not have to use it. Be sure that when they do, it is easy to understand, has full lists of your route as far as you know it and lists of your supplies.

The rescue plan itself. The plan can cover such data as reserves carried and what action to take but will vary according to the expedition concerned and a host of other variables. For those wishing to peruse a precedent plan of this kind, the Joint Services West East Sahara Expedition of 1975 produced a comprehensive rescue plan and the report on this expedition is held by the Royal Geographical Society. An extract from this report covering one sector is reproduced on the facing page; this is a part of what would be on the person's desk getting the non-arrival call. Note the inclusion of logistical/supplies information.

Case study: Extract from a rescue plan covering one sector

Non-arrival at destination – overdue action

9. Sub-section A1 – Ouadane – Tessalit

a. Route description and alternative destinations. Estimated 1300 miles (2090 km); no road, track, previous route, habitation, fuel or water en route and the most demanding leg of the whole expedition. The worst physical hazard is a 50-60 mile (80-96 km) band of dunes running across the route about 200 miles (300 km) from Ouadane; the vehicles will still be heavy with fuel and water when this obstacle is encountered – about 300 lb down from max payload. After this the Mréyyé, the centre of the Mauritanian Empty Quarter, is reputed to be relatively easy going for about 700 miles (1120 km) of rock / gravel before Tadhak (2030N, 0000W) where a 3-day stop for collection of carbonatite rock specimens is planned. After this the remaining 75 miles (120 km) or so to the Mali military post at Tessalit is through very bad rocky country but a form of track – likely the Tessalit-Taoudenni track – is shown on the map. Skylab photo-cover of this area is being obtained. The only alternative destination to shorten the route is Arouane, 250 miles (400 km) north of Tombouctou and approximately 100 miles (160 km) south of the expedition's track. There is believed to be a Mali military post at Arouane.

b. Rescue criteria
Leg length: Ouadane-Tessalit 1280 miles (2060 km)
Fuel carried: 906 gallons
Water carried: 340 gallons

Estimated duration of crossing: 16 days (inc 3 days at Tadhak)

Effective fuel reserve: 25%+100 miles (160 km) = 420 miles (675 km) = 210 gallons
Effective water reserve: 6 days = 96 gallons.

c. Action. At ETA + 4 days, initiate air search between last known position and Tessalit. Any non-arrival situation is likely to be preceded by a communication failure (otherwise the nature of the emergency will be known). After 2 days of no communications, the British Embassy Dakar, the US Embassy in Bamako and Petty Ray in UK should be informed so that action can be taken. Over Mauritania, a request by the UK Embassy via Texaco (see Appendix 2) for help from the French Air Force at Dakar is probably the best bet for air search; the Atlantique aircraft is specially equipped for search operations.

In Mali, Petty Ray are likely to be the most cost-effective source of assistance and search (see also Appendix 2)

The above was the plan. The amount of research and permission-seeking to get this down on paper may be imagined!

Be sure rescue plan provides information on supplies, fuel and water you carry to give an idea how long you can last. Put yourself in rescuer's position – tense!

Acknowledgements and thanks:

Special thanks to:

Vladislav Sudenov, Cospas-Sarsat Secretariat, London UK

Section 6

Index